PEARSON ALWAYS LEARNING

Ideas to Innovation

Third Edition

With contributions from Monica E. Cardella, Heidi A. Diefes-Dux, David Dux, Stephen R. Hoffmann, Alice Pawley and edited by Monica E. Cardella, Chell E. Nyquist, Matthew W. Ohland, and Amy Van Epps.

Taken from:

MATLAB® for Engineers, Second Edition
by Holly Moore

Thinking Like an Engineer: An Active Learning Approach, Second Edition
by Elizabeth A. Stephan, David R. Bowman, William J. Park, Benjamin L. Sill, and Matthew W. Ohland

Engineering Communication, Second Edition
by Hillary Hart

Engineering Success, Third Edition
by Peter Schiavone

Cover Art: Courtesy of PhotoDisc/Getty Images

Taken from:

MATLAB® for Engineers, Second Edition
by Holly Moore
Copyright © 2009, 2007 by Pearson Education, Inc.
Published by Prentice Hall
Upper Saddle River, New Jersey 07458

Thinking Like an Engineer: An Active Learning Approach, Second Edition
by Elizabeth A. Stephan, David R. Bowman, William J. Park, Benjamin L. Sill, and Matthew W. Ohland
Copyright © 2013, 2011 by Pearson Education, Inc.
Published by Prentice Hall

Engineering Communication, Second Edition
By Hilary Hart
Copyright © 2009, 2005 by Pearson Education, Inc.
Published by Prentice Hall

Engineering Success, Third Edition
By Peter Schiavone
Copyright 2007 by Pearson Education, Inc.
Published by Prentice Hall

Pearson Learning Solutions, 501 Boylston Street, Suite 900, Boston, MA 02116
A Pearson Education Company
www.pearsoned.com

Printed in the United States of America

2 3 4 5 6 7 8 9 10 V092 17 16 15 14 13 12

000200010271668107

TF/MM

ISBN 10: 1-256-71919-6
ISBN 13: 978-1-256-71919-9

CONTENTS

COPYRIGHT ACKNOWLEDGMENTS

Grateful acknowledgment is made to the following sources for permission to reprint material copyrighted or controlled by them:

"Engineering Majors," and "Profiles of Engineers," reprinted from *Engineering Your Future: A Brief Introduction to Engineering,* 2009–2010 Edition, edited by William C. Oakes, Les L. Leone, and Craig J. Gunn, Oxford University Press.

"Documentation," reprinted from *Pocket Book of Technical Writing for Engineers and Scientists,* Third Edition, edited by Leo Finkelstein, Jr.

"Building Teams and Work Groups," and "Project Management," reprinted from *Interpersonal Skills in Organizations,* Second Edition, edited by Suzanne C. De Janasz, Karen O. Dowd, and Beth Z. Schneider, McGraw Hill Companies.

"Tips for Working Successfully in a Team," by Randy Pausch, reprinted from *Building Virtual Worlds Course at Carnegie Mellon* (spring 1998), by permission of David Black Literary Agency.

"Teamwork Skills and Problem Solving," reprinted from *Teamwork and Project Management,* Third Edition, edited by Karl A Smith and P.K. Imbrie, McGraw Hill Companies.

"Applications in Numerical Analysis," by Amos Gilat, reprinted from *MATLAB: An Introduction with Applications,* edited by Amos Gilat (2008), by permission of John Wiley & Sons, Inc.

Excerpts reprinted from *MatLab® Programming for Engineers,* by Stephen J. Chapman, by permission of Cengage Learning.

CHAPTER 1
ENGINEERING MAJORS

Objectives

By learning the material in this chapter, you should be able to

- list and describe various engineering job functions
- list and describe various engineering job disciplines/majors

1.1 INTRODUCTION

Engineers produce things that impact us every day. They invent, design, develop, manufacture, test, sell, and service products and services that improve the lives of people. The Accreditation Board for Engineering and Technology (ABET), which is the national board that establishes accreditation standards for all engineering programs, defines engineering as follows [Landis]:

> *Engineering is the profession in which a knowledge of the mathematical and natural sciences, gained by study, experience, and practice, is applied with judgment to develop ways to utilize, economically, the materials and forces of nature for the benefit of mankind.*

Frequently, students early in their educational careers find it difficult to understand exactly what engineers do, and often more to the point, where they fit best in the vast array of career opportunities available to engineers.

Common reasons for a student to be interested in engineering include:

1. Proficiency in math and science
2. Suggested by a high school counselor
3. Has a relative who is an engineer
4. Heard it's a field with tremendous job opportunity
5. Read that it has high starting salaries

While these can be valid reasons, they don't imply a firm understanding of engineering. What is really important is that a student embarking upon a degree program, and ultimately a career, understands what that career entails and the options it presents. We all have our own strengths and talents. Finding places to use those strengths and talents is the key to a rewarding career.

The purpose of this chapter is to provide information about some of the fields of engineering in order to help you decide if this is an area that you might enjoy. We'll explore the role of engineers, engineering job functions, and the various engineering disciplines.

Taken from *Engineering Your Future: A Brief Introduction to Engineering*, 2009–2010 Edition, by William C. Oakes, PhD, Les L. Leone, PhD, and Craig J. Gunn, MS.

1.1.1 The Engineer and the Scientist

To better understand what engineers do, let's contrast the roles of engineers with those of the closely related field of the scientist. Many students approach both fields for similar reasons: they were good at math and science in high school. While this is a prerequisite for both fields, it is not a sufficient discriminator to determine which is the right career for a given individual.

The main difference between the engineer and the scientist is in the object of each one's work. The scientist searches for answers to technological questions to obtain a knowledge of why a phenomenon occurs. The engineer also searches for answers to technological questions, but always with an application in mind.

Theodore Von Karman, one of the pioneers of America's aerospace industry, said, "Scientists explore what is; engineers create what has not been." [Paul Wright, *Introduction to Engineering*].

In general, science is about discovering things or acquiring new knowledge. Scientists are always asking, "Why?" They are interested in advancing the knowledge base that we have in a specific area. The answers they seek may be of an abstract nature, such as understanding the beginning of the universe, or more practical, such as the reaction of a virus to a new drug.

The engineer also asks, "Why?" but it is because of a problem which is preventing a product or service from being produced. The engineer is always thinking about the application when asking why. The engineer becomes concerned with issues such as the demand for a product, the cost of producing the product, the impact on society and the environment of the product.

Scientists and engineers work in many of the same fields and industries but have different roles. Here are some examples:

- Scientists study the planets in our solar system to understand them; engineers study the planets so they can design a spacecraft to operate in the environment of that planet.
- Scientists study atomic structure to understand the nature of matter; engineers study the atomic structure in order to build smaller and faster microprocessors.
- Scientists study the human neurological system to understand the progression of neurological diseases; engineers study the human neurological system to design artificial limbs.
- Scientists create new chemical compounds in a laboratory; engineers create processes to mass-produce new chemical compounds for consumers.
- Scientists study the movement of tectonic plates to understand and predict earthquakes; engineers study the movement of tectonic plates to design safer buildings.

1.1.2 The Engineer and the Engineering Technologist

Another profession closely related to engineering is engineering technology. Engineering technology and engineering have similarities, yet there are differences; they have different career opportunities. ABET, which accredits engineering technology programs as well as engineering programs, defines engineering technology as follows:

> *Engineering technology is that part of the technological field which requires the application of scientific and engineering knowledge and methods combined with technical skills in support of engineering activities; it lies in the occupational spectrum between the craftsman and engineering at the end of the spectrum closest to the engineer.*

Technologists work with existing technology to produce goods for society. Technology students spend time in their curricula working with actual machines and equipment that are used in the jobs they will accept after graduation. By doing this, technologists are equipped to be productive in their occupation from the first day of work.

Both engineers and technologists apply technology for the betterment of society. The main difference between the two fields is that the engineer is able to create new technology through research, design and development. Rather than being trained to use specific machines or processes, engineering students study additional mathematics and engineering science subjects. This equips engineers to use these tools to advance the state of the art in their field and move technology forward.

There are areas where engineers and engineering technologists perform very similar jobs. For example, in manufacturing settings, engineers and technologists are employed as supervisors of assembly line workers. Also, in technical service fields both are hired to work as technical support personnel supporting equipment purchased by customers. However, most opportunities are different for engineering and engineering technology graduates.

- The technologist identifies the computer networking equipment necessary for a business to meet its needs and oversees the installation of that equipment; the engineer designs new computer boards to transmit data faster.
- The technologist develops a procedure to manufacture a shaft for an aircraft engine using a newly developed welding technique; the engineer develops the new welding machine.
- The technologist analyzes a production line and identifies new robotic equipment to improve production; the engineer develops a computer simulation of the process to analyze the impact of the proposed equipment.
- The technologist identifies the equipment necessary to assemble a new CD player; the engineer designs the new CD player.
- The technologist identifies the proper building materials and oversees the construction of a new building; the engineer determines the proper support structures, taking into account the local soil, proposed usage, earthquake risks and other design requirements.

1.1.3 What Do Engineers Do?

Engineering is an exciting field with a vast range of career opportunities. In trying to illustrate the wide range of possibilities, Professors Jane Daniels and Richard Grace from Purdue University constructed the cubic model of Figure 1.1. One edge of the cube represents the engineering disciplines that most students identify as the potential majors. A second edge of the cube represents the different job functions an engineer can have within a specific engineering discipline. The third edge of the cube represents industrial sectors where engineers work. A specific engineering position, such as a mechanical engineering design position in the transportation sector, is the intersection of these three axes. As one can see from the cube, there is a vast number of possible engineering positions.

In the following sections of this chapter, the engineering functions and majors are described. The remaining axis, the industrial sectors, are dependent on the companies and governmental agencies that employ engineers.

To obtain more information about the various industrial sectors:

- Explore your school's placement center
- Visit job fairs
- Attend seminars on campus sponsored by various companies
- Search the Internet (visit Web sites describing career opportunities)
- Talk to faculty familiar with a certain industry
- "Shadow" a practicing engineer

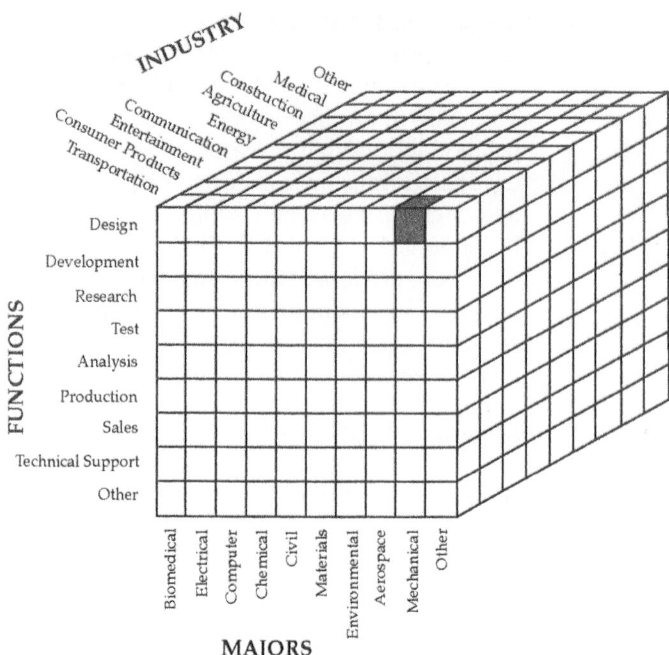

Figure 1.1 Engineering positions. [Grace and Daniels]

- Work as an intern or co-op engineer
- Take an engineering elective course

Most engineering curricula include common courses within an engineering major for the first two years of study. It is not until the junior or senior year that students take technical electives that can be industry specific. Students are encouraged to explore various career opportunities so they can make better decisions when required to select their junior and senior level electives.

EXAMPLE 1.1

Let's consider a mechanical engineer (an "ME") who performs a design function to illustrate how a specific job in one industrial sector can vary from that in another sector.

- **Aerospace**—*Design of an aircraft engine fan blade:* Detailed computer analyses and on-engine testing are required for certification by the FAA. Reliability, efficiency, cost and weight are all design constraints. The design engineer must push current design barriers to optimize the design constraints, potentially making tradeoffs between efficiency, cost and weight.
- **Biomedical**—*Design of an artificial leg and foot prosthesis giving additional mobility and control to the patient:* Computer modeling is used to model the structure of the prosthesis and the natural movement of a leg and foot. Collaboration with medical personnel to understand the needs of the patient is a critical part of the design process. Reliability, durability and functionality are the key design constraints.
- **Power**—*Design of a heat recovery system in a power plant, increasing the plant productivity:* Computer analyses are performed as part of the design process. Cost, efficiency and reliability are the main design constraints. Key mechanical components can be designed with large factors of safety since, weight is not a design concern.

- **Consumer products**—*Design of a pump for toothpaste for easier dispensing:* Much of the development work might be done with prototypes. Cost is a main design consideration. Consumer appeal is another consideration and necessitates extensive consumer testing as part of the development process.
- **Computer**—*Design of a new ink-jet nozzle with resolution approaching laser printer quality:* Computer analyses are performed to ensure that the ink application is properly modeled. Functionality, reliability and cost are key design concerns.

1.2 ENGINEERING FUNCTIONS

Within engineering there are basic classifications of jobs that are common across the various engineering disciplines. What follows are brief descriptions of these different engineering job functions. A few examples are provided for each function. It is important to realize that all the fields of engineering have roles in each of the main functions described here.

1.2.1 Research

The role of the engineering researcher is the closest to that of a scientist of all the engineering functions. Research engineers explore fundamental principles of chemistry, physics, biology and mathematics in order to overcome barriers preventing advancement in their field. Engineering researchers differ from scientists in that they are interested in the application of a breakthrough, whereas scientists are concerned with the knowledge that accompanies a breakthrough.

Research engineers conduct investigations to extend knowledge using various means. One of the means is conducting experiments. Research engineers may be involved in the design and implementation of experiments and the interpreting of the results. Typically, the research engineer does not perform the actual experiment. Technicians are usually called upon for the actual testing. Large-scale experiments may involve the coordination of additional supporting personnel including other engineers, scientists, technologists, technicians and craftspeople.

Research is also conducted using the computer. Computational techniques are developed to calculate solutions to complex problems without having to conduct costly and time-consuming experiments. Computational research requires the creation of mathematical models to simulate the natural occurring phenomena under study. Research engineers also might develop the computational techniques to perform the complex calculations in a timely and cost-effective fashion.

Most research engineers work for some type of research center. A research center might be a university, a government laboratory such as NASA, or an industrial research center. In most research positions an advanced degree is required, and often a Ph.D. is needed. If research appeals to you, a great way to explore it is by doing an undergraduate research project with an engineering professor. This will allow you to observe the operation of a laboratory first-hand and find out how well you enjoy being part of a research team.

1.2.2 Development

Development engineers bridge the gap between laboratory research and full-scale production. The development function is often coupled with research in so-called R&D (research and development) divisions. Development engineers take the knowledge acquired by the researchers and apply it to a specific product or application. The researcher may prove something is possible in a laboratory setting; the development engineer shows that it will work on a large, production-size scale and under actual conditions encountered in the field. This is done in pilot manufacturing plants or by using prototypes.

Development engineers are continuously looking for ways to incorporate the findings of researchers into prototypes to test their feasibility for use in tomorrow's products. Often, an idea proven in a laboratory needs to be significantly altered before it can be introduced on a mass production scale. It is the role of development engineers to identify these areas and work with the design engineers to correct them before full-scale production begins.

An example of a development process is the building of concept cars within the automotive industry. These are unique cars that incorporate advanced design concepts and technology. The cars are then used as a test case to see if the design ideas and technology actually perform as predicted. The concept cars are put through exhaustive tests to determine how well the new ideas enhance a vehicle's performance. Each year, new technology is introduced into production automobiles that was first proven in development groups using concept vehicles.

1.2.3 Testing

Test engineers are responsible for designing and implementing tests to verify the integrity, reliability and quality of products before they are introduced to the public. The test engineer devises ways to simulate the conditions a product will be subjected to during its life. Test engineers work closely with development engineers in evaluating prototypes and pilot facilities. Data from these initial development tests are used to decide whether full production versions will be made or if significant changes are needed before a full-scale release. Test engineers work with design engineers to identify the changes in the product to ensure its integrity.

A challenge that engineers face is simulating the conditions a product will face during its life span, and doing so in a timely, cost-effective manner. Often the conditions the product will face are difficult to simulate in a laboratory. A constant problem for the test engineer is simulating the aging of a product. An example of such a testing challenge is the testing of a pacemaker for regulating a patient's heart which is designed to last several decades. An effective test of this type cannot take 20 years or the product will be obsolete before it is introduced. The test engineer must also simulate conditions within the human body without exposing people to unnecessary risks.

Other challenges facing test engineers involve acquiring accurate and reliable data. The test engineer must produce data that show that the product is functioning properly or that identify areas of concern. Test engineers develop data acquisition and instrumentation methods to achieve this. Techniques such as radio telemetry may be used to transmit data from the inside of a device being tested. The measurement techniques must not interfere with the operation of the device, presenting a tremendous challenge for small, compact products. Test engineers must cooperate with design engineers to determine how the device being tested can be fitted with instrumentation yet still meet its design intent.

EXAMPLE 1.2

Test engineers must understand the important parameters of their tests. The development of a certain European high-speed train provides an example of the potential consequences which may result when test engineers fail to understand these parameters. A test was needed to show that the windshield on the locomotive could withstand the high-velocity impacts of birds or other objects it might encounter. This is also a common design constraint encountered in airplane design. The train test engineers borrowed a "chicken gun" from an aerospace firm for this test. A chicken gun is a mechanism used to propel birds at a target, simulating in-flight impact. With modern laws governing cruelty to animals, the birds are humanely killed and frozen until the test.

On the day of the test, the test engineers aimed the gun at the locomotive windshield, inserted the bird and fired. The bird not only shattered the windshield but put a hole through the engineer's seat.

The design engineers could not understand what went wrong. They double-checked their calculations and determined that the windshield should have held. The problem became clear after the test engineers reviewed their procedure with the engineers from the aerospace firm from whom they had borrowed the equipment. The aerospace test engineers asked how long they had let the bird thaw.

The response was, "Thaw the bird?"

There is a significant difference in impact force between a frozen eight-pound bird and a thawed bird. The test was successfully completed later with a properly thawed bird.

Test engineers must have a wide range of technical and problem-solving skills. They must also be able to work in teams involving a wide range of people. They work with design and development engineers, technicians, and craftspeople, as well as management.

1.2.4 Design

The design function is what many people think of when they think of engineering, and this is where the largest number of engineers are employed. The design engineer is responsible for providing the detailed specifications of the products society uses.

Rather than being responsible for an entire product, most design engineers are responsible for a component or part of the product. The individual parts are then assembled into a product such as a computer, automobile, or airplane. Design engineers produce detailed dimensions and specifications of the part to ensure that the component fits properly with adjoining pieces. They use modern computer design tools and are often supported by technicians trained in computer drafting software.

The form of the part is also a consideration for the design engineer. Design engineers use their knowledge of scientific and mathematical laws, coupled with experience, to generate a shape to meet the specifications of the part. Often, there is a wide range of possibilities and considerations. In some fields, these considerations are ones that can be calculated. In others, such as in consumer products, the reaction of a potential customer to a shape may be as important as how well the product works.

The design engineer also must verify that the part meets the reliability and safety standards established for the product. The design engineer verifies the integrity of the product. This often requires coordination with analysis engineers to simulate complex products and field conditions, and with test engineers to gather data on the integrity of the product. The design engineer is responsible for making corrections to the design based on the results of the tests performed.

In today's world of ever increasing competition, the design engineer must also involve manufacturing engineers in the design process. Cost is a critical factor in the design process and may be the difference between a successful product and one that fails. Communication with manufacturing engineers is therefore critical. Often, simple design changes can radically change a part's cost and affect the ease with which the part is made.

Design engineers also work with existing products. Their role includes redesigning parts to reduce manufacturing costs and time. They also work on redesigning products that have not lived up to expected lives or have suffered failure in the field. They also modify products for new uses. This usually requires additional analysis, minor redesigns and significant communication between departments.

1.2.5 Analysis

Analysis is an engineering function performed in conjunction with design, development and research. Analysis engineers use mathematical models and computational tools to provide the necessary information to design, development or research engineers to help them perform their function.

Analysis engineers typically are specialists in a technology area important to the products or services being produced. Technical areas might include heat transfer, fluid flow, vibrations, dynamics, system modeling, and acoustics, among others. They work with computer models of products to make these assessments. Analysis engineers often possess an advanced degree and are experienced in their area of expertise.

In order to produce the information required of them, they must validate their computer programs or mathematical models. To do so may require comparing test data to their predictions. This requires coordination with test engineers in order to design an appropriate test and to record the relevant data.

An example of the role of analysis is the prediction of temperatures in an aircraft engine. Material selection, component life estimates and design decisions are based in large part on the temperature the parts attain and the duration of those temperatures. Heat transfer analyses are used to determine these temperatures. Engine test results are used to validate the temperature predictions. The permissible time between engine overhauls can depend on these temperatures. The design engineers then use these results to ensure reliable aircraft propulsion systems.

1.2.6 Systems

Systems engineers work with the overall design, development, manufacture and operation of a complete system or product. Design engineers are involved in the design of individual components, but systems engineers are responsible for the integration of the components and systems into a functioning product.

Systems engineers are responsible for ensuring that the components interface properly and work as a complete unit. Systems engineers are also responsible for identifying the overall design requirements. This may involve working with customers or marketing personnel to accurately determine market needs. From a technical standpoint, systems engineers are responsible for meeting the overall design requirements.

Systems engineering is a field that most engineers enter only after becoming proficient in an area important to the systems, such as component design or development.

Some graduate work often is required prior to taking on these assignments. However, there are some schools where an undergraduate degree in systems engineering is offered.

1.2.7 Manufacturing and Construction

Manufacturing engineers turn the specifications of the design engineer into a tangible reality. They develop processes to make the products we use every day. They work with diverse teams of individuals, from technicians on the assembly lines to management, in order to maintain the integrity and efficiency of the manufacturing process.

It is the responsibility of manufacturing engineers to develop the processes for taking raw materials and changing them into the finished pieces that the design engineers detailed. They utilize state-of-the-art machines and processes to accomplish this. As technology advances, new processes often must be developed for manufacturing the products.

The repeatability or quality of manufacturing processes is an area of increasing concern to modern manufacturing engineers. These engineers use statistical methods to determine the precision of a process. This is important, since a lack of precision in the manufacturing process may result in inferior parts that cannot be used or that may not meet the customer's needs. Manufacturing engineers are very concerned about the quality of the products they produce. High quality manufacturing means lower costs since more parts are usable, resulting in less waste. Ensuring quality means having the right processes in place, understanding the processes and working with the people involved to make sure the processes are being maintained at peak efficiency.

Manufacturing engineers also keep track of the equipment in a plant. They schedule and track required maintenance to keep the production line moving. They also must track the inventories of raw materials, partially finished parts and completely finished parts. Excessive inventories tie up substantial amounts of cash that could be used in other parts of the company. The manufacturing engineer is also responsible for maintaining a safe and reliable workplace, including the safety of the workers at the facility and the environmental impact of the processes.

Manufacturing engineers must be able to work with diverse teams of people including design engineers, tradesmen and management. Current "just in time" manufacturing practices reduce needed inventories in factories but require manufacturing engineers at one facility to coordinate their operation with manufacturing engineers at other facilities. They also must coordinate the work of the line workers who operate the manufacturing equipment. It is imperative that manufacturing engineers maintain a constructive relationship with their company's trade workers.

Manufacturing engineers play a critical role in modern design practices. Since manufacturing costs are such an important component in the success of a product, the design process must take into account manufacturing concerns. Manufacturing engineers identify high cost or high risk operations in the design phase of a product. When problems are identified, they work with the design engineers to generate alternatives.

In the production of large items such as buildings, dams and roads, the production engineer is called a construction engineer rather than a manufacturing engineer. However, the role of the construction engineer is very similar to that of the manufacturing engineer. The main difference is that the construction engineer's production facility is typically outdoors while the manufacturing engineer's is inside a factory. The functions of construction engineers are the same as mentioned above when "assembly line" and "factory" are replaced with terms like "job site," reflecting the construction of a building, dam or other large-scale project.

1.2.8 Operations and Maintenance

After a new production facility is brought on-line, it must be maintained. The operations engineer oversees the ongoing performance of the facility. Operations engineers must have a wide range of expertise dealing with the mechanical and electrical issues involved with maintaining a production line. They must be able to interact with manufacturing engineers, line workers and technicians who service the equipment. They must coordinate the service schedule of the technicians to ensure efficient service of the machinery, minimizing its downtime impact on production.

Maintenance and operations engineers also work in non-manufacturing roles. Airlines have staffs of maintenance engineers who schedule and oversee safety inspections and repairs. These engineers must have expertise in sophisticated inspection techniques to identify all possible problems.

Large medical facilities and other service sector businesses require operations or maintenance engineers to oversee the operation of their equipment. It is obviously critical that emergency medical equipment be maintained in peak working order.

1.2.9 Technical Support

A technical support engineer serves as the link between customer and product and assists with installation and setup. For large industrial purchases, technical support may be included in the purchase price. The engineer may visit the installation site and oversee a successful start-up. For example, a new power station for irrigation might require that the technical support engineer supervises the installation and helps the customer solve problems to get the product operational. To be effective, the engineer must have good interpersonal and problem-solving skills as well as solid technical training.

The technical support engineer may also trouble-shoot problems with a product. Serving on a computer company's help line is one example. Diagnosing design flaws found in the field once the product is in use is another example.

Technical support engineers do not have to have in-depth knowledge of each aspect of the product. However, they must know how to tap into such knowledge at their company.

Modern technical support is being used as an added service. Technical support engineers work with customers to operate and manage their own company's equipment as well as others. For example, a medical equipment manufacturer might sell its services to a hospital to manage and operate its highly sophisticated equipment. The manufacturer's engineers would not only maintain the equipment, but also help the hospital use its facilities in the most efficient way.

1.2.10 Customer Support

Customer support functions are similar to those of technical support as a link between the manufacturer and the customer. However, customer support personnel also are involved in the business aspect of the customer relationship. Engineers are often used for this function because of their technical knowledge and problem solving ability. Typically, these positions require experience with the products and customers, and also require some business training.

The customer support person works with technical support engineers to ensure proper customer satisfaction. Customer support is also concerned with actual or perceived value for customers. Are they getting what they paid for? Is it cost-effective to continue current practices? Customer support persons are involved in warranty issues, contractual agreements and the value of trade-in or credits for existing equipment. They work very closely with the technical support engineers and also with management personnel.

1.2.11 Sales

Engineers are valuable members of the sales force in numerous companies. These engineers must have interpersonal skills conducive to effective selling. Sales engineers bring many assets to their positions.

Engineers have the technical background to answer customer questions and concerns. They are trained to identify which products are right for the customer and how they can be applied. Sales engineers can also identify other applications or other products that might benefit the customer once they become familiar with their customer's needs.

In some sales forces, engineers are utilized because the customers are engineers themselves and have engineering-related questions. When airplane manufacturers market their aircraft to airlines, they send engineers. The airlines have engineers who have technical concerns overseeing the maintenance and operation of the aircraft. Sales engineers have the technical background to answer these questions.

As technology continues to advance, more and more products become technically sophisticated. This produces an ever-increasing demand for sales engineers.

1.2.12 Consulting

Consulting engineers are either self-employed or they work for a firm that does not provide goods or services directly to consumers. Such firms provide technical expertise to organizations that do. Many large companies do not have technical experts on staff in all areas of operation. Instead, they use consultants to handle issues in those technical areas.

For example, a manufacturing facility in which a cooling tower is used in part of the operation might have engineers who are well versed in the manufacturing processes but not in cooling tower design. The manufacturer would hire a consulting firm to design the cooling tower and related systems. Such a consultant might oversee the installation of such a system or simply provide a report with recommendations. After the system is in place or the report is delivered, the consultant would move on to another project with another company.

Consulting engineers also might be asked to evaluate the effectiveness of an organization. In such a situation, a team of consultants might work with a customer and provide suggestions and guidelines for improving the company's processes. These might be design methods, manufacturing operations or even business practices. While some consulting firms provide only engineering-related expertise, other firms provide both engineering and business support and require the consulting engineers to work on business-related issues as well as technical issues.

Consulting engineers interact with a wide range of companies on a broad scope of projects, and come from all engineering disciplines. Often a consultant needs to be registered as a professional engineer in the state where he or she does business.

1.2.13 Management

In many instances, engineers work themselves into project management positions, and eventually into full-time management. National surveys show that more than half of all engineers will be involved in some type of management responsibilities—supervisory or administrative—before their career is over. Engineers are chosen for their technical ability, their problem solving ability and their leadership skills.

Engineers may manage other engineers or support personnel, or they may rise to oversee the business aspects of a corporation. Often, prior to being promoted to this level of management, engineers acquire some business or management training. Some companies provide this training or offer incentives for employees to take management courses in the evening on their own time.

1.2.14 Other Fields

Some engineering graduates enter fields other than engineering, such as law, education, medicine and business. Patent law is one area in which an engineering or science degree is almost essential. In patent law, lawyers research, write, and file patent applications. Patent lawyers must have the technical background to understand what an invention does so that they can properly describe the invention and legally protect it for the inventor.

Another area of law that has become popular for engineering graduates is corporate liability law. Corporations are faced with decisions every day over whether to introduce a new product, and must weigh potential risks. Lawyers with technical backgrounds have the ability to weigh technical as well as legal risks. Such lawyers are also used in litigation for liability issues. Understanding what an expert witness is saying in a suit can be a tremendous advantage in a courtroom and can enable a lawyer to effectively cross-examine the expert witness. Often, when a corporation is sued over product liability, the lawyers defending the corporation have technical backgrounds.

Engineers are involved in several aspects of education. The one students are most familiar with is engineering professors. College professors usually have their Ph.D.s. Engineers with master's degrees can teach at community colleges and in some engineering technology programs. Engineering graduates also teach in high schools, middle schools, and elementary schools. To do this full-time usually requires additional training in educational methods, but the engineering background is a great start. Thousands of engineers are involved in part-time educational projects where they go to classes as

EXAMPLE 1.3

A dean of a New York engineering school passed along a story about her faculty, which was concerned that most of that year's graduates had not accepted traditional engineering positions. The largest employers were firms that hire stockbrokers. The school's engineering graduates were prized for their ability to look at data and make rational conclusions from the data. In other words, they were very effective problem solvers. They also had the ability to model the data mathematically. This combination made the engineering graduates a perfect fit for Wall Street. This is not an isolated story. Many engineering graduates find themselves in careers unrelated to their engineering education. All engineers are trained problem solvers, and in today's technically advanced society, such skills are highly regarded.

guest speakers to show students what "real engineers" do. The beginning of this chapter described one such engineer. The American Society for Engineering Education (ASEE) is a great resource if you are interested in engineering education.

Engineers also find careers in medicine, business, on Wall Street and in many other professions. In modern society, with its rapid expansion of technology, the combination of problem solving ability and technical knowledge makes engineers very valuable and extremely versatile.

1.3 ENGINEERING MAJORS

The following section is a partial listing of the various engineering disciplines in which engineering students can earn degrees. The list includes all of the most common majors. Some smaller institutions may offer programs that are not mentioned in this chapter. Be aware that some disciplines are referred to by different names at various institutions. Also, some programs may be offered as a subset of other disciplines. For instance, aeronautical and industrial engineering is sometimes combined with mechanical engineering. Environmental engineering might be offered as part of civil or chemical engineering.

These descriptions are not meant to be comprehensive. To describe a field completely, such as electrical engineering, would take an entire book by itself. These descriptions are meant to give you an overview of the fields and to answer some basic questions about the differences among the fields. It is meant to be a starting point. When selecting a major, a student might investigate several sources, including people actually working in the field.

An engineering student should keep in mind that the list of engineering fields is fluid. Areas such as aerospace, genetic, computer and nuclear engineering did not even exist 50 years ago. Yet men and women developed the technology to create these fields. In your lifetime, other new fields will be created. The objective is to gain the solid background and tools to handle future challenges. It is also important to find a field you enjoy.

EXAMPLE 1.4

"Show me the money!" As academic advisors, we see students regularly who are interested in engineering but not sure which discipline to pursue. Students are tempted to decide which field to enter by asking which offers the greatest salary. There are two issues a student should consider when looking at salaries of engineers.

First, all engineers make a good starting salary—well over the average American household income. However, a high salary would not make up for a job that is hated. The salary spread between the engineering disciplines is not large, varying only by about 10% from the average. The career you embark on after graduation from college will span some forty years—a long time to spend in a discipline you don't really enjoy.

Second, if you consider money a critical factor, you should consider earning potential, not starting salary. Earning potential in engineering is dependent, to a large extent, on job performance. Engineers who do well financially are those who excel professionally. Again, it is very rare for someone to excel in a field that he or she does not enjoy.

1.3.1 Aerospace Engineering

Aerospace engineering was previously referred to as aeronautical and astronautical engineering. Technically, aerospace engineering involves flight within the Earth's atmosphere and had its birth when two bicycle repairmen from Dayton, Ohio, made the first flight at Kitty Hawk, North Carolina, in 1903. Since that time, aerospace engineers have designed and produced aircraft that have broken the sound barrier, achieved near-orbit altitudes, and become the standard mode of transportation for long journeys. Aerospace engineering involves flight in space which began on October 4, 1957, when the Soviet Union launched Sputnik into orbit. The United States achieved one of its proudest moments in the field of aerospace on July 20, 1969, when Neil Armstrong set foot on the moon's surface—the first person ever to do so. In order to describe what the broad field of aerospace engineering has become, it can be separated into the categories of aerodynamics, propulsion, structures, controls, orbital mechanics, and life sciences.

Aerodynamics is the study of the flow of air over a streamlined surface or body. The aerodynamicist is concerned with the lift that is produced by a body such as the wing of an aircraft. Similarly, there is a resistance or drag force when a body moves through a fluid. An engineer looks to optimize lift and minimize drag. While mechanical, civil and chemical engineers also study flow over bodies, the aerospace engineer is interested especially in high-speed air flows. When the speed of the aircraft approaches or exceeds the speed of sound, the modeling of the airflow becomes much more complex.

Air-breathing propulsion systems that power airplanes and helicopters include propellers, and gas turbine jets, as well as ramjets and scram-jets. Propulsion systems used to launch or operate spacecraft include liquid and solid rocket engines. **Propulsion engineers** are continually developing more efficient, quieter and cleaner-burning conventional engines as well as new engine technologies. New engine concepts include wave rotors, electric propulsion, and nuclear-powered craft.

The structural support of an aircraft or spacecraft is critical. It must be both lightweight and durable. These conditions are often mutually exclusive and provide challenges for structural design engineers. **Structural engineers** utilize new alloys, composites and other new materials to meet design requirements for more efficient and more maneuverable aircraft and spacecraft.

The control schemes for aircraft and spacecraft have evolved rapidly. The new commercial airplanes are completely digitally controlled. Aerospace engineers work with electrical engineers to design **control systems** and subsystems used to operate the craft. They must be able to understand the electrical and computational aspects of the control schemes as well as the physical systems that are being controlled.

Aerospace engineers are also interested in **orbital mechanics.** They calculate where to place a satellite to operate as a communication satellite or as a global positioning system (GPS). They might also determine how to use the gravity fields of the near-Earth planets to help propel a satellite to the outskirts of the solar system.

An aerospace engineer must be aware of human limitations and the effects of their craft on the human body. It would serve no useful purpose to design a fighter plane that was so maneuverable it incapacitated the pilot with a high G-force. Designing a plane and a system which keeps the pilot conscious is an obvious necessity. Understanding the physiological and psychological affects of lengthy exposure to weightlessness is important when designing a spacecraft or space station.

The American Institute of Aeronautics and Astronautics (AIAA) is one of the most prominent aerospace professional societies. It is composed of the following seven technical groups, which include 66 technical committees.

- Engineering and Technology Management
- Aircraft Technology Integration and Operations
- Propulsion and Energy
- Space and Missile Systems
- Aerospace Sciences
- Information and Logistics Systems
- Structures, Design and Testing

1.3.2 Agricultural Engineering

Agricultural engineering traces its roots back thousands of years to the time when people began to examine ways to produce food and food products more efficiently. Today, the role of the agricultural engineer is critical to our ability to feed the ever-expanding population of the world. The production and processing of agricultural products is the primary concern of agricultural engineers. Areas within agricultural engineering include power machinery, food processing, soils and water, structures, electrical technologies, and bioengineering.

The mechanical equipment used on modern farms is highly sophisticated and specialized. **Harvesting equipment** not only removes the crop from the field but also begins to process it and provides information to the farmers on the quality of the harvest. This requires highly complicated mechanical and electrical systems that are designed and developed by the agricultural engineer.

Often, once the food is harvested it must be processed before it reaches the marketplace. Many different technologies are involved in the efficient and safe processing and delivery of food products. **Food process engineers** are concerned with providing healthier products to consumers who increasingly rely on processed food products. This often requires the agricultural engineer to develop new processes. Another modern-day concern is increased food safety. Agricultural engineers design and develop means by which food is produced free of contamination such as the irradiation techniques used to kill potentially harmful bacteria in food.

The effective management of **soil and water resources** is a key aspect of productive agriculture. Agricultural engineers design and develop means to address effective land use, proper drainage and erosion control. This includes such activities as designing and implementing an irrigation system for crop production and designing a terracing system to prevent erosion in a hilly region.

Agricultural **structures** are used to house harvested crops, livestock and their feed. Agricultural engineers design structures including barns, silos, dryers and processing centers. They look for ways to minimize waste or losses, optimize yields and protect the environment.

Electrical and information technology development is another area important to the agriculture community due to the fact that farms are typically located in isolated regions. Agricultural engineers design systems that meet the needs of the rural communities.

Bioengineering has rapidly evolved into a field with wide uses in health products as well as agricultural products. Agricultural engineers are working to harness these rapidly developing technologies to further improve the quality and quantity of the agricultural products necessary to continue to feed the world's population.

The American Society of Agricultural Engineers (ASAE) is one of the most prominent professional societies for agricultural engineers. It has eight technical divisions which address areas of agricultural engineering:

- Food Processing
- Information and Electrical Technologies
- Power and Machinery
- Structures and Environmental
- Soil and Water
- Forest
- Bioengineering
- Aqua culture

1.3.3 Architectural Engineering

In ancient times, major building projects required a master builder. The master builder was responsible for the design and appearance of the structure, for selecting the appropriate materials, and for personally overseeing construction. With the advent of steel construction in the 19th century, it became necessary for master builders to consult with specialists in steel construction in order to complete their designs. As projects became more complex, other specialists were needed in such areas as mechanical and electrical systems. Modern architectural engineers facilitate the coordination between the creativity of the architect and the technical competencies of a variety of technology specialists.

Architectural engineers are well-grounded in the engineering fundamentals of structural, mechanical and electrical systems, and have at least a foundational understanding of aesthetic design. They know how to design a building and how the various technical systems are interwoven within that design. Their strengths are both creative and pragmatic.

The National Society of Architectural Engineers, which is now the Architectural Engineering Institute, defined architectural engineering as:

> *". . . the profession in which a knowledge of mathematics and natural sciences, gained by study, experience, and practice, is applied with judgment to the development of ways to use, economically and safely, the materials and forces of nature in the engineering design and construction of buildings and their environmental systems."* [Belcher]

There are four main divisions within architectural engineering: structural; electrical and lighting; mechanical systems; and construction engineering and management.

Structural is primarily concerned with the integrity of the structure of buildings. Determining the integrity of a building's structure involves the analysis of loads and forces resulting from normal usage and operation as well as from earthquakes, wind forces, snow loads, or wave impacts. The structural engineer takes the information from the analysis, and designs the structural elements that will support the building while at the same time meeting the aesthetic and functional needs involved.

The area of **electrical and lighting** systems is concerned with the distribution of utilities and power throughout the building. This requires knowledge of electricity and power distribution as well as lighting concerns. Lighting restrictions may require energy-efficient lighting systems that are sufficient to meet the functional requirements related to use of the building. The architectural engineer also must insure that the lighting will complement the architectural designs of the building and the rooms within that structure.

Mechanical systems control the climate of a building, which includes cooling and heating the air in rooms as well as controlling humidity and air quality. Mechanical systems are also used to distribute water through plumbing systems. Other mechanical systems include transportation by way of elevators and escalators within a building. These systems must be integrated to complement the architectural features of the building.

The fourth area is **construction engineering and management,** which combine the technical requirements with the given financial and legal requirements to meet project deadlines. The architectural engineer is responsible for implementing the design in a way which assures the quality of the construction and meets the cost and schedule of the project. Modern computer tools and project management skills are implemented to manage such complex projects.

Other areas which are merging for architectural engineers include energy management, computerized controls, and new building materials including plastics and composites and acoustics.

Architectural engineers are employed by consulting firms, contractors, and government agencies. They may work on complex high-rise office buildings, factories, stadiums, research labs, or educational facilities. They also may work on renovating historic structures or developing affordable low-income housing. As the construction industry continues to grow and as projects continue to become more complex, the outlook for architectural engineers is bright.

There are less than 20 ABET accredited programs in architectural engineering in the United States. Some of these are four-year programs while others provide the combined engineering foundation and architectural insights in a five-year program.

The Architectural Engineering Institute (AEI) was formed in 1998 with the merger of the National Society of Architectural Engineers and the American Society of Civil Engineers Architectural Engineering Division. AEI was created to be the home for professionals in the building industry. It is organized into divisions, which include:

- Commercial Buildings
- Industrial Buildings
- Residential Buildings
- Institutional Buildings
- Military Facilities
- Program Management
- Mitigation of the Effects of Terrorism
- Building Systems
- Education
- Architectural Systems
- Fully Integrated and Automated Project Process
- Glass as an Engineered Material
- Sick/Healthy Buildings
- Designing for Facilities for the Aging

Reference: Belcher, M. C., Magill's Survey of Science: Applied Science, Salem Press, Pasadena, CA, 1993.

1.3.4 Biomedical Engineering

Biomedical engineering is one of the newer fields of engineering, first recognized as a discipline in the 1940s. Its origins, however, date back to the first artificial limbs made of wood or other materials. Captain Ahab in "Moby Dick" probably didn't think of the person who made his wooden leg as a biomedical engineer, yet he was a predecessor for biomedical engineers who design modern prosthetics.

Biomedical engineering is a very broad field that overlaps with several other engineering disciplines. In some institutions, it may be a specialization within another discipline. Biomedical engineering applies the fundamentals of engineering to meet the needs of the medical community. Because of the wide range of skills needed in the fields of engineering and medicine, biomedical engineering often requires graduate work. The broad field of biomedical engineering encompasses the three basic categories of medical, clinical, and bioengineering.

Bioengineering is the application of engineering principles to biological systems. This can be seen in the production of food or in genetic manipulation to produce a disease-resistant strain of a plant or animal. Bioengineers work with geneticists to produce bioengineered products. New medical treatments are produced using genetically altered bacteria to produce human proteins needed to cure diseases. Bioengineers may work with geneticists in producing these new products in the mass quantities needed by consumers.

The medical aspect of biomedical engineering involves the design and development of devices to solve medical challenges. This includes designing mechanical devices such as a prosthesis which give individuals the desired mobility. It also involves the development of the chemical processes necessary to make an artificial kidney function and the electrical challenges in designing a new pacemaker.

Medical engineers develop instrumentation for medical uses including non-intrusive surgical instruments. Much of the trauma of surgery results from the incisions made to gain access to the area of concern. Procedures allowing a surgeon to make a small incision, such as orthoscopic surgery, have greatly reduced risk and recovery time for patients.

Rehabilitation is another area in which biomedical engineers work. It involves designing and developing devices for the physically impaired. Such devices can expand the capabilities of impaired individuals, thereby improving their quality of life or shortening recovery times.

Clinical engineering involves the development of systems to serve hospitals and clinics. Such systems exhaust anesthetic gases from an operating room without impairing the surgical team. Air lines in ventilating systems must be decontaminated to prevent microorganisms from spreading throughout the hospital. Rehabilitation centers must be designed to meet the needs of patients and staff.

1.3.5 Chemical Engineering

Chemical engineering differs from most of the other fields of engineering in its emphasis on chemistry and the chemical nature of products and processes. Chemical engineers take what chemists do in a laboratory and, applying fundamental engineering, chemistry and physics principles, design and develop processes to mass-produce products for use in our society. These products include detergents, paints, plastics, fertilizers, petroleum products, food products, pharmaceuticals, electronic circuit boards and many others.

The most common employment of chemical engineers is in the design, development and operation of large-scale chemical production facilities. In this area, the design function involves the **design of the processes** needed to safely and reliably produce the final product. This may involve controlling and using chemical reactions, separation processes, or heat and mass transfer. While the chemist might develop a new compound in the laboratory, the chemical engineer would develop a new process to make the compound in a pilot plant, which is a small-scale version of a full-size production facility. An example would be the design of a process to produce a lower-saturated-fat product with the same nutritional value yet still affordable. Another example would be the development of a process to produce a higher-strength plastic used for automobile bumpers.

With respect to **energy sources,** chemical engineers are involved in the development of processes to extract and refine crude oil and natural gas. Petroleum engineering grew out of chemical engineering and is described in a separate section. Chemical engineers are also involved in alternative fuel development and production.

The processing of petroleum into plastics by chemical engineers has created a host of consumer products that are used every day. Chemical engineers are involved in adapting these products to meet new needs. GE Plastics, for instance, operates a research house in Massachusetts made entirely from plastic. It is used as a research facility to develop new building materials that are cheaper and more beneficial to the consumer.

Many of the chemicals and their byproducts used in industry can be dangerous to people and/or the environment. Chemical engineers must develop processes that minimize harmful waste. They work with both new and traditional processes to treat hazardous byproducts and reduce harmful emissions.

Chemical engineers are also very active in the bio-products arena. This includes the **pharmaceutical industry,** where chemical engineers design processes to manufacture new lines of affordable drugs. Geneticists have developed the means to artificially produce human proteins that can be used successfully to treat many diseases. They use genetically altered bacteria to produce these proteins. It is the job of the chemical engineer to take the process from the laboratory and apply it to a larger-scale production process to produce the quantities needed by society.

Chemical engineers are also involved in **bio-processes** such as dialysis, where chemical engineers work along with other biomedical engineers to develop new ways to treat people. Chemical engineers might be involved in the development of an artificial kidney. They could also be involved in new ways to deliver medicines, such as through skin implants or patches.

Chemical engineers have become very active in the production of **circuit boards,** such as those used in computers. To manufacture the very small circuits required in modern electronic devices, material must be removed and deposited very precisely along the path of the circuit. This is done using chemical techniques developed by chemical engineers. With the demand for smaller and faster electronics, challenges continue for chemical engineers to develop the processes to make them possible.

Chemical engineers are also involved in the **modeling of systems.** Computer models of manufacturing processes are made so that modifications can be examined without having to build expensive new facilities. Managing large processes involving facilities which could be spread around the globe requires sophisticated scheduling capabilities. Chemical engineers who developed these capabilities for chemical plants have found that other large industries with scheduling challenges, such as airlines, can utilize these same tools.

The American Institute of Chemical Engineering (AIChE) is one of the most prominent professional organizations for chemical engineers. It is organized into 13 technical divisions that represent the diverse areas of the chemical engineering field:

- Catalysis and Reaction Engineering
- Computing and Systems Technology
- Engineering and Construction Contracting
- Environmental
- Food, Pharmaceutical, and Bioengineering
- Forest Products
- Fuels and Petrochemicals
- Heat Transfer and Energy Conversion
- Management
- Materials Engineering and Sciences
- Nuclear Engineering
- Safety and Health
- Separations

1.3.6 Civil Engineering

Ancient examples of early **civil engineering** can be seen in the pyramids of Egypt, the Roman roads, bridges and aqueducts of Europe, and the Great Wall in China. These all were designed and built under the direction of the predecessors to today's civil engineers. Modern civil engineering continues to face the challenges of meeting the needs of society. The broad field of civil engineering includes these categories: structural, environmental, transportation, water resources, surveying, urban planning, and construction engineering.

A humorous aside perhaps illustrates one aspect of civil engineering. . . . An Air Force general with an engineering background was asked what the difference is between civil and aerospace engineers. "That's easy," he responded. "The aerospace engineers build modern, state-of-the-art weapon systems and the civil engineers build the targets."

Structural engineers are the most common type of civil engineer. They are primarily concerned with the integrity of the structure of buildings, bridges, dams and highways. Structural engineers evaluate the loads and forces to which a structure will be subjected. They analyze the structural design in regard to earthquakes, wind forces, snow loads or wave impacts, depending on the area in which the building will be constructed.

A related field of structural engineering is **architectural engineering,** which is concerned with the form, function and appearance of a structure. The architectural engineer works alongside the architect to ensure the structural integrity of a building. The architectural engineer combines analytical ability with the concerns of the architect.

Civil engineers in the **environmental** area may be concerned with the proper disposal of wastes—residential and industrial. They may design and adapt landfills and waste treatment facilities to meet community needs. Industrial waste often presents a greater challenge because it may contain heavy metals or other toxins which require special disposal procedures. Environmental engineering has come to encompass much more and is detailed in a later section of this chapter.

Transportation engineers are concerned with the design and construction of highways, railroads and mass transit systems. They are also involved in the optimization and operation of the systems. An example of this is **traffic engineering.** Civil engineers develop the tools to measure the need for traffic control devices such as signal lights and to optimize these devices to allow proper traffic flow. This can become very complex in cities where the road systems were designed and built long ago but the areas around those roads have changed significantly with time.

Civil engineers also work with water resources as they construct and maintain dams, aqueducts, canals and reservoirs. **Water resource engineers** are charged with providing safe and reliable supplies of water for communities. This includes the design and operation of purification systems and testing procedures. As communities continue to grow, so do the challenges for civil engineers to produce safe and reliable water supplies.

Before any large construction project can be started, the construction site and surrounding area must be mapped or surveyed. **Surveyors** locate property lines and establish alignment and proper placement of engineering projects. Modern surveyors use satellite technology as well as aerial and terrestrial photogrammetry. They also rely on computer processing of photographic data.

A city is much more than just a collection of buildings and roads. It is a home and working place for people. As such, the needs of the inhabitants must be taken into account in the design of the city's infrastructure. **Urban planning engineers** are involved in this process. They incorporate the components of a city (buildings, roads, schools, airports, etc.) to meet the overall needs of the population. These needs include adequate housing, efficient transportation and open spaces. The urban planning engineer is always looking toward the future to fix problems before they reach a critical stage.

Another civil engineering area is **construction engineering.** In some institutions, this may even be a separate program. Construction engineers are concerned with the management and operation of construction projects. They are also interested in the improvement of construction methods and materials. Construction engineers design and develop building techniques and building materials that are safer, more reliable, cost-effective and environmentally friendly. There are many technical challenges that construction engineers face and will continue to face in the coming decades.

An example of one such construction challenge is the rebuilding of a city's infrastructure, such as its sewers. While the construction of a sewer may not seem glamorous or state-of-the-art, consider the difficulty of rebuilding a sewer under an existing city. A real problem facing many cities is that their Infrastructure was built decades or centuries ago, but it has a finite life. As these infrastructures near the end of their expected lives, the construction engineer must refurbish or reconstruct these systems without totally disrupting the city.

The American Society of Civil Engineers (ASCE) is one of the most prominent professional organizations for civil engineers. It is organized into the following 16 technical divisions covering the breadth of civil engineering:

- Aerospace
- Air Transport
- Architectural Engineering
- Construction Division
- Energy
- Engineering Mechanics
- Environmental Engineering
- Geomatics
- Highway
- Materials Engineering
- Pipeline
- Urban Planning and Development

- Urban Transportation
- Water Resources Engineering
- Water Resources Planning and Management
- Waterways, Ports, Coastal and Ocean Engineering

1.3.7 Computer Engineering

Much of what computer and electrical engineers do overlaps. Many **computer engineering** programs are part of electrical engineering or computer science programs. However, computer technology and development have progressed so rapidly that specialization is required in this field, and thus computer engineering is treated separately. Given the wide range of computer applications and their continued growth, computer engineering has a very exciting future.

Computer engineering is similar to computer science, yet distinct. Both fields are extensively involved with the design and development of software. The main difference is that the computer scientist focuses primarily on the software and its optimization. The computer engineer, by contrast, focuses primarily on computer hardware—the machine itself. Software written by the computer engineer is often designed to control or to interface more efficiently with the hardware of the computer and its components.

Computer engineers are involved in the design and development of operating systems, compilers and other software that requires efficient interfacing with the components of the computer. They also work to improve computer performance by optimizing the software and hardware in applications such as computer graphics.

Computer engineers work on the design of computer architecture. Designing faster and more efficient computing systems is a tremendous challenge. As faster computers are developed, applications arise for even faster machines. The continual quest for faster and smaller microprocessors involves overcoming barriers introduced by the speed of light and by circuitry so small that the molecular properties of components become important.

Computer engineers develop and design electronics to interface with computers. These include modems, Ethernet connections and other means of data transmission. Computer engineers created the devices that made the Internet possible.

In addition to having computers communicate with each other, the computer engineer is also interested in having computers work together. This may involve increasing the communication speed of computer networks or using tightly coupled multiple processors to improve the computing speed.

Security is becoming a bigger concern as more and more information is transferred using computers. Computer engineers are developing new means of commercial and personal security to protect the integrity of electronic communications.

Artificial intelligence, voice recognition systems and touch screens are examples of other technologies with which computer engineers are involved. The computers of the future will look and operate much differently than they do now, and it is the computer engineer who will make this happen.

1.3.8 Electrical Engineering

Considering the wide range of electronic devices people use every day, it is not surprising that **electrical engineering** has become the most populated of the engineering disciplines. Electrical engineers have a wide range of career opportunities in almost all of the industrial sectors. In order to provide a brief discussion of such a broad field, we will divide electrical engineering into eight areas: computers, communications, circuits and solid state devices, control, instrumentation, signal processing, bioengineering, and power.

Engineers specializing in **computer** technology are in such high demand that numerous institutions offer a separate major for computer engineering. Please refer back to the earlier section which described computer engineering separately.

Electrical engineers are responsible for the explosion in **communication** technologies. Satellites provide nearly instantaneous global communication. Global positioning systems (GPS) allow anyone with the required handheld unit to pinpoint precisely where they are located anywhere in the world. Fiber optics and lasers are rapidly improving the reliability and speed with which information can be exchanged. Wireless communication allows people to communicate anywhere, with anyone. Future breakthroughs in this field will have a tremendous impact on how we live in tomorrow's society.

Electrical engineers also design and develop electronic **circuits.** Circuit design has changed rapidly with the advent of microelectronics. As circuits continue to shrink, new barriers such as molecular size emerge. As the limits of current technology are approached, there will be incentives to develop new and faster ways to accomplish the same tasks.

Almost all modern machines and systems are digitally controlled. **Digital controls** allow for safer and more efficient operation. Electronic systems monitor processes and make corrections faster and more effectively than human operators. This improves reliability, efficiency and safety. The electrical engineer is involved in the design, development and operation of these control systems. The engineer must determine the kind of control required, what parameters to monitor, the speed of the correction, and many other factors. Control systems are used in chemical plants, power plants, automotive engines, airplanes and a variety of other applications.

For a control system to operate correctly, it must be able to measure the important parameters of whatever it is controlling. Doing so requires accurate **instrumentation,** another area for the electrical engineer. Electrical engineers who work in this area develop electrical devices to measure quantities such as pressure, temperature, flow rate, speed, heart rate and blood pressure. Often, the electrical devices convert the measured quantity to an electrical signal that can be read by a control system or a computer. Instrumentation engineers also design systems to transmit the measured information to a recording device, using telemetry. For example, such systems are needed for transmitting a satellite's measurements to the recording computers back on earth as it orbits a distant planet.

Signal processing is another area where electrical engineers are needed. In many instances the electrical signals coming from instrumentation or other sources must be conditioned before the information can be used. Signals may need to be electronically filtered, amplified or modified. An example is the active noise control system on a stethoscope which allows a paramedic to listen to a patient's heart while in a helicopter. The active noise control system can block out the sound of the helicopter so the paramedic can make a quick, accurate assessment of the patient. Signal processing also comes into play in areas such as voice recognition for computers.

Electrical engineers also work in biomedical, or **bioengineering,** applications, as described earlier. Electrical engineers work with medical personnel to design and develop devices used in the diagnosis and treatment of patients. Examples include non-intrusive techniques for detecting tumors through magnetic resonance imaging (MRI) or through computerized axial tomography (CAT) scans. Other examples include pacemakers, cardiac monitors and controllable prosthetic devices.

The generation, transmission and distribution of electric **power** is perhaps the most traditional aspect of electrical engineering. Electrical engineers work closely with mechanical engineers in the production of electrical power. They also oversee the distribution of power through electrical networks and must ensure reliable supplies of electricity to our communities. With modern society's dependence on electricity, interruptions in the flow of electricity can be catastrophic. Many of today's power-related challenges revolve around reliability and cost of delivery. Electrical engineers also work with materials engineers to incorporate superconductivity and other technology in more efficient power transmission.

The Institute of Electrical and Electronics Engineers (IEEE) is the largest and most prominent professional organization for electrical engineers. It is organized into 37 technical divisions, which indicates the breadth of the field of electrical engineering. The technical divisions include:

- Aerospace and Electronic Systems
- Antennas and Propagation
- Broadcast Technology
- Circuits and Systems
- Communications
- Components Packaging and Manufacturing Technology
- Computer
- Consumer Electronics
- Control Systems
- Dielectrics and Electrical Insulation
- Education
- Electromagnetic Compatibility
- Electron Devices
- Engineering in Medicine and Biology
- Engineering Management
- Instrumentation and Measurement
- Lasers and Electro-Optics
- Magnetics
- Microwave Theory and Techniques
- Neural Networks
- Nuclear and Plasma Sciences
- Oceanic Engineering
- Power Electronics
- Power Engineering
- Professional Communication
- Reliability
- Robotics and Automation
- Signal Processing
- Social Implications of Technology
- Solid-State Circuits
- Geoscience and Remote Sensing
- Industrial Electronics
- Industrial Applications
- Information Theory
- Systems, Man, and Cybernetics
- Ultrasonics, Ferroelectrics, and Frequency Control
- Vehicular Technology

1.3.9 Environmental Engineering

Environmental engineering is a field which has evolved to improve and protect the environment while maintaining the rapid pace of industrial activity. This challenging task has three parts to it: disposal, remediation, and prevention.

Disposal is similar to that covered under civil engineering. Environmental engineers are concerned with disposal and processing of both industrial and residential waste. Landfills and waste treatment facilities are designed for residential waste concerns. The heavy metals and other toxins found in industrial wastes require special disposal procedures. The environmental engineer develops the techniques to properly dispose of such waste.

Remediation involves the cleaning up of a contaminated site. Such a site may contain waste which was improperly disposed of, requiring the ground and/or water to be removed or decontaminated. The environmental engineer develops the means to remove the contamination and return the area to a usable form.

Prevention is an area that environmental engineers are becoming more involved in. Environmental engineers work with manufacturing engineers to design processes that reduce or eliminate harmful waste. One example is in the cleaning of machined parts. Coolant is sprayed on metal parts as they are cut to extend the life of the cutting tools. The oily fluid clings to the parts and has to be removed before the parts are assembled. An extremely toxic substance had been used in the past to clean the parts because there was not a suitable alternative. Environmental engineers discovered that oil from orange peels works just as well and is perfectly safe (even edible). Since this new degreasing fluid did not need to be disposed of in any special way, manufacturing costs were reduced, and the environment of the workers improved.

Environmental engineers must be well grounded in engineering fundamentals and current on environmental regulations. Within their companies, they are the experts on compliance with the ever-changing environmental laws. An environmental engineer must be able to understand the regulations and know how to apply them to the various processes they encounter.

1.3.10 Industrial Engineering

Industrial Engineering is described by the Institute of Industrial Engineers as the design, improvement and installation of integrated systems of people, material and energy. Industrial engineering is an interdisciplinary field that involves the integration of technology, mathematical models and management practices. Traditional industrial engineering is done on a factory floor. However, the skills of an industrial engineer are transferable to a host of other applications. As a result, industrial engineers find themselves working within a wide variety of industries. Four of the main areas of emphasis for industrial engineers are production, manufacturing, human factors, and operations research.

The **production** area includes functions such as plant layout, material handling, scheduling, and quality and reliability control. An industrial engineer would examine the entire process involved in making a product, and optimize it by reducing cost and production time, and by increasing quality and reliability. In addition to factory layout, industrial engineers apply their expertise in other ways. For example, with an amusement park an industrial engineer would analyze the flow of people through the park to reduce bottlenecks and provide a pleasant experience for the patrons.

Manufacturing differs from production in that it addresses the components of the production process. While production concerns are on a global scale, manufacturing concerns address the individual production station. The actual material processing, such as machining, is optimized by the industrial engineer.

The **human factors area** involves the placement of people into the production system. An industrial engineer in this area studies the interfaces between people and machines in the system. The machines may include production machinery, computers or even office chairs and desks. The industrial engineer considers ergonomics in finding ways to improve the interfaces. He or she looks for ways to improve productivity while providing a safe environment for workers.

Operations research is concerned with the optimization of systems. This involves mathematically modeling systems to identify ways to improve them. Project management techniques such as critical path identification fall under operations research. Often, computer simulations are required to either model the system or to study the effects of changes to the system. These systems may be manufacturing systems or other organizations. The optimizing of sales territories for a pharmaceutical sales force provides a non-manufacturing example.

The Institute for Industrial Engineering (IIE) is one of the most prominent professional organizations for industrial engineers. It is organized into three societies, 10 technical divisions and 8 interest groups. The following technical divisions show the breadth of industrial engineering:

- Aerospace and Defense
- Energy, Environment, and Plant Engineering
- Engineering Economy
- Facilities Planning and Design
- Financial Services
- Logistics Transportation and Distribution
- Manufacturing
- Operations Research
- Quality Control and Engineering Reliability
- Utilities

1.3.11 Marine and Ocean Engineering

Nearly 80 percent of the Earth's surface is covered with water. Engineers concerned with the exploration of the oceans, the transportation of products over water, and the utilization of resources in the world's oceans, seas and lakes are involved in **marine and ocean engineering.**

Marine engineers focus on the design, development and operation of ships and boats. They work together with **naval architects** in this capacity. Naval architects are concerned with the overall design of the ship. They focus on the shape of the hull in order to provide the appropriate hydrodynamic characteristics. They are also concerned with the usefulness of the vessel for its intended purpose, and with the design of the ship's subsystems including ventilation, water and sanitary systems to allow the crew to work efficiently.

The **marine engineer** is primarily concerned with the subsystems of the ship which allow the ship to serve its purpose. These include the propulsion, steering and navigation systems. The marine engineer might analyze the ship for vibrations or stability in the water. The ship's electrical power distribution and air-conditioning fall under the responsibility of marine engineers. They also might be involved in the analysis and design of the cargo handling systems of the ship.

The responsibilities of an **ocean engineer** involve the design, development and operation of vehicles and devices other than boats or ships. These include submersible vehicles used in the exploration of the oceans and in the obtaining of resources from the ocean depths. He or she might be involved in the design of underwater pipelines or cables, offshore drilling platforms and offshore harbor facilities.

Ocean engineers also are involved with the interaction of the oceans and things with which oceans come in contact. They study wave action on beaches, docks, buoys, moorings and harbors. Ocean engineers design ways to reduce erosion while protecting the marine environment. They study ways to protect and maintain marine areas which are critical to our food supply. Ocean engineers become involved with pollution control and treatment in the sea and alternative sources of energy from the ocean.

One of the professional societies to which these engineers may be involved is the Society of Naval Architects and Marine Engineers. The society is subdivided into the following nine technical and research committees:

- Hull Structure
- Hydrodynamics
- Ship's Machinery
- Ship Technical Operations
- Offshore
- Ship Production
- Ship Design
- Ship Repair and Conversion
- Small Craft

1.3.12 Materials Engineering

The origins of **materials engineering** can be traced to around 3000 B.C. when people began to produce bronze for use in creating superior hunting tools. Since that time, many new materials have been developed to meet the needs of society. Materials engineers develop these new materials and the processes to create them. The materials may be metals or non-metals: ceramics, plastics and composites. Materials engineers are generally concerned with four areas of materials: structure, properties, processes, and performance.

Materials engineers study the **structure** and composition of materials on a scale ranging from the microscopic to the macroscopic. They are interested in the molecular bonding and chemical composition of materials. The materials engineer is also concerned with the effect of grain size and structure on the material properties.

The **properties** in question might include strength, crack growth rates, hardness and durability. Numerous technological advances are impeded by a lack of materials possessing the properties required by the design engineers. Materials engineers seek to develop materials to meet these demands.

A given material may have very different properties depending on how the material is **processed.** Steel is a good example. Cooling can affect its properties drastically. Steel that is allowed to cool in air will have different properties than steel that is cooled through immersion in a liquid. The composition of a material also can affect its properties. Materials such as metallic alloys contain trace elements that must be evenly distributed throughout the alloy to achieve the desired properties. If the trace elements are not well distributed or form clumps in the metal, the material will have very different properties than the desired alloy. This could cause a part made with the alloy to fail prematurely. Materials engineers design processes and testing procedures to ensure that the material has the desired properties.

The materials engineer also works to ensure that a material meets the **performance** needs of its application by designing testing procedures to ensure that these requirements are met. Both destructive and nondestructive testing techniques are used to serve this process.

Materials engineers develop new materials, improve traditional materials and produce materials reliably and economically through synthesis and processing. Subspecialties of materials engineering, such as metallurgy and ceramics engineering, focus on classes of materials with similar properties.

Metallurgy involves the extraction of metals from naturally occurring ore for the development of alloys for engineering purposes. The metallurgical engineer is concerned with the composition, properties and performance of an alloy. Detailed investigation of a component failure often identifies design flaws in the system. The materials engineer can provide useful information regarding the condition of materials to the design engineer.

Ceramics is another area of materials engineering. In ceramic engineering, the naturally occurring materials of interest are clay and silicates, rather than an ore. These non-metallic minerals are employed in the production of materials that are used in a wide range of applications, including the aerospace, computer and electronic industries.

Other areas of materials engineering focus on polymers, plastics and composites. **Composites** are composed of different kinds of materials which are synthesized to create a new material to meet some specific demands. Materials engineers are also involved in **biomedical** applications. Examples include the development of artificial tissue for skin grafts, or bone replacement materials for artificial joints.

One of the professional societies to which materials engineers may belong is the Minerals, Metals and Materials Society. It is organized into the following five technical divisions:

- Electronic, Magnetic, and Photonic Materials
- Extraction and Processing
- Light Metals
- Materials Processing and Manufacturing
- Structural Materials

1.3.13 Mechanical Engineering

Mechanical engineering is one of the largest and broadest of the engineering disciplines. It is second only to electrical engineering in the number of engineers employed in the field. Fundamentally, mechanical engineering is concerned with machines and mechanical devices. Mechanical engineers are involved in the design, development, production, control, operation and service of these devices. Mechanical engineering is composed of two main divisions: design and controls, and thermal sciences.

The **design** function is the most common function of mechanical engineering. It involves the detailed layout and assembly of the components of machines and devices. Mechanical engineers are concerned about the strength of parts and the stresses the parts will need to endure. They work closely with materials engineers to ensure that correct materials are chosen. Mechanical engineers must also ensure that the parts fit together by specifying detailed dimensions.

Another aspect of the design function is the design process itself. Mechanical engineers develop computational tools to aid the design engineer in optimizing a design. These tools speed the design process by automating time-intensive analyses.

Mechanical engineers are also interested in controlling the mechanical devices they design. **Control** of mechanical devices can involve mechanical or hydraulic controls. However, most modern control systems incorporate digital control schemes. The mechanical engineer models controls for the system and programs or designs the control algorithm.

The noise generated from mechanical devices is often a concern, so mechanical engineers are often involved in acoustics—the study of noise. The mechanical engineer works to minimize unwanted noise by identifying the source and designing ways to minimize it without sacrificing a machine's performance.

In the **thermal sciences,** mechanical engineers study the flow of fluids and the flow of energy between systems. Mechanical engineers deal with liquids, gases and two-phase flows, which are combinations of liquids and non-liquids. Mechanical engineers might be concerned about how much power is required to supply water through piping systems in buildings. They might also be concerned with aerodynamic drag on automobiles.

The flow of energy due to a temperature difference is called **heat transfer,** another thermal science area in which mechanical engineers are involved. They predict and study the temperature of components in environments of operation. Modern personal computers have microprocessors that require cooling. Mechanical engineers design the cooling devices to allow the electronics to function properly.

Mechanical engineers design and develop **engines.** An engine is a device that produces mechanical work. Examples include internal combustion engines used in automobiles and gas turbine engines used in airplanes. Mechanical engineers are involved in the design of the mechanical components of the engines as well as the overall cycles and efficiencies of these devices.

Performance and efficiency are also concerns for mechanical engineers involved in the production of power in large **power generation systems.** Steam turbines, boilers, water pumps and condensers are often used to generate electricity. Mechanical engineers design these mechanical components needed to produce the power that operates the generators. Mechanical engineers also are involved in alternative energy sources including solar and hydroelectric power, and alternative fuel engines and fuel cells.

Another area in the thermal sciences is **heating, ventilating, and air-conditioning** (HVAC). Mechanical engineers are involved in the climate control of buildings, which includes cooling and heating the air in buildings as well as controlling humidity. In doing so, they work closely with civil engineers in designing buildings to optimize the efficiency of these systems.

Mechanical engineers are involved in the **manufacturing processes** of many different industries. They design and develop the machines used in these processes, and develop more efficient processes. Often, this involves automating time-consuming or expensive procedures within a manufacturing process. Mechanical engineers also are involved in the development and use of **robotics** and other automated processes.

In the area of **biomedical engineering,** mechanical engineers help develop artificial limbs and joints that provide mobility to physically impaired individuals. They also develop mechanical devices used to aid in the diagnosis and treatment of patients.

The American Society of Mechanical Engineering (ASME) is one of the most prominent professional societies for mechanical engineers. It is divided into 35 technical divisions, indicating the diversity of this field. These divisions are:

- Advanced Energy Systems
- Aerospace Engineering
- Applied Mechanics
- Basic Engineering Technical Group
- Bioengineering
- Design Engineering

- Dynamic Systems and Control
- Electrical and Electronic Packaging
- FACT
- Fluids Engineering
- Fluids Power Systems and Technology Systems
- Heat Transfer
- Information Storage/Processing
- Internal Combustion Engine
- Gas Turbine
- Manufacturing Engineering
- Materials
- Materials Handling Engineering
- Noise Control and Acoustics
- Non-destructive Evaluation Engineering
- Nuclear Engineering
- Ocean Engineering
- Offshore Mechanics / Arctic Engineering
- Petroleum
- Plant Engineering and Maintenance
- Power
- Pressure Vessels and Piping
- Process Industries
- Rail Transportation
- Safety Engineering and Risk Analysis
- Solar Energy
- Solid Waste Processing
- Technology and Society
- Textile Engineering
- Tribology

1.3.14 Mining Engineering

Modern society requires a vast amount of products made from raw materials such as minerals. The continued production of these raw materials helps to keep society functioning. **Mining engineers** are responsible for maintaining the flow of these raw materials by discovering, removing and processing minerals into the products society requires.

Discovering the ore involves exploration in conjunction with geologists and geophysicists. The engineers combine the utilization of seismic, satellite and other technological data, utilizing a knowledge of rocks and soils. The exploration may focus on land areas, the ocean floor, or even below the ocean floor. In the future, mining engineers may also explore asteroids, which are rich in mineral deposits.

Once mineral deposits are identified, they may be **removed.** One way minerals are removed is by way of mining tunnels. The engineers design and maintain the tunnels and the required support systems including ventilation and drainage. Other times, minerals are removed from open pit mines. Again, the engineers analyze the removal site and design the procedure for removing the material. The engineer also develops a plan for returning the site to a natural state. Mining engineers use boring, tunneling and blasting techniques to create a mine. Regardless of the removal technique, the environmental impact of the mining operation is taken into account and minimized.

The mining engineer is also involved in the **processing** of the raw minerals into usable forms. Purifying and separating minerals involves chemical and mechanical processes. While mining engineers may not be involved in producing a finished product that consumers recognize, they must understand the form their customers can use and design processes to transform the raw materials into usable forms.

Mining engineers also become involved in the **design** of the specialized equipment required for use in the mining industry. The design of automated equipment capable of performing the most dangerous mining jobs helps to increase safety and productivity of a mining operation. Since mines typically are established in remote areas, mining engineers are involved in the **transportation** of minerals to the processing facility.

The expertise of mining engineers is not used exclusively by the mining industry. The same boring technology used in developing mines is used to create subway systems and railroad tunnels, such as the one under the English Channel.

1.3.15 Nuclear Engineering

Nuclear engineers are concerned primarily with the use and control of energy from nuclear sources. This involves electricity production, propulsion systems, waste disposal and radiation applications.

The production of **electricity** from nuclear energy is one of the most visible applications of nuclear engineering. Nuclear engineers focus on the design, development and operation of nuclear power facilities. This involves using current fission technology as well as the development of fusion, which would allow sea water to be used as fuel. Nuclear energy offers an environmentally friendly alternative to fossil fuels. A current barrier to production of nuclear facilities is the high cost of construction. This barrier provides a challenge for design engineers to overcome. Research is currently being performed on the viability of smaller, more efficient nuclear reactors.

Nuclear power is also used in **propulsion systems.** It provides a power source for ships and submarines, allowing them to go years without refueling. It is also used as a power source for satellites. Nuclear-powered engines are being examined as an alternative to conventional fossil-fueled engines, making interplanetary travel possible.

One of the main drawbacks to nuclear power is the production of **radioactive waste.** This also creates opportunities for nuclear engineers to develop safe and reliable means to dispose of spent fuel. Nuclear engineers develop ways to reprocess the waste into less hazardous forms.

Another area in which nuclear engineers are involved is the use of **radiation** for medical or agricultural purposes. Radiation therapy has proven effective in treating cancers, and radioactive isotopes are also used in diagnosing diseases. Irradiating foods can eliminate harmful bacteria and help ensure a safer food supply.

Due to the complex nature of nuclear reactions, nuclear engineers are at the forefront of advanced computing methods. High-performance computing techniques, such as parallel processing, constitute research areas vital to nuclear engineering.

The American Nuclear Society (ANS) is one of the professional societies to which nuclear engineers belong. It is divided into these 16 technical divisions:

- Biology and Medicine
- Decommissioning, Decontamination, and Reutilization

- Education and Training
- Environmental Sciences
- Fuel Cycle and Waste Management
- Fusion Energy
- Human Factors
- Isotopes and Radiation
- Materials Science and Technology
- Mathematics and Computations
- Nuclear Criticality Safety
- Nuclear Operations
- Nuclear Installations Safety
- Power
- Radiation Protection and Shielding
- Reactor Physics

1.3.16 Petroleum Engineering

Petroleum and petroleum products are essential components in today's society. **Petroleum engineers** maintain the flow of petroleum in a safe and reliable manner. They are involved in the exploration for crude oil deposits, the removal of oil, and the transporting and refining of oil.

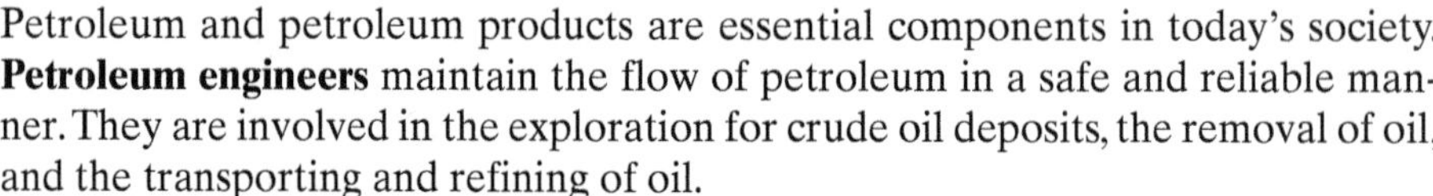

Petroleum engineers work with geologists and geophysicists to identify potential oil and gas reserves. They combine satellite information, seismic techniques and geological information to **locate deposits of gas or oil.** Once a deposit has been identified, it can be removed. The petroleum engineer designs, develops and operates the needed drilling equipment and facilities. Such facilities may be located on land or on offshore platforms. The engineer is interested in removing the oil or gas in a safe and reliable manner—safe for the people involved as well as for the environment. **Removal of oil** is done in stages, with the first stage being the easiest and using conventional means. Oil deposits are often located in sand. A significant amount of oil remains coating the sand after the initial oil removal. Recovery of this additional reserve requires the use of secondary and tertiary extraction techniques utilizing water, steam or chemical means.

Transporting the oil or gas to a processing facility is another challenge for the petroleum engineer. At times this requires the design of a heated pipeline such as the one in Alaska to carry oil hundreds of miles over frozen tundra. In other instances this requires transporting oil in double-hulled tankers from an offshore platform near a wildlife refuge. Such situations necessitate extra precautions to ensure that the wildlife is not endangered.

Once the oil or gas arrives at the processing facility, it must be **refined** into usable products. The petroleum engineer designs, develops and operates the equipment to chemically process the gas or oil into such end products. Petroleum is made into various grades of gasoline, diesel fuel, aircraft fuel, home heating oil, motor oils, and a host of consumer products from lubricants to plastics.

1.3.17 Other Fields

The most common engineering majors have been described in this chapter. However, there are other specialized engineering programs at some institutions. Here is a partial listing of some of these other programs:

- Automotive Engineering
- Acoustical Engineering

- Applied Mathematics
- Bioengineering
- Engineering Science
- Engineering Management
- Excavation Engineering
- Fire Engineering
- Forest Engineering
- General Engineering
- Genetic Engineering
- Geological Engineering
- Inventive Design
- Manufacturing Engineering
- Packaging Engineering
- Pharmaceutical Engineering
- Plastics Engineering
- Power Engineering
- Systems Engineering
- Theatre Engineering
- Transportation Engineering
- Welding Engineering

1.4 EMERGING FIELDS

The fields of engineering have been, and will continue to be, dynamic. As new technologies emerge, new definitions are needed to classify disciplines. The boundaries will continue to shift and new areas will emerge. The explosion of technological advances means that there is a good chance you will work in a field that is not currently defined. Technological advances are also blurring the traditional delineations between fields. Areas not traditionally linked are coming together and providing cross-disciplinary opportunities for engineers. A good example of this is in the development of smart buildings which sense the onset of an earthquake, adapt their structures to survive the shaking, and then return to normal status afterward. Research is being conducted on these technologies that bridge computer engineering with structural (Civil) engineering to produce such adaptable buildings.

The incredible breakthroughs in biology have opened many new possibilities and will continue to impact most of the fields of engineering. Historically, biology has not been as integrated with engineering as has physics and chemistry, but that is rapidly changing and will have enormous impact on the future of engineering. The ability to modify genetic codes has implications in a wide range of engineering applications including the production of pharmaceuticals that are customized for individual patients, alternative energy sources, and environmental reclamation.

Nanotechnology is an area that is receiving a great deal of attention and resources, and is blurring the boundaries of the fields of engineering. Nanotechnology is an emerging field in which new materials and tiny structures are built atom-by-atom, or molecule-by-molecule, instead of the more conventional approach of sculpting parts from pre-existing materials. The possibilities for nano-applications include:

- the creation of entirely new materials with superior strength, electrical conductivity, resistance to heat, and other properties
- microscopic machines for a variety of uses, including probes that could aid diagnostics and repair

- a new class of ultra-small, super-powerful computers and other electronic devices, including spacecraft
- a technology in which biology and electronics are merged, creating "gene chips" that instantly detect food-borne contamination, dangerous substances in the blood, or chemical warfare agents in the air
- the development of "molecular electronics" and devices that "self assemble," similar to the growth of complex organic structures in living organisms

Nanotechnology requires specialized laboratory and production facilities that provide further challenges and opportunities for future engineers.

The explosion of information technology with the Internet and wireless communication has produced a melding of disciplines to form new fields in information science and technology. Information management and transfer is an important and emerging issue in all disciplines of engineering and has opened opportunities for engineers who want to bridge the gaps between the traditional fields and information technologies.

Undoubtedly, more new fields will open and be discovered as technology continues to advance. As the boundaries of the genetic code and molecular-level device are crossed, new frontiers will open. As an engineer, you will have the exciting opportunity to be part of the discovery and definition of these emerging fields which will have tremendous impact on society's future.

1.5 CLOSING THOUGHTS

The information presented in this chapter is meant to provide a starting point on the road to choosing a career. There may have been aspects of one or more of these engineering fields that appealed to you, and that's great. The goal, however, is not to persuade you that engineering is for everyone; it is not. The goal is to provide information to help you decide if engineering would be an enjoyable career for *you.*

As a student, it is important to choose a career path that will be both enjoyable and rewarding. For many, an engineering degree is a gateway to just such a career. Each person has a unique set of talents, abilities and gifts that are well matched for a particular career. In general, people find more rewarding careers in occupations where their gifts and talents are well used. Does engineering match your talents, abilities and interests?

Right now, choosing a career may seem overwhelming. But at this point, you don't have to. What you are embarking on is an education that will provide the base for such decisions. Think about where a degree in engineering could lead. One of the exciting aspects of an engineering education is that it opens up a wide range of jobs after leaving college. Most students will have several different careers before they retire, and the important objective in college is obtaining a solid background that will allow you to move into areas that you enjoy later in life.

As you try to make the right choice for you, seek out additional information from faculty, career centers, professional societies, placement services and industrial representatives. Ask a lot of questions. Consider what you would enjoy studying for four years in college. What kind of entry level job would you be able to get with a specific degree? What doors would such a degree open for you later in life? Remember, your decision is unique to you. No one can make it for you.

REFERENCES

Burghardt, M.D., *Introduction to the Engineering Profession,* 2nd Edition, Harper Collins College Publishers, 1995.

Garcia, J., *Majoring {Engineering},* The Noonday Press, New York, New York, 1995.

Grace, R., and J. Daniels, *Guide to 150 Popular College Majors,* College Entrance Examination Board, New York, New York, 1992, pp. 175–178.

Kemper, J.D., *Engineers and Their Profession,* 4th Edition, Oxford University Press, New York, 1990.

Irwin, J.D., *On becoming An Engineer,* IEEE Press, New York, 1997.

Landis, R., *Studying Engineering, A Road Map to a Rewarding Career,* Discovery Press, Burbank, California, 1995.

Smith, R.J., B.R. Butler, W.K. LeBold, *Engineering as a Career,* 4th Edition, McGraw-Hill Book Company, New York, 1983.

Wright, P.H., *Introduction to Engineering,* 2nd Edition, John Wiley and Sons, Inc., New York, 1994.

EXERCISES AND ACTIVITIES

1.1 Contact a practicing engineer in a field of engineering that interests you. Write a brief report on his or her activities and compare them to the description of that field of engineering as described in this chapter.

1.2 For a field of engineering that interests you, make a list of potential employers that hire graduates from your campus, and list the cities in which they are located.

1.3 Visit a job fair on your campus and briefly interview a company representative. Prepare a brief report on what that company does, what the engineer you spoke to does, and the type of engineers they are looking to hire.

1.4 Make a list of companies that hire co-op and/or Intern students from your campus. Write a brief report on what these companies are looking for and their locations.

1.5 Select a company that employs engineers in a discipline that interests you, and visit their web page. (You can search for them using Yahoo or Alta Vista, or you can call them and ask for their Web address.) Prepare a brief report on what the company does, hiring prospects, engineering jobs in that organization, and where the company is located.

1.6 Contact a person with an engineering degree who is not currently employed in a traditional engineering capacity. Write a one-page paper on how that person uses his or her engineering background in their job.

1.7 Write a one-page paper on an engineering field that will likely emerge during your lifetime (a field that does not currently exist). Consider what background an engineering student should obtain in preparation for this emerging field.

1.8 Draft a sample letter requesting a co-op or intern position.

1.9 Identify a modern technological problem. Write a brief paper on the role of engineers and technology in solving this problem.

1.10 Select an engineering discipline that interests you and a particular job function within that discipline. Write a brief paper contrasting the different experiences an engineer in this discipline would encounter in each of three different industries.

1.11 Make a list of your own strengths and talents. Write a brief report on how these strengths are well matched with a specific engineering discipline.

1.12 Pick an engineering discipline that interests you. List and briefly describe the technical and design electives available in that discipline for undergraduates.

1.13 Select a consumer product you are familiar with (a stereo, clock radio, automobile, food product, etc.). List and briefly describe the role of all the engineering disciplines involved in producing the product.

1.14 Select an engineering discipline that interests you. Write a brief paper on how the global marketplace has altered this discipline.

1.15 Write a brief paper listing two similarities and two differences for each of the following engineering functions:

- **(a)** research and development
- **(b)** development and design
- **(c)** design and manufacturing
- **(d)** manufacturing and operations
- **(e)** sales and customer support
- **(f)** management and consulting

1.16 Find out how many engineering programs your school offers. How many students graduate each year in each discipline?

1.17 Which of the job functions described in this chapter is most appealing to you? Write a brief paper discussing it why it is appealing.

1.18 Write a paper about an engineer who made a significant technical contribution to society.

1.19 Report on the requirements for becoming a registered professional engineer in your state. Also report on how registration would be beneficial to your engineering career.

1.20 Make a list of general responsibilities and obligations you would have as an engineer.

1.21 Write a brief paper on the importance of ethical conduct as an engineer.

1.22 Select one of the industrial sectors within engineering and list five companies that do business in that sector. Briefly describe job opportunities in each.

1.23 Prepare a report on how the following items work and what engineering disciplines are involved in their design and manufacture:

- **(a)** CD player
- **(b)** CAT scan machine
- **(c)** Computer disk drive
- **(d)** Dialysis machine
- **(e)** Flat TV screen

1.24 Answer the following questions and look for themes or commonality in your answers. Comment on how engineering might fit into these themes.

- **(a)** If I could snap my fingers and do whatever I wanted, knowing that I wouldn't fail, what would I do?
- **(b)** At the end of my life, I'd love to be able to look back and know that I had done something about ____________________.
- **(c)** What would my friends say I'm really interested in or passionate about?
- **(d)** What conversation could keep me talking late into the night?
- **(e)** What were the top five positive experiences I've had in my life, and why were they meaningful to me?

1.25 Write a short paper describing your dream job, regardless of pay or geographical location.

1.26 Write a short paper describing how engineering might fit into your answer to 1.25.

1.27 List the characteristics a job must have for you to be excited to go to work every morning. How does engineering fit with those characteristics?

1.28 List the top ten reasons why a student should study engineering.

1.29 List the ten inappropriate reasons for a student to choose to study engineering.

1.30 Select an industrial sector and describe what you suppose a typical day is like for:

- **(a)** Sales engineer
- **(b)** Research engineer
- **(c)** Test engineer
- **(d)** Manufacturing engineer
- **(e)** Design engineer

1.31 Make a list of five non-engineering careers an engineering graduate could have and describe each one briefly.

1.32 Identify one of the student branches of an engineering professional society on your campus and prepare a report on the benefits of involvement with that organization for an engineering student.

1.33 Write a letter to a 9th grade class explaining the exciting opportunities in your chosen major within engineering. Include a short discussion of the classes they should be taking to be successful in that same major.

1.34 Write a letter to a 9th grade class describing the opportunities a bachelor's degree in engineering provides in today's society.

1.35 Write a letter to your parents detailing why you are going to major in the field you have chosen.

1.36 Write a one-page paper describing how your chosen field of engineering will be different in 25 years.

1.37 Select one field of engineering and write a one page paper on how the advances in biology have influenced that field.

1.38 Select one field of engineering and write a one page paper on how the advances in nanotechnology have influenced that field.

1.39 Select one field of engineering and write a one page paper on how the advances in information technology influenced that field.

1.40 Select two fields of engineering and describe problems that span these two disciplines.

1.41 Write a brief paper on an emerging area within engineering. Relate the area to your chosen engineering major.

1.42 Research the current spending priorities of the U.S. government in the area of technical research. How will these priorities impact your chosen major?

1.43 For each grouping of engineering disciplines, describe applications or problems that span the disciplines.

- **(a)** Aerospace, Materials and Civil
- **(b)** Mechanical, Agricultural, and Computer
- **(c)** Biological and Environmental
- **(d)** Industrial, Chemical, and Electrical
- **(e)** Biomedical and Nuclear
- **(f)** Agricultural and Aerospace
- **(g)** Materials and Biomedical
- **(h)** Civil and Computer

1.44 Select one professional organization and find out how they handle new and emerging technologies within their society (where do they put them and where can people working in emerging areas find colleagues?)

1.45 Interview a practicing engineering and a faculty member from the same discipline about their field. Compare and contrast their views of the discipline.

1.46 Select two engineering majors and compare and contrast the opportunities available between the two.

1.47 Identify how your skills as an engineer can be used within your local community—either as full time work or as a volunteer. Share your findings with the class by preparing a short oral presentation.

CHAPTER 2
PROFILES OF ENGINEERS

Objective

By learning the material in this chapter, you should be able to

- explain how the profiles of engineers' careers inform their choice of a major and their career planning

This chapter contains a collection of profiles of engineering graduates to let you read firsthand accounts of what it is really like to be an engineer. Each engineer wrote his or her own profile.

Our intent is to provide you with a glimpse of the diversity of the engineering workforce. Engineers are people just like you, and had varying reasons for pursuing engineering as a career. Engineering graduates also take very diverse career paths.

In order to capture a flavor of this diversity, each engineer was asked to address three areas:

1. Why or how they became an engineer
2. Their current professional activities
3. Their life outside of work

This is not a comprehensive survey of the engineering workforce. To truly represent the breadth of engineering careers and the people in those careers would take several volumes, not just one chapter. This is meant to be only a beginning. It is also arranged simply to show you the wide range of engineering careers that are possible. To keep the wide-ranging feel, we've avoided ranking the profiles by subject, and instead present them alphabetically. This makes it easier to see the common bonds across all the disciplines.

We recommend that you follow up and seek out other practicing engineers or engineering students, to get more detailed information about the specific career path you might follow. As with the information we have collected in other chapters of this text, our goal is to assist you in finding that career path which is right for you. You are the one who must ultimately decide this for yourself.

Table 2.1 summarizes those who provided profiles.

Taken from *Engineering Your Future: A Brief Introduction to Engineering,* 2009–2010 Edition, by William C. Oakes, PhD, Les L. Leone, PhD, and Craig J. Gunn, MS.

Table 2.1 Summary of Profiled Engineers

Name	BS Degree	Graduate Degree	Current Job Title
Moyosola Ajaja	BS/EE		Software Engineer
Artagnan Ayala	BS/Aero		Combustion Engineer
Sandra Begay-Campbell	BS/CE	MS/CE	Executive Director of AISES
Raymond C. Barrera	BS/EE	MS/Software	Computer Engineer
Linda Blevins	BS/ME	MS/ME & Ph.D.	Mechanical Engineer with NIST
Timothy Bruns	BS/EE		Software Manager
Jerry Burris	BS/EE	MBA	General Manager
Bethany Fabin	BS/ABE		Design Engineer
Bob Feldmann	BS/EE	MS/Comp, MBA	Director, Tactical Aircraft Systems
Steven Fredrickson	BS/EE	Ph.D.	Project Manager, NASA
Myron Gramelspacher	BS/ME		Manufacturing Manager
Karen Jamison	BS/IE	MBA	Operations Manager
James Lammie	BS/CE	MS/CE	Member of Board of Directors
Mary Maley	BS/AgE		Product Manager
Jeanne Mordarski	BS/IE	MBA	Sales Manager
Mark Pashan	BS/EE	MS/EE & MBA	Director, Hardware Operations
Patrick Shook	BS/ME	MS/ME	Senior Engineer
Nana Tzeng	BS/ME	MS/ME	Design Engineer
Jack Welch	BS/ChE	MS/ChE & Ph.D.	Chief Executive Officer (retired)

PROFILE OF A COMPUTER ENGINEER: MOYOSOLA O. AJAJA, CHANDLER, ARIZONA

Occupation

Software Engineer at Intel Corporation

Education

BS, Computer and Electrical Engineering, 1997

Studying Engineering

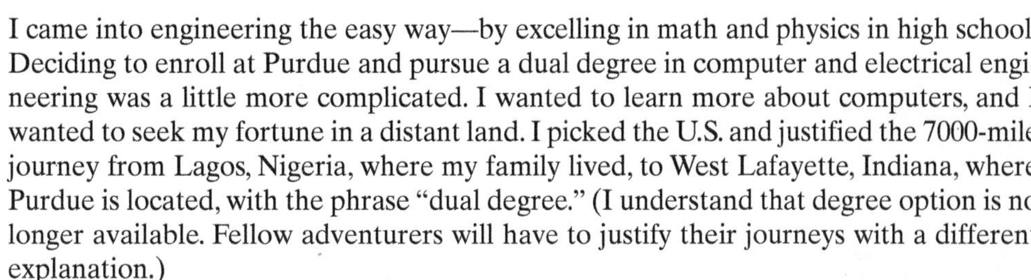

I came into engineering the easy way—by excelling in math and physics in high school. Deciding to enroll at Purdue and pursue a dual degree in computer and electrical engineering was a little more complicated. I wanted to learn more about computers, and I wanted to seek my fortune in a distant land. I picked the U.S. and justified the 7000-mile journey from Lagos, Nigeria, where my family lived, to West Lafayette, Indiana, where Purdue is located, with the phrase "dual degree." (I understand that degree option is no longer available. Fellow adventurers will have to justify their journeys with a different explanation.)

During my first year at Purdue I set two goals for myself: first, find a scholarship to fund my education, and second, gain useful work experience. I applied for dozens of scholarships. I was partial to those offered by engineering firms that provided internships, since internships for first-year engineering students were very scarce. In addition, I attended every resume or interview preparation workshop offered during that year. My efforts paid off. I was invited to join the cooperative education program with a summer placement with Intel Corporation, and later I was awarded an Intel Foundation scholarship which paid my tuition.

Career Life

Today, I work as a software engineer with Intel in Arizona. I develop hardware emulation units and validation test suites for new processors. What that means in plain English: I take descriptions of hardware features and functions and write software programs that behave like the hardware should. This is cheaper than fabricating silicon devices each time a change is made during design. As an Intel engineer with access to the latest and greatest technologies, I am constantly challenged to learn new things to remain at the leading edge of computer technology.

Life Outside of Work

I have tried to maintain a balance between my work and my non-work activities. My weekend mornings are spent running with my dog or hiking up Camelback Mountain in Phoenix. The evenings are spent in classes like dog training, theology, or photography. My real passion is traveling, and through engineering school, internships, and my current assignment, I have met people who helped fuel my interest in increasingly diverse destinations.

I've discovered that engineering is a *discipline,* not just a major. The distinction here is that a discipline involves the development of the faculties through instruction and exercise, while a major is simply a field of study, an area of mental focus, or a concentration. For me this means the qualities of an engineer should be apparent in all I do. The guide I use is the Code of Ethics approved by the IEEE.

PROFILE OF AN AEROSPACE ENGINEER:
ARTAGNAN AYALA, GILBERT, ARIZONA

Occupation

Combustion Engineer, Diversity Organizations Manager, Honeywell

Education

BS, Aeronautical and Astronautical Engineering, 1995
MS (in progress), Mechanical & Aerospace Engineering

Studying Engineering

I have been interested in space since I was very young, I always wanted to be an Astronaut. This was my motivation to become an engineer. I figured that, if one day I was to climb on a rocket and go to outer space, I'd better know how it works. I am still working towards that goal.

My education has definitely met my expectations. I have applied what I learned in my job, and some of it to life in general. Engineering is not only a field you go into, but also a way of thinking. You are thought to solve problems, which can be applied to everything you do.

If I could start over, I would interact more with professors, take better notes, and learn more about statistics.

Career Life

Currently I am a Combustion Engineer, a Six Sigma Plus Black Belt, and the Diversity Organizations Manager for Society of Hispanic Professional Engineers at Honeywell Engines & Systems.

As a combustion engineer I design and develop combustion systems that are installed in Auxiliary Power Units and Industrial Power Generators. I have finished the development on one system, designed a technology demonstrator, and am currently designing a premixed fuel delivery system.

As a Six Sigma Plus Black Belt I apply statistical tools to improve all sorts of processes, from combustion system development and manufacturing.

As Diversity Organizations Manager, I am responsible for the company's contact and participation with the Society.

What I like the most about what I do is the diversity of my responsibilities. I get to apply my engineering skills every day, and I get to learn more skills. This has allowed me to receive my Black Belt certification, and participate in the Honeywell Quest for Excellence, a company event where teams with outstanding results present their work in a competition to win the Premier Achievement Award, the biggest team honor. I am particularly proud of my participation as presenter in 2 events, and making it to the finals in one of them.

Life Outside of Work

My wife Laura, a Graphic Designer, and I recently expanded our family with the arrival of our first daughter, Deanna Isabella. I devote most of my free time to my family and some to my studies.

Before we had a baby, I participated in a volleyball league, went dancing at clubs and concerts on weekends, and traveled outside of Arizona.

PROFILE OF A CIVIL ENGINEER: SANDRA BEGAY-CAMPBELL, BOULDER, COLORADO

Occupation

AISES Executive Director

Education

BSCE, 1987; MS, Structural Engineering, 1991

Studying Engineering

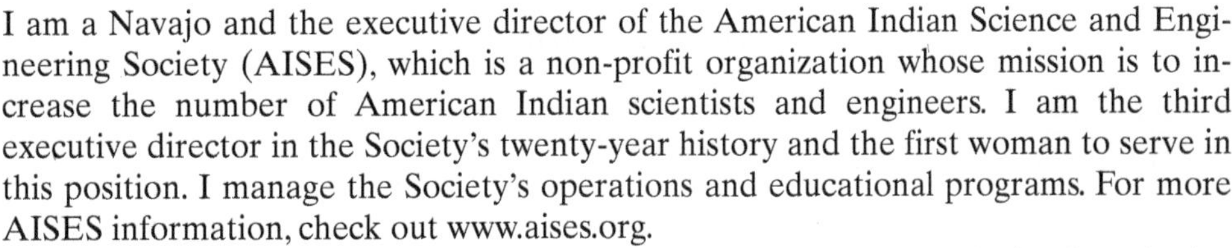

I am a Navajo and the executive director of the American Indian Science and Engineering Society (AISES), which is a non-profit organization whose mission is to increase the number of American Indian scientists and engineers. I am the third executive director in the Society's twenty-year history and the first woman to serve in this position. I manage the Society's operations and educational programs. For more AISES information, check out www.aises.org.

In 1987, I received a BSCE degree from the University of New Mexico. I worked at Lawrence Livermore National Laboratories before I earned a MS, Structural Engineering degree from Stanford University. I also worked at Los Alamos National Laboratory and Sandia National Laboratories before accepting my current leadership position. Within AISES, I served as a college chapter officer, a national student representative, and board of directors member. I was the first woman AISES board of directors Chairperson.

In the sixth grade, I was very interested in architecture, but I knew I was not an artist. I also enjoyed math and solving problems so I looked into the engineering profession. I attended a "minority introduction to engineering" program as a high school junior and I discovered that civil engineers worked on a variety of interesting public projects, which included work with architects. This program solidified my decision to become an engineer.

Career Life

One of the earliest challenges I faced was in continuing my structural engineering studies following the 1989 San Francisco Bay-Area earthquake. I was a first quarter graduate student at Stanford when the earthquake hit. Through prayer and reflection, I understood my unique role as an American Indian engineer. I must use my best knowledge to design structures for earthquake resistance, but my cultural heritage taught me the wisdom that engineers ultimately cannot control Nature and that we have to accept the consequences from natural phenomena.

Life Outside of Work

Life outside of work is difficult to describe at this point in time. With the re-building of the AISES organization and relocation of the offices, I don't have much time for outside activities. I have also been commuting between Boulder, Colorado, and Albuquerque, New Mexico. In brief, my hobbies are watching college basketball, watching movies, and working on my home's backyard. My husband and I have two dogs and a cat.

PROFILE OF A COMPUTER ENGINEER: RAYMOND C. BARRERA, GAITHERSBURG, MD

Occupation

Computer Engineer, Advanced Concepts and Engineering Division, Space and Warfare Systems Command Systems Center, San Diego

Education

BS, Electrical and Computer Engineering 1989
MS, Software Engineering 1999

Studying Engineering

I was very fortunate during high school to work for an archaeologist and her husband who were great mentors. To me archaeology is like detective work—finding bits of information here and there and putting them together to form the big picture. Dr. Bernice McAllister taught me the scientific methodology an archaeologist needs to base sound conclusions on evidence. I think I would be happy had I become an archaeologist, but I really enjoy building things. My dad's training as an electronic technician had gotten me interested in electronics when I was very young. That, with some encouragement from Dr. McAllister's husband, Capt. James McAllister, USN (ret) helped convince me to select Electrical Engineering as my specialty.

Career Life

I work at a research, development, test and evaluation laboratory for the US Navy. I am involved in testing and system engineering of command and control systems. Command and control systems are used by tactical commanders for decision making and direction. I began working here in 1989 so I was here during Desert Storm. Perhaps even more important than the technical work is the ability to communicate. Not very many engineers work alone. A former Navy Admiral, Grace Hopper (who is said to have coined the computer term "bug") used a length of wire to describe a nanosecond to programmers. It was about a foot long, the distance that electricity could travel in one billionth of a second. But then she showed a microsecond—a coil of wire almost a thousand feet long. She was trying to convince programmers not to waste even a microsecond. Often the most difficult engineering challenge is to share an idea with others in oral and written presentations, but that is the only way these ideas can come to life.

Life Outside of Work

My wife Martha and I spend most of our time outside of work with our new daughter Laura. I do have some flexibility on my work schedule so I can spend more time with her. I've been able to select job assignments that don't require too much travel. Since this is a research laboratory there are always new things to do. In the over ten years I've been here, no two have been the same. In this command alone there are engineers working with supercomputers, lasers, networking, marine mammals, 3-D displays, simulators, and sensors.

PROFILE OF A MECHANICAL ENGINEER: LINDA G. BLEVINS, GAITHERSBURG, MARYLAND

Occupation

Mechanical Engineer, National Institute of Standards and Technology

Education

BSME, 1989; MSME, 1992; PhD, 1996

Studying Engineering

During high school I discovered that I enjoyed mathematics. I learned about engineering when I participated in a six-week summer honors program at the University of Alabama before my senior year in high school. I took college calculus that summer, and I was hooked. I chose to study mechanical engineering because the course subjects are diverse and the industrial demand for mechanical engineers remains steady. As a co-op at Eastman Chemical Co., I worked on engineering problems in power and chemical plants. The concepts that I learned in classes came to life during the alternate semesters that I worked, and the money I earned helped pay for school. After earning a BS degree from the University of Alabama, I obtained an MS degree from Virginia Tech, and a PhD degree from Purdue University. I never would have set or achieved these goals without encouragement and advice from faculty members. Because these mentors played such valuable roles in my life, I would advise college students to get to know their professors well. These personal investments will be rewarding for years to come.

Career Life

I am a mechanical engineer in the Building and Fire Research Laboratory at the National Institute of Standards and Technology (NIST), a national research laboratory operated by the U.S. Department of Commerce, located in Gaithersburg, Maryland. Our goals are to study the ways that fires ignite, spread, and extinguish so that our nation can minimize the loss of lives and property to fires. My primary job function is to improve the accuracy of measurements made during fire research. A few things routinely measured are toxic gas concentration, temperature, and heat intensity. I spend my time developing laser-based instrumentation, devising computer (math) models of instrument behavior, designing laboratory equipment, tinkering with electronics, publishing papers, writing and reviewing research proposals, and presenting talks at conferences. In addition, I work on a project funded by the National Aeronautics and Space Administration (NASA) to study fires in space. Working in a research laboratory ensures that I am constantly learning and growing, and I realize every day how lucky I am to be here. My job is exciting, fun, and rewarding.

Life Outside of Work

During my free time, I enjoy hiking, rollerblading, and reading. I participate in a weekly bowling league and I manage a softball team each summer. I also volunteer as a member of the Mechanical Engineering Advisory Board at the University of Alabama. This allows me to travel home to Alabama (and visit my family) several times a year. Finally, I volunteer regularly to educate children and community members about the excitement of engineering.

PROFILE OF AN ELECTRICAL ENGINEER: TIMOTHY J. BRUNS, ST. LOUIS, MISSOURI

Occupation

Software Manager at Boeing Co.

Education

BSEE, 1983

Studying Engineering

I became interested in electronics at a young age by building electronic kits from companies like Radio Shack and Heathkit. As a teenager, I became very active in local citizen's band (CB) radio groups. It was an easy decision for me to pursue a degree in engineering. The technology has changed so much since I graduated, and I have needed to stay current with the latest technology and to find ways to apply it to my line of work. If you are just starting out in engineering, I encourage you to apply yourself and do your very best in all your classes. When I arrived at Purdue I felt as if I was the least prepared of any of my classmates, but I worked hard and did very well. Some of the better prepared students did not apply themselves from the beginning and suffered as a result. One thing I would have done differently is to get to know my professors and teaching assistants better. In large universities and organizations it is easy to get lost in the crowd, and I wish that I had formed better friendships and relationships with my instructors.

Career Life

I am the software manager for a team of 15 developers that is creating a Windows NT application. This application uses the latest technologies such as MFC, COM and ActiveX. A typical day is spent reviewing the technical work of the team, along with reviewing schedules and making estimates for future work. I often meet with customers of our product and suppliers of our software development tools. Since our program is just getting started, I have been spending a lot of time interviewing people who would like to join our team. It is difficult to say how I apply my engineering training directly to my current job. I know that my engineering degree has given me the ability to plan and organize the work of our team, and to solve the many problems that come up. The thing I like best about my job is the wide variety of assignments I have had in my 15 years with Boeing. Working in a large company gives me the ability to have several "mini-careers," all while working for the same company. A significant accomplishment that I have made while working at Boeing is the introduction of new tools and technology into the software development process. One tool that we have introduced automatically produces source code from a graphical representation. This tool enables us to bypass much of the labor-intensive and error-prone aspects of software design.

Life Outside of Work

In the engineering field, particularly in electrical and computer engineering, you will find that the technology changes very rapidly. In my case, I stay abreast of the latest technologies by enrolling in evening computer classes through the local universities. I enjoy home "engineering" projects such as designing a new deck. My wife, Donna, and I keep very busy raising our two sons, Garrett and Gavin.

PROFILE OF AN ELECTRICAL ENGINEER: JERRY W. BURRIS, LOUISVILLE, KENTUCKY

Occupation

General Manager of Refrigeration Programs for General Electric Appliances

Education

BSEE, 1985; MBA, 1994

Studying Engineering

I have always had a curiosity about how things work (especially electronic devices). My parents recognized this at a very early age. They encouraged me to think about becoming an engineer. I was the child in the family who was always asked to fix the TV or electronic games. This continued through high school, where I excelled in math and science.

Purdue University was a natural choice for me, not only for its reputation for engineering excellence, but also due to the added bonus of having Marion Blalock and her Minority Engineering Program. This program has served as a recruiting magnet for Purdue and also has served as a mechanism for helping retain and matriculate students of color at Purdue.

While at Purdue, I was active in many extracurricular activities including leadership roles with NSBE and Kappa Alpha Psi fraternity. My early involvement in academics and extracurricular activities led to a full scholarship, which I received from PPG during my freshman year. Summer internships with PPG and IBM were invaluable in terms of giving me insight into what career path I wanted to pursue (design, manufacturing, or sales/marketing).

Career Life

I chose the technical sales and marketing route with General Electric's Technical Leadership Program. This premier program gave me advantages over direct hires in terms of exposure and training. After working six years I earned an MBA from Northwestern's Kellogg School of Management; I focused on global business, teamwork, and marketing.

My career has taken me from a role as a sales engineer, calling on industrial and OEM customers, to branch manager, with profit and loss responsibility, leading a team of nine people; to general manager of Refrigeration Programs at GE Appliances, where I now manage a $2 billion refrigeration product line.

I have been blessed with a lovely wife, who is also a Purdue and Northwestern graduate. We have two active children—Jarret, who is 7, and Ashlee, 4. We are managing dual careers at GE. This comes with significant challenges. However, GE has been very supportive of both of our careers.

Life Outside of Work

Life can not be all about work! You have to strive for balance. I have sought to keep God first in my life. I enjoy coaching my children in soccer, baseball and basketball, and I try to stay active with my own personal sporting activities. My favorite activities are listening to jazz music, traveling to exotic locations, managing our investment portfolio, and improving my golf game.

PROFILE OF AN AGRICULTURAL ENGINEER: BETHANY A. ELKIN FABIN, WATERLOO, IOWA

Occupation

Design Engineer, 8000 Chassis Design Team – John Deere Waterloo Works

Education

BS, Agricultural and Biological engineering

Studying Engineering

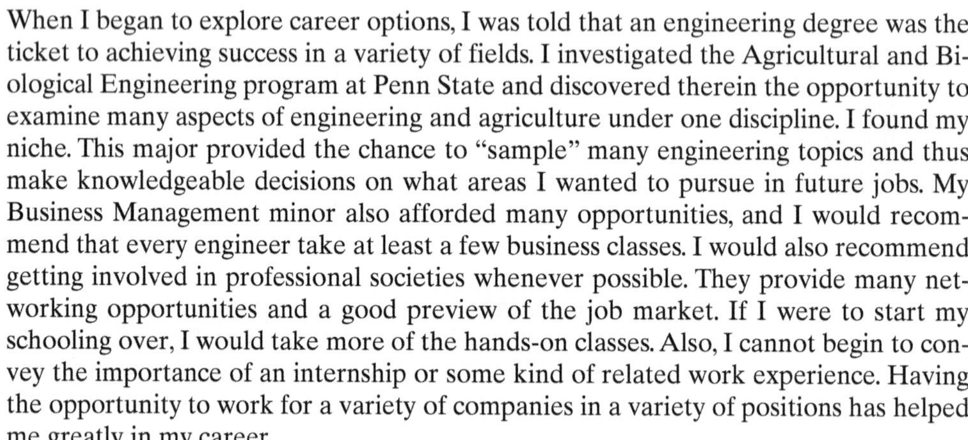

When I began to explore career options, I was told that an engineering degree was the ticket to achieving success in a variety of fields. I investigated the Agricultural and Biological Engineering program at Penn State and discovered therein the opportunity to examine many aspects of engineering and agriculture under one discipline. I found my niche. This major provided the chance to "sample" many engineering topics and thus make knowledgeable decisions on what areas I wanted to pursue in future jobs. My Business Management minor also afforded many opportunities, and I would recommend that every engineer take at least a few business classes. I would also recommend getting involved in professional societies whenever possible. They provide many networking opportunities and a good preview of the job market. If I were to start my schooling over, I would take more of the hands-on classes. Also, I cannot begin to convey the importance of an internship or some kind of related work experience. Having the opportunity to work for a variety of companies in a variety of positions has helped me greatly in my career.

Career Life

In my current position as a chassis design engineer for John Deere, I work with others to design parts for tractor frames, coordinate homologation and standard reviews for update programs, and coordinate projects with supporting teams. In the latter role, I develop general specifications to ensure that we meet customer requirements and implement verification processes.

In a typical day of work, I spend a couple of hours working on Pro/E software designing and modeling parts. I also spend time working with suppliers and purchasing personnel to get parts quoted and ordered. In addition, I spend some time in our shop checking on prototype builds or test procedures, and some time in meetings working with different groups to keep people informed. The thing I like best about my job is the freedom I have to work on a variety of projects. It's nice to work for a company that has developed a strong name for itself and works diligently to stand behind their products.

Life Outside of Work

Outside of work, I welcome every opportunity to travel with my husband and play host to out-of-state friends, relatives, and foreign exchange students. MBA classes are taking up much of my time off the job currently, but in my free time I find I enjoy music, sports, rowing, training my dog, remodeling my house, and gardening. My membership in the local chapter of American Society of Agricultural Engineers also keeps me busy with meetings and seminars.

PROFILE OF AN ELECTRICAL ENGINEER: BOB FELDMANN, ST. LOUIS, MISSOURI

Occupation

Director, Tactical Aircraft Mission Systems, The Boeing Company

Education

BSEE, 1976; MS, Computer Science, 1980; MBA, 1999

Studying Engineering

My interest in engineering evolved naturally from my lifelong interest in science. Mathematics, while not my life's ambition, was interesting and satisfying. High school offered me the opportunity to enjoy learning about science, and I knew that I wanted to explore it even more in college.

In the mid-1970s, computers were not commonplace except in colleges, and I was hooked with my first FORTRAN programming class as a freshman. From that point on, I wanted to learn more about the hardware and software that made computers work. I oriented my electrical engineering curriculum toward digital electronics and used every elective I could to take software or software theory courses. While in college, I began a four-quarter stint as a cooperative engineering student at McDonnell Douglas in St. Louis. As a co-op, I was able to design software in the flight simulators (McDonnell was a world leader in simulation) and to work on a research design team for advanced flight control systems. Each semester when I went back to school, I would be at the library when Aviation Week magazine arrived, and I would read it cover to cover. When I graduated, I started my career as a software designer. My first day on the job, I was told that I would be responsible for the design of the software that controls the automatic carrier landing system on the F/A-18 aircraft. Ever since that first day, I have never been disappointed with the technical issues that have challenged me.

Career Life

Today I am leading a team of over 800 engineers in the design and production of Mission Systems (also known as avionics) for the F-15, the F/A-18, the AV-8B, and the T-45 aircraft. My role as team leader for the organization is to ensure that the various product teams are providing outstanding value to our customers with the quality of our designs. I no longer write software, but I interact with the technical teams, coaching and guiding them through the difficult challenges of today's technically-exploding world. My proudest recent accomplishment was leading a team of engineers in the design and flight test of a reconnaissance system for the F/A-18. That system will provide the United States with its first manned tactical reconnaissance capability since the mid-1980s.

Life Outside of Work

My life outside the office centers around outdoor activities and my family. My wife and I have three sons, all of whom play soccer and baseball (I have coached each one at various times). I really enjoy golf, bike riding, and other outdoor activities. My wife and I receive great pleasure from watching our sons grow up.

PROFILE OF A COMPUTER ENGINEER: STEVEN E. FREDRICKSON, HOUSTON, TEXAS

Occupation

Project manager of the Autonomous Extravehicular Robotic Camera for NASA; Electronics Engineer, NASA Johnson Space Center, 1995 – present

Education

BS, Computer and EE 1992; PhD, Engineering Science, 1995

Studying Engineering

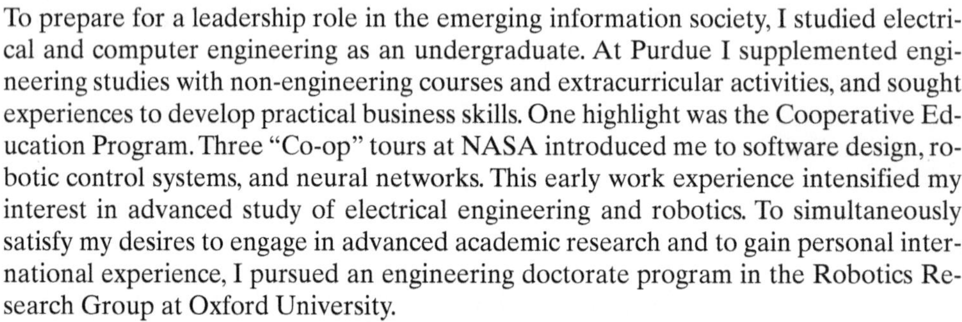

To prepare for a leadership role in the emerging information society, I studied electrical and computer engineering as an undergraduate. At Purdue I supplemented engineering studies with non-engineering courses and extracurricular activities, and sought experiences to develop practical business skills. One highlight was the Cooperative Education Program. Three "Co-op" tours at NASA introduced me to software design, robotic control systems, and neural networks. This early work experience intensified my interest in advanced study of electrical engineering and robotics. To simultaneously satisfy my desires to engage in advanced academic research and to gain personal international experience, I pursued an engineering doctorate program in the Robotics Research Group at Oxford University.

I am extremely pleased with the universities I attended and the fields of study I completed to prepare for my current career. I would offer three recommendations to anyone pursuing an engineering path: 1) participate in Co-op or similar programs, 2) develop effective oral and written communications skills, 3) explore opportunities to study abroad.

Career Life

When I returned to NASA as a robotics research engineer, I transitioned from specialized research in artificial neural networks to broadly focused applied engineering. As project manager of the Autonomous Extravehicular Robotic Camera (AERCam) project, I have led a multidisciplinary team of engineers in development of a free-flyer robotic camera to provide "bird's eye" views of the Space Shuttle or International Space Station. Despite this deliberate transition to a project leadership role, it has been imperative for me to maintain my core technical skills. To ensure continued technical proficiency, I participate in several training courses and technical conferences every year.

Life Outside of Work

As much as I enjoy working at NASA, I believe it is essential to maintain outside interests. For me, that starts by spending time with my wife, Becky. Since Becky is pursuing a joint engineering and medical career, it can be demanding at times. The key for us has been to develop outside activities that we can enjoy together. Currently these include teaching Sunday school, participating in Bible study, attending concerts and plays, jogging, lifting weights, climbing at an indoor rock gym, and traveling. In addition, we allow each other time to pursue individual interests, which for me include reading, aviation, and golf.

PROFILE OF A MECHANICAL ENGINEER: MYRON D. GRAMELSPACHER, HARTLAND, WI

Occupation

Manufacturing Manager, General Electric

Education

BSME, 1989

Studying Engineering

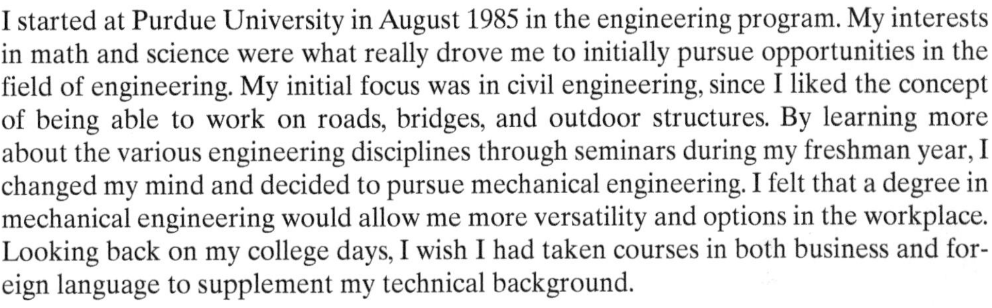

I started at Purdue University in August 1985 in the engineering program. My interests in math and science were what really drove me to initially pursue opportunities in the field of engineering. My initial focus was in civil engineering, since I liked the concept of being able to work on roads, bridges, and outdoor structures. By learning more about the various engineering disciplines through seminars during my freshman year, I changed my mind and decided to pursue mechanical engineering. I felt that a degree in mechanical engineering would allow me more versatility and options in the workplace. Looking back on my college days, I wish I had taken courses in both business and foreign language to supplement my technical background.

Career Life

I graduated from Purdue University in 1989 with a degree in mechanical engineering, and started with General Electric (GE) as part of the Manufacturing Management Program. This program provided me with an opportunity to have six-month rotational assignments in two GE businesses. My first year was with GE Transportation Systems in Grove City, Pennsylvania, followed by a year with GE Aircraft Engines in Cincinnati, Ohio. In 1991, I transferred to the GE Medical Systems division in Milwaukee, Wisconsin. Since that time, I have held various positions in the Sourcing group, including supplier quality engineer, buyer, and team leader of the mechanical sourcing department. I also had the opportunity to live in Paris, France, for a year, heading up an Eastern European initiative. During that time, my efforts focused on the identification and qualification of suppliers in Eastern Europe. This position required that I travel throughout Europe, making it possible for me to experience different cultures and surroundings. This was a truly challenging and rewarding experience, both for my wife and me.

I currently hold the position of a Black Belt in GE's Six Sigma quality program. I utilize the Six Sigma tools and methodology to drive both process and product improvements that reduce costs, and ultimately impact our customers. The analytical skills and systematic problem solving techniques that I gained through my undergraduate engineering courses have greatly contributed to the many opportunities and successes I have had in my professional career.

Life Outside of Work

I now am attending Marquette University, working toward my MBA. An MBA will complement my technical background and enable me to strengthen my overall business knowledge. Outside work, I enjoy making landscaping improvements around the house and tackling various wood-working activities. My wife, Kim, and I enjoy traveling in our spare time. I also enjoy playing golf, tennis, and softball.

PROFILE OF AN INDUSTRIAL ENGINEER: KAREN JAMISON, DAYTON, OHIO

Occupation

Operations Manager, Jamison Metal Supply, Inc.

Education

BSIE, 1988; MBA, 2000

Studying Engineering

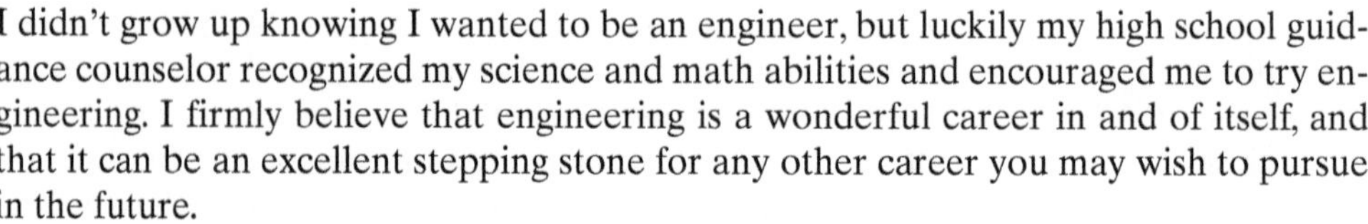

I didn't grow up knowing I wanted to be an engineer, but luckily my high school guidance counselor recognized my science and math abilities and encouraged me to try engineering. I firmly believe that engineering is a wonderful career in and of itself, and that it can be an excellent stepping stone for any other career you may wish to pursue in the future.

I chose industrial engineering because I am highly interested in improving the processes people use to do their work. Industrial engineering provides both technical challenges and the opportunity to work with all kinds of people.

If you are just starting to think about engineering or are trying to choose a specific discipline, talk to as many practicing engineers and professors as you can. Become involved in organizations on campus that will let you interact with other engineering students and practicing engineers.

I also highly recommend the co-op program. I had over two years of work experience when I graduated, and I knew what types of work I would enjoy. It is definitely to your advantage during interviews to know what type of job will best suit you, and to be able to speak intelligently on that subject.

Finally, remember that grades aren't everything but that your education is invaluable. If I were to do one thing differently, I would study to truly learn and understand the content instead of with the goal of getting a good grade in the class.

Career Life

Until last year, I was a consultant focusing on process improvement and business process re-engineering. Now I am learning to run Jamison Metal Supply, which is a business my parents founded 25 years ago. My job includes anything and everything that needs to be done. My primary responsibilities are overseeing operations to ensure quality products and timely deliveries, ordering steel for inventory and special orders, and pricing the material we sell.

I use my engineering training in all kinds of ways. I am working on updating our physical inventory system to better utilize warehouse floor space; I schedule customer orders to meet promised delivery times; and I am updating our computer system. Most importantly, engineering has taught me how to approach solving a problem and how to manage my time.

Life Outside of Work

My time outside of work is concentrated on completing my MBA degree, but I do find time for having fun as well. One of my favorite hobbies is crewing for a hot air balloon. I also teach a sign language class at the University of Dayton, and am vice president of the Purdue Club of Greater Dayton, Ohio. I think engineering is a very flexible field that allows individuals to prioritize their lives any way they wish.

PROFILE OF A CIVIL ENGINEER: JAMES L. LAMMIE, NEW YORK, NY

Occupation

Board of Directors, Parsons Brinckerhoff, Inc.

Education

BS, Civil Engineering, 1953; MS, Civil Engineering, 1957

Career Life

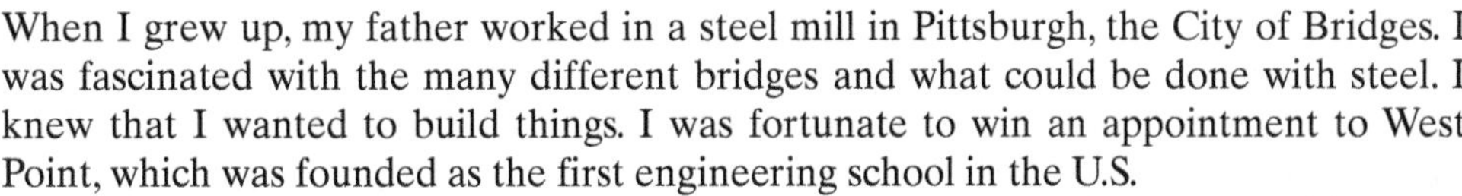

When I grew up, my father worked in a steel mill in Pittsburgh, the City of Bridges. I was fascinated with the many different bridges and what could be done with steel. I knew that I wanted to build things. I was fortunate to win an appointment to West Point, which was founded as the first engineering school in the U.S.

After graduation, I spent 21 years in the Army Corps of Engineers working on a wide variety of military and civil engineering projects all over the world. After retiring from the Army I knew I wanted to be a Project Manager on big projects, so I joined Parsons Brinckerhoff, Inc. and spent seven years as a consultant Project Manager for design and construction on the Metropolitan Atlanta Rapid Transit project (MARTA), the most rewarding period of my professional career. Today, my grandchildren ride what I helped build—a most rewarding feeling.

After MARTA, I had the pleasure of serving as the CEO of Parsons Brinckerhoff, Inc., the largest transportation design firm in the U.S., for the next fourteen years. Today, as a member of the Board of Directors of our employee-owned firm, I am still involved in some of our mega projects: the Central Artery Highway project in Boston, the new Taiwan High-Speed Rail system, the Bay Area Rapid Transit extension to the San Francisco Airport, and many others. The high point of my job is getting involved in critical project decisions and being able to "kick the tires" of work under construction.

Life Outside of Work

Thanks to my varied career in engineering, construction and management, I am also able to participate in a variety of outside activities: the Transportation Research Board (TRB), the Institute for Civil Infrastructure Systems (ICIS), the Engineering Advisory Board at Purdue University, and the National Academy of Engineering (NAE). I also teach and lecture on Project Management, Leadership, and Engineering Ethics. During my career, the high points have been presenting proposals and winning major jobs, election to the National Academy of Engineering, and receiving an Honorary Doctorate at Purdue University.

I always enjoyed participating in a variety of sports, until my knees gave out. The most personally rewarding aspect of my life over the years has been the companionship of my wife, three children (all in the medical profession, thanks to my wife's nursing career), and my eight grandchildren (with three going to colleges close by, permitting frequent visits).

PROFILE OF AN AGRICULTURAL ENGINEER: MARY E. MALEY, BATTLE CREEK, MICHIGAN

Occupation

Product Manager,
Kellogg Company

Education

BS, Agricultural Engineering (food engineering)

Studying Engineering

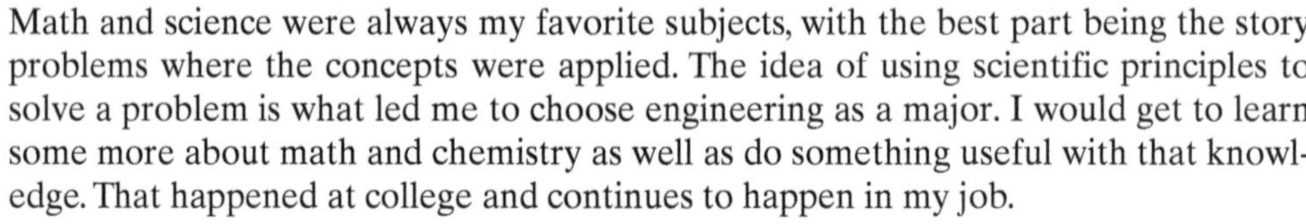

Math and science were always my favorite subjects, with the best part being the story problems where the concepts were applied. The idea of using scientific principles to solve a problem is what led me to choose engineering as a major. I would get to learn some more about math and chemistry as well as do something useful with that knowledge. That happened at college and continues to happen in my job.

Career Life

Today at Kellogg Company, the work I do is varied from day to day. My role is to make sure our manufacturing facilities have all the information they need, at the right time, to bring new products to market. That means coordinating the work from many different departments and gaining a consensus on the critical tasks to meet the timeline. You might ask, "What does that have to do with engineering?" Primarily, I bring together a myriad of details into one final outcome, just as all engineers do in combining the known facts to reach a solution. I just get to add some more unknowns and assumptions, such as dealing with people and changing requirements. The biggest challenge is getting the project accomplished to meet the needs of the consumer (that's you) before any of our competitors do.

Since Kellogg Company is a global company, my work affects the entire world. These days I work on projects for North America, Mexico, and Southeast Asia. I have had the opportunity to learn about other cultures and adapt our food products to fit their lifestyles. With manufacturing being located outside the U.S. as well, I encounter the varying work procedures and government regulations of each country. It makes my job challenging and enjoyable.

Life Outside of Work

Certainly, working at Kellogg's is not all that I do. My job is just one part of life. I find I need outlets for creative activities and for making contributions for the betterment of our world. Through sailboat racing I find a time of total concentration and a chance to apply aerodynamic principles. This also provides a fun way to have some competition. On the creative side, I participate in the handbell choir at my church. For me, music is a way to use my whole brain in the interpretation of notes into an emotional song of praise.

PROFILE OF AN INDUSTRIAL ENGINEER: JEANNE MORDARSKI, ALBUQUERQUE, NM

Occupation

Sales Manager, LightPath Technologies, Inc.

Education

BSIE; MBA

Studying Engineering

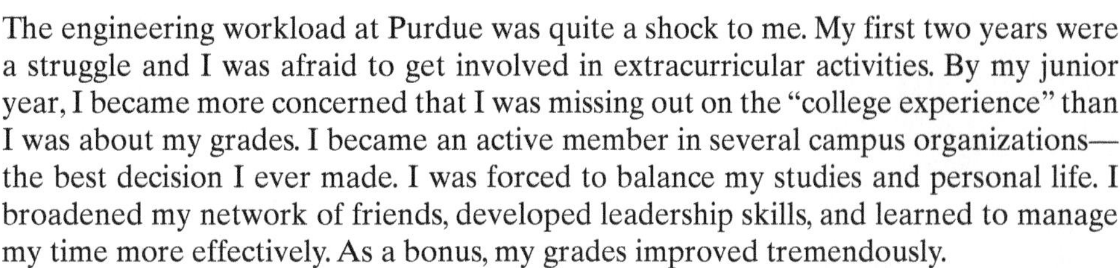

The engineering workload at Purdue was quite a shock to me. My first two years were a struggle and I was afraid to get involved in extracurricular activities. By my junior year, I became more concerned that I was missing out on the "college experience" than I was about my grades. I became an active member in several campus organizations—the best decision I ever made. I was forced to balance my studies and personal life. I broadened my network of friends, developed leadership skills, and learned to manage my time more effectively. As a bonus, my grades improved tremendously.

My emphasis within the IE curriculum was on Production and Manufacturing Systems. I accepted a production supervisor position with Corning Inc. after graduation. This role put me in the middle of the action, and taught me to think on my feet and make sound decisions. For eight years I worked at Corning in various engineering and manufacturing capacities. During this time, I was able to land a one-year tenure in Japan implementing Process Management Systems at our facility in Shizuoka.

For three years I took evening classes working toward an MBA from Syracuse University. In my course work, I realized how much I enjoyed the business side of things. Upon completion of my degree, I accepted a sales manager position at Corning in the telecommunications market.

Career Life

I recently left Corning to work as a sales manager for a start-up company, LightPath Technologies, Inc. Working for a large company directly from college gave me invaluable experience. The structure enabled me to work more effectively. However, as I progressed through the ranks at Corning, I realized that this same structure was limiting my ability to contribute because of the many management layers. In my current role at LightPath, we are introducing new products to the telecommunications market.

Life Outside of Work

I have an eclectic mix of interests outside of work. I truly enjoy exercise and the outdoors. On weekends, you'll find me skiing, camping, hiking, rock climbing, or biking. I love international travel and scuba diving, and take every opportunity I can to participate in both. I have recently taken up Latin social dance and kickboxing. I am also involved with the Purdue Alumni Association in Albuquerque. I like to keep busy and have worked very hard to strike a balance between my career and personal life. I seldom work more than 40 hours a week. I made it a goal to be more productive during work hours to minimize overtime and unnecessary stress. It usually works.

PROFILE OF AN ELECTRICAL ENGINEER: MARK ALLEN PASHAN, RED BANK, NEW JERSEY

Occupation

Director of Hardware Development, Lucent Technologies

Education

BS; MS; MBA

Studying Engineering

When I was in high school trying to decide which career to pursue, I had a number of criteria: I wanted a job that I'd look forward to each day, that offered continuous learning, and that offered a reasonable level of financial stability. Engineering satisfied those criteria for me. I enjoyed math and science (the foundations of engineering) in high school, but engineering is more than number crunching. The field of engineering rewards creativity, the ability to find a better way to solve a problem. If I had to do it over again, I'd still choose engineering, but I'd also have bought more shares of Wal-Mart, Lucent, and Yahoo when they were first offered.

Career Life

In my career, I have advanced through a number of levels of technical management, and currently have about 130 engineers reporting to me. My job is no longer at the level of designing integrated circuits. I guide my team's progress on a number of new product development activities. I work to make sure we have the right people working on the right things at the right time. I set priorities among the competing needs of the business, and evaluate new business opportunities. To do my job, I use a combination of business and technical judgment: what are the future customer needs, what are the available and soon-to-be-available technologies, what are my competitors doing and what may they do next, who can do the work and work well together, and can we get the work done in time and at a reasonable cost. The end results are new products introduced into the marketplace that turn a profit for the business. That goal can only be achieved through others. A good part of my job is getting my teams to achieve more than they thought possible.

This is the best time in history to be an engineer. There are more available alternatives than ever—from startup companies to large established firms, from full-time to part-time work hours. There are more opportunities for continuing education and there is the potential for significant financial reward for those willing to take a risk.

My organization is spread across three states and I have customers and suppliers all over the world. My job requires travel and long hours, and I couldn't do my job and have a family without the support of my wife, Reem. But we do it together and the kids are a joy (even when they don't always obey). I enjoy a number of activities outside of work such as basketball, traveling, and dining out.

PROFILE OF A MECHANICAL ENGINEER: PATRICK J. SHOOK, COLUMBUS, INDIANA

Occupation

Senior Engineer, New Product Development, Cummins Engine Company

Education

BSME, 1992; MSME, 1994

Studying Engineering

Mr. Myers, my high school chemistry teacher, had a discussion with me one day about Purdue's co-operative education program. He could see my interest in math and science and pointed me toward a field which I knew very little about—engineering. I investigated, and with high expectations, made the decision to attend Purdue to study and to prepare for what seemed to be a very interesting career.

By the end of the first semester during my freshman year, I had decided to pursue a mechanical engineering degree. This was after many discussions with junior and senior engineering students as well as with my father and a few professors. I had grown up in a family which owned a general contracting business (house construction, remodeling, etc.) and the broad variety of topics of study within mechanical engineering seemed to fit my desires. I also signed up to become a co-op student in order to obtain valuable work experience as well as to help pay for my education.

After graduating with my BSME, I entered into a research assistantship at Purdue for an intense (but extremely rewarding) two years on the way to obtaining my MSME. The most exciting task given to me by Prof. Fleeter was to build and operate a helicopter engine compressor test stand.

After graduating with my MSME, I hired on at Cummins Engine Company and worked for four years as a mechanical development engineer. This time was filled with designing abuse tests for semi-truck engines and determining how to improve the components that wore out during those tests. Without a doubt, learning how to work with people is easily 50-percent of my job. Since I have been at Cummins, I have learned that being clear with people concerning the goals of a plan is extremely important. As in a football huddle, everyone on the "field" needs to know what the "play" is and how to execute it.

Since July 1998, I have been working in a new position which focuses on engine cycle simulation. This has been primarily computer work and has re-sharpened my skills in fluid mechanics, thermodynamics, and heat transfer. The variety in my job has been enjoyable: from defining customer requirements for specific components to maximizing work processes within the structure of a large company.

Life Outside of Work

Outside of work, my wife and I do our best to serve the Lord and our church. In the past, we have both taken and taught classes on what the Bible says about marriage. We wanted to build on a good foundation and have enjoyed our marriage more and more with each year.

PROFILE OF A MECHANICAL ENGINEER: NANA TZENG, SEATTLE, WASHINGTON

Occupation

Design Engineer, The Boeing Company

Education

BSME, 1997; MSME, 1998

Studying Engineering

What I enjoyed most about being an engineering student was making stuff—in other words designing and fabricating mechanical parts. While I was at Purdue, I participated in the Solar Racing Club. As one of the few mechanical engineers on a team dominated by electrical engineers, I helped improve the braking system, performed computer aided stress analysis on the chassis, learned to weld, machined rotors and other parts, and got to be driver of the solar car. The experience was not only rewarding, it also helped me relate what I read about in textbooks with applying that knowledge. College offers many extracurricular opportunities and I would encourage any engineering student to become involved in hands-on activities and research projects.

Career Life

My career really is rocket science! I currently work in the Instrumentation Development and Design group at Rocketdyne, the division of The Boeing Company that designs and develops rocket engines. The team I work with is responsible for all the sensors and electrical components on the Space Shuttle Main Engine. My latest project is the redesign of the spark ignition system. This involves the design of components and tooling, creating and updating of drawings, and working with the manufacturing team to improve the fabrication process. I also help the members of my team analyze sensor data from hot fire tests and space shuttle flights. Because the nature of my work is highly technical, I regularly use the knowledge and skill I gained as an engineering student. Now that I am familiar with the complexity of rocket engines and the detailed work that goes into building one, it's even more amazing when I see everything come together during launch.

Life Outside of Work

Ever since I finished school, I have been able to develop other interests and hobbies, some of which are golf, photography and snowboarding. I also often enjoy hiking, camping, rollerblading, shopping, concerts, clubs, etc. The best advice I have to offer to students of any discipline is to keep an open mind and take advantage of your opportunities.

PROFILE OF A CHEMICAL ENGINEER:
JACK WELCH, FAIRFIELD, CONNECTICUT

Occupation

CEO of General Electric (Retired, 2002)

Education

BSChE; MSChE; PhD

Career Life

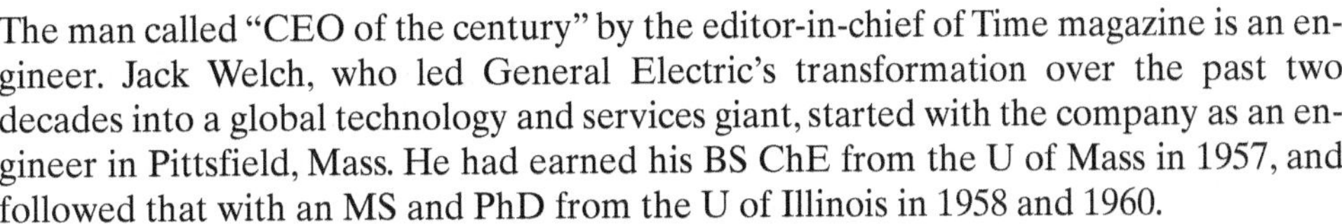

The man called "CEO of the century" by the editor-in-chief of Time magazine is an engineer. Jack Welch, who led General Electric's transformation over the past two decades into a global technology and services giant, started with the company as an engineer in Pittsfield, Mass. He had earned his BS ChE from the U of Mass in 1957, and followed that with an MS and PhD from the U of Illinois in 1958 and 1960.

In high school he had captained the hockey and golf teams and earned the distinction of being voted "Most Talkative and Noisiest Boy" by his classmates. "No one in my family had ever gone to college, but I had that ambition," Welch recalls. "Of course, believe me, my mother had that ambition for both of us."

"Life is a series of experiences, a series of steps if you will," he continues. "Every time you're reaffirmed, every time someone tells you you're Okay, you can go on to the next step, the next challenge. Well, my teachers in the Engineering Department told me I was Okay. In fact, they told me I was really good. A couple of them practically adopted me, and told me I had what it took to go on to graduate school. I had never even thought of graduate school. But they really believed in me."

After earning his PhD, Welch returned to Massachusetts and GE's Chemicals Division for his first job as a development specialist. It was on that first job that he demonstrated many of the leadership traits that characterize him to this day.

"I was an entrepreneur in a small business outside the mainstream of GE—the plastics business. My technician and I were partners working on the same thing. We had two people, then four people, then eight people, then 12. Today, GE Plastics is a $6 billion business. But it started that way. Everyone's involved. Everyone knows. Everyone's got a piece of the action. The organization's flat. All these things are from when I was 26 years old."

Welch's rapid rise in GE continued, and in 1981 he became the eighth chairman and CEO of the company that was founded in 1892. Although he recently retired, the organization he led was named "Most Admired" by Fortune magazine and "Most Respected" by the Financial Times.

Yet he described his job running a company with 1998 revenues of approximately $100 billion as "not rocket science." Instead he saw his key role as allocating both human and financial resources in a way that will continue GE's growth. "My job is allocating capital, human and financial, and transferring the best practices. That's all. It's transferring ideas, putting the right people in the right jobs and giving them the resources to win," he says.

Welch, now the father of four and recently a grandfather for the fourth time, continues on the golf course his winning ways that began in high school. He's twice won his club championship and has even bested well-known pros in friendly play.

EXERCISES AND ACTIVITIES

2.1 Select five of the engineers profiled in this chapter. Prepare a one-page summary of their current responsibilities.

2.2 Select five other engineers profiled in this chapter. What were some of the common factors that got them interested in engineering or helped them succeed in school?

2.3 Of the engineers profiled in this chapter, describe three who have unique, non-engineering jobs.

2.4 Make a list summarizing the current jobs and responsibilities of five of the engineers in this chapter.

2.5 What types of career paths are available to engineers? Make a list of seven different career paths taken by engineers in this chapter.

2.6 Select a historical engineering figure. Prepare a one-page profile on this person using the format used in this chapter.

2.7 Interview a practicing engineer and prepare a profile on him or her, similar to the format used in this chapter.

2.8 Select five of the engineers profiled in this chapter and list some of the challenges they had to overcome during their education and/or career.

2.9 Prepare a one-page paper summarizing some of the challenges engineers face today.

2.10 Select one of the engineers profiled in this chapter and prepare an oral presentation on that engineer's company or organization.

2.11 Which career path presented in this chapter sounds most appealing to you?

2.12 Which of the engineers' stories can you relate to the most? Why?

2.13 What are your goals for your life outside of work? In this chapter, did you read about anyone with similar goals and/or interests? Explain.

2.14 Imagine yourself five years from now. Write your profile using the same format as presented in this chapter.

2.15 Imagine yourself ten years from now. Write your profile from that perspective.

2.16 Imagine yourself 25 years from now. Write your profile from that perspective.

2.17 What are your thoughts about the success and fulfillment found by engineers who obtained an advanced degree outside the field of engineering?

2.18 Based on the profiles and your own experience, what are the advantages and disadvantages of getting a graduate degree in engineering?

2.19 Prepare a matrix of the bachelor's degrees the engineers in this chapter received and their current positions. How many work in jobs traditionally associated with bachelor's degrees?

2.20 Select your preferred major and prepare a list of potential career paths it could lead to. Provide a brief explanation for each option.

2.21 Today's engineering workforce is truly diverse, with both men and women from all ethnic backgrounds working together. This was not always the case. Select a historical figure who was a woman or minority engineer and prepare a one-page profile which discusses the difficulties she or he had to overcome.

2.22 Research a company you would be interested in working for and list the engineers in their upper-level management structure. Identify the highest level of management currently held by an engineer in that company.

2.23 Prepare a one-page paper on how some of the engineers profiled have addressed family responsibilities amidst an engineering career.

2.24 A stereotype of engineers is that they are boring loners who only care about numbers and technology. Based on the personal-interest sections of the profiles, prepare a report refuting this stereotype.

CHAPTER 3
DOCUMENTATION

Objectives

By learning the material in this chapter, you should be able to

- describe three considerations for gathering information
- list and apply three criteria for evaluating the trustworthiness of information resources
- list and gather necessary elements of a citation

Your technical writing teacher has just assigned a large research report that must have at least 10 sources, not including encyclopedias or websites. To save time and effort, you obtain everything you need from (where else?) an encyclopedia or website. Then, using that information, you whip up a complete research report. Next, through quick Web searches and a superficial skimming of newspapers, magazines, and books, you identify multiple sources that somehow relate, even tangentially, to the topics about which you have already written. These become the "sources" that you reference in your paper to keep the teacher happy.

The problem with this approach—besides leading to a paper with inferior content and throwing all standards of individual integrity and academic ethics into the dumpster—is that it compromises the role of documentation in technical writing. It ignores the need for complete, accurate source citations in the most serious form of business and scientific writing.

Technical writing often involves big business, lots of money, and a competitive, unforgiving environment. Proper documentation is an essential element of technical writing—an element that can have serious legal, ethical, and credibility implications for those who fall short of the mark. Documentation requirements are something that any technical writer must take seriously.

3.1 WHAT IS DOCUMENTATION?

In its most general meaning, *documentation* refers to creating virtually anything recorded or "documented" on paper. All the documents described in this book are forms of technical documentation. However, this chapter focuses on the kind of documentation that involves referencing sources. In this sense of the word, documentation gives formal credit to a person, organization, or publication for an idea or information

Taken from *Pocket Book of Technical Writing for Engineers and Scientists,* Third Edition, by Leo Finkelstein, Jr.

that either is not original or is not common knowledge of the field. It represents an acknowledgment of your indebtedness to the source.

For example, if you need to quote the performance specifications for, say, the Thumper City Water Treatment Plant, you must document that technical report. Those specifications represent ideas that are not original—in other words, they are not your ideas. On the other hand, if you use Ohm's law to show that 10 volts across a 1-ohm load produces 10 amperes of current, you do not need to document your source. Even though $I = E/R$ is not your idea, it is common knowledge in the field of electronics and, as such, does not need to be referenced.

Whether something is common knowledge of the field is often a judgment call. Normally, we think of something as being common knowledge when the average skilled person in the field should already be familiar with it. However, the best approach is to document any source when you are in doubt. Not only does this ensure that those who deserve credit receive it, but also it usually enhances the credibility of your writing by adding some authority to the argument.

Your goal in providing documentation should be to give enough information about the sources you have used to enable your reader to find and consult those sources conveniently and independently. Sources typically include print media such as books, journals, periodicals, newspapers, conference proceedings, and dissertations; electronic media such as websites, file transfer protocol (FTP) servers, newsgroups, and forums; storage media such as CDs and DVDs; and other material such as lectures and interviews.

Documentation Styles

Many style guides exist today for documenting sources. Here are a few: *MLA Handbook for Writers of Research Papers,*[1] *The Chicago Manual of Style,*[2] the *Government Printing Office Style Manual,*[3] the *APA Publications Manual,*[4] the *American Chemical Society's Manual for Authors and Editors,*[5] the *American Institute of Physics Style Manual,*[6] and *The Council of Biology Editors Manual for Editors and Publishers.*[7] The best approach is to use the style guide specified by your employer, your teacher, or your field. If a style guide is not specified, you can use any consistent form of documentation that provides the necessary information, including the simplified method provided in this chapter.

3.2 WHEN TO DOCUMENT SOURCES

As a technical writer, you should document sources for any or all of the following reasons.

To Meet Legal Requirements

Legally, when using copyrighted sources, you are required to document these sources. Federal copyright statutes control the reproduction of original works, including books, music, drama, computer programs, databases, videos, sculptures, and virtually any other media. Although copyright laws do not specifically protect the ideas contained in these works, they do protect the expression of ideas by these works. Also, some works, such as photographs, contain ideas that are intertwined with expression and cannot be separated easily.

You may use copyrighted material, either with permission of the copyright holder or without permission if your use is within the scope of the Fair Use Doctrine. Fair Use provides for limited reproduction of copyrighted material without the permission of the owner for noncommercial, teaching, and research purposes. Fair Use also requires that the original work be fully documented (referenced). If you do not provide this documentation, then it is not Fair Use—it is a violation of copyright law.[8]

To Meet Academic Standards

Academic standards require that you document any nonoriginal ideas, except those that represent common knowledge of the field. You must document not only direct and indirect quotations, but also paraphrases or any other discussions that specifically refer to or include original ideas that are not yours.

To Establish Credibility

You should support your original assertions or conclusions, which are not based on common knowledge, when you can show complementing positions on the part of authoritative sources. The purpose here is to establish the credibility of your position. Avoid making unsupported assertions in technical documents. If your assertions are consistent with the ideas of a recognized authority or previous work, document (reference) that authority or work to establish your credibility.

3.3 HOW TO DOCUMENT SOURCES

Generally speaking, two different approaches exist for documenting: *notational* and *parenthetical.*

- *Notational documentation* places footnote or endnote superscript numbers in your paper at the point where you need to document a source. You include the actual source citation either as a footnote at the bottom of the page, or as an endnote at the conclusion of the report (or a subsection of the report).
- *Parenthetical documentation* places a source citation in parentheses in your paper at the point where you need to document a source. You include a list of references at the end of the report (or major subsection). The citations are keyed to that list of references by either number or author's last name. Most technical documents use parenthetical documentation because it is simple and effective. Parenthetical documentation also gives the reader more information at the point of the citation.

Parenthetical documentation consists of two parts: the list of references at the end of the report or subsection and the parenthetical references cited within the text of the paper.

- The *list of references* (also called *list of sources, sources, references, notes, works cited,* or, frankly, whatever sounds reasonable) is essentially a bibliography that provides specific information (author, title, publication, date) about the works used or considered by the writer. You can list the references alphabetically by the first significant word, which is usually the author's last name. Or you can sequentially number your sources. If you list your references alphabetically, you usually can reference the source with the author's last name. Numbering your sources will make things even easier because you can reference each source in the paper by its number in the list.

- The parenthetical references are inserted into the text of the paper as the source citations. In the parentheses, first you identify the source by either source number or author's last name along with the date of publication, and then you add the specific pages being referenced (if applicable—some sources do not have page numbers). For example, consider the following paragraph:

  The Megatube XL is a high-power transmitting tube normally used in class C radio-frequency applications. However, as research commissioned by the Village Thumpers so clearly demonstrates, the tube can be used successfully as a power amplifier in class A audio applications as well. Its power, distortion, and signal-to-noise performance specifications are quite impressive in this regard. (3, pp. 22–23) or (Yinburg 2007, pp. 22–23)

This particular paragraph needs a reference to the Village Thumpers' commissioned research. Either of the two sample citations will work. The first example uses a source number, whereas the second example uses the source's last name—in this case Dr. Robert W. Yinburg's last name because he is Thumper Enterprises' chief scientist who wrote the referenced report. Also notice that the year *2007* is included after Yinburg's last name. Including the year of publication provides the reader with more information at the point of the citation; the year can also help differentiate one reference from another reference by the same author in the same list of references.

As mentioned, the sources themselves are listed at the end of the report. This list of references might look something like the following:

List of References

1. Pradeep Misra, "Order Recursive Gaussian Elimination," *IEEE Transactions on Aerospace and Electronic Systems*, AES-32 (January 1996), pp. 396–401.
2. Thomas S. Kuhn, *The Structure of Scientific Revolutions*, 2d ed. Enlarged. Chicago: The University of Chicago Press, 1970.
3. Robert W. Yinburg, "Preliminary Report on the Metatube XL in Audio Service," TR-05-0022. Thumper Station, N.Y.: Thumper Enterprises, September 2007.

The parenthetical documentation in our example was either (3, pp. 22–23) or (Yinburg 2007, pp. 22–23). Notice that both point to the same source in our list of references. Whichever parenthetical format you decide to use, be consistent throughout the entire report. Do not list a source by number in one section and by author's last name in another.

You may also want to add sources that you consulted but did not specifically use. The idea is not to pad your reference list, but to acknowledge sources that may have influenced your thinking even though you did not specifically cite them. These latter sources should be included in a separate list of references clearly indicating that they were consulted but not used. In other words, you might end up with a "List of Sources Consulted and Used" and a "List of Sources Consulted but Not Used"—or perhaps "Sources Cited" and "Sources Consulted."

Again, it is best to use the style guide specified by your organization, your boss, your teacher, or your field. However, if you do not have a specified format, the simple approach provided in this chapter should be adequate for documenting the most commonly used sources in technical writing.

Of course, several different types of sources exist, and each type is handled differently in the list of references. The following examples will show you how to handle the most common types of sources.

3.4 PRINT MEDIA EXAMPLES

The following examples provide a general guide for documenting the most commonly used forms of print media.

Books

Include the author(s), title, edition, city of publication, publisher, and date of publication:

1. T. Sudkamp, *Languages and Machines: An Introduction to the Theory of Computer Science,* 3d ed. New York: Addison-Wesley, 2006.

Journals

Include the author(s), article title, journal, volume (and number if necessary), date, and inclusive pages:

2. Brad Bryant and Marian K. Kazimierczuk, "Modeling the Closed-Current Loop of PWM Boost DC-DC Converters Operating in CCM with Peak Current-Mode Control," *IEEE Transactions on Circuits and Systems,* Vol. 52, No. 11, November 2005.

Conference Papers

Include the author(s), paper title, conference or transactions information, date, and inclusive pages:

3. R. V. Grandhi and L. Wang, "High-Order Failure Probability Calculation Using Nonlinear Approximations," 37th SDM Conference, Salt Lake City, Utah, April 1996, pp. 1292–1306.

Encyclopedias

Include article, encyclopedia, edition, place of publication, publisher, date, and inclusive pages:

4. "Acceleration," *Von Nostrand's Scientific Encyclopedia*, 9th ed., New York: Wiley-Interscience, 2002, p. 10.

Newspapers

Include author(s) if known, article title, newspaper name, date, section, and page(s):

5. George Will, "Volcano's Reverberations Still Felt?" *Dayton Daily News*, May 22, 2003, sec. A, p. 15.

Note: In this case, the author is listed. If no author is listed, you would alphabetize the entry by the first significant word of the article title.

Nonjournal Entries

Include author, article title, publication, date, and inclusive pages:

6. Harry Goldstein, "Irradiation Nation," *IEEE Spectrum*, August 2003, pp. 24–29.

Technical Reports

Include author, title, number, agency, place, and date:

7. Fred D. Garber, "Synthetic Aperture Radar Automatic Strategic Relocatable Target Identification System," WL-TR-93-1145, Wright Laboratory, Wright-Patterson Air Force Base, Ohio, October 1993.

Dissertations and Theses

Include author, title, degree level, school, and date:

8. Albert J. Rosa, "Luminescent and Electrical Properties of Sodium Implanted Zinc Selenide," Ph.D. dissertation, University of Illinois at Urbana-Champaign, 1975.

3.5 ELECTRONIC MEDIA EXAMPLES

The following examples provide a general guide for documenting electronic media. Documenting electronic media, especially sources that exist solely in cyberspace, represents significant challenges for the technical writer. Sources range from specialized databases (e.g., Lexis-Nexis), to online service databases (e.g., AOL), to forums and news groups (e.g., USENET), and to the mass of material now available to anyone on millions of Internet websites. In addition, there are wide variations in styles for documenting electronic media. You should always check with your teacher or employer to see if a specific style format is required.

When you document cyberspace sources, also keep in mind the differences between cyberspace and traditional sources. For example, an Internet address does more than just indicate where a source is located. It also provides the detailed electronic directions, including the precise path, for accessing the source. In effect, a cyberspace address not only shows you where the source is located, but it also takes you there.

Unfortunately, computer networks are absolutely unforgiving of errors in addresses. If you make even the slightest mistake in order, spelling, or punctuation, you will not reach your desired Internet site. To make matters worse, long-held use of certain marks of punctuation such as periods and slashes is often incompatible with Internet addresses. For example, you may not be able to use a period at the end of a sentence when working with Web addresses. Consider this sentence:

For more information on Dr. Finkelstein's courses, go to http://www.finkelnet.com.

If you are Web-savvy and do not enter the trailing period, you will reach the author's finkelnet.com Web page, which is used to support his classes. If you enter the final period, however, the finkelnet.com address will fail, resulting in a "server not found" error. Where universal resource locators (URLs) and domain name service (DNS) are involved, the period's function has nothing to do with English grammar and punctuation. Consequently, you would have to add a space before the ending period (the terminal mark of punctuation), or invert the sentence to move the Web address away from the end of the sentence, or even omit the final period altogether.

Another problem with cyberspace documents is the lack of key information. The goal when you are documenting an electronic source "in a perfect world" is to provide the reader with all the relevant information about that source. But in cyberspace, the world is far from perfect. For example, the author's name may not be included on the Web page, and the title may be missing or only included in a /title tag in the HTML code. Additionally, the universal resource locator (URL) or Web address may be redirected from one page to another without your knowledge or any obvious indication. You may not be getting the information from where you think you are.

Finally, cyberspace addresses tend to be unreliable over time. Websites come and go, and material on websites is "here today and gone tomorrow." On some sites, Web addresses are dynamically assigned to time-sensitive materials, then reassigned once the materials are archived. In other words, an address that works today may not work tomorrow—or even later today! Generally, the best advice when you are documenting a cyberspace source is to do the best you can do with the information available. Remember, your goal in documentation is to provide your reader with enough information so that he or she can independently locate the source. When all else fails, even providing partial information—perhaps a topic or an author's name—might be enough with modern search engines to track down the source. When documenting electronic sources, however, you are obligated, to the maximum extent possible, to include all the relevant information. In this case, the information would include the author, title, database record identifier (file name and path), medium, and date of posting (or date of access, if the posting date is unknown).

Here are a few examples.

Large, Complex Website

Include author (if known), article title, host agency or organization, department or office (if relevant), Web URL, and date of access:

9. "SOI Tax Stats – Corporation Complete Report." Internal Revenue Service, http://www.irs.ustreas.gov/taxstats/bustaxstats/article/0,,id=112834,00.html (accessed December 22, 2005).

In this example, the author is not known, so the reference begins with the title.

University Website

Include author (if known), article title, document title (if relevant), Web URL, and date of access:

10. "Understanding Earthquakes," *Rensselaer Research Review,* Rensselaer Polytechnic Institute, http://www.rpi.edu/research/magazine/fall05/earthquakes_1.html (accessed December 1, 2005).

Online Forum

Include author (or topic), title, medium, site owner, complete network address, and date:

11. Figure Skating, "ISU Press Conference Transcript of April 1, 2003." Internet: google.com: groups.google.com/groups?hl=en&lr=&ie=UTF-8&group=rec.skate (accessed June 2, 2003).

FTP Site

Include author (if known), title, file name, medium, site owner, complete network address, and access date:

12. Leo Finkelstein, Jr., "College Recruiting Game" (file=ecsslots.exe). Internet: College of Engineering and Computer Science, Wright State University, Dayton, Ohio, ftp.cs.wright.edu/~lfinkel (June 1998).

Computer Local Storage Media (Computer Disk, Flash Card, etc.)

Include file name, medium title, medium type, version, series or ID number, and date:

13. "Readme," Apple Hardware Test—iMac, CD, version 2.0, 691-4199A, 2003.

3.6 OTHER EXAMPLES

Interview

Interviews include most situations where you pose questions to a source and receive answers. Interviews do not have to occur face to face or in real time. Include interviewee, method, topic, affiliation, place, and date:

14. Leo Finkelstein, Jr., Personal Interview, Topic: "The Ethics of Using the Finkel-KICK for Self-Defense." Office of the Dean, College of Engineering and Computer Science, Wright State University, Dayton, Ohio, April 21, 2002.

Lecture

Include lecturer, occasion, topic, location, and date:

15. Leo Finkelstein, Jr., EGR 335 class lecture, Topic: "The Grammar Hammer." College of Engineering and Computer Science, Wright State University, Dayton, Ohio, January 17, 2006.

CHECKLIST FOR DOCUMENTATION

- Have I used source citations throughout the text keyed to my list of references?
- Have I documented all uses of copyrighted material?
- Have I documented all nonoriginal ideas that are not common knowledge?
- Have I referenced authoritative sources that support assertions I have made that are not otherwise supported?
- Have I used the prescribed method and form of documentation (if applicable)?
- Have I been consistent in the method and form of documentation I have used?

NOTES

1. *MLA Handbook for Writers of Research Papers*, 6th ed. New York: The Modern Language Association, 2003.
2. *The Chicago Manual of Style*, 15th ed. Chicago: University of Chicago Press, 2003.
3. *Style Manual*, rev. ed. Washington, D.C.: U.S. Government Printing Office, 1984.
4. *Publication Manual of the American Psychological Association*, 5th ed. Washington, D.C.: American Psychological Association, 2001.
5. *The ACS Style Guide: A Manual for Authors and Editors*. Washington, D.C.: American Chemical Society, 1986.
6. *AIP Style Manual,* 4th ed. New York: American Institute of Physics, 1990.
7. //, 6th ed. New York: Cambridge University, 1994.
8. For more information, see "About Copyright," Internet: the United States Copyright Office www.loc.gov/copyright/ (last accessed December 20, 2005).

CHAPTER 4

BUILDING TEAMS AND WORK GROUPS

Objectives

By learning the material in this chapter, you should be able to

- form a team and help it progress through developmental stages
- form or join a high-performance work team
- ensure that all members of a team contribute equally
- handle differences in values and work styles in a team setting
- allocate team roles and responsibilities
- motivate a team to achieve its objectives

Jeremy was perplexed. He had been looking forward to the first team project in his new job. He had heard how much his new employer valued teamwork. At his previous job, he hadn't encountered teams. He had done virtually all his work on his own, as an individual contributor. This job was going to be different.

At the outset of the project, the group was given a series of projects on which to work. Over the course of the quarter, the group was supposed to evolve into what the team leader called a high-performance work team. But now, at the project's midpoint, Jeremy felt his group was anything but high-performance. Things had started out great. Right away, Jeremy hit it off with his fellow teammates. While the team was diverse in terms of gender, ethnicity, and function, most members had similar interests and got along well with each other. They had even gotten together socially a couple of times during the quarter. At the beginning, the group was very task oriented. They seemed to communicate well and were able to clarify their objective, determine their topic and research priorities, allocate roles and responsibilities, and set up a planning schedule working backwards from their project due date at the end of the quarter.

After a few initial organizing meetings, the group members were left to work on their own. That's where the problems started occurring. In preparation for an interim project due date, Jeremy and his team had planned a team meeting the day before to combine everyone's work and produce the deliverable that the team leader expected the next day. To his chagrin, Jeremy discovered that only he and one other team member were ready. The others had procrastinated and thought they could "wing it." He was contemplating pulling an all-nighter to make up the others' work. "This project is

---

Taken from *Interpersonal Skills in Organizations,* Second Edition, by Suzanne C. De Janasz, Karen O. Dowd, and Beth Z. Schneider.

going nowhere," he thought. "Why didn't I just do everything on my own? I could have done better working on my own. This team stuff isn't all it's cracked up to be."

1. What is the situation Jeremy faces? What are the core issues here?
2. How did this situation develop? What could have been done to achieve a different outcome?
3. How would you feel if you were Jeremy? Has a similar situation happened to you?
4. What would you do if you were Jeremy?
5. What should Jeremy do?

> "We are a pack animal. From earliest times we have used the strength of the group to overcome the weakness of the individual. And that applies as much to business as to sport."[1]
>
> Tracey Edwards
> (Skippered the First Women's
> Crew to Circumnavigate
> the Globe)

From the popular NBC reality show *The Apprentice* to most of the *Fortune* 500 and many high-tech start-up firms to competitive sports, teams are an everyday occurrence in our personal and work lives. As the nature of work progresses from individually based work to group settings, understanding teams and how to work in team settings and in work groups has become a crucial interpersonal skill. Not everyone is convinced that teams are more effective than individuals working on their own. But the reality is that many organizations are attempting to set up a team-based structure when tackling particular issues or processes, and the ability to work as a team is one of the most commonly required skills in the work environment.[2]

This chapter covers the basics of teamwork. We define teams and detail their importance in business today. We discuss strategies for forming teams and tips for making teams effective and successful. We also include several exercises at the end of the chapter for you to further enhance your team skills, and list resources available for further exploration.

4.1 WHAT IS TEAMWORK?

A team is a formal work group consisting of people who work together to achieve a common group goal.[3] The word *team* is not synonymous with *group*. A **group** is a collection of people who work together but aren't necessarily working collectively toward the same goal. A **team** is composed of three or more interdependent individuals who are consciously working together to achieve a common objective, such as product development, service delivery, or process improvement. A group becomes a team when members demonstrate a commitment to each other and to the end goal toward which they are working. In a team, there is a higher degree of cohesiveness and accomplishment than in a group.[4]

From earliest times, human beings have used teams or groups to overcome the limitations of individuals. Collections of nomads in search of food and land, kingdoms composed of villagers and their leaders, native settlements, wagon trains and pioneers, the crews of ships—all were formed with the idea that more could be accomplished together than by an individual.[5] Even Adam and Eve decided to band together, as do the quasi-"alliances" on the CBS television show *Survivor.* Aside from gains in sheer horsepower, as in the case of a ship's crew, teams exist because few individuals possess all the knowledge, skills, and abilities needed to accomplish all tasks. Simply put, two heads are often better than one.

Within many professional sports teams, we can find shining examples of teamwork. Michael Jordan, one of the world's greatest basketball players and author of the book, *I Can't Accept Not Trying*, writes, "One thing I believe to the fullest is that if you think and achieve as a team, the individual accolades will take care of themselves. Talent wins games, but teamwork and intelligence win championships." He says he never forgot that he was only one-fifth of the effort at any time.[6] Staying with sports for a moment, consider the differences between a gymnastics team and a football team. In gymnastics, the members of a team may work together, but the ultimate achievement of a team is based on the collective efforts of the individual gymnasts. A winning team has the highest combined score. In football, a great quarterback is nothing without a great wide receiver, tight end, or offensive line that can keep him or her from getting sacked. The football team wins when all members work interdependently toward the same goal—passing and rushing their way toward touchdowns.

Returning to the workplace, it is estimated that between 70 and 82 percent of U.S. companies use the team concept, making teamwork skills one of the most commonly required skills in the work environment.[7] Many businesses are adopting a collaborative management approach that encourages sharing ideas and strategies throughout the organization. This collaboration provides many benefits to the organization as well as to the individuals who make up the teams.[8]

4.1.1 Why Teams?

Teaming is more than a phrase or a buzzword. If it didn't work, organizations would abandon this strategy for getting work done. There is much evidence that teams can be effective, especially when tasks are complex and task interdependence is high. It is not always appropriate, of course, for work to be done in teams. But when a team structure is employed, and those teams work effectively, many benefits accrue to the organization and to the team members themselves.

- *Increased creativity, problem solving, and innovation*: Bringing together a group of individuals who possess a wealth of ideas, perspectives, knowledge, and skills can result in a synergy through which new ideas can be entertained. We each have a unique set of skills. Working with others allows us to combine our skills and talents to create new approaches to solving problems.[9] An example is a team of marketers where each

BENEFITS OF TEAMS

- Increased creativity, problem solving, and innovation.
- Higher-quality decisions.
- Improved processes.
- Global competitiveness.
- Increased quality.
- Improved communication.
- Reduced turnover and absenteeism and increased employee morale.

person applies his or her strengths to the issue at hand. One person who is very creative can lead the process of coming up with ideas; another who is detail-oriented can do the initial research; a third person who is skilled in graphic applications can put together a great sales presentation.

- *Higher-quality decisions*: Teamwork enhances the quality of the outcomes. Teamwork involves the collective effort of a group of people who represent diverse backgrounds and experiences. As more ideas are produced and alternatives are considered, the team gets closer to optimal decisions—decisions that are stronger because they have been made with various perspectives and interests in mind.
- *Improved processes*: Teamwork results in a systematic approach to problem solving. Because of the necessary coordination between and transfer of learning among team members, teamwork results in organized approaches to the situation at hand. For example, a team is more likely than an individual to set up project checkpoints and planning systems to enable all team members to contribute to the project as it unfolds. Teamwork also permits distribution of workloads for faster and more efficient handling of large tasks or problems.[10] When members representing different organizations work together to improve a process that cuts across multiple organizational functions, more glitches and interdependencies will be uncovered and addressed than would be by individuals working independently.
- *Global competitiveness*: Teamwork enables companies to compete globally. Firms in the United States are relying increasingly on diverse teams to compete in the global economy.[11] Diverse teams have skill sets and perspectives that are superior to what a single individual can bring to the table. For example, when Clairol marketed its popular Mist Stick in parts of Germany, it flopped. Had the Clairol marketing team included someone of German origin, they could have informed the group that mist was a slang word for "manure." As we continue developing and marketing our products in a global marketplace, combining diverse perspectives is essential.
- *Increased quality*: Studies show that those large, complex, global companies that have moved to teams show increases in productivity, employee ownership of and accountability for their work, timeliness, efficiency, and customer service.[12] This results in higher-quality standards than are possible when individuals or groups of individuals, who lack a common goal, are doing the work.
- *Improved communication*: The use of teams in the workplace enhances employee communication. In a traditional, hierarchical organization, communication tends to flow primarily in one direction—downward. In a team-based organization, communication flows laterally, upward, downward, and even outside the organization's boundaries (e.g., customers and suppliers). Teamwork requires collective action that is grounded in words and actions. It's not sufficient for one person to determine how he or she wants to work. Each person must get others on board before proceeding. In effective teams, there is rich sharing of information and ideas that improves communication within the team and between the team and the organization.[13]
- *Reduced turnover and absenteeism and increased employee morale*: Teamwork results in changes in employee behaviors and attitudes. Teamwork fosters a camaraderie that helps many employees to feel more a part of the organization than when working independently. They feel ownership of the problems on which they work, get immediate feedback from teammates, see the fruits of their labors, and feel they have an impact on their job and the organization. Compared with the alienation employees often experience in traditional firms, employees in team-based organizations are happier, more committed, and more loyal to their organization.

The chart below contains examples of the positive outcomes that resulted when organizations embraced and encouraged team-based work:

EXAMPLES OF SUCCESSES BY SELF-MANAGED TEAMS[14]

Organization	Reported Successes
Harley-Davidson	Returned to profitability in six years.
Hallmark	200 percent reduction in design time. Introducing 23,000 new card lines each year.
Liberty Mutual	50 percent reduction in contract process time. Saving of more than $50 million per year.
Johns Hopkins Hospital	Patient volume increased by 21 percent. Turnover reduced, absenteeism reduced by 20 percent.
Monsanto	Quality and productivity improved by 47 percent in 4 years.
Saab and Volvo	4 percent increase in production output. Inventory turnover increased from 9 to 21 times a year.

4.1.2 Potential Limitations of Teams

While this chapter focuses primarily on the effectiveness of teams and work groups and how-tos for being a productive team member, there are some concerns about teams and their ability to make the most effective decisions. Some of these concerns are expressed briefly below.

LIMITATIONS OF TEAMS

- **Groupthink:** Groupthink[15]—or individuals agreeing reluctantly with a group's decision—is a potential problem for teams. Groupthink can happen when a decision is made in a hurry, when one or a few members are extremely dominant in a group setting, or when one or more members present believe they haven't had a chance to air their concerns before an action is taken.
- **Social loafing:** By definition a team is a collection of three or more people. Invariably, a team will be composed of members with different work ethics and work styles, and this can result in some individuals doing more work than others.
- **Quality concerns:** Ironically, although there is much evidence that teams produce quality outcomes, the fact is that some individuals have the expert knowledge necessary to be able to make decisions independently without the benefit of a team.
- **Timeliness:** Individuals can make decisions more quickly than teams, especially if gaining buy-in from others is not an essential component of the action under consideration.
- **Diversity:** In general, diversity of background and thought process is a good way to ensure that multiple perspectives will be incorporated into a particular decision. Sometimes, especially when expedience is desired or when management has a clear preference for a particular course of action, a homogenous group can make decisions more quickly and easily than can a more diverse group.

Organizing work into teams is the wave of the future. In fact, many organizations now have "virtual teams," in which much or all of the work is done by group members who may be dispersed geographically and communicate with each other primarily via e-mail and the Internet. But like any new phenomenon, it is important to understand that teams have both upsides and downsides. Teams may not be optimal for every business situation. When you are placed in a team, be aware of the potential problems and develop strategies early on to overcome these challenges.

4.2 TYPES OF TEAMS

In the same way sports teams differ in function, makeup, and ultimate goal or purpose, so do teams in the workplace. The more commonly used team types are described below.

Cross-functional Teams: These include members from various departments or business specialties such as marketing, information systems, communications, public relations, operations, human resources, accounting, finance, planning, research and development, and legal. Cross-functional teams are usually charged with developing new products or investigating and improving a companywide problem such as the need to increase speed and efficiency across departmental lines or the need to adopt a new companywide computer system. Cross-functional teams derive their strength from diversity. By including representatives from all or most of an organization's primary functional areas, the team can diagnose a problem from multiple perspectives simultaneously, ensuring that all relevant points of view are taken into account. This can speed up the problem-solving process and result in an outcome that the various departments affected by the change more readily accept.

Case in point: Prior to producing its LH line of cars, Chrysler followed what most would call a serial design process. Engineering would design a car and throw it over the wall to manufacturing. "We can't build this," manufacturing replied, and sent it back over the wall to engineering. This would continue for months or years until marketing was charged with marketing a car that no one wanted. From product inception to market, this process could take as long as six years or more. By that time, technologies were obsolete and other companies easily stole market share. Realizing this, Chrysler moved to a simultaneous, cross-functional team-based design process. Everyone who had a stake in or was affected by the design of a new product was on a team that hashed it out—together. This included people from marketing, sales, engineering, design, and many others. These meetings had conflict, but the conflict was actually helpful. Chrysler was able to reduce the cycle time from over six years to less than 18 months!

Another example of a cross-functional team is a top management team. In many large organizations, the CEO typically makes strategic decisions in collaboration with the leaders of the major functional areas. Even at this level in the organization, top management recognizes their individual strengths and weaknesses and the value that diverse perspectives can add when making key organizational decisions.

Self-managed Teams: These are "groups of employees who are responsible for a complete, self-contained package of responsibilities that relate either to a final product or an ongoing process."[16] Also known as self-directed, self-maintained, or self-regulating, self-managed teams are typically given a charge by senior management and then are given virtually complete discretion over how, when, and what to do to attain their objective. Self-managed teams are expected to coordinate their work without ongoing direction from a supervisor or manager. Self-managed teams set their own norms, make their own planning schedules, set up ways to keep relevant members and others informed of their progress, determine how the work is going to be accomplished, and are held accountable for their end product or "deliverable." Many of these teams are responsible for hiring, training, and firing team members. The flattening of organizational structures, resulting in less hierarchy and fewer managers, makes self-directed teams a popular concept in business today. Of course, it's not as if management flips a switch and a team becomes self-managing. It's a long process of team building and teamwork combined with sufficiently greater responsibility and accountability gained through the team's demonstrated capabilities and performance.

Task Force: This is an ad hoc, temporary project team assembled to develop a product, service, or system or to solve a specific problem or set of problems. Companies are always faced with the challenge of getting ongoing, day-to-day work done while utilizing available resources to work on various change processes or product innovations. For example, a technology company might designate a group to study the next wave in software development while others are maintaining and servicing existing software programs. Often task force members are individuals who have demonstrated interest or skill in the area being examined by the task force, so the members are enthusiastic about the project and its potential. The task force process is very common in business today. It is lower in cost than hiring an outside consultant or group of contract workers and allows for management to allocate resources at will to various projects as the needs of the company and the interests of its employees change.

Process Improvement Teams: These teams focus on specific methods, operations, or procedures and are assembled with the specific goal of enhancing the particular component being studied. Process improvement teams are typically composed of individuals with expertise and experience in the process being reviewed. They are assigned the tasks of eliminating redundant steps, looking for ways to reduce costs, identifying ways to improve quality, or finding means for providing quicker, better customer service.[17] Process improvement teams are often given training on problem-solving tools and techniques to help them map processes, identify root causes of problems, and prioritize potential solutions.

To analyze a system and make recommendations for changes, process improvement team members diagnose the current state of a process and chart how it occurs step by step. They review customer or internal data and collect data from other sources such as managers, competitors, and others as needed. They identify ways the process can be enhanced, make their recommendations, and sometimes assist the operating units involved in implementing the changes. Process improvement teams are usually temporary and disband once the process being studied has been changed to the satisfaction of management.

Learning Teams: Teams in the workplace (including all the types of teams described previously in this section) are typically focused on performance. That is, the goal of the team is the completion of a task and completing that task on time, on budget, to specifications, etc. The examples given in the previous sections show that the typical metrics of success of typical workplace teams are money (higher production rates, lower personnel cost, fewer worker's compensation claims, lower meeting costs), time (less time to design a car), and safety (lower injury rate). Along the way, other objectives are met whether intentionally or serendipitously. For example, the use of virtual teams not only saves meeting costs, but by reducing air travel, there is a significant reduction in the environmental impact of the travel generally associated with face-to-face meetings of people who must travel by airplane. Learning teams have an entirely different measure of success, which is the degree to which each member of the team meets the learning objectives. As a result, learning teams will not have the same performance focus as teams in the workplace. In the workplace, if only one team member has developed the needed skills to present the team's work, then that person will be designated the spokesperson for the team for any presentations to executives, other internal teams, the public, and/or any other audiences. In a learning team, however, if one of the learning objectives is for all team members to develop presentation skills, it will be important for all the team members to present the work of the team so they can learn to do it well. In the process, there may be some times when the work of the team is not presented as well as it could have been presented by the student who already knew how to present. This reduction in performance is offset by the learning experience of the other three team members so that they can be better presenters in the future. While workplace team members learn as well, and sometimes learning is required to complete the team's objectives, this trade-off between learning and performance exists in teams where learning is the primary focus.

4.2.1 Team Developmental Stages

Groups typically pass through a series of stages as they grow and evolve into teams. Theorists postulate that a team goes in and out of at least five stages in its life cycle:[18] forming, storming, norming, performing, adjourning. This process is fluid—teams may revisit a stage, or skip one or more altogether. Each phase has distinguishing characteristics and presents particular challenges to team members and their managers.

Stage One—Forming

In this stage, a team is established to accomplish a particular task. Typically the group members will not know each other, and even if they do, there is a feeling of uncertainty and tentativeness because people haven't had a chance yet to get to know one another and set group objectives.[19] In the **forming** stage, members will engage in behaviors such as defining the initial assignment, discussing how to divvy up the necessary tasks, understanding the broad scope and objectives of the project, and learning about the resources (time, equipment, personnel) available to the team as it works to complete the project. In this stage, there is some testing by members of leadership roles, some discovery of personality similarities and differences, some initial disclosure, and usually relatively little progress on the task.

As a team member or team leader, your role in stage one is to encourage the group to establish its mission and purpose, set up a work schedule, get to know one another, and establish some initial norms for working together.

Stage Two—Storming

In this stage, a group experiences differences over factors such as direction, leadership, work style and approach, and perceptions about the expected quality and state of the end product or deliverable. As is true of any relationship, conflict is inevitable. Many couples feel bad when they experience their first fight, and teams are no exception. When the first conflict among group members emerges, some or all of the members begin to feel less enthusiastic about the group and might even doubt the group can come together and achieve its objective. There may be struggles over leadership ("my way is best"), power ("if you don't agree we'll leave you behind") and roles ("who appointed you chief?"). In the **storming** stage, feelings emerge such as resistance to the task or approach being taken by the group, resentment about differences in workload, anger about roles and responsibilities, and changes in attitude about the group or toward individual group members and concerns. Typically in the storming stage, the group is in conflict and chaos, as the group has not yet established ways to communicate about these differences. During this stage, few if any processes and procedures are in place, as the need for them wasn't anticipated due to the lack of prior conflict. All of this can result in arguing among members, emergence of subgroups, and disunity. If and when a group in which you are working enters this stage, what can you do?

In the storming stage, your role as a group member or leader is to refrain from taking sides. Encourage the group to develop communication channels. Help your group members focus on the task and not on personal differences. Promote an environment of open communication to ensure that the inevitable conflict is healthy and results in improved communication and commitment to the group's task. Remember that an appropriate level of tension motivates a team, but too much or too little can affect productivity.[20] If your group cannot resolve or work effectively with conflict, request the assistance of a trained process consultant or facilitator. A group that can't learn how to handle conflict may never achieve its deliverable.

Stage Three—Norming

In this stage, the group faces its issues, conflicts, and power and leadership struggles openly and directly. The members establish and adhere to patterns of acceptable behavior and learn to incorporate new methods and procedures into their working together. In the **norming** stage, members feel a new ability to express constructive criticism; they feel part of a working team and a sense of relief that everything will work out.[21] In this stage, members attempt to achieve harmony by avoiding unnecessary conflict, acting more friendly toward and trusting of each other, and developing a sense of team unity ("together, we can solve this"). Norms don't have to be established about every single decision or policy, only those that are particularly significant to team members.[22]

As a team member or leader, your role is to encourage team members to take on more responsibility, work together to create means acceptable for solving problems, set challenging goals, and take personal responsibility for team success. As a leader, you set the tone. Don't expect others to "do as you say, but not as you do." If you are seen bickering with colleagues and secretly plotting political moves, team members are less likely to emulate the helpful norming behaviors and may regress to the storming stage.

Stage Four—Performing

In the **performing** stage, teams have worked through their differences. Their membership is stable, the task is clear, and eyes are on the prize. Team members are highly motivated to accomplish their task and focused on team objectives rather than individual interests. Through working closely together, team members have developed insights into each other's strengths and weaknesses (many even finish each other's sentences), feel satisfied with the team's progress, and believe the team will successfully reach or even exceed its goals. In this stage, members engage in constructive self-change for the good of the group; experience greatly enhanced ability to communicate with and give feedback to each other; are able to anticipate, prevent, or work through group problems; and, as a result, develop a close attachment to the team.[23]

As a team member or leader, your role at this stage is to encourage members to provide support to and serve as resources for each other. Make sure the team continues with its progress and maintains its cohesion and morale, and guide it toward success. Do remain vigilant, however. It's easy to kick back and relax, believing that once a team gets to this phase of development, it stays there. That may or may not be true. Changes in membership, scope of the task, or broader organizational changes can cause a team to regress developmentally. In addition, the close attachments members have to a team could possibly blind them to other developing problems.

Stage Five—Adjourning

After successfully completing the task or objective, teams may disband permanently or take a temporary break. Some may get new members or receive a new objective. This stage is usually brought on by an imminent deadline. At the **adjourning** stage, members are likely to feel disappointment—if the experience was positive—or gratitude—if the experience was negative. The task at this stage is to tie up loose ends and complete final follow-up on projects.

As a team member or leader, your role at this end stage is to encourage the team members to debrief the project, discussing the lessons learned that members can take with them to new projects and convey to new teams tackling similar issues. It is also helpful at this stage to recognize the team for its efforts. This could take the form of public recognition (a blurb on the team's accomplishments in the monthly newsletter), a reward (some organizations reward teams with a percentage of the savings or revenues realized as a result of the team's work), or other benefit (use company funds to take the team out for lunch). By providing encouragement and recognizing accomplishments, hard work, and efforts, you help to continue momentum and build motivation.[24] Of course, ongoing work project teams may not physically adjourn. They may remain intact, continuing with a new set of objectives once a particular project is complete. In this case, rather than adjourning, the team members may choose to debrief at certain checkpoints along the way, evaluating their processes and communication efforts to ensure they're keeping current and are as productive as they can be.

It is healthy for groups to move through some or all of these stages as they evolve into a team. Not all groups go through all the stages, and some go through them at different paces. For example, if a group's members knew each other previously and had similar values and goals—as well as a tight deadline—they might be able to move almost immediately to the norming stage. In another case, where the group members don't know each other well and they have some time before the deliverable is due, they might take longer to reach the norming phase and coalesce as a real team just before the deliverable is due. Some may get stuck in one of the stages and disband before progressing to the next stage or perform at a lower level than what might have been possible. A group stuck in the storming stage but facing an imminent deadline has to continue performing. In this case, it is likely that its performance will suffer due to the inability to function cohesively. In some extreme cases, a group will be dysfunctional and will require outside intervention in order to complete its task. As is true with relationships, teams have developmental cycles. Understanding this ahead of time can help you develop strategies for helping your group evolve into a team and to increase its effectiveness every step of the way.

4.2.2 Characteristics of High-Performance Teams

As former Notre Dame coach Lou Holtz said, "Winning is never accidental. To win consistently you must have a clear plan and intense motivation." As we have said, not all teams are alike. As a team member or leader, your primary goal is to encourage your group to evolve into a motivated, goal-oriented, successful team; we refer to these types of teams as high-performance teams. In **high-performance teams**, there is a commitment to quality and a dedication to producing the best outcome possible. Research shows that most high-performance work teams possess the following characteristics:[25]

- *Common purpose and goals:* High-performing teams have a clearly defined mission, purpose, and goals. Individual team members understand why the team has been formed and what is expected from the team.[26]

- *Intention:* According to researcher Barry Ekman, the best teams are not ad-hoc or unstructured. Instead, they are planned or structured to achieve a specific goal or address a specific challenge. In structured team building, the importance is on intentionally striving to achieve sustainable outcomes by matching team psychology with change and technology.[27]
- *Clear roles:* High-performing teams have clarity about roles and responsibilities. Team members understand their roles and assignments and how they impact the group, have clear and stable boundaries, are aware of how their work affects other members, and know the direction that is needed to get there.[28]
- *Communication processes:* High-performing teams have extensive communication mechanisms. They communicate regularly with each other either in person, via telephone, or through e-mail and keep those unable to attend meetings informed of the group's progress. They constantly update their planning calendar and communicate about adjustments, as they are needed.[29]
- *Accepting and supportive leadership:* Studies have found that team leaders who function more as coaches than managers facilitate the development of participative, motivated teams.[30] These leaders were proactive and committed to the team, and they provided encouraging, positive influence over the team and its members. A manager pulls a group along; a coach gently pushes it from behind. A manager works to maintain control; a coach works to give up control.[31]
- *Small size:* The size of the team can be essential to a team's success. The optimal size is between 6 and 10. This is large enough to accomplish the work and provide enough human resources and ideas, and small enough for a team to coalesce and reach consensus on major issues.[32]
- *High levels of technical and interpersonal skills:* High-performing teams are composed of members who have a breadth of both specialty and people skills. Understanding how to work with and through others, problem solving, managing project work flow, giving and receiving feedback, goal setting, time management, and conflict management are some of the most valuable skills in team settings.[33]
- *Open relationships and trust:* In high-performing teams, the members develop cooperative behaviors including understanding what is needed from one another; defining the interrelated activities necessary to complete the project; volunteering to assist each other in doing what's needed; and completing assigned tasks competently, on time, accurately, and with quality. Trust is built through behaviors such as being dependable, doing what is agreed upon, being kept informed and informing others of necessary facts and information, keeping confidential information private, and allowing others to use their specialized knowledge and abilities.[34]
- *Accountability:* High-performance team members understand for what (and to what degree) they and others are held accountable. The team receives the message from the organization that performance matters—that it makes a difference whether goals are achieved or not. Expectations are clarified, and members are held responsible as individuals as well as members of the team.[35]
- *Reward structures:* High-performing teams are rewarded for team accomplishments in addition to individual recognition. Organizations that support the team concept organize their recruiting, training, development, sales, business development, strategic planning, compensation, performance appraisal, and promotion strategies to support and reward teamwork.[36] When these strategies don't match with or undermine team processes or philosophies, the organization sends a mixed message and members find ways to "game" the system—often at the expense of their team. If an individual team member who "saves the day" for the department is rewarded for individual behavior, it sends the message that collaboration is not as valued as individual contributions or heroics, even if management's rhetoric suggests teams are truly valued.

4.3 TIPS FOR EFFECTIVE TEAMS

As a member of a team, it is important to be self-directed and work for the betterment of your team. You and your team members will be working with minimal supervision, and it is everyone's responsibility to make the team work. As athletes have learned, if one team member doesn't come through, the quality and performance of the entire team is affected. Teamwork requires full dedication and participation by all members of the team.

The following tips can help make your next team experience more positive and successful.

- *Be focused.* Cooperate with your team members in concentrating on the current issues they face. Cooperation builds trust and mutual respect. Be willing and dedicated to working toward the common purpose.
- *Handle conflict directly* and be willing to compromise. Be willing to explore conflict in a constructive, win–win fashion. Stand up for things that are important to you, but don't insist on getting your way in every discussion. When working together, put personalities aside and confront issues that arise. Resolve conflicts and walk away from sessions with regard, respect, and esteem for yourself and your team members.[37]
- *Focus on both process and content.* Pay attention to the *process* of becoming and working together as a team as well as the *result* or end goal expected from the team. Teamwork is more than producing a deliverable. It also entails the approach or process used when people are working together.[38] The ends don't necessarily justify the means if team members despise and lack respect for team members because of the way decisions and outcomes are rammed through when teams fail to use a consensus approach. At team meetings, review both the processes being used as well as the status of the project.
- *Actively participate*, and encourage others to do the same. At the beginning of a project, talk about roles and responsibilities. Also talk frankly about team members' schedules and their availability to participate fully in the project. Set up checkpoints to ensure that all are contributing equally.
- *Keep sensitive issues private.* At the beginning of a project, discuss the importance of confidentiality. All teams engage in discussions that could be hurtful if made public. Have a pact that private information and views shared will be just that—not relayed to others outside the group. "What's said in the room, stays in the room."
- *Communicate openly and positively.* In order to have full team participation, and for the team to learn and develop, it is essential that team members do not embarrass, reject, mock, or punish someone for speaking up and sharing ideas and perceptions. Foster a climate of psychological safety in order to motivate members to participate, admit errors, and share ideas and beliefs openly and comfortably.[39]
- *Take time to establish operating guidelines* and clarify expectations. Make sure everyone is present for initial discussions of roles, responsibilities, and operating guidelines. For these guidelines to work, it is best that everyone participate in establishing and agreeing to uphold them. Put them in writing and have everyone sign them.
- *Monitor what's going on with the team.* Watch for reactions, nonverbal cues, level of participation (or lack thereof), and general changes in the group's dynamics. Develop observational skills to help the team reach its full potential. A side benefit of doing this is that you increase your own interpersonal skills as you try to set a tone that is conducive to all members enjoying and participating in the team experience.[40]
- *Practice giving (and receiving) effective feedback.* Express support and acceptance by praising and seeking other members' ideas and conclusions. If you disagree with others' viewpoints, criticize ideas but not the people. Be specific about the ideas that concern you and accept others' concerns about your ideas.

- *Work with underperformers* to keep them in the flow of the project and prevent them from becoming excluded from the group.[41] If slackers are an issue in your team, talk with them immediately, preferably one on one. Find out if there is a personal problem preventing the member from being more engaged. Offer to be supportive but don't carry the workload. Give that team member specific, manageable tasks and hold him or her accountable. If the underperformance continues, talk with your manager or instructor. The person may need to be removed from the group or reassigned to a different team.
- *Energize the team* when motivation is low by suggesting new ideas, through humor or use of enthusiasm. Encourage a time-out, if one is needed, or suggest a work or coffee break.
- *Be reliable and conscientious.* Respect other members by honoring deadlines, commitments, and project milestones.[42] If you are having difficulty making a deadline, don't wait until the last minute—discuss the problem immediately with a team member or with the team. There might be a different way of approaching it. It's easier for a team to be flexible when there is adequate time to review the situation and come up with a different plan.
- *When needed, give direction to the team's work* by stating and restating the purpose of assignments, setting or calling attention to time limits, and offering procedures on how to complete the assignment most effectively.
- *Be supportive of your team members.* Always ask how you can help. It's a great way to remind everyone you're a team with collective objectives, not a group of individual contributors competing against each other.

4.4 WHY TEAMS FAIL

A note of caution: for teams and teamwork to succeed, there must be ample time in which to complete an assignment. Also needed are adequate resources to achieve the stated objectives and full management support of the team's effort. While the concept of teamwork is prevalent in both work and nonwork settings, not all situations warrant or are conducive to teams. Teams may be faced with tight deadlines; merging of processes and responsibilities; technological challenges; mismatched skills and abilities; unresolvable personality clashes, styles, and behaviors; limited work or teaming experience; or power struggles. In these situations, or in cases where there is no interdependence or need for collaboration, teamwork is going to be difficult if not impossible. These issues should be addressed early so that modifications can be made if necessary.

For example, if a team lacks the proper skill sets, additional members or training sessions can be added. If a power struggle is unfolding, a facilitator can be appointed. Inexperienced team members can be assigned informal mentors or coaches. Sometimes, if it's in the best interests of an organization, a team can be disbanded altogether. Perhaps the mission wasn't clearly defined at the outset of a project and the team members find they are unable to devote the time necessary to do the job. Or perhaps management requested individuals to work on a team project but made no allowances for mandatory day-to-day tasks. In situations such as these, it's appropriate for the team to be reconfigured (or disbanded) so that the original objective can be attained through either a different team or a different approach. Oftentimes, teams ignore early problems—perhaps believing such problems can be overcome—and become dysfunctional.[43] Intervening early, in a proactive way, can turn a team around or cause the organization to consider other, non-team-based approaches to solving a problem.

How can you deal with team members who aren't performing? Following are some tips.

DEALING WITH PROBLEM TEAM MEMBERS

- **Absentee member:** A member can become distracted by a work or personal problem that prevents him or her from following through on commitments made to the team. In this case, the best strategy is to be direct immediately. Discuss the situation with the team member in a way in which the person does not feel he or she is being put on the defensive. Explain the problem and find out the team member's perception of the situation. Ask specifically if the team member still has the time necessary for the team. If not, part ways if possible. If this is not possible, determine a way for the team member to make contributions outside of the normal meeting times and make the person accountable for a specific segment of the work that limits reliance on the team.
- **Social loafer:** As mentioned earlier, it is not uncommon for one or more persons on a team to be able to "hide" the fact they're not contributing. This typically happens when the team members' work ethics differ and one or more team members "step up to the plate" and take on additional responsibility to ensure the work gets done, effectively covering for the less productive team members. Work standards will always vary from person to person. A strategy for dealing with this is to raise the issue at the onset of the project. Divide the responsibilities and set up checkpoints to ensure each member is contributing roughly equally. If a discrepancy appears, try to quantify it and reallocate the workload so all members are contributing roughly equally.
- **Procrastinator:** We're all human, and a seemingly human tendency is to "put off until tomorrow what we should be working on today." This is particularly problematic for work teams. Teams are composed of individuals with different work schedules and work styles. Some people thrive on the pressure of imminent deadlines while others find waiting until the last minute to be overly stressful. In this situation it is best to do two things: (a) set up interim checkpoints, or minideadlines, to ensure the work progresses at a reasonable pace, and (b) be realistic when work schedules are drawn up and deadlines determined. Prior to establishing deadlines, ask all team members to check personal and work calendars to catch any problems before they occur. At each meeting reclarify the commitments that might affect a person's inability to adhere to a deadline set earlier. And build in some slack: set the final deadline for a few days before the *actual* deadline—just in case!

Teams may not be a cure for all that ails an organization. But, teams can be very effective if the team structure makes sense and members practice the suggestions outlined in the chapter. Other steps team members and their managers can take to improve the likelihood of team success are summarized in the chart below:

TIPS FOR MANAGING FOR OUTSTANDING RESULTS

- Care about the people you work with—understand them, know what's important to them, and be able to motivate them.
- Don't worry about who gets the credit—emphasize team effort and rewards; use the "whatever is best for the team" approach.
- Respect individual differences—accept individuals and work to emphasize strengths and minimize weaknesses.
- Subordinate yourself to a higher purpose—keep the common goal in the forefront.

- Know yourself—be aware of your strengths and admit your weaknesses; surround yourself with people who can compensate for your weaknesses.
- Don't be afraid to follow—some of the best teams are those where the leader doesn't call all the shots.

Source: Stephen Covey, "Team Up for a Superstar Office," *USA Weekend,* Sept. 4–6, 1998, p. 10.

4.5 TEAMWORK AND PROJECT MANAGEMENT

To achieve the benefits of a team culture, some changes in management behavior are needed, as shown in Table 4.2. To learn more about the behaviors listed on the right-hand side of Table 4.2, read on.

Organization—Team Norms

A common way to promote more constructive and productive teamwork is to have the team create a set of guidelines for the team, sometimes called team norms. Take a minute and list some things (attitudes, behaviors, and so on) that you have found (or believe) can help a team be more effective. Then compare your list with the following two lists, both of which are from McNeill, Bellamy, and Foster (1995). The first was adapted from the Boeing Airplane Group's training manual for team members and the second is from the Ford Motor Company.

Table 4.1 Team Task and Maintenance Roles

Team Task Roles	Team Maintenance Roles
Initiating	Encouraging
Seeking information	Expressing feelings
Giving information	Harmonizing
Seeking opinions	Compromising
Giving opinions	Facilitating communications
Clarifying	Setting standards or goals
Elaborating	Testing agreement
Summarizing	Following

Taken from *Teamwork and Project Management,* Third Edition, by Karl A. Smith.

Table 4.2 Management Behavior Change Needed for Team Culture

From	To
Directing	Guiding
Competing	Collaborating
Relying on rules	Focusing on the process
Using organizational hierarchy	Using a network
Consistency/sameness	Diversity/flexibility
Secrecy	Openness/sharing
Passivity	Risk taking
Isolated decisions	Involvement of others
People as costs	People as assets
Results thinking	Process thinking
Source: McNeill, Bellamy, and Foster, 1995.	

Code of Cooperation

1. *Every* member is responsible for the team's progress and success.
2. Attend all team meetings and be on time.
3. Come prepared.
4. Carry out assignments on schedule.
5. Listen to and show respect for the contributions of other members; be an active listener.
6. *Constructively* criticize ideas, not persons.
7. Resolve conflicts constructively.
8. Pay attention; avoid disruptive behavior.
9. Avoid disruptive side conversations.
10. Only one person speaks at a time.
11. Everyone participates; no one dominates.
12. Be succinct; avoid long anecdotes and examples.
13. No rank in the room.
14. Respect those not present.
15. Ask questions when you do not understand.
16. Attend to your personal comfort needs at any time, but minimize team disruption.
17. Have fun.
18. ?

Ten Commandments: An Effective Code of Cooperation

- Help each other be right, not wrong.
- Look for ways to make new ideas work, not for reasons they won't.
- If in doubt, check it out. Don't make negative assumptions about each other.
- Help each other win, and take pride in each other's victories.
- Speak positively about each other and about your organization at every opportunity.
- Maintain a positive mental attitude no matter what the circumstances.
- Act with initiative and courage, as if it all depends on you.

- Do everything with enthusiasm; it's contagious.
- Whatever you want, give it away.
- Don't lose faith.
- Have fun!

Team norms are common today not only in business and industry, but also in academic and research settings. The box "Tips for Working Successfully in a Team" presents a list developed by Randy Pausch for use in a course he taught at Carnegie Mellon University (Pausch, 2002). Having an agreed-upon, abided-by code of cooperation such as Pausch's will help teams get started toward working effectively. However, if team members haven't developed the requisite communication, trust, loyalty, organization, leadership, decision-making procedures, and conflict management skills, then the team will very likely struggle or at least not perform up to its potential. One way a team can develop such a code is to create a *team charter*—a sample format for a team charter is given below.

TEAM CHARTER GUIDELINES

- Team name, membership, and roles
- Team mission statement
- Anticipated results (goals)
- Specific tactical objectives
- Ground rules/guiding principles for team participation
- Shared expectations/aspirations

Team charters typically are created during a team meeting early in the project life cycle. Involvement of all team members in creating the charter helps build commitment of each to the project and to other members. A set of guidelines such as the Team Charter Guidelines often helps the team through this process.

Let's look more deeply into the mystery of teamwork skills with a summary of our work on teamwork skills in learning groups.

TIPS FOR WORKING SUCCESSFULLY IN A TEAM

Meet people properly. It all starts with the introduction. Then exchange contact information and make sure you know how to pronounce everyone's names. Exchange phone numbers, and find out when it is acceptable to call.

Find things you have in common. You can almost always find something in common with another person, and starting from that baseline, it's much easier to then address issues where you have differences. This is why cities benefit from professional sports teams, which are socially galvanizing forces that cut across boundaries of race and wealth. If nothing else, you probably have in common things like the weather.

Make meeting conditions good. Have a large surface to write on, make sure the room is quiet and warm enough, and that there aren't lots of distractions. Make sure no one is hungry, cold, or tired. Meet over a meal if you can; food *softens* a meeting. That's why they "do lunch" in Hollywood.

Let everyone talk. Even if you think what's being said is stupid, don't interrupt. Cutting someone off is rude and is not worth whatever small time gain you might make. Don't finish people's sentences for them; they can do it themselves. And remember: talking louder or faster doesn't make your idea any better.

Check your egos at the door. When you discuss ideas, immediately label them and write them down. The labels should be descriptive of the idea, not the originator, e.g., "the troll bridge story," not "Jane's story."

Praise each other. Find something nice to say, even if it's a stretch. Even the worst of ideas has a silver lining inside it, if you just look hard enough. Focus on the good, praise it, and then raise any objections or concerns you have about the rest of it.

Put it in writing. Always write down who is responsible for what, by when. Be *concrete.* Never assume that someone's roommate will deliver a phone message. Also, remember that "politics is when you have more than two people"—with that in mind, always copy any piece of e-mail within the team, or to me, to *all members* of the team. This rule should *never* be violated; don't try to guess what your teammates might or might not want to hear about.

Be open and honest. Talk with your team members if there's a problem, and talk with me if you think you need help. The whole point of this course is that it's tough to work across cultures. If we all go into it knowing that's an issue, we should be comfortable discussing problems when they arise—after all, that's what this course is really about. Be forgiving when people make mistakes, but don't be afraid to raise the issues when they come up.

Avoid conflict at all costs. When stress occurs and tempers flare, take a short break. Clear your heads, apologize, and take another stab at it. Apologize for upsetting your peers, even if you think someone else was primarily at fault; the goal is to work together, not start a legal battle over whose transgressions were worse. It takes two to have an argument, so be the peacemaker.

Phrase alternatives as questions. Instead of "I think we should do A, not B," try "What if we did A, instead of B?" That allows people to offer comments, rather than defend one choice.

Source: Randy Pausch, for the Building Virtual Worlds course at Carnegie Mellon, Spring 1998.

In-Class Activities

ICA 4-1

Bridge Building

Groups of four to six are tasked with creating a bridge out of the materials provided. You have 30 minutes in which to complete this task. When the project is complete or time is called—whichever comes first—your instructor will roll a ball across your bridge to ensure it meets the project specifications. Following this activity, discuss these questions in your group.

Questions

1. How did your group decide how to build the bridge? Did it make a plan or did it just start building?
2. Did anyone play a leadership role in the task? Explain.
3. What made building the bridge as a group, rather than as an individual, more difficult?
4. In what ways did the group make the project easier? Explain.
5. Was your group a group or team? Explain.

ICA 4-2

The Story: A Team Exercise

Read the instructions and story below and answer the corresponding questions. Next, complete the same task in your assigned group.

What Does the Story Tell?

INSTRUCTIONS

Read the following story and take for granted that everything it says is true. Read carefully because, in spots, the story is deliberately vague. Don't try to memorize it since you can look back at it at any time.

Then read the numbered statements about the story and decide whether you consider each one true, false, or questionable. Circling the "T" means you feel sure the statement is definitely true. Circling the "F" means you feel sure the statement is definitely false. Circling the "?" means you cannot tell whether it is true or false. If you feel doubtful about any part of a statement, circle the question mark.

Take the statements in turn and do not go back later to change any of your answers. Do not reread any of the statements after you have answered them.

STORY

The owner of the Adams Manufacturing Company entered the office of one of his foremen where he found three employees playing cards. One of them was Carl Young, brother-in-law of foreman Henry Dilson. Dilson, incidentally, often worked late. Company rules did not specifically forbid gambling on the premises, but the president had expressed himself forcibly on the subject.

STATEMENTS ABOUT THE STORY

1.	In brief, the story is about a company owner who found three men playing cards.	T	F	?
2.	The president walked into the office of one of his foremen.	T	F	?
3.	Company rules forbade playing cards on the premises after hours.	T	F	?

		T	F	?
4.	While the card playing took place in Henry Dilson's office, the story does not state whether Dilson was present.	T	F	?
5.	Dilson never worked late.	T	F	?
6.	Gambling on the premises of the Adams Manufacturing Company was not punished.	T	F	?
7.	Carl Young was not playing cards when the president walked in.	T	F	?
8.	Three employees were gambling in a foreman's office.	T	F	?
9.	While the card players were surprised when the owner walked in, it is not clear whether they will be punished.	T	F	?
10.	Henry Dilson is Carl Young's brother-in-law.	T	F	?
11.	The president is opposed to gambling on company premises.	T	F	?
12.	Carl Young did not take part in the card game in Henry Dilson's office.	T	F	?

Questions

1. What process did you use to come up with the group answers?
2. Did anyone act as a leader or facilitator in the exercise? Explain.
3. In what ways was it difficult to achieve a group decision?
4. Which behaviors blocked the group's process? Which ones helped?
5. What are the advantages or disadvantages of working in a group compared to working as an individual?

ICA 4-3

Case Study on Gaining Appropriate Membership on Teams

This is the team's third meeting. The team's task, deliverables, and membership have been dictated by a steering committee that oversees the division's teaming efforts. Members represent different areas and management levels within the division. A new team member who missed the first two meetings enters the room. Let's eavesdrop:

SCRIBE: "Okay. Here's our agenda. Does this sound ok to everyone?"

NEW TEAM MEMBER: "Well, not exactly. I have a question regarding the team's task. I know I missed the first two meetings, but I'm unclear about our purpose. I mean, without a well-understood purpose, are we ready to talk about membership? I'm not even sure if I should be here!"

SCRIBE: "Well, I suppose we can add "team purpose" to the agenda. How much time should we allot?"

TEAM LEADER: (Feeling strained by all the necessary structure.) "Could we hold off with the agenda for a few minutes . . . I know we need the agenda, but I think we should talk about purpose for a few minutes at least; then we can get back to the regular agenda. She (the new team member) brings up a good point."

Some discussion ensues. It becomes clear that the team's purpose *is* unclear. Other additional information is revealed, such as the fact that there had been three other team members who, shortly after being appointed by the steering committee, decided to excuse themselves from the team. Also, the team leader brought a new person in (call her Possible New Member), who is not really a full-fledged member until the steering committee approves it.

SCRIBE: "Back to the agenda. Were there any corrections to the minutes? (No response.) Okay, now for today's meeting roles . . . oh, our timekeeper isn't here today."

NEW TEAM MEMBER: (Looking at Possible New Member) "Would you like to keep time?"

TEAM LEADER: "Well, we're not sure if she is an official team member yet. Remember, the steering committee hasn't okayed her yet. Should she keep time if she's not?"

NEW TEAM MEMBER: "What's the difference? And why do we need the steering committee's blessing? Let's just do it."

TEAM LEADER: "Actually, there are some other names, in addition to Possible Team Member, that we've submitted to the steering committee. After all, we've lost three people since the team began."

NEW TEAM MEMBER: "Do we need additional people? Why? Again, doesn't it depend on what we're trying to accomplish?"

Questions

1. Why is it important to clarify a team's purpose? Once the task is given, why is clarification necessary?
2. What role does this purpose play in defining team membership? Why do you suppose others have "excused themselves" from the team?
3. How effective is the team leader? Explain.
4. Meeting management techniques—using agendas, having a scribe and timekeeper—are intended to make meetings more effective. In what ways could these techniques have the opposite effect?
5. If you were asked to participate in this meeting, what would you do to get the process back on track? Explain.

ICA 4-4

The Case of the Take-Charge Team Leader

You are a member of a team that is meeting for the third time. Your goal is to reduce the number and dollar amount of workers' compensation claims. The team consists of members from safety, human resources, legal, and medical (e.g., staff nurses and doctors) departments. The team leader—a senior level manager—demonstrates a "take-charge" approach in that he or she believes he or she knows more about the task and assignment than anyone on the team. Early in the team's existence, the leader shared a project milestone chart that the team accepted. While the group has kept up with its assignments and is working rather effectively, the team leader seems impatient with the team's progress. In fact, the leader would like to exert greater control over the team's activities because he or she already has supporting data from outside groups and departments about the task and wants to complete the project in record time. However, you and other team members are concerned that (1) there may be other issues that have not yet surfaced, and (2) if his or her ideas are accepted, one of the team members may lose his or her position in the firm.

Questions

1. What issues are at play? How would you feel in this situation?
2. If the leader is so capable, why do you suppose management created a team to address this particular (and highly visible) problem?
3. At this point, what would you do and why?
4. If no changes were made, what do you think the final outcome would be?

ICA 4-5

Reflection/Action Plan

This chapter focused on teams in the workplace—what they are, why they are important, and how to improve your skill in this area. Complete the worksheet below upon completing all the reading and experiential activities for this chapter.

1. The one or two areas in which I am most strong are:
2. The one or two areas in which I need more improvement are:
3. If I did only one thing to improve in this area, it would be to:

SUMMARY

Workplaces in the United States and abroad have embraced teaming. This is no accident. Organizations that implemented work teams as a way to improve products, services, and processes have witnessed tremendous measurable benefits. Some of these benefits accrue because of synergies—the notion that teams produce more and better solutions than individuals—gained from combining various skill sets, perspectives, abilities, and work styles on a single team. Not all teams produce phenomenal outcomes. By understanding the normal phases of group development and ways to gain and maintain group productivity and motivation, you can help your teams reach their full potential.

KEY TERMS AND CONCEPTS

Absentee member
Adjourning
Cross-functional teams
Forming
Group
Groupthink
High-performance team
Norming
Performing
Process improvement team
Procrastinator
Self-managed team
Social loafing/loafer
Storming
Task force
Team

ENDNOTES

1. Quote by Tracey Edwards in "Teaming with Talent," by Jim White, *Management Today,* Sept. 1999, p. 56.

2. Lillian Chaney and Julie Lyden, "Making U.S. Teams Work," *Supervision,* Jan. 2000, p. 6.

3. Karl L. Smart and Carol Barnum, "Communication in Cross-Functional Teams: An Introduction to This Special Issue," *Technical Communication,* Feb. 2000, p. 19.

4. Kevin McManus, "Do You Have Teams?" *IIE Solutions,* April 2000, p. 21.

5. Jim White, "Teaming with Talent," *Management Today,* Sept. 1999, p. 56.

6. Harvey Mackay, "Get on the Team and Be a Winner," *Providence Business News,* August 16, 1999, p. 38.

7. Chaney and Lyden, "Making U.S. Teams Work."

8. McManus, "Do You Have Teams?"

9. Ibid.

10. Smart and Barnum, "Communication in Cross-Functional Teams."

11. Chaney and Lyden, "Making U.S. Teams Work."

12. Mohsen Attaran and Tai T. Nguyen, "Succeeding with Self-managed Work Teams," *Industrial Management,* July–August 1999, p. 24.

13. Larry Cole and Michael Scott Cole, "Teamwork is Spelled Incorrectly: Teamwork = Communication," *Communication World,* April 2000, p. 56.

14. Attaran and Nguyen, "Succeeding with Self-managed Work Teams." Reprinted by permission of the Institute of Industrial Engineers, 25 Technology Park, Norcross, GA 30092, 770-449-0461. Copyright © 1999.

15. Irving I. Janis, *Groupthink,* 2nd ed. (Boston, MA: Houghton-Mifflin, 1982).

16. Attaran and Nguyen, "Succeeding with Self-managed Work Teams."
17. David Rohlander, "Building High-Performance Teams," *Credit Union Executive,* March 2000, p. 36.
18. Bruce W. Tuckman, "Developmental Sequences in Small Groups," *Psychological Bulletin* 63 (1965), pp. 384–99. The stage theory of team development was first identified by Tuckerman. Subsequent research has found the stages occur in a slightly different order. While the original model is reflected in this chapter, some researchers have found that teams more likely progress through conforming before entering the storming stage. See R. E. Quinn and K. S. Cameron, "Organizational Life Cycles and Shifting Criteria of Effectiveness," *Management Science* 29 (1983), pp. 37–61. Also see K. S. Cameron and D. A. Whetten, "Perceptions of Organizational Effectiveness in Organizational Life Cycles," *Administrative Science Quarterly* 27 (1981), pp. 525–44.
19. Peter R. Scholtes, *The Team Handbook* (Madison, WI: Joiner and Associates, 1988).
20. John R. Myers, "What It Takes to Make a Team," *Purchasing,* Sept. 2, 1999, p. 91.
21. Scholtes, *The Team Handbook.*
22. Daniel C. Feldman, "The Development and Enforcement of Group Norms," *Academy of Management Review* 9, no. 1 (1984), pp. 47–53.
23. Scholtes, *The Team Handbook.*
24. Rona Leach, "Supervision: From Me to We," *Supervision,* Feb. 2000, p. 8.
25. Ruth Wageman, "Critical Success Factors for Creating Superb Self-Managing Teams," *Organizational Dynamics,* Summer 1997, p. 49.
26. Rohlander, "Building High-Performance Teams."
27. Barry Ekman and Emmanuela Ginngregorio, "Establishing Truly Peak Performance Teams—Beyond Metaphoric Challenges," *Human Resource Management International Digest,* 11, no. 3 (2003), p. 2.
28. American Management Association, "HR Update: Creating Real Teamwork at the Top," *HR Focus,* Jan. 2000, p. 2.
29. Smart and Barnum, "Communication in Cross-Functional Teams."
30. Paulo Vieira Cunha and Maria Joao Louro, "Building Teams That Learn," *The Academy of Management Executives,* Feb. 2000, p. 152.
31. Renee Evenson, "Team Effort: Beyond Employees to Team, beyond Manager to Coach," *Supervision,* Feb. 2000, p. 11.
32. Chaney and Lyden, "Making U.S. Teams Work."
33. Avan R. Jassawalla and Hemant C. Sashittal, "Building Collaborative Cross-Functional New Product Teams," *The Academy of Management Executive,* August 1999, p. 50.
34. Cole and Cole, "Teamwork Is Spelled Incorrectly."
35. Russ Forrester and Allan B. Drexler, "A Model for Team-Based Organizational Performance," *The Academy of Management Executive,* August 1999, p. 36.
36. Becky L. Nichol, "Top Ten Reasons Teams Become Dysfunctional," *National Public Accountant,* Feb. 2000, p. 12.
37. Jassawalla and Sashittal, "Building Collaborative Cross-Functional New Product Teams."
38. Cole and Cole, "Teamwork Is Spelled Incorrectly."
39. Cunha and Louro, "Building Teams."
40. Myers, "What It Takes to Make a Team."
41. Ted Gautschi, "Strengthen Your Team," *Design News,* Oct. 18, 1999, p. 158.
42. Myers, "What It Takes to Make a Team."
43. Smart and Barnum, "Communication in Cross-Functional Teams."

CHAPTER 5
PROJECT MANAGEMENT

Objectives

By learning the material in this chapter, you should be able to

- keep projects on track
- help your team meet deadlines
- ensure project members agree on and maintain the necessary standards or quality
- handle multiple projects simultaneously
- incorporate your personal project time lines into your professional project time lines
- keep long-term objectives in mind while working on day-to-day objectives
- handle unexpected events that interfere with your preplanned schedule

Carol Marshall is a bright young engineer in a large manufacturing facility. Although she's been out of college for three years, she's been promoted twice and is now in a supervisory position. She is very comfortable with projects in which she is the key contributor. She has high work standards and always goes the extra mile to bring projects in on time and budget. Working autonomously, she has developed good systems that allowed her to accumulate an enviable success record. Her managers, noticing her leadership potential, have given her a very important task force to oversee. A lot depends on the results of the task force.

Carol has devoted a lot of energy to the task force. She has helped them build confidence in and rapport with each other. She has involved the group in several social gatherings to strengthen their comfort level in working with each other. She has good communication with the group as a whole and with each of the five other group members. They've been together for four months, and the deadline for their task force deliverable is drawing near. Carol heard two weeks ago that they were on schedule and today she's expecting to see the final report.

In looking over the project report, Carol is shocked to discover the development subcommittee is behind schedule and needs more time to complete the final report. Carol is worried; she has a presentation to senior management scheduled for the end of the week. There's no way she's going to be ready by then. She wonders, "What happened? What could I have done differently? How come this always happens?" She concludes she's not cut out for supervision and thinks she needs to go to her managers and request

---

Taken from *Interpersonal Skills in Organizations,* Second Edition, by Suzanne C. De Janasz, Karen O. Dowd, and Beth Z. Schneider.

a reassignment. "From now on," she mutters, "I'll just do important things like this on my own. I'm not going to depend on anyone else but me."

1. Why was Carol left in this situation?
2. What could Carol have done over the four months to ensure timely completion of the project?
3. Do you think Carol should give up supervision? Why or why not?
4. Has something like this ever happened to you before? How did you react? What did you learn from this experience?

"Plan the work. Work the plan."

This old saying is the cornerstone of management today. If you don't plan, you will be so busy reacting to situations that you will not have time to take advantage of new opportunities.[1] It's easy for most people to develop plans. What separates successful plans from unsuccessful ones is the implementation. For a plan to become reality, it needs to be operationalized—brought to life. This chapter introduces the concept of project management and discusses how this concept can be used to organize projects and assignments that are managed by teams. The definition and importance of project management, steps involved in managing projects, and strategies and tips for honing your project management skills are discussed. We also include information on tools available to help you manage projects.

5.1 WHAT IS PROJECT MANAGEMENT?

Have you ever been involved in a team project where team members had different definitions of quality? Or different interpretations of the phrase "on time"? Or where everyone procrastinated until the last minute? When used effectively, project management can help prevent or reduce the likelihood of these problems. **Project management** is the coordination of your work and that of others such that organizational objectives can be achieved while meeting time, budget, and quality standards or expectations.[2]

Project management is a systematic process through which almost all the steps involved in starting and completing a project are anticipated and outlined in advance.[3] We use the word "almost" because no one can predict everything that will happen between the present and the project deadline. In project management, the known steps are anticipated and accounted for; in addition, the schedule includes some "slack" to account for unforeseen difficulties or events that invariably arise. Project management involves tracking a project from its inception to completion. This includes scheduling steps, allocating tasks to various team members, creating and overseeing time and financial budgets for projects, monitoring progress made toward goals, and overall project resource management.

5.1.1 Why Project Management?

In today's rapidly changing and highly competitive workplace, managers are being asked to reduce costs while increasing productivity. This imperative forces managers to develop new models of operating for every aspect of the organization.[4] One way to "do more with less" is to encourage employees to be efficient in plotting their work flow, whether on independent or team-based projects. As employees work increasingly in teams, it is essential to have a system to help team members work collectively on a project that has multiple milestones or deadlines. This is especially true when individual members are involved in multiple projects. They, and their managers, must juggle many balls simultaneously. Being involved in multiple individual and team-based projects, project managers and project team members have a lot—perhaps too much—on their plates today. Project planning and management becomes essential as project managers attempt to adapt to changing technology, coordinate with multiple people and departments, meet financial goals, and manage business strategy while simultaneously monitoring multiple projects with day-, week-, or year-long or more time spans. And all of this must get done while getting the day-to-day work done![5]

Projects that encompass many tasks and run over several weeks or months require planning and coordination with other projects and activities, both personal and professional. As a manager or employee, your ongoing job priorities and commitments have to be factored in when planning new projects. The same is true for students. Coursework and extra assignments need to be incorporated into your plans, as do personal commitments. Vacations, medical appointments, sports competitions, community involvement, carpooling, child care, and elder care are examples of personal commitments that should be taken into account when planning project schedules either independently or with others.

5.2 BENEFITS OF PROJECT MANAGEMENT

Applying a project management approach to your work has numerous benefits for organizations and individuals. We've mentioned the need to "do more with less" or perhaps "work smart, not hard." Project management helps organizations do this and ensures that:

- *Resources such as time, money, and personnel are appropriately allocated to the organization's numerous priorities and objectives.*[6] Through advance planning, individual project calendars can be adjusted to be in sync with other organization commitments. For example, in planning a major new product rollout, a company can ensure that it occurs at a time when other projects aren't absorbing needed time and energy of the managers and employees involved in the rollout effort.[7]
- *Long-term objectives can be kept in mind while short-term objectives are being implemented.* Through thinking strategically about an organization's long-term objectives, short-term activities that help move the organization toward the longer-term goal can be planned and implemented. Using project management, a company can ensure that weekly or monthly tasks and objectives—in addition to those responsible for them—are included in plans that support a new marketing strategy. If a company strives to expand sales by 20 percent by adding an online business to complement its brick and mortar business within two years, it could set up multiple milestones that track this progress. Within 3 months, content for the website is researched; within 6 months, the website is up and running; within one year, sales should increase by 5 percent; within 18 months, sales should increase by 15 percent, and so on.

- *Contingencies can be anticipated.* By articulating in advance the known steps to complete a project and building in some slack in the schedule, each unanticipated event that occurs during the project time line does not have to be treated as a crisis that affects the ultimate deadline or deliverable. Let's say a company is implementing a new integrated computer system that tracks inventory, sales, costs, and operations. The consultants who are installing the package estimate that complete installation and implementation will take eight months. This includes installation of software, training all employees, testing and debugging the system, and making modifications. For project planning purposes, it's best to add 10 to 20 percent additional time to each phase. This will ensure that slack is built into the schedule to accommodate the unexpected, such as incompatibility with previous hardware, heavier than usual sales, or vacations and holidays. By allocating extra time to projects at the outset, you have a better chance of getting ahead of your workload and staying there.[8] Sarah Gavit, an experienced project manager at NASA's Jet Propulsion Laboratory, notes, "Manage the risk. There always will be certain parts more susceptible to going wrong. Before we ever lay out a schedule, we look at four or five areas with high risk. We develop contingency plans and watch extra closely. Other project managers sometimes don't look until they're up against the wall."[9]
- *Project output is made more consistent.* By developing quality standards in advance, team members, managers, and employees have the opportunity to discuss and clarify their perceptions of the project objectives and their expectations for the end product, or project deliverable(s). For example, when developing a new interviewer training program, a company can outline the legal requirements, research industry benchmarks or best practices, and develop a set of specifications for the project that all members of the planning team agree to in advance. By getting all involved on board before any project output is generated, the quality of the components comprising the end product will be higher and more harmonious than if everyone established his or her own quality standards independently.

Project management has numerous benefits for the individuals involved as well as the organization. In addition to enabling individuals to be more efficient and organized, through project planning and management:

- *Collegiality is enhanced.* Through meeting with other team members and organizational employees who have a stake in the success of a project, you have the opportunity to build relationships that contribute to a sense of belonging in the organization.[10] Let's say you are part of a group tasked with implementing a new budget tracking system for the company. By meeting regularly as a team and with department heads and other stakeholders, you are able to form relationships that contribute to the success of the project at hand and last beyond the duration of the project. These relationships facilitate your knowledge and understanding of where you and your work fit with that of others in the organization. This enhances your perspective and enables you to think more globally in how you do your work. In addition, by being connected or networked with others in the organization, trust and helping behaviors—part of collegiality—are increased.[11]
- *Morale is enhanced.* No one likes feeling that they're all alone in overcoming a mountain of work at the office. Planning work in advance and achieving the desired outcome successfully boosts your morale and the morale of others involved in the effort. For example, tackling a thorny problem such as designing a new budget monitoring system can be a tedious task. When the various components of the task are articulated, planned for, and carried out systematically and incrementally, what might be an overwhelming task appears more manageable. And when you are able to

make progress on this task—even one small component at a time—your self-efficacy increases along with your morale. "Projects that succeed are just about the most satisfying work experience you can have. It's as much fun as you can have and still get paid," notes Steve McMenamin, Vice President of Customer Service at Southern California Edison Co.[12]

- *Job satisfaction is increased.* Once we have mastered the basics of any job, many of us want more. Once we prove our capabilities, many people want to be involved in greater levels of responsibility, more variety of work, and more complex work.[13] Being involved in multiple projects or tasks affords you this opportunity to stretch and grow further and, as a result, experience enhanced job satisfaction. Let's say that in recognition for your outstanding capabilities as a waitress, the owner of a busy restaurant asks you to participate in a task force that is evaluating ways to improve customer service. Project management gives you the tools needed to juggle both roles simultaneously, facilitating your ability to take on both roles and, in so doing, increasing your ability multitask and contribute to the organization beyond your daily job.
- *Learning is enhanced.* Project management results in learning about others' jobs and work styles, not just your own. Working with others on projects increases your understanding of how your and others' roles and responsibilities fit into the whole. This increases your knowledge of the complexities and interdependencies in the organization, enabling you to make more substantive and appropriate contributions to the organization's success. For example, you might be involved in a group project at school where the ultimate deliverable is a presentation on a cutting-edge business topic. By planning the project in advance with other team members, you exchange ideas about preferred ways to approach the project, manage time, communicate with each other, make decisions, and solve problems. This collaboration increases everyone's skills and knowledge base.
- *Creativity and synergy are enhanced.* Through planning a project in advance with your manager and team members, you are more likely to envision a new way to approach the situation than if you simply did the work in the same way it's always been done. Imagine you are part of a team charged with implementing a membership expansion campaign for a fraternity. By planning the project in advance, you can ask big-picture questions such as, "What do we want to accomplish?" "How can we do things better than before?" "What worked and what didn't work previously?" "Ideally, what would we like the new program to look like?" By brainstorming with other team members to answer these questions, you're likely to tap into the synergistic potential that resides in most diverse groups. This process energizes a group toward identifying more creative, innovative, and better solutions than could have been produced by any one team member working on his or her own.

Let's face it. Despite, or perhaps because of, all the technology that is now available, working today is harder and more pressure-filled than ever. The average workday for today's white-collar worker is longer today than it was in the 1960s.[14] With the availability of e-mail, fax machines, and voice mail, our expectations for quick turnaround have changed from a week or so to an hour or two! Customers want service now. Managers want deliverables yesterday. With all this pressure, it's a wonder that any projects with a time line of more than a few days get done. Managing projects can be tedious and time-consuming work. The time that an organization or individual invests in planning will yield paybacks and returns through reduced implementation time and costs.[15] A project management mindset can serve as a way to spread the work around, making working on projects more effective and enjoyable.

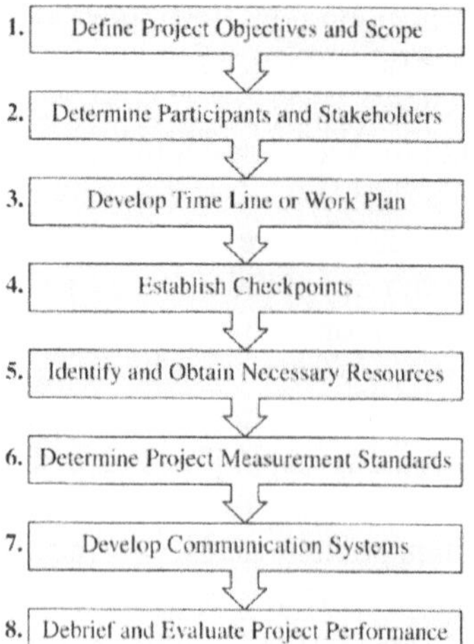

Figure 5.1 Steps to managing projects.

5.2.1 Eight Steps to Managing Projects

The eight steps for managing projects (see Figure 5.1) can help you clarify, organize, and implement projects or complex tasks. First, we must define *what* we are managing before we plan *how* we manage it.

Step One—Define Project Objectives and Scope

As a group, discuss the goals of the project. What deliverables and outcomes are expected? What would you ideally like to accomplish? The answers to these questions may be different. If so, focus first on the essentials or must haves, and then, if there is room in the schedule, incorporate the optionals or nice to haves. For example, an essential element would be to meet the deadline imposed by the instructor or manager. An optional element would be to have deliverables prepared a week ahead of time. After going through all the steps of project management, you'll then be able to assess whether getting done a week early is possible.

- Relate the project goals to overall organizational goals and strategy. For example, if your team's goal is to produce a set of recommendations for consideration by senior management, determine your boss's objectives—as well as those of his or her boss—to ensure your project goals support the organization's broader goals. Without taking this step, you risk "doing things right" instead of "doing the right things."
- Clarify the scope of the project. Making recommendations is not the same as implementing them. Aside from the time required, these differing outcome expectations can be a source of frustration and chaos for a team.
- Clarify project objectives with the project manager or instructor to ensure everyone's on the same page about the expected outcome. This might surprise you, but the phrase "zero defects" means different things to different people. Quality of 99.9 percent is impressive, unless you consider that a .1 percent error rate equates, for example, to Americans consuming over 14,000 cans of "bad" soda in a single year. The clarification of project objectives and scope can be one of the most critical steps in the process of project management.

Step Two—Determine Project Participants and Stakeholders

Now that you are clear about what to do, it makes sense to consider who should be included in the project. Even though some people may not seem necessary at first, the

PROJECT MANAGEMENT IN ACTION[16]

Pam Statz, an analyst for HotWired—a company that creates and manages websites for other entities—used to struggle with reaching deadline until her department began using project management. Pam and her staff would continually fall short of expected deadlines because they were unable to work together toward stated objectives. They would also have to spend their weekends and late nights in the office to try and accomplish their goats. Once they installed and began using Microsoft Project, specific objectives were defined as was the person responsible for achieving them. It focused the department on using a time line and plan to follow. The project management tools and approach provided a means for the group members to communicate and share files without having to be physically together. Project management enabled Pam's department to become a cohesive unit that met their deadlines in a relatively stress-free manner. It also enabled HotWired to efficiently and effectively design websites—and satisfy their customers—often before project deadlines.

fact that their work or organization is affected by the outcomes of the project, thereby making them **stakeholders**, may suggest that their inclusion is more important than you might think. Key considerations for this stage include the following:

- Make sure that vital employees and teammates are made and kept a part of the project and that key stakeholders—those who have a stake in the outcome such as your manager or instructor—are either involved in or kept apprised of the group's efforts throughout the project.[17] For example, a functional organization charged with procuring materials for projects became frustrated with a system that took anywhere from four weeks to 18 months to obtain even simple, low-cost items. The group worked together and devised a new system designed to save countless hours and, hence, costs. But they weren't done. The proposed system required extensive changes in the way accounts payable did its work. The group presented their plan to their management as well as members of accounts payable, and then asked representatives from the latter to join their group to flesh out the details and then implement the new system. Had they not included this step, the group might have faced an uphill battle—even though their proposed new system could save valuable resources.
- Once the project group has been assembled, begin a master calendar on which members' availability (and lack thereof) is noted. Indicate specific dates in which one or more of the team members will not be available to work on the project. Holidays, vacation days, anticipated personal days, travel days, meeting days, or commitments to other projects should be noted and accounted for when designating project steps and entering to do items on the project calendar. Some dates may have to be skipped completely if key group members are unavailable, while others may be okay to include as long as tasks performed by others are unaffected by individual absences.
- Discuss what the group members' interests are—their strengths and desired contributions to the project. One might volunteer to contribute by doing research, another by doing data entry, and a third by doing analysis, and so on. Two things for the team to consider: (1) if possible, allow members not only to do what they do best but also afford them the opportunity to develop other skills, and (2) if individuals don't volunteer, or if all members lack needed skills, roles will have to be assigned regardless of personal interest or strengths. For example, give someone with a computer background the chance to take on a marketing role if possible and if the person desires. While he or she may be better equipped to prepare the final report or

presentation, allowing members to stretch and possibly cross functional lines builds their skills for future projects.

- Consider the team members' planning and organizing skills. Discuss expectations regarding meeting project deadlines as well as what each person can contribute to the task. When allocating project steps to specific team members, assign tasks that stretch but don't overextend any one team member.

Step Three—Develop a Timeline or Work Plan

The next step is to create a specific plan that takes into account all the various steps—large and small—as well as the relationship among the steps. For example, in building a car, you would never install the headrests before installing the seats. Figure 5.2 shows a work plan for a five-member team presentation project. It includes all the steps necessary to complete the project, a time frame to allow for completion of the project, and assignment of responsibilities for individual team members. Some tactics for developing a timeline or work plan include these:

- Working with a large blackboard, whiteboard, easel and newsprint, or computer program (something that can be seen by all involved), begin brainstorming all the steps that will be needed to complete the project. If possible, start with the end goal and work backwards from there. This process is called **backscheduling** and involves looking backward from a target date, beginning with your goal or objective and then plotting out the means to achieve it. This is done by:

1. Identifying the individual tasks necessary to achieve the objective.
2. Estimating how long it will take you to complete each task and determining the best time to do it.
3. Listing each task on a calendar, appropriately backdating each task from the project due date.[18]

Let's take you away from business to share an example of backscheduling. If you were preparing a meal, the Spanish *paella* to be exact, you wouldn't put all the ingredients in at the same time. This complex dish includes meats (sausage, chicken), seafood (fish,

Project: Team presentation on business topic of current interest
Due Date: December 3
Team Members' Names and Initials: James Smith (JS), Mary Conover (MC), Jesse Baron (JB), Nomi Hussein (NH), Maria Santanella (MS)

Step	Date	Initials
1. Meet with team; decide topic	10/8	All
2. Discuss key components of topic	10/12	All
3. Assign individual research topics	10/15	MS
4. Re-group to share results	10/29	All
5. Further research and develop outline	11/5	JS, MC
6. E-mail to group to solicit and incorporate feedback	11/12	JS, MC
7. Develop presentation and share draft with others, edit	11/19	JB, NH
8. Plan presentation, prepare slides, and share with group	11/26	MS
9. Rehearse	11/29	All
10. Prepare copies for distribution	12/1	JB
11. Present	12/3	All
12. Arrange, have debrief and lunch session	12/5	NH

Figure 5.2 Sample work plan.

shrimp, mussels), and vegetables (carrots, peppers), each of which has an optimal cooking time. If you were planning to serve the dish in 40 minutes, you would put the meats in first, as they would take the longest to cook. Then you'd add the vegetables, and finally the seafood. Shrimp that has cooked for 40 minutes tastes mushy, and the fish would fall apart and taste dried out. If you put the meats in last, say with only 10 minutes to go, you may subject your guests to undercooked meats (and the problems that brings). When you backschedule, you determine what happens last, next to last, next to next to last, and so on. For the example in Figure 5.2, the team would need to start with the presentation date and work backwards to determine when they would need to begin the project to ensure quality and timely completion. By doing so, they would determine that they will need eight weeks to allow for successfully creating this particular presentation.

If the project is complex and it's easier to start at the beginning, do so. List each step and allocate all steps to specific dates on the calendar. Realize that some tasks are serial (one must precede another) while others are parallel (two noninterrelated tasks that can occur simultaneously).

- Determine and specify the dependencies that exist between all the tasks, participants, and activities in a project plan. Each step relates to others in the plan. Understanding these interrelationships can help the group know where potential problems could arise or where a delay or lag could change the process.[19] If employees at the manufacturer supplying the upholstery material for the car seats are on strike, this impacts not only car seat readiness, but also the installation of the headrests.
- As a group, clarify the objectives when specific tasks are assigned. Clearly communicate the expected deliverables and the desired results. Monitor tasks delegated and record to whom specific tasks are allotted. Set precise and realistic deadlines for short-term deliverables, adjusting the timeline as necessary throughout the project.
- Build in time for the unexpected. Planning and communication with teammates are essential here. Watch for the tendency to try to make up losses late in the project cycle. It's not atypical for a project to stay on schedule for the first 80 percent of the time and then fall apart due to overconfidence ("We're practically done"), reduced attention to the schedule ("We know what we have to do . . . who needs to see the schedule?"), or just procrastination. Once group members recognize this slippage, they stress and rush to completion, resulting in lower quality output than would have been the case had the original timeline been adhered to. Many people and teams grossly underestimate the time needed toward the end to complete details that bring a final deliverable up to quality standards. Let's say your team is assembling a report based on a survey conducted over a six-month time period. Who's going to check the accuracy of the data? Who will proofread? Edit? Check for content? Run the report by the research and legal departments? Share a preview copy with a few stakeholders to ensure buy-in? Copy and prepare presentation materials, or ensure they're available online? All these minute details take much more time than most people imagine. It's wise to build them into the schedule from the outset of the project.

Talking through these kinds of details with a project group has several benefits. It helps the group become realistic about what can and cannot be accomplished. It helps individuals think of additional steps that might otherwise have been omitted from the planning phase. And it helps team members to begin defining in real terms the quality standards for the project.

- Avoid the tendency to wait until late in the project to buy time for these important details. Budget for them up front. Stay vigilant and look at the whole project to determine where time can be bought earlier on in the process. Taking time for this discussion will pay off in a higher quality outcome, and with less stress than "winging it!"[20]

- Some final advice from a veteran project manager. "Be very flexible. In this day where we're on these faster, better, cheaper programs, with very high turnaround and very high-risk technologies, you can come up with a great master plan, but things never go according to plan. You have to be flexible when changes come in to rapidly replan and not be discouraged by it."[21] The goal of your project is set, but the action plan or means of getting to your end result must constantly be adapted to address deviations from the original path. Effective project managers recognize when and how to change directions as well as to ask for help when extra resources are needed.[22]

Step Four—Establish Checkpoints and Control Mechanisms

Step four involves setting up a series of checkpoints, or points at which progress on the project will be checked, and entering these onto the project calendar. Even after your group lists all the tasks, identifies interdependencies, and assigns specific due dates, it is wise to establish periodic checkpoints. These may be progress meetings where members can check status, clarify expectations, or raise issues. If unanticipated problems arise, these checkpoint meetings can be used to problem-solve and make necessary adjustments to the schedule.

- Evaluate your project for important steps or tasks to be completed and insert interim deadlines or checkpoints in the project plan. In step three, we broke the project into smaller tasks or objectives. In this step, break these down further into milestones or incremental steps in order to determine when checks and tests should be completed. For example, break a 30-day project into three 10-day subsections, instituting a checkpoint after each one. This will help to shorten the time between when an error or misunderstanding occurs and when it can be discovered and corrected.[23] It will also help to prevent or reduce the possibility of time line slippage.
- Review and update the project plan regularly. Monitor other projects and events that might interfere with your project schedule and adjust accordingly. One suggestion is to post the project plan in an area visible to all group members. Don't confine the schedule to the conference room in which you meet only monthly. Instead, put it in a hallway that all members pass through, such as the hallway to the bathroom or break-room. By keeping the plan highly visible, potential interferences and problems can be raised and dealt with before they impact the expected outcomes.

Step Five—Identify and Obtain Necessary Resources

Project managers and their teams must identify and obtain the resources that are needed to complete the project within the specified time frame, cost parameters, or budget in order to meet quality standards. It is therefore necessary to:

- Look through the tasks and objectives and discuss what will be required to carry out the assignment. Be realistic about what can be accomplished given the resources available and time constraints inherent in the project; this will facilitate effective ***resource management*** over the course of the project. If your group anticipates a shortfall of personnel, budget, time, computer support, administrative support, or supplies, now is the time—before you roll up your sleeves and begin the project—to discuss these needs with your manager. If the resources can be provided, great. If not, it's important to "push back" on management and negotiate which elements of the deliverable can be achieved, given the resources available. Don't assume you can get these resources later. Get what you need before you start or, if the resources are not forthcoming, manage stakeholders' expectations about the group's ability to achieve a desired outcome.

- Know when to let a project go or when to start over. Sometimes a project team discovers early on that the project expectation is unrealistic or the scope of the project is more complex than originally envisioned. Perhaps the team thought its job was to make recommendations when their manager saw the task as ending with implementation of the recommendations. These perceptions differ substantially. Or perhaps a pilot project is expanded to include the entire organization. The project team might need to reconsider its objectives and change course. If this happens to you, consult with your manager or instructor. Perhaps the task can be reconceived. Don't let politics, pride, or the thought of failure keep you from asking for help or from scrapping a project that is not going to contribute to the organization. Use active decision making throughout to help you make these determinations.[24] Communicate frequently and clearly about these determinations with appropriate stakeholders.

Step Six—Determine How Project Results Will Be Measured

Before the project starts, understand how the project will be evaluated and who will assess it. This will ensure that steps are built into the process to obtain the data needed to evaluate the success of the project. If your group's task is to improve customer satisfaction, how will you know whether you've done it? Are they happier? Do they file fewer complaints? Is the wait time for help shorter? Especially in a case like this, your group might first have to measure and establish a baseline. How do you know if the wait time is shorter after your recommendations are implemented if you don't assess the wait time before you begin? In some organizations, teams are rewarded with a percentage of total savings—another good reason to establish and assess results.

Step Seven—Set Up an Ongoing Communication System

There is no substitute for effective communication in project management. Typically, projects get in trouble when people are unsure of their role or responsibilities relative to other roles and responsibilities. To avoid confusion, members must see over the horizon and convey to others their ideas, perceptions, and the objective with clarity and confidence. It also requires listening skills. It's important to:

- Communicate with team members and stakeholders. The ability to deal with people—using your interpersonal skills—can be the primary factor in the success of a project.[25] Important skills to use throughout the process are listening, giving and receiving feedback, persuasion, delegation, seeing things from another's perspective, and getting people to respond to you.[26]
- Start the project with face-to-face or telephone contact if possible. This is important for both traditional and virtual teams. Research shows that e-mail contact can occur once the group is formed and people are clear on their roles and responsibilities. Misunderstanding is less likely to occur when members are able to meet and fully discuss project expectations and concerns in real time, with the benefit of nonverbal language.
- Meet regularly (in person or virtually) to check on project status and progress. Meetings can keep a project on task by enabling members to check and recheck their understanding of dates and deliverables. To be effective, meetings should be primarily decision oriented. In addition to sharing status, meetings can be used to

1. Choose carefully. Projects should be large enough to be worthwhile and should suit your skills and qualifications.
2. Establish a realistic time line.
3. Let employees know how important the project is.
4. Keep employees informed and involved so they understand the constraints under which they're operating.
5. Meet across boundaries—involve people from various parts of the organization if possible.
6. Keep in touch with the progress and morale of the crew.
7. Share bad news and information when things aren't going well—don't keep employees in the dark.
8. Make trade-off decisions crisply to minimize big changes, but be flexible to adjust to marketplace developments and changes.
9. Know when to give up.
10. Breed healthy competition.

Figure 5.3 Project management tips from Bill Gates.[29]

maintain agreed-upon deadlines, discuss changes that might be necessary in the plan or work schedule, address questions and issues, and clarify roles and expectations.

- Revisit initial decisions made by the group if they are not working. An important aspect of project management is continuously reviewing the initial prioritization of steps. Continuously cross-check all interrelated project components to make sure that the critical aspects and requirements are being implemented. Constantly review and modify where necessary, ensuring your ability to deliver what is promised by your deadlines.[27]
- Keep people informed by issuing progress reports. This can be done face to face, but written methods (e.g., an e-mail sent to the team) may provide an easier and more efficient means for tracking individual and collective progress. Err on the side of going overboard on updating people on how your objectives or tasks are measuring up to the goals of the project.[28]
- Ensure a positive, open atmosphere. Provide encouragement throughout the project. If the project occurs over an extended period of time, plan some fun get-togethers to build camaraderie, trust, and rapport among team members.
- Monitor performance and catch problems early on. If this is not done, you risk marginalization, wherein the poor performers bring down the group's standards rather than the other way around. Since a change to a single step can have a ripple effect on the whole project and system, communicating instantly is critical in keeping projects on time and on budget.[30] Providing constructive feedback as soon as possible can do this. A good project manager will be able to question others and give feedback without alienating the members.[31]
- Give less experienced team members more initial attention and direction. As they acquire experience and confidence, you can be less involved in overseeing their work.
- Be clear on accountability and clarify where overall responsibility for the ultimate quality of each deliverable lies. Make sure everyone understands and is held accountable for the responsibilities they assume.
- Develop records that document the group's progress on the project. This will help the group stay on track without having to replicate earlier discussions. This also aids future groups working on similar projects. The records can be print or electronic and should include the original project plan and changes that are made, meeting schedules and minutes, team to-do lists, memos and e-mail correspondence, and samples of interim and final deliverables.

Step Eight—Debrief and Evaluate the Process and Results at Project End

Remember that all processes and efforts can be improved. Keep notes of lessons learned throughout the process and share them with group members at the end of the project. Discuss what worked well and what didn't. Discuss what everyone learned from the group's mistakes and how similar mistakes can be prevented in future team projects. This allows for all involved to offer feedback and to share ideas for improving group behaviors and processes in the future.

5.2.2 Project Management Tools

Several tools are available to help you track progress on projects. One of the more common and simple tools is the **Gantt chart.** Named after its developer, Henry Gantt, this chart describes the temporal relationships of events of tasks that unfold over time.[32] It can also show projected and actual schedules. Figure 5.4 shows how another

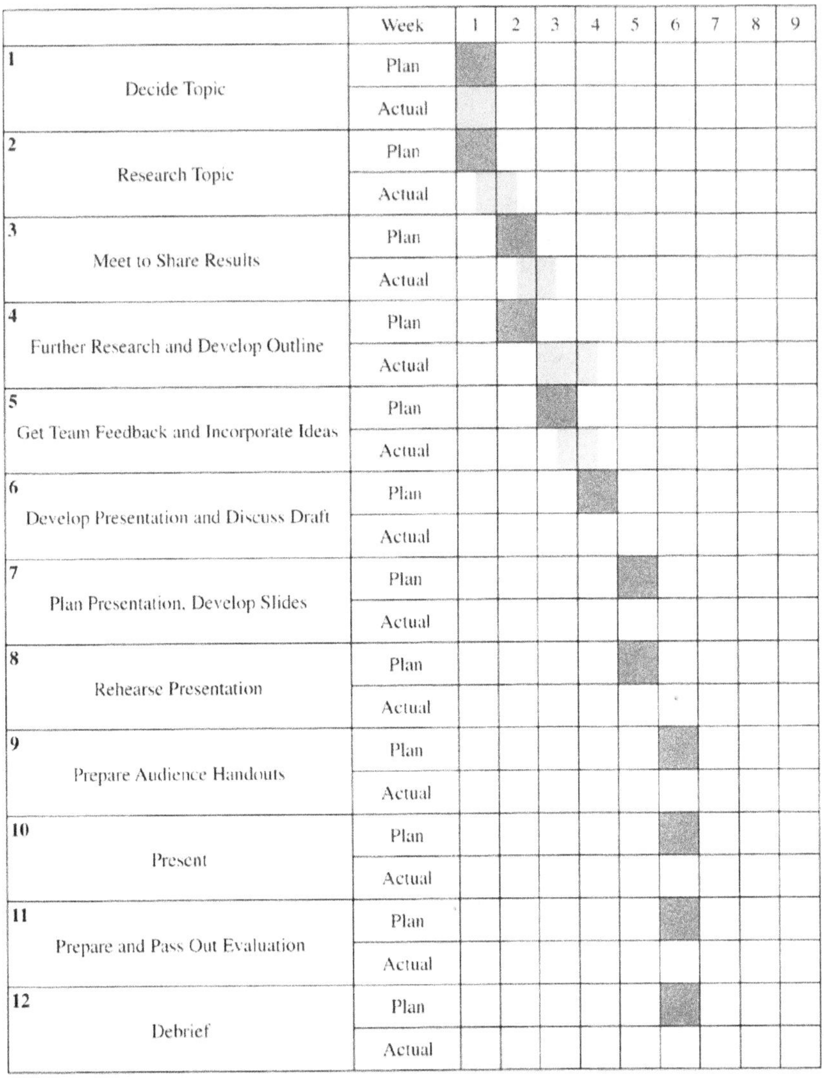

		Week	1	2	3	4	5	6	7	8	9
1	Decide Topic	Plan									
		Actual									
2	Research Topic	Plan									
		Actual									
3	Meet to Share Results	Plan									
		Actual									
4	Further Research and Develop Outline	Plan									
		Actual									
5	Get Team Feedback and Incorporate Ideas	Plan									
		Actual									
6	Develop Presentation and Discuss Draft	Plan									
		Actual									
7	Plan Presentation, Develop Slides	Plan									
		Actual									
8	Rehearse Presentation	Plan									
		Actual									
9	Prepare Audience Handouts	Plan									
		Actual									
10	Present	Plan									
		Actual									
11	Prepare and Pass Out Evaluation	Plan									
		Actual									
12	Debrief	Plan									
		Actual									

Figure 5.4 A Gantt chart on the development of a team presentation.

project team engaged in project management when given the same task as the team in Figure 5.2. From this chart, the team can track the planned activities, control individual activities, and identify delays or deviations from the original plan. The team can see where they have lost time and can plan and make adjustments to complete the project on time. The Gantt chart will also be helpful when debriefing the project and team process for future improvements on their next assignment.

To make a Gantt chart,

1. Brainstorm all the tasks necessary to complete the final project.
2. Reorganize this list in order from beginning to ending tasks.
3. Create a grid (or use graph paper) wherein the columns represent weeks (or days if the project is very short) and the rows represent specific tasks. Plan to post this where all group project members can see it.
4. List each task in order and estimate the time needed to complete each task. Traditionally, this would be represented by a rectangle whose endpoints show the start and finish time of the task; the longer the rectangle, the longer it would take to complete this task.
5. You could also include two rows for each task—one that shows the projected or planned time (using an opaque rectangle) and one that shows the actual time (using a shaded rectangle).

While it may not be critical to have the planned and actual schedules on a Gantt chart, adding the actual schedule helps in at least two ways. First, you will be able to make real-time adjustments to the schedule, especially when a preceding, interdependent task was delayed in starting or finishing. Second, the comparisons will help in the overall project debrief and provide feedback and lessons learned for future projects and planning.

Another common tool used in project management is the **PERT (Program Evaluation and Review Technique)** chart. A PERT chart diagrams all the steps involved in completing a project and estimates the length of time needed in each phase of the project. By mapping out tasks in a flowchart pattern, the PERT helps identify sequences of dependent activities (see Figure 5.5).[33] It answers the questions of what are the most optimistic estimates of the time to complete the project under the best conditions,

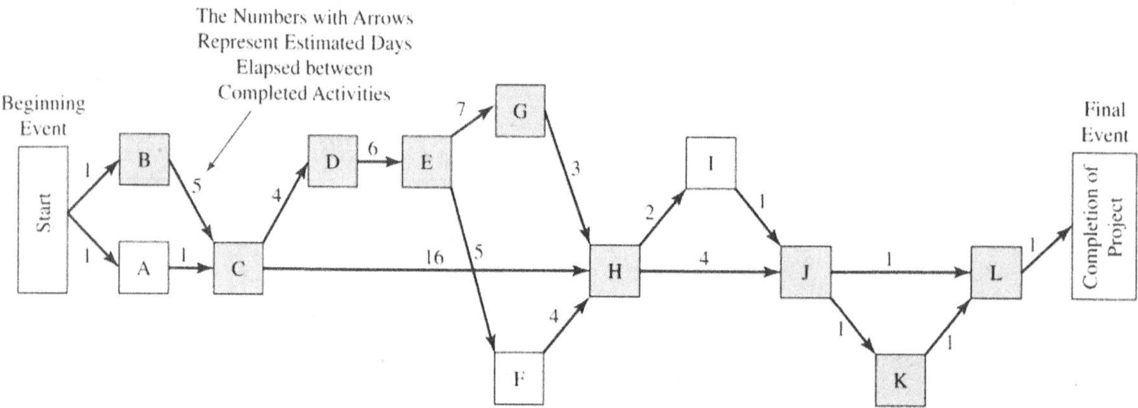

Figure 5.5 PERT Chart for development of team presentation.

Note: Shaded boxes show critical path (B→C→D→E→G→H→J→K→L) of 33 days what's the most pessimistic under the worst conditions, and what is the most likely under normal conditions.[34] The PERT process can also determine the longest anticipated single line of activity from start to finish,[35] which is known as **critical path method (CPM).**

To make a PERT chart and determine the critical path:[36]

1. Define the project and all of its significant activities and tasks.
2. Develop the relationships among the activities. Decide which activities must precede and follow others.
3. Draw the network connecting all the activities.
4. Assign time and/or cost estimates to each activity.
5. Compute the longest time path through the network; this is called the critical path.
6. Use the network to help plan, schedule, monitor, and control the project.

The critical path represents tasks and activities that, if delayed, will cause the entire project to be delayed. Teams can use this information to identify noncritical tasks for replanning, rescheduling, and reallocating resources to gain flexibility and allow for alterations. Therefore, PERT and CPM can play a major part in controlling a project. Figure 5.5 illustrates a team presentation project showing the relationship between the activities and the estimated time needed to complete the presentation. The critical path shows that they will need a minimum of 33 days to complete all the steps and identifies which steps are critical and which ones have some slack time.

Both of these methods are immensely helpful in planning out a project. By creating either chart, most groups discover missing steps, clarify whether the anticipated time line is realistic (or not), and identify critical dependencies and resources. One recommendation for creating a first draft Gantt or PERT chart is to use Post-Its or other easily movable notes. Since so many hidden tasks or issues arise in the building of these charts, the use of Post-Its can reduce group members' frustration in the process. Software programs can also be used to create PERT charts; the team identifies the tasks and time estimates, and the programs prepare the charts.

Numerous Web-oriented software programs are available. These programs enable group members to enter tasks, estimate time lines and other dependencies, and create the project management chart.[37] One benefit of these programs is that changes—added tasks, modified time lines—create instant adjustments to the overall schedule, enabling members to see the immediate impact of a midterm slippage. Another benefit is that many of these programs can be "connected" to company systems, enabling stakeholders such as department heads and customers to access information on how a project that concerns them is progressing, while the project team maintains control over the project.[38] This allows for others, besides the team members, to participate and have easy access to project information. Of course, as is true of any computer program, their availability does not replace the need for human interaction. Keeping people informed through personal contact is an important complement to electronic communication about project status.[39]

SUMMARY

In today's environment, company and individual success comes more readily to those who can do more with less while working smarter, not harder. One way to do this is to make effective use of project management skills and tools. This becomes especially important when you are involved in one or more complex projects. Taking time to clarify project expectations, determine contributors and stakeholders, establish specific objectives or milestones, create contingency plans, and communicate regularly with stakeholders are among the steps needed to make all your projects a success. In the final analysis, others expect project outcomes or deliverables—on time and on budget—not excuses or explanations!

KEY TERMS AND CONCEPTS

Backscheduling
Critical path method (CPM)
Gantt chart
Program Evaluation and Review Technique (PERT)
Project management
Project time line
Resource management
Stakeholders
Work plan

ENDNOTES

1. David L. Coles, "Step Back to Get Ahead; The Key to Completing Projects on Time Is Working Backward from Your Deadlines," *Coles and Associates,* March–April 1988, p. 14.
2. Joe E. Beck, Worley Johnson, and R. Steve Konkel, "Project Management Insights," *Occupational Health and Safety,* June 2000, p. 22.
3. Alexander Laufer, "Project Planning: Timing Issues and Path of Progress," *Project Management Journal,* June 1991, p. 39.
4. Robert D. Landel and J. Robb Dixon, "Assessing the Potential for Office-Productivity Improvement," *Operations Management Review,* Fall 1983, pp. 3–8.
5. Kathleen Melymuka, "Born to Lead Projects: Some People Have Innate Talents for Managing Projects," *Computerworld,* March 27, 2000, p. 62.
6. Howard Millman, "On Track and in Touch," *Computerworld,* June 26, 2000, p. 88.
7. Sonia Tellez, "Think Globally When Designing a PM Solution," *Computing Canada,* Dec. 10, 1999, p. 28.
8. Coles, "Step Back."
9. Quoted in article by Kathleen Melymuka, "Project Management Top Guns," *Computerworld,* Oct. 20, 1997, pp. 108–109.
10. Lawrence Todryk, "The Project Manager as Team Builder: Creating an Effective Team," *Project Management Journal,* Dec. 1990, p. 17.
11. M. C. Higgins, "The More the Merrier? Multiple Developmental Relationships and Work Satisfaction," *Journal of Management Development,* 19, no. 4 (2000), pp. 277–296.
12. Melymuka, "Project Management Top Guns."
13. See J. Richard Hackman, "Motivation through the Design of Work—Test a Theory," *Organizational Behavior and Human Performance,* Aug. 1976, p. 250; J. R. Hackman, "Is Job-Enrichment Just a Fad," *Harvard Business Review,* Sept.–Oct. 1975, p. 129.
14. See Frank Swoboda, "Workers Generally Worse Off Than a Decade Ago, Study Finds," *Washington Post,* Sept. 7, 1992, p. 25; and Susan Cartwright, "Taking the Pulse of Executive Health in the U.K.," *The Academy of Management Executive,* May 2000, p. 16.
15. Lloyd A. Rogers, "Project Team Training: A Proven Key to Organizational Teamwork and Breakthrough in Planning Performance," *Project Management Journal,* June 1990, p. 9.

16. Pam Statz (2001). "Wanna Be a Project Manager?" *WebMonkey.* (http://hotwired.lycos.com/webmonkey/01/18/index3a.html?tw=jobs).
17. Robert Thompson, "More Heads Better Than One in Project Management," *Computing Canada,* Dec. 10, 1999, p. 27.
18. Coles, "Step Back."
19. Paul S. Adler, "Never-Ending Mission to Find Magic Solution," *Computing Canada,* Oct. 1, 1999, p. 17.
20. Don Reinertsen, "The Best-Laid Plans Become the Enemy of Vigilance," *Electronic Design,* March 20, 2000, p. 57.
21. Quote attributed to Uwe Weissflog, manager of strategic planning Structural Dynamics Research Corp., as captured by Kathleen Melymuka, "Project Management Top Guns."
22. Rogers, "Project Team Training."
23. Don Reinertsen, "Projects Can Slip by More Than One Day at a Time," *Electronic Design,* March 6, 2000, p. 56.
24. Daphne Main and Carolyn L. Lousteau, "Don't Get Trapped," *Strategic Finance,* Nov. 1999, p. 74.
25. Melymuka, "Project Management Top Guns."
26. Melymuka, "Born to Lead Projects."
27. Yourdon, Ed, "The Value of Triage," *Computerworld,* March 20, 2000.
28. "Ask Bill Gates (Project Management Tips)," *Management Today,* Feb. 2000, p. 38.
29. "Ask Bill Gates." Reprinted with permission from "Ask Bill Gates," *Management Today,* February 2000, p. 38.
30. Tellez, "Think Globally."
31. Melymuka, "Born to Lead Projects."
32. Peter R. Scholtes, *The Leader's Handbook* (Washington, DC: McGraw-Hill, 1998), p. 205.
33. Scholtes, *The Leader's Handbook,* pp. 99 and 205.
34. Haidee E. Allerton, "How To," *Training and Development,* Nov. 1999, p. 15.
35. Scholtes, *The Leader's Handbook,* p. 205.
36. Barry Render and Ralph M. Stair, Jr., *Introduction to Management Science* (Boston, MA: Allyn & Bacon, 1992), p. 368.
37. "Get a Grip," *Fortune,* Summer 2000, Supplement, pp. 74–90.
38. Matthew J. Liberatore, "A Decision Support System Linking Research and Development Project Selection with Business Strategy," *Project Management Journal,* Nov. 1988, p. 14.
39. Thompson, "More Heads Better Than One."

EXERCISES AND ACTIVITIES

5.1 Team Project Worksheet

1. As a team, use the following sheet to develop a work plan for your team project. Use the guidelines outlined in this chapter, and be sure to break down large objectives into smaller components.
2. For each project step, collectively decide on a due date as well as the persons ultimately accountable. Even if a task requires input from all team members, one person must accept the responsibility for coordinating this task.

3. Before approving the plan, each member should compare his/her project tasks with other requirements or deadlines listed in his/her day planner. Potential conflicts should be discussed and adjusted accordingly. Slack time should be incorporated as well.
4. Present your team's work plan to the class or group. Obtain feedback from them about steps that might have been overlooked or time lines that may be unrealistic. Adjust accordingly. Remember to make adjustments both on the team work plan and in your own day planner.

Team Project Work Plan

Project:
Due Date:
Names and Initials of Team Members:

Project Steps:	Date:	Initials:
1.		
2.		
3.		
4.		
5.		
6.		
7.		
8.		
9.		
10.		
11.		
12.		
13.		
14.		

(continue with additional steps on reverse or on blank sheet of paper)

5.2 Individual Day Planner Update

Each person should bring two sharpened pencils and his or her own personal day planner to this session.

1. Make a list of all activities and projects, personal and professional, in which you're currently involved. This can include work activities or classes in which you're enrolled, children's commitments such as carpooling or after-school activities, family, church or community obligations, exercise, planned travel (trip, vacation, holidays), and medical appointments.
2. Working through the list, enter all known dates for all commitments, activities, and appointments into your personal day planner, using a pencil. Be as thorough as possible. For example, if you are a student, enter all class sessions, exams, paper and project due dates, and vacation schedules. If you are unsure of a specific date, write the activity in the expected week, month, quarter, or semester in which it is likely to occur.
3. Make adjustments as you discover conflicts.
4. Keep this list up to date. As your schedule changes or as additional activities and deadlines are made known, add these into your day planner on a regular basis.

Discuss in small groups:

1. How does it feel to devote time to planning and scheduling activities and commitments?
2. What impact does planning have on our tendency to procrastinate or not devote ample time to what's really important?
3. What other tools or strategies are used to ensure the regular planning and achieving of goals and objectives?

5.3 Personal Project Time Line

You will need your up-to-date individual day planner and project sheet or computer project management program.

1. Working on your own, consider a project in which you're currently involved or in which you anticipate being involved soon.* The project can be personal, such as planning a trip; academic, such as preparing to give a class presentation; or professional, such as conducting an analysis of available products that compete against those of your company.
2. Develop a work plan for the project, following the steps outlined in this chapter. Starting backwards from the project deadline, list every step needed to complete the project. Use a pencil if working on paper. Be as thorough as possible. Assign initials and projected dates for each step.
3. Now transfer each of these dates (in pencil if using paper) to your personal day planner. If there are conflicts between this project and other classes, projects, or activities that are already in your planner, adjust the dates accordingly on both the project work plan and in your personal day planner.
4. Share your project work plan with a partner and obtain feedback on how realistic and how detailed your plan is, as well as on any suggested steps for adding or deleting. Modify your plan accordingly.

*If you can't think of a project, imagine it is the start of the fall semester and you are asked to prepare a 20-page term paper and presentation on a cutting-edge business topic by the end of the semester. You have 12 weeks in which to plan and complete this project. Other ideas: Building a new house, opening a retail store, producing a TV documentary, manufacturing and marketing a new product.

5.4 R & D Project Planning*

You are part of a newly formed task team that is taking over a project presently being handled by Research and Development. You have been assigned responsibility and authority for planning the project, and then, after top management has reviewed and accepted your plans, for carrying out the project. How do you get (and keep) a project running smoothly from start to finish?

Your instructor will provide additional materials to complete this activity.

*Referenced with permission from Human Synergistics International's Project Planning Simulation #SM17101.

5.5 Product Recall

The Scenario

You are part of the Yum Yum Bubblegum's management team. Yum Yum Bubblegum manufactures and sells bubble gum in the United States and Canada.

You have three manufacturing plants:

- Chewing, Mississippi
- Bubbleton, Alabama
- Poppingsburg, South Dakota

The same products are manufactured at all plants and then sent to Yum Yum's distribution center in Shipit, Arkansas, where they are then shipped to customers via distribution trucks. Assume that the company has no contingency or preventive product recall plans.

The Problem

- The company has just been notified that six people have been hospitalized for toxic poisoning related to substances found in Yum Yum Bubblegum.
- Three of the hospitalized individuals purchased gum in Dallas, Texas; one in San Antonio; one in San Diego, California; and one is believed to have purchased the gum in an airport in Utah.

Questions and Task

Using the tips and techniques provided in the chapter, work as a team to manage the clean-up project.

1. How should you as managers attack this problem? What's your plan? Create a list of key steps and time frame for each.
2. Next, choose your project team. Who should be on this team? What is each team member's role? Who should be the leader?
3. Determine a contingent plan of attack that specifies how to approach the problem and how to control the process.
4. Finally, determine a preventive plan for the future, assuming that this fiasco does not *blow* the company's ability to continue to do business.
5. Discuss the importance of project management in preventing or dealing with crises.

Source: Permission provided by creator Sherry Ghodes, JMU MBA Student, presented Fall 2000.

5.6 Tools of Project Management

1. Research existing project management tools and resources on the Internet, such as Microsoft Project. Bring an example of a new product that you think looks particularly effective to your class or group.
2. Contact your computer department and ask them for recommendations of new software programs that can be used easily for tracking projects. Try one out and report to your group on its effectiveness and potential applicability to your group's project.
3. Visit a local office supply or stationery store and investigate the current day planner systems that are available. Make a note of the particular strengths and limitations of each. Report to the class or group on the top one or two that you believe are the best available for your group's purposes.

5.7 Reflection/Action Plan

This chapter focused on project management—what it is, why it's important, and how to improve your skills in this area. Complete the worksheet below upon finishing all the reading and experiential activities for this chapter.

1. The one or two areas in which I am most strong are:

____

____

____

____

2. The one or two areas in which I need more improvement are:

____

____

____

____

3. If I did only one thing to improve in this area, it would be to:

____

____

____

____

4. Making this change would probably result in:

____

____

____

____

5. If I did not change or improve in this area, it would probably affect my personal and professional life in the following ways:

____

____

____

____

CHAPTER 6

EXCEL WORKBOOKS

Objectives

By learning the material in this chapter, you should be able to

- create Excel spreadsheets that use relative, absolute, and mixed references appropriately
- use Excel functions to accomplish a task
- learn to use a new function from the Excel Help features
- use logic, conditionals, conditional formatting, and sorting to answer questions about tabular data and support decision making

The following is an example of the level of knowledge of Excel needed to proceed with this chapter. *If you are not able to quickly recreate an Excel Worksheet similar to the one shown, including equations and formatting, please review worksheet basics in the appendix materials before proceeding.*

The wind chill temperature is calculated using the following empirical formula:

$$WC = 35.74 + 0.6215\,T - 35.75\,v^{0.16} + 0.4275\,Tv^{0.16}$$

where WC = Wind Chill Temperature [degrees Fahrenheit, °F], T = Actual Air Temperature [degrees Fahrenheit, °F], and v = Wind Speed [miles per hour, mph].

Create a single cell to hold the wind speed, set at 5 miles per hour, in Column A. Create a vertical series of actual air temperatures: $T = 30, 10, 0, -10$. Enter the equation for wind chill, referencing the cells and not the actual numerical values. A sample worksheet is shown below.

	A	B	C	D	E
1					
2					
3					
4					
5					
6					
7	Wind Speed	Actual Temperature (T) [deg F]			
8	(v) [mph]	30	10	0	-10
9	5	24.7	1.2	-10.5	-22.3

Taken from *Thinking Like an Engineer: An Active Learning Approach,* by Elizabeth A. Stephan, David R. Bowman, William J. Park, Benjamin L. Sill, and Matthew W. Ohland.

6.1 CELL REFERENCES

EXAMPLE 6-1

Suppose we are given a list of XY coordinates in a worksheet. We want to calculate the distance between each point. We can find the distance between two XY coordinates by using Pythagoras' theorem:

$$d = \sqrt{(x_2 - x_1)^2 + (y_2 - y_1)^2}$$

This example demonstrates how to handle Excel's order of operations and cell references.

Row	Point 1 X	Point 1 Y	Point 2 X	Point 2 Y
7	27	20	25	10
8	25	4	7	8
9	4	6	24	3
10	25	26	13	24
11	19	24	26	1
12	29	10	0	5
13	7	29	13	13
14	3	20	19	16
15	20	7	5	17
16	20	26	19	3
17	13	15	13	14
18	23	22	17	25
19	3	27	10	22
20	30	16	30	17

To solve this problem, we must adhere to the default behavior of Excel in order to properly calculate the distance between the coordinates. First, we must observe the order of operations that Excel follows to determine how we need to write our equations. Second, we must determine how to use **cell references** to translate the x_2, x_1, y_2, and y_1 values in the equation shown above into locations in our worksheet.

Let us rewrite Pythagoras' theorem in the notation shown above using what we know about order of operations in Excel:

$$d = ((x_2 - x_1)\text{^}2 + (y_2 - y_1)\text{^}2)\text{^}(1/2)$$

Let us calculate the distance between Point 1 and Point 2 in column G. In cell G7, we need to translate the equation into an equation that replaces the x_1, y_1 and x_2, y_2 variables with addresses to cells in the worksheet. Since each row represents a single calculation, we know that for the first data pair, $x1$ is located in cell A7, y_1 is in B7, x_2 is in D7, and y_2 is in E7.

The equation we need to type into cell G7 becomes

= ((D7 − A7)^2 + (E7 − B7)^2)^(1/2)

If we copy that equation down for the other pairs of XY coordinates, our sheet should now contain a column of all the distance calculations.

	A	B	C	D	E	F	G	H	I
1	**Distance Between XY Coordinates**								
2	This example demonstrates how to handle Excel's order of operations and cell references.								
3									
4									
5	Point 1			Point 2					
6	X	Y		X	Y		Distance		
7	27	20		25	10		10.20		
8	25	4		7	8		18.44		
9	4	6		24	3		20.22		
10	25	26		13	24		12.17		
11	19	24		26	1		24.04		
12	29	10		0	5		29.43		
13	7	29		13	13		17.09		
14	3	20		19	16		16.49		
15	20	7		5	17		18.03		
16	20	26		19	3		23.02		
17	13	15		13	14		1.00		
18	23	22		17	25		6.71		
19	3	27		10	22		8.60		
20	30	16		30	17		1.00		
21									

Suppose we start off with a slightly modified worksheet that requires us to calculate the distance between all the points in the first column of XY values to a single point in the second column.

We can calculate the distance between all the points in the first column to the single point through the use of absolute addressing. An absolute address allows an equation to reference a single cell that will remain constant regardless of where the equation is copied in the worksheet. An **absolute reference** is indicated by a dollar sign ($) in front of the row and column designators. In this example, we want to use an absolute reference on cells D7 and E7 in all distance calculations. The equation we need to type in cell G7 becomes:

$$= ((\$D\$7 - A7)\text{^}2 + (\$E\$7 - B7)\text{^}2)\text{^}(1/2)$$

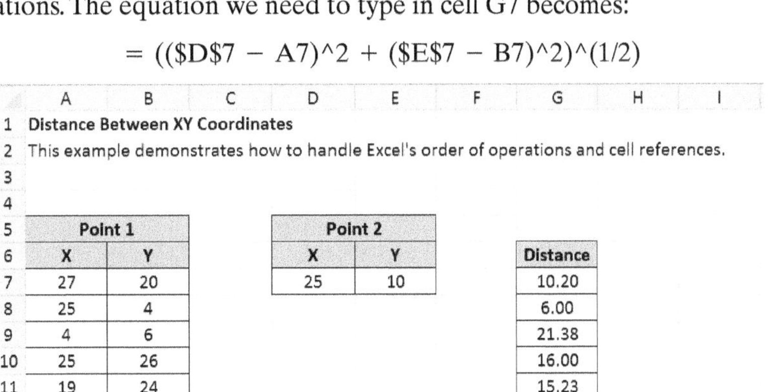

	A	B	C	D	E	F	G	H	I
1	**Distance Between XY Coordinates**								
2	This example demonstrates how to handle Excel's order of operations and cell references.								
3									
4									
5	Point 1			Point 2					
6	X	Y		X	Y		Distance		
7	27	20		25	10		10.20		
8	25	4					6.00		
9	4	6					21.38		
10	25	26					16.00		
11	19	24					15.23		
12	29	10					4.00		
13	7	29					26.17		
14	3	20					24.17		
15	20	7					5.83		
16	20	26					16.76		
17	13	15					13.00		
18	23	22					12.17		
19	3	27					27.80		
20	30	16					7.81		
21									

6.1.1 Relative Addressing

- A **relative cell address** used in a formula will always *refer to the cell in the same relative position* to the cell containing the formula, no matter where the formula is copied in the worksheet. For example, if "=B2" is typed into cell C4 and then copied to cell C7, the formula in cell C7 would read "=B5". In this case, the cell reference is to call the cell two rows up and one cell to the left.
- When we insert or change cells, the formulas automatically update. This is one of a worksheet's major advantages: easily applying the same calculation to many different sets of data.

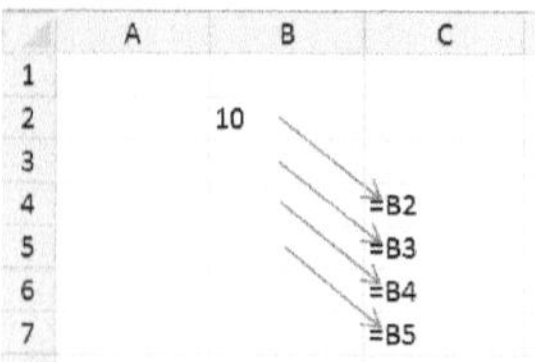

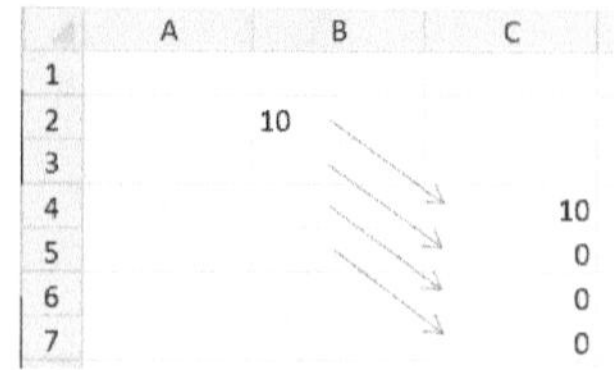

6.1.2 Absolute Addressing

- Absolute addressing is indicated by the presence of a dollar sign ($) immediately before both the column and row designators in the formula (e.g., $C$5; $AB$10).
- An **absolute cell address** will *always refer to the same cell* if the formula is copied to another location. For example, if "=$B$2" is typed into cell C4 and then copied to cell C7, the formula in cell C7 would read "=$B$2".

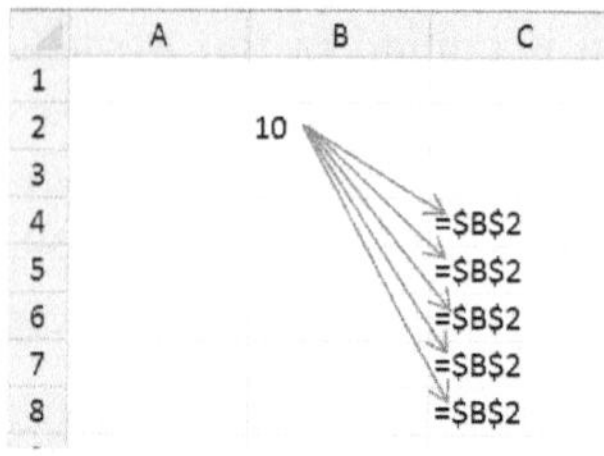

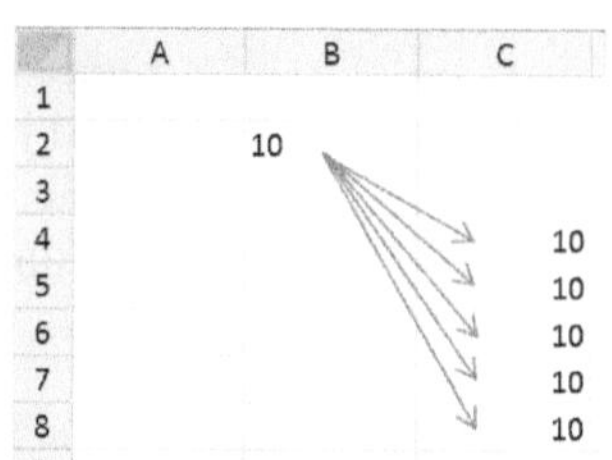

6.1.3 Mixed Addressing

- In **mixed addressing**, *either the row or the column designator is fixed* (by the $), but the other is relative (e.g., $C5; AB$10; $AB10).
- It may not be immediately obvious why this capability is desirable, but many problems are dramatically simplified with this approach. We will study this in more detail later.

COMPREHENSION CHECK 6-1

Type "5" in cell E22 and "9" in cell E23; type "=E22 + 4" in cell F22. Copy cell F22 to cell F23.

- Is this an example of absolute, mixed, or relative addressing?
- What is displayed in cell F23?

COMPREHENSION CHECK 6-2

Type "20" into cell G22 and "=$G$22 + 10" in cell H22. Copy cell H22 down to row 26 using the fill handle.

- Is this an example of absolute, mixed, or relative addressing?
- What is displayed in cell H26?

COMPREHENSION CHECK 6-3

Type "25" into cell A28 and "=A$28 + 5" in cell D28. Copy cell D28 down to row 30 using the fill handle. Copy cell D28 across to column F using the fill handle.

- Is this an example of absolute, mixed, or relative addressing?
- What is displayed in cell F28?

COMPREHENSION CHECK 6-4

Type "=$A28 + 5" in cell G28. Copy cell G28 down to row 30 using the fill handle. Copy cell G28 across to column J using the fill handle.

- Is this an example of absolute, mixed, or relative addressing?
- What is displayed in cell J28?

6.2 FUNCTIONS IN EXCEL

Hundreds of functions are built into Excel. Tables 6.1 through 6.4 list a few functions commonly used in engineering applications. Table 6.5 contains common error messages you may encounter. There are several things you should note when using these functions.

- You must make certain to *use the correct name of the function.* For example, the average function is written as AVERAGE and cannot be abbreviated AVE or AVG.
- *All functions must be followed by parentheses.* For example, the value of p is given as PI(), with nothing inside the parentheses.
- The argument of the function (the stuff in the parentheses) can include numbers, text, expressions, or cell references, as long as they are appropriate for the function.
- Many functions can *accept a list or range of cells as the argument.* These can be expressed as a list separated by commas [e.g., A6, D7, R2, F9], as a rectangular block designated by the top-left cell and bottom-right cell separated by a colon [e.g., D3:F9], or as a mixed group [e.g., A6, R2, D3:F9]. To insert cells into a formula, type the formula up to the open parenthesis and select the desired cells. You can also type in the references directly into the formula.
- Most functions will also *accept another function as the argument.* These can be fairly simple [e.g., SIN (RADIANS (90))] or more complicated [e.g., AVERAGE (SQRT(R2), COS(S4 + C4), MIN (D3:F9) + 2)].
- Some functions, such as trigonometric functions, require specific arguments. *Trigonometric functions must have an argument in units of radians, not units of degrees.* Be sure you are aware of any limitations of the functions you are using. Look up an unfamiliar function in the **HELP** menu.

- Note that some functions can be *expressed in several different ways*. For example, raising the number 2 to the fifth power can be written as = 2^5 or as POWER(2,5).

Table 6.1 Trigonometric functions in Excel

Function as written in Excel	Definition
ACOS (cell)	Calculates the inverse cosine of a number (also ASIN)
COS (angle in radians)	Calculates the cosine of an angle (also SIN)
DEGREES (angle in radians)	Converts radians to degrees
PI()	Calculates pi (π) to about 15 significant figures
RADIANS (angle in degrees)	Converts degrees to radians

Table 6.2 Mathematical functions in Excel

Function as written in Excel	Definition
EXP (cell)	Raises e (base of the natural log) to the power "cell"
POWER (cell, power)	Raises the cell to "power"
PRODUCT (cells)	Finds the product of a list of cells
SQRT (cell)	Finds the square root of cell
SUM (cells)	Finds the sum of a list of cells

Table 6.3 Statistical functions in Excel

Function as written in Excel	Definition
AVERAGE (cells)	Finds the mean or average value of a list of cells
MAX (cells)	Finds the maximum value in a list of cells
MEDIAN (cells)	Finds the median value of a list of cells
MIN (cells)	Finds the minimum value in a list of cells
STDEV (cells)	Finds the standard deviation value of a list of cells
VAR (cells)	Finds the variance value of a list of cells

Table 6.4 Miscellaneous functions in Excel

Function as written in Excel	Definition
COUNT (cells)	Counts number of cells that are not blank and that do not contain an error
COUNTIF (cells, criteria)	Counts number of cells that meet the stated criteria, such as a numerical value, text, or a cell reference
COUNTIF (cells1, criteria1, cells2, criteria2, . . .)	Counts number of cells that meet multiple stated criteria, such as a numerical value, text, or a cell reference
INTERCEPT (*y* values, *x* values)	Calculates linear line for range of (x, y) pairs and returns the intercept value of y (where $x = 0$)
ROUND (cell, number of decimal places)	Rounds a number to a specific number of decimal places
SLOPE (*y* values, *x* values)	Calculates linear line for range of (x, y) pairs and returns the slope value
TRUNC (cell, number of digits)	Truncates a number to a specific number of digits

Table 6.5 Common error messages in Excel and possible solutions

Error	Explanation	Possible Fix	Example
#####	Column is not wide enough to display a number	Make column wider	−125,000,500 will not fit in a cell with a standard width
#DIV/0!	Formula has resulted in division by zero	Check values in denominator of formula contained in the cell	If cell A1 contains 12 and cell A2 is empty, the formula =A1/A2 will return #DIV/0!
#NAME?	Excel does not recognize something you have typed	Check spelling! Check operators for missing * or : Check for missing " " around text	Formula names: MXA should be MAX; PI should be PI() Range of cells: 2A:B3 should be A2:B3 Operators: (A7)(B6) should be (A7)*(B6)
#NULL!	You specify a set of cells that do not intersect	Check formulas for spaces, missing commas	= SUM(A2:A5 B4:B6) will return this error; fix as = SUM(A2:A5,B4:B6)
#VALUE!	Formula contains invalid data types	Arguments of functions must be numbers, not text Sometimes, part of a required function is missing; check for all required elements	If cell A2 contains "2 grams" and cell A3 contains 3, the formula = A2 + A3 will result in this error since A2 is text (the word grams makes the cell text, not a number) = VLOOKUP(A2:B5,2,FALSE) will result in this error since a LOOKUP function must contain four parts in the argument, not three
#N/A	Formula has called a value that is not available	Check for lookup value in data table (see Section 10.4 on LOOKUP function)	If A2 contains 11, and the data table contains values 1 to 10 in the first column, this error will appear since the value 11 is not in the first column of the data table
#REF!	Invalid cell reference	Check formula for data table size and number of column to return (see Section 6.4 on LOOKUP function)	= VLOOKUP(A2,A2:B5,3,FALSE) will return this error because there are not three columns available in the lookup table
#NUM!	Formula results invalid numeric values	Check numerical result expected is between -1×10^{307} and 1×10^{307} Check number of iterations	If the calculation results in a value outside the range given, such as 2×10^{400}, this error will appear

EXAMPLE 6-2

Assume we are studying the number of fatal accidents that occur during different times of the day. Given the data shown, we want to use Excel to analyze our data to determine the average, minimum, or maximum number of accidents, as well as a few other items that might be of significance.

	A	B
1	**Fatal Vehicular Accidents**	
2	This worksheet demonstrates the proper use of Excel Functions	
3		
4	**Week**	**Number Fatal Accidents**
5	A	190
6	B	202
7	C	179
8	D	211
9	E	160
10	F	185
11	G	172
12	H	205
13	I	177
14	J	120
15	K	235
16	L	183
17	M	177
18	N	193
19		

NOTE

The ROUND function refers to number of decimal places, although the Excel help menu calls this "num_digits." Be sure to always read ALL the help menu file when using a new function.

Total accidents: = SUM (B5:B18)
Total samples: = COUNT (B5:B18)
Mean: = AVERAGE (B5:B18)
Median: = MEDIAN (B5:B18)
Variance: = VAR (B5:B18)
Standard deviation: = STDEV (B5:B18)

Note that decimal values appear when we calculate the mean, variance, and standard deviation of the accident data. Since it makes sense to round these values up to the nearest whole number, we need to type those functions as the argument to a rounding function. Start by modifying the equation for the mean by typing the ROUND function. Notice that as you start typing the **ROUND** function in the cell, a drop-down menu with a list of all of the functions that start with the letters ROUND appears below the cell. Note that Excel contains a function called **ROUNDUP** that will round a number up to the nearest whole value away from zero.

2589
14
=round
ROUND — Rounds a number to a specified number of digits
703 ROUNDDOWN / ROUNDUP
26.51694461

After we select the ROUNDUP function, a new box below the cell documents the arguments the function requires. Note that we need to provide the value we want to round as the first argument and the number of decimal places to which we want to round the number (in this case, 0).

Total Accidents	2589
Total Samples	14
Mean	=ROUNDUP(
Median	184
Variance	703.1483516
Standard Deviation	26.51694461

The new function we need to type ultimately becomes

= ROUNDUP (AVERAGE (B5:B18), 0)

Repeat this with the equations for calculating the median and the standard deviation.

Suppose we want to determine how many of the samples reported accidents greater than the calculated average number of accidents. Note that the **COUNTIF** function requires a "criteria" argument, which can take on a number of different values. For example, if we want to count the number of values greater than 200 in the range B5:B18, we need to type the criteria ">.200" (in double quotes) as the 2nd argument to the COUNTIF function.

= COUNTIF (B5:B18,">200")

In this example, we want to compare our COUNTIF result to a value calculated in a different cell. Since we cannot type cell references inside of double quotes (">E21"), we need to use the **ampersand** operator (&) to **concatenate** the logical operator to the cell reference (">"&E21).

Samples Greater than Mean: = COUNTIF (B5:B18,">"&B22)

Similarly, we could use the **COUNTIFS** function to calculate the number of samples that have a number of accidents between (and including) 180 and 200. COUNTIFS is a special function that contains a variable number of arguments, with a minimum of two arguments required (range1, criteria1) to use the function. Since we have two criteria that must be met (>180 and <200), we must pass in four arguments to the COUNTIFS function (range1, criteral, range2, criteria2). In this example, range1 and range2 must be the same range of cells since we are enforcing the criteria on the same set of data. We will place the bounds in the worksheet as follows:

Lower Bound in D23: 180 Upper Bound in E23: 200

Samples Between: = COUNTIFS (B5:B18,">="&D23, B5:B18, "<="&E23)

NOTE

Concatenate means to join things together. In Excel, the ampersand sign (&) will join two elements together.
=3&75 will result in 375
=3&"grams" will result in 3 grams

Your final worksheet should appear as shown.

	A	B	C	D	E
1	**Fatal Vehicular Accidents**				
2	This worksheet demonstrates the proper use of Excel Functions				
3					
4	**Week**	**Number Fatal Accidents**			
5	A	190			
6	B	202			
7	C	179			
8	D	211			
9	E	160			
10	F	185			
11	G	172			
12	H	205			
13	I	177			
14	J	120			
15	K	235			
16	L	183			
17	M	177			
18	N	193			
19					
20	Total Accidents	2589	Samples Greater than Mean		
21	Total Samples	14	6		
22	Mean	185			
23	Median	184	Samples Between	180	200
24	Variance	704	4		
25	Standard Deviation	27			

COMPREHENSION CHECK 6-5

Launch a new worksheet. Type the following Excel expressions into the specified cells. Be certain you understand why each of the following yields the specific result. Note that not all functions shown in this table are valid Excel functions. If the formula returns an error, how can the formula be changed to correctly display the desired result?

In Cell . . .	Enter the Formula . . .	The Cell Will Display . . .
A1	= SQRT (144)	
A2	= MAX (5, 8, 20/2, 5 + 6)	
A3	= AVERAGE (5, SQRT(100), 15)	
A4	= POWER (2, 5)	
A5	= PI()	
A6	= PI	
A7	= PRODUCT (2, 5, A2)	
A8	= SUM (2 + 7, 3 2, A1:A3)	
A9	= RADIANS (90)	
A10	= SIN (RADIANS (90))	
A11	= SIN (90)	
A12	= ACOS (0.7071)	
A13	= DEGREES(ACOS(0.7071))	
A14	= CUBRT(27)	

EXAMPLE 6-3

The maximum height (H) an object can achieve when thrown can be determined from the velocity (v) and the launch angle with respect to the horizontal (θ):

$$H = \frac{v^2 \sin(\theta)}{2g}$$

Note the use of a cell (E7) to hold the value of the acceleration due to gravity. This cell will be referenced in the formulae instead of our inserting the actual value into the formulae. This will allow us to easily work the problem in a different gravitational environment (e.g., Mars) simply by changing the one cell containing the gravitational constant.

	A	B	C	D	E	F	G
1	**Basic Examples of Trig Functions and Cell Addressing**						
2	The following data is used to illustrate built-in trig functions and mixed references						
3							
4							
5							
6							
7	Planet	Earth		Gravity (g)	9.8	[m/s²]	
8							
9	Velocity	Angle (θ) [degrees]					
10	(v)[m/s]	50	60	70	80		
11	10						
12	12						
13	14						
14	16						
15	18						
16	20						
17							

For the following, assume that the angle 50° is in cell B10. After setting up the column of velocities and the row of angles, we type the following into cell B11 (immediately below 50°)

= $A11^2 * SIN (RADIANS (B$10)) / (2*$E$7)

Note the use of absolute addressing (for gravity) and mixed addressing (for angle and velocity). For the angle, we allow the column to change (since the angles are in different columns) but not the row (since all angles are in row 10). For the velocity, we allow the row to change (since the velocities are in different rows) but the column is fixed (since all velocities are in column A). This allows us to write a single formula and replicate it in both directions.

The sine function requires an argument in units of radians, and the angle is given in units of degrees in the problem statement. In this example, we used the RADIANS function to convert from degrees into radians. Another method is to use the relationship 2p radians is equal to 360 degrees, or

= $A11^2 * SIN ((2 * PI() / 360) * B$10) / (2*$E$7)

We replicate the formula in cell B11 across the row to cell E11, selecting all four formulae in row 11 and replicating to row 16. If done correctly, the values should appear as shown.

Velocity (v) [m/s]	Angle (θ) [°]			
	50	60	70	80
20	3.91	4.42	4.79	5.02
12	5.63	6.36	6.90	7.24
14	7.66	8.66	9.40	9.85
16	10.01	11.31	12.27	12.86
18	12.66	14.32	15.53	16.28
20	15.63	17.67	19.18	20.10

Here, we consider the planet to be Mars with a gravity of 3.7 meters per second squared in cell E7. The worksheet should automatically update, and the values should appear as shown.

Velocity (v) [m/s]	Angle (θ) [°]			
	50	60	70	80
10	10.35	11.70	12.70	13.31
12	14.91	16.85	18.29	19.16
14	20.29	22.94	24.89	26.08
16	26.50	29.96	32.51	34.07
18	33.54	37.92	41.14	43.12
20	41.41	46.81	50.79	53.23

Now, we consider the planet to be Moon with a gravity of 1.6 meters per second squared in cell E7. The worksheet should automatically update, and the values should appear as shown.

Velocity (v) [m/s]	Angle (θ) [°]			
	50	60	70	80
10	23.94	27.06	29.37	30.78
12	34.47	38.97	42.29	44.32
14	46.92	53.04	57.56	60.32
16	61.28	69.28	75.18	78.78
18	77.56	87.69	95.14	99.71
20	95.76	108.25	117.46	123.10

6.3 LOGIC AND CONDITIONALS

Outside of the realm of computing, logic exists as a driving force for decision making. Logic transforms a list of arguments into outcomes based on a decision.

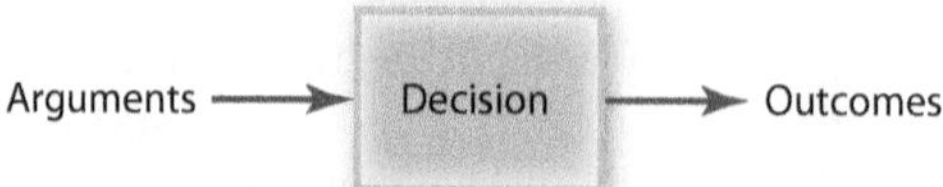

Some examples of every day decision making:

- If the traffic light is red, stop. If the traffic light is yellow, slow down. If the traffic light is green, go.

Argument: three traffic bulbs   Decision: is bulb lit?   Outcomes: stop, slow, go

- If the milk has passed the expiration date, throw it out; otherwise, keep the milk

Argument: expiration date   Decision: before or after?   Outcomes: garbage, keep

To bring decision making into our perspective on problem solving, we need to first understand how computers make decisions. **Boolean logic** exists to assist in the decision-making process, where each argument has a binary result and our overall outcome exhibits binary behavior. **Binary behavior**, depending on the application, is any sort of behavior that results in two possible outcomes.

> **NOTE**
>
> AND is true if and only if all arguments are true.
>
> OR is true if at least one of the arguments is true.

In computing, we often refer to the outcome of Boolean calculations as "yes" and "no." Alternatively, we may refer to the outcomes as "true" and "false," or "1" and "0." To connect all the Boolean arguments to make a logical decision, we have a few operators that allow us to relate our arguments to determine a final outcome.

- **AND:** The AND logical operator enables us to connect two Boolean arguments and return the result as TRUE if and only if *both* Boolean arguments have the value of TRUE. In Excel, the AND function accepts more than two arguments and is TRUE if all the arguments are TRUE.
- **OR:** The OR logical operator enables us to connect two Boolean arguments and return the result as TRUE if *only one* of the Boolean arguments has the value of TRUE. In Excel, the OR function accepts two or more arguments and is TRUE if at least one of the arguments is TRUE.
- **NOT:** The NOT logical operator enables us to invert the result of a Boolean operation. In Excel, the NOT function accepts one argument. If the value of that argument is TRUE, the NOT function returns FALSE. Likewise, if the argument of the function is FALSE, the NOT function returns TRUE.

To determine the relationship between two cells (containing numbers or text), we have a few operators, listed in Table 6.6, that allow us to compare two cells to determine whether or not the comparison is true or false.

Table 6.6 Relational operators in Excel

Operator	Meaning
>	Greater than
<	Less than
>=	Greater than or equal to
<=	Less than or equal to
=	Equal to
<>	Not equal to

These relational operators are usually placed between two different cells to determine the relationship between the two values. This expression of cell–operator–cell is typically called a **relational expression**. Relational expressions can be combined by means of logical operators to create a **logical expression**. If no logical operator is required in a particular decision, then the single relational expression can be the logical expression.

Conditional statements are commands that give some decision-making authority to the computer. Specifically, the user asks the computer a question using conditional statements, and then the computer selects a path forward based on the answer to the question. Sample statements are given below:

- If the water velocity is fast enough, switch to an equation for turbulent flow!
- If the temperature is high enough, reduce the allowable stress on this steel beam!
- If the RPM level is above red line, issue a warning!
- If your grade is high enough on the test, state: You Passed!

In these examples, the comma indicates the separation of the condition and the action that is to be taken if the condition is true. The exclamation point marks the end of the statement. Just as in language, more complex conditional statements can be crafted with the use of "else" and "otherwise" and similar words. In these statements, the use of a semicolon introduces a new conditional clause, known as a nested conditional statement. For example:

- If the collected data indicate the process is in control, continue taking data; otherwise, alert the operator.
- If the water temperature is at or less than 10 degrees Celsius, turn on the heater; or else if the water temperature is at or greater than 80 degrees Celsius, turn on the chiller; otherwise, take no action.

6.3.1 Single Conditional Statements

In Excel, conditional statements can be used to return a value within a cell based upon specified criteria. The IF conditional statement within Excel takes the form

= IF (logical test, value if true, value if false)

Every statement must contain three and only three parts:

1. **A logical test, or the question to be answered**
   The answer to the logical test must be TRUE or FALSE.
   Is the flow rate in Reactor #1 higher than Reactor #5?
2. **A TRUE response,** if the answer to the question is yes
   Show the number 1 to indicate Reactor #1.
3. **A FALSE response,** if the answer to the question is no
   Show the number 5 to indicate Reactor #5.

The whole statement for the above example would read:

= IF (B3 > B4, 1, 5)

	A	B	C
1			
2			
3	Reactor #1 Flowrate	10	[gpm]
4	Reactor #5 Flowrate	25	[gpm]
5	Maximum Flowrate in Reactor #	5	

6.3.2 Special Things to Note

- **To leave a cell blank, type a set of quotations with nothing in between (" ").** For example, the statement = IF (C3>10, 5," ") is blank if C3 is less than 10.
- For display of a text statement, *the text must be stated within quotes ("text goes in here")*. For example, the statement = IF (E5 > 10, 5,"WARNING") would display the word WARNING if E5 is less than 10.

EXAMPLE 6-4

For the following scenarios, write a conditional statement to be placed in cell B5 to satisfy the conditions given. Below each statement are sample outcomes of the worksheet in different scenarios.

(a) Display the pressure difference between upstream station 1 (displayed in cell B3) and downstream station 2 (displayed in cell B4) if the pressure difference is positive; otherwise, display the number 1.

	A	B	C
1			
2			
3	Station #1 Pressure	2.4	[atm]
4	Station #2 Pressure	2.8	[atm]
5	Pressure Difference	1	[atm]

	A	B	C
1			
2			
3	Station #1 Pressure	3.2	[atm]
4	Station #2 Pressure	2.8	[atm]
5	Pressure Difference	0.4	[atm]

$$Answer: = IF((B3 - B4) > 0, B3 - B4, 1)$$

(b) Display the value of the current tank pressure if the current pressure is less than the maximum tank pressure; otherwise, display the word "MAX".

	A	B	C
1			
2			
3	Maximum Tank Pressure	5	[atm]
4	Current Tank Pressure	2	[atm]
5	Pressure Status	2	[atm]

	A	B	C
1			
2			
3	Maximum Tank Pressure	5	[atm]
4	Current Tank Pressure	10	[atm]
5	Pressure Status	MAX	[atm]

Answer: = IF (B3 > B4, B4, "MAX")

(c) If the sum of the temperature values shown in cells B2, B3, and B4 is greater than or equal to 100, leave the cell blank; otherwise, display a warning to the operator that the temperature is too low.

	A	B	C
1			
2	Temperature Reading #1	25	[°C]
3	Temperature Reading #2	50	[°C]
4	Temperature Reading #3	45	[°C]
5	Cumulative Temperature		

	A	B	C
1			
2	Temperature Reading #1	25	[°C]
3	Temperature Reading #2	10	[°C]
4	Temperature Reading #3	45	[°C]
5	Cumulative Temperature	Too Low	

Answer: = IF (SUM(B2:B4) > = 100, B4, " ", "Too Low")

COMPREHENSION CHECK 6-6

Are the logical expressions displayed in Example 6-4 the only logical expressions that could be used to display the required outcomes? Write out a logically equivalent expression that could be typed into cell B5 for each situation.

6.3.3 Nested Conditional Statements

If more than two outcomes exist, the conditional statements in Excel can be nested. The nested IF conditional statement within Excel can take the form

= IF(logical test #1, value if #1 true, IF (logical test #2, value if #2 true, value if both false))

Note that the number of parenthesis must match (open and closed) and must be placed in the proper location. Recall that every statement must contain three and only three parts. For the first IF statement, they are:

1. **The first logical test, or the first question to be answered**
   The answer to the logical test must be TRUE or FALSE.
   Is the score for Quiz #1 less than the score for Quiz #2?
2. **A true response, or what to do if the answer to the first question is yes**
   Show the score for Quiz #1.
3. **A false response,** or what to do if the answer to the first question is no
   Proceed to the logical question for the second IF statement.

For the second IF statement, the three parts are:

1. **The second logical test, or the second question to be answered**
   The answer to the logical test must be TRUE or FALSE.
   Is the score for Quiz #2 less than the score for Quiz #1?
2. **A true response,** or what to do if the answer to the second question is yes
   Show the score for Quiz #2.
3. **A false response,** or what to do if the answer to the second question, and by default both questions, is no
   Show the text "equal".

The whole statement typed in cell B5 for the above example would read

= IF (B3 < B4, B3, IF (B3 > B4, B4, "equal"))

	A	B	C
1			
2			
3	Quiz Grade #1	70	
4	Quiz Grade #2	70	
5	Lowest Quiz Score	Equal	

	A	B	C
1			
2			
3	Quiz Grade #1	90	
4	Quiz Grade #2	70	
5	Lowest Quiz Score	70	

	A	B	C
1			
2			
3	Quiz Grade #1	50	
4	Quiz Grade #2	70	
5	Lowest Quiz Score	50	

There can be a maximum of 64 nested IF statements within a single cell. The nested IF can appear as either the true or false response to the first IF logical test. In the above example, only the false response option is shown.

EXAMPLE 6-5

Write the conditional statement to display the state of water (ice, liquid, or steam) based upon temperature displayed in cell B4, given in degrees Celsius. Below are sample outcomes of the worksheet in different scenarios.

	A	B	C
1			
2			
3			
4	Temperature of Mixture	75	[°C]
5	State of Mixture	Liquid	

	A	B	C
1			
2			
3			
4	Temperature of Mixture	110	[°C]
5	State of Mixture	Steam	

	A	B	C
1			
2			
3			
4	Temperature of Mixture	10	[°C]
5	State of Mixture	Ice	

Here, there must be two conditional statements because there are three responses:

- If the temperature is less than or equal to zero, display "ice";
- If the temperature is greater than or equal to 100, display "steam";
- Otherwise, display "liquid".

Answer: = IF(B4 < = 0, "ice", IF (B4 > = 100, "steam", "liquid"))

COMPREHENSION CHECK 6-7

Is the logical expression displayed in Example 6-5 the only logical expression that could be used to display the phase of the water? Write out a logically equivalent expression that could be typed into cell B5.

6.3.4 Compound Conditional Statements

If more than two logic tests exist for a single condition, conditional statements can be linked together by AND, OR, and NOT functions. Up to 255 logical tests can be compared in a single IF statement (only two are shown in the box below). The compound IF conditional statement takes the form

= IF (AND (logical test #1, logical test #2), value if both tests are true, value if either test is false)

= IF (OR (logical test #1, logical test #2), value if either test is true, value if both tests are false)

EXAMPLE 6-5

Write the conditional statement that meets the following criteria:

(a) If the product has cleared all three quality checks (given in cells B2, B3, and B4) with a score of 80 or more on each check, mark the product as "OK" to ship; otherwise, mark the product as "Recycle."

	A	B	C
1			
2	Quality Check #1 Rating	90	
3	Quality Check #2 Rating	80	
4	Quality Check #3 Rating	85	
5	Mark Product	OK	

	A	B	C
1			
2	Quality Check #1 Rating	60	
3	Quality Check #2 Rating	80	
4	Quality Check #3 Rating	85	
5	Mark Product	Recycle	

Answer: = IF(AND (B2 >= 80, B3 >= 80, B4 >= 80), "OK", "Recycle")

(b) If the product has cleared all three quality checks (given in cells B2, B3, and B4) with a minimum score of 80 on each check, mark the product as "OK" to ship; otherwise, if the product scored a 50 or below on any check, mark the product as "Rejected"; otherwise, mark the product as "Rework."

	A	B	C
1			
2	Quality Check #1 Rating	90	
3	Quality Check #2 Rating	80	
4	Quality Check #3 Rating	85	
5	Mark Product	OK	

	A	B	C
1			
2	Quality Check #1 Rating	40	
3	Quality Check #2 Rating	80	
4	Quality Check #3 Rating	85	
5	Mark Product	Rejected	

	A	B	C
1			
2	Quality Check #1 Rating	60	
3	Quality Check #2 Rating	80	
4	Quality Check #3 Rating	85	
5	Mark Product	Rework	

Answer: = IF(AND (B2 >= 80, B3 >= 80, B4 >= 80), "OK", IF (OR (B2 <= 50, B3 <= 50, B4 <= 50), "Rejected", "Rework"))

COMPREHENSION CHECK 6-8

Is the logical expression displayed in Example 6-6(a) the only logical expression that could be used to display the desired outcome? Write out a logically equivalent expression that could be typed into cell B5.

6.4 CONDITIONAL FORMATTING

You can use conditional formatting to change the font color or background of a cell based upon the values found in that cell. As an example:

- On a blank worksheet, type the value of 20 in cell A4, a value of 30 in cell B4, and a value of 50 in cell C4.
- Select cells A4 to C4.
- Select the **Conditional Formatting** drop-down menu in **Home > Styles** and click the **Manage Rules** item.

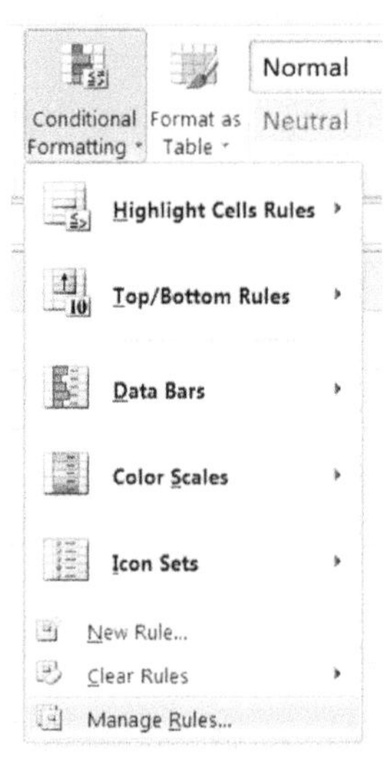

- In the Conditional Formatting Rules Manager window, click the New Rule button to open the New Formatting Rule wizard. In this window, you can now select several options. Under Select a Rule Type, click the option **Format only cells that contain** to bring up the interface for creating custom formats based on certain conditions. In the first drop-down menu, you can choose among **Cell Value** and a few other options. For this activity, use only Cell Value.
- In the second drop-down menu, you can choose various conditional statements such as “between” or “less than.” To begin this problem, choose “less than” from this list.
- The choice of “less than” will combine the next two boxes into a single box. You can enter a number or formula, or reference a cell within the worksheet.

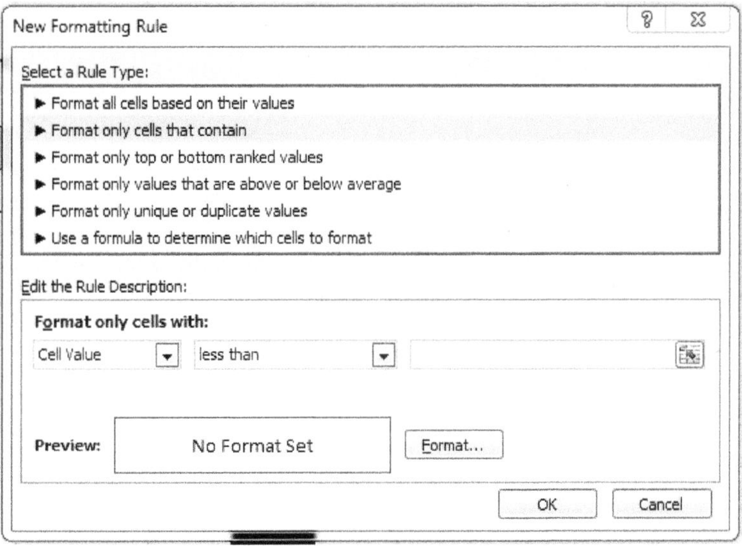

For this example, enter the value “25.” Note: If you enter a formula, the same rules apply for absolute and relative referencing. In addition, if you select a cell within the worksheet, the program automatically defaults to an absolute reference.

- Click the **Format** button. Select the formatting you want to apply when the cell value meets the condition or the formula returns the value TRUE. You can change the font, border, or background of the cell. For this example, choose a green background on the Fill tab. When you are finished, click **OK**.
- To add another condition, click **New Rule**. Additionally, in this window, you can edit or delete existing conditional formatting options. For this condition, make it greater than 40, with a font of white, bolded on a red background. Click **OK**. To apply the

conditions in the Conditional Formatting Rules Manager window, click the **Apply** button, then click **OK**.

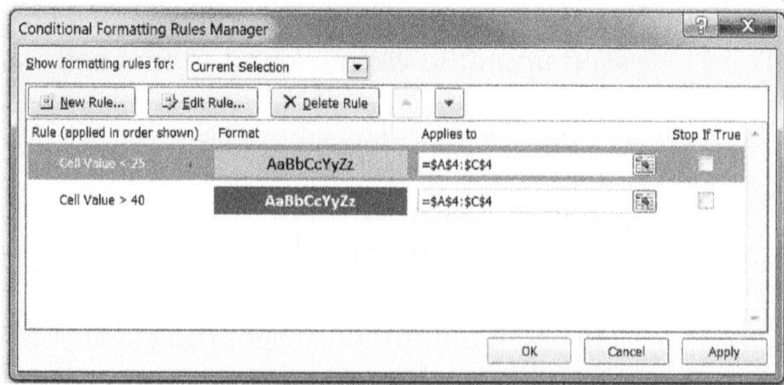

Your worksheet should now look like the one shown. If none of the specified conditions are TRUE, the cells keep their existing formats.

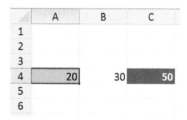

	A	B	C
1			
2			
3			
4	20	30	50
5			
6			

EXAMPLE 6-8

Let us assume we want to build an interactive worksheet that changes the format of a cell to model the behavior of a traffic light. We want the user to input the number of seconds it takes for a light (which is initially green) to turn red. In addition, the user must also be able to provide the "warning" so that the light can switch from green to yellow and then to red.

- The green light (bottom) will only be lit if the time remaining is greater than the warning time.
- The yellow light (middle) will only be lit if the time remaining is greater than 0 seconds, but less than the warning time.
- The red light (top) will only be lit if the time remaining is 0 seconds.

Before we set up the conditional formatting for each cell, we need to write IF statements in the light cells that will be used as a trigger for conditional formatting.

For Cell E5 (the red light): = IF(A5 = 0, "R", "")
For Cell E9 (the yellow light): = IF(AND (A5 <=B5, A5 > 0), "Y", "")
For Cell E13 (the green light): = IF(A5 < B5, "G", "")

Next, we add a set of conditional formatting rules for each cell.

For the red light, we click E5 and select the Manage Rules item from the Conditional Formatting menu to create a rule that turns the fill color red when the cell has the letter "R" in the text.

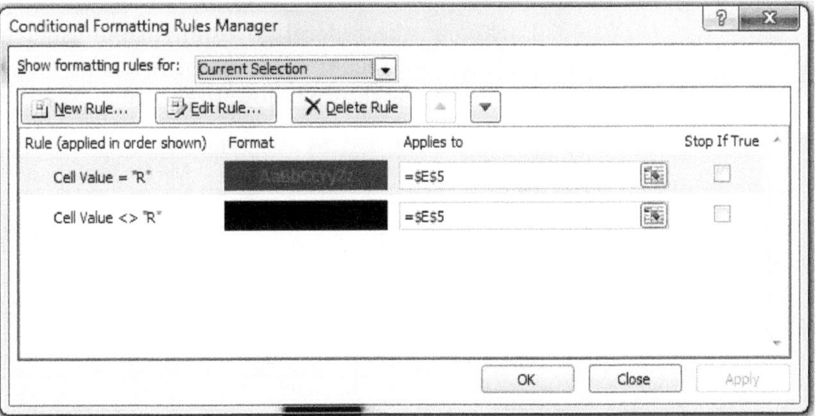

For the yellow light, we click E9 and repeat this process to turn the fill color yellow when cell has the letter "Y" in the text. For the green light, we click E13 and repeat this process to turn the fill color green when cell has the letter "G" in the text.

The final worksheet should appear as shown. Note that cell formats should change when the time remaining changes.

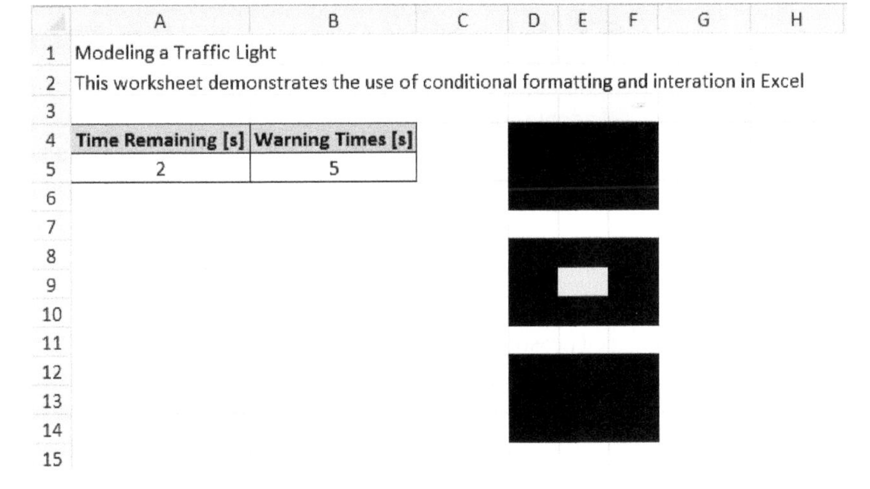

COMPREHENSION CHECK 6-10

Open the worksheet you created in Example 6-3 and modify it to highlight all heights greater than 100 meters with a light blue background and all heights less than 25 meters with a dark blue background with a white font.

6.5 SORTING AND FILTERS

Excel provides a number of built-in tools for sorting and filtering data in a worksheet. This section describes how to use these tools effectively without causing unintended side effects.

Each year, the federal government publishes a list of fuel economy values. The complete lists for recent years can be found at www.fueleconomy.gov/feg. A partial list of 2009 vehicles is shown below. In the table, MPG = miles per gallon.

Make	Model	MPG City	MPG Highway	Annual Fuel Cost
Jeep	Liberty 4WD	15	21	$1835
BMW	X5 xDrive 30i	15	21	$1927
Honda	Civic Hybrid	40	45	$ 743
Volkswagen	Jetta 2.5L	20	29	$1301
Ford	Mustang 5.4L	14	20	$2166
Bentley	Continental GTC	10	17	$2886
Honda	Fit	27	33	$1039

Given this information, assume you are to present it with some sort of order. What if you want to sort the data on text values (Make or Model) or numerical values (MPG City, MPG Highway, Annual Fuel Cost), or what if you want to view only certain vehicles that meet a certain condition?

6.5.1 Sorting Data in a Worksheet

- Select the cells to be sorted. You can select cells in a single column or row, or in a rectangular group of cells.
- Select **Home > Editing > Sort & Filter.** By default, two commonly used sorting tools (Sort A to Z and Sort Z to A) appear, in addition to a button for Custom Sort. With a group of cells selected, the common sorting tools will sort according to the values in the leftmost column. If the leftmost column contained numerical values, the options would have read Sort Smallest to Largest/Largest to Smallest. Since it is often desired to involve multiple sorting conditions, click **Custom Sort**.
- The sorting wizard is displayed as shown. If your selected group of cells had a header row (a row that displays the names of the columns and not actual data) the "My data has headers" checkbox should be selected.

  By default, Excel automatically detects whether the top row of your selected data is a header or a data row. Since you selected the data including the header rows, the "Sort by" drop-down menu will contain the header names. If you had not included the header row, the "Sort by" drop-down menu would show the column identifiers as options. It is good practice to select the headers in addition to the data to make sorting easier to understand.

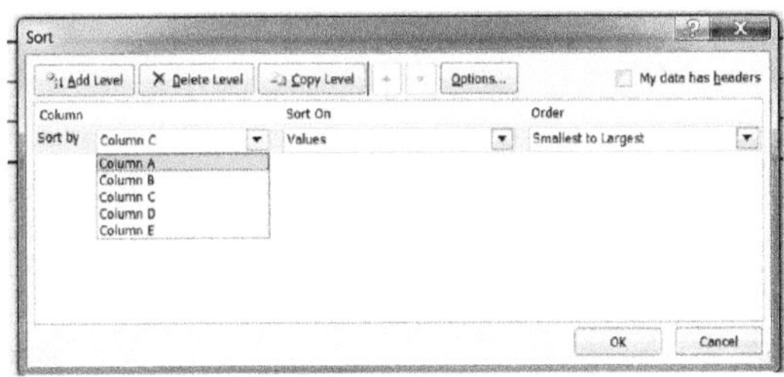

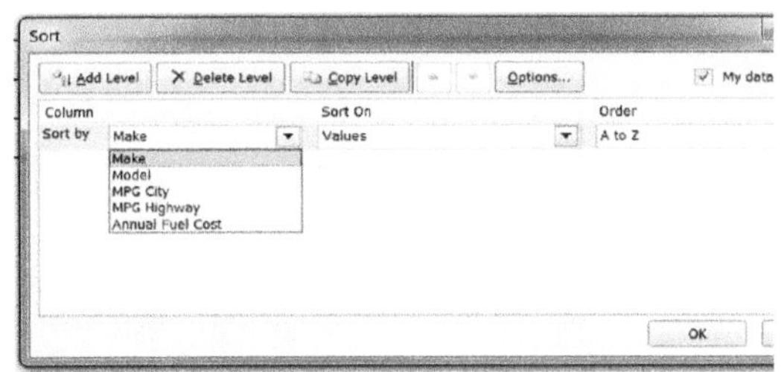

- Assume you want to sort the list alphabetically (A to Z) by the make, then by smallest-to-largest annual fuel cost. Click the Add Level button to add two levels of sorting since there are two conditions. In the sorting wizard, the topmost sorting level will be the sort applied first, and then the next level will sort each data group that forms from the first sort. In the example, there is more than one Honda vehicle, so the second level will place the Civic Hybrid above the Fit, since the Civic Hybrid has a smaller annual fuel cost.

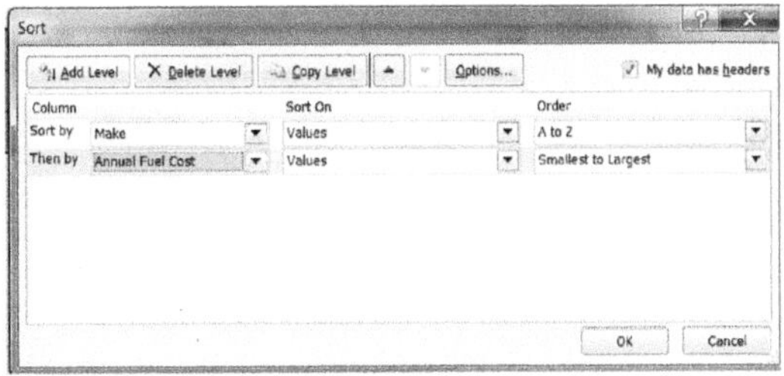

The resulting sorted data appear as shown.

	A	B	C	D	E
1	**Fuel Economy of Vehicles**				
2	This worksheet demonstrates the use of sorting and filtering in excel				
3					
4	**Make**	**Model**	**MPG City**	**MPG Highway**	**Annual Fuel Cost**
5	Bentley	Continental GTC	10	17	$2,885
6	BMW	X5 xDrive 30i	15	21	$1,927
7	Ford	Mustang 5.4L	14	20	$2,165
8	Honda	Civic Hybrid	40	45	$743
9	Honda	Fit	27	33	$1,039
10	Jeep	Liberty 4WD	15	21	$1,835
11	Volkswagon	Jetta 2.5L	20	29	$1,301
12					

NOTE

To "undo" a sort, either choose the "Undo" arrow button on the top menu or use CTRL-Z.

It is important to be sure to select all of the data when using the sort functions because it is possible to corrupt your data set. To demonstrate, select only the first three columns (Make, Model, MPG City) and sort the data smallest to largest on the MPG City column.

Notice after sorting that the last two columns (MPG Highway, Annual Fuel Cost) are not the correct values for the vehicle. There is no way to recover the original association if you were to save the file and open it at a later time, so it is critical that when using the built-in sorting functions, you verify the correctness of your data before saving your workbook. In this case, you can click Excel's Undo button or CTRL-Z to unapply the last sort.

	A	B	C	D	E
1	**Fuel Economy of Vehicles**				
2	This worksheet demonstrates the use of sorting and filtering in excel				
3					
4	**Make**	**Model**	**MPG City**	**MPG Highway**	**Annual Fuel Cost**
5	Bentley	Continental GTC	10	17	$2,885
6	Ford	Mustang 5.4L	14	21	$1,927
7	BMW	X5 xDrive 30i	15	20	$2,165
8	Jeep	Liberty 4WD	15	45	$743
9	Volkswagon	Jetta 2.5L	20	33	$1,039
10	Honda	Fit	27	21	$1,835
11	Honda	Civic Hybrid	40	29	$1,301
12					

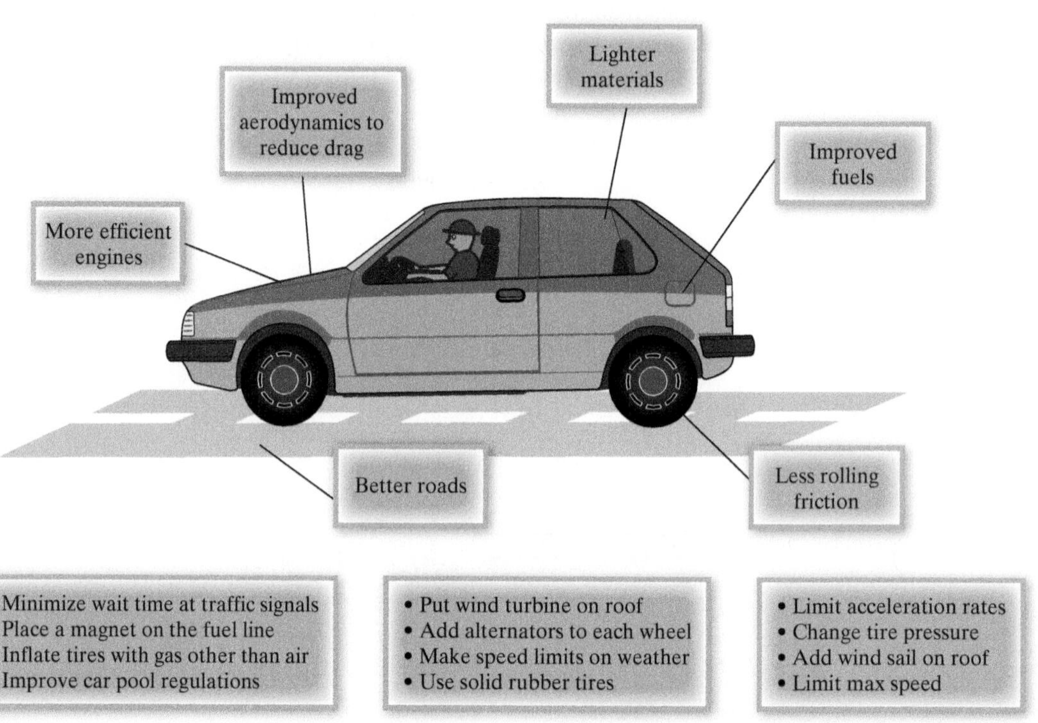

Improving automotive gas mileage while keeping costs under control is a complex puzzle, involving many different types of engineers. Below are some ways to possibly improve fuel efficiency. Some really work, some are false claims, and some are fictitious. Can you tell the difference? What other ways can you think of to improve today's automobiles?

COMPREHENSION CHECK 6-11

In 1980, the Environmental Protection Agency (EPA) began the Superfund Program to help cleanup highly polluted areas of the environment. There are over 1,300 Superfund sites across the country. Not all Superfund sites are from deliberate pollution. Some sites are old factories, where chemicals were dumped on the ground; landfills where garbage was dumped along with other poisonous waste; remote places where people secretly dumped hazardous waste because they did not know what to do with it; or old coal, iron ore, or silver mines.

According to the EPA (http://www.epa.gov/superfund/index.htm), the following groundwater contaminants were found in South Carolina Superfund sites in Greenville, Pickens, Oconee, and Anderson counties.

- Sort by city in ascending order. Examine the result: Which city appears first?
- Sort again: first by city in descending order, then by site name in descending order. Examine the results: Which site name now appears first?
- Sort again by contaminant in ascending order, then by site name in ascending order. Examine the results: Which site name appears last?

Contaminants	Site Name	City
Polycyclic aromatic hydrocarbons	Sangamo Weston	Pickens
Volatile organic compounds	Beaunit Corporation	Fountain Inn
Polycyclic aromatic hydrocarbons	Beaunit Corporation	Fountain Inn
Polycyclic aromatic hydrocarbons	Para-Chem Southern, Inc.	Simpsonville
Volatile organic compounds	Golden Strip Septic Tank Service	Simpsonville
Volatile organic compounds	Para-Chem Southern, Inc.	Simpsonville
Metals	Para-Chem Southern, Inc.	Simpsonville
Polycyclic aromatic hydrocarbons	Rochester Property	Travelers Rest
Volatile organic compounds	Sangamo Weston	Pickens
Polychlorinated biphenyl	Sangamo Weston	Pickens
Metals	Rochester Property	Travelers Rest
Metals	Golden Strip Septic Tank Service	Simpsonville
Metals	Beaunit Corporation	Fountain Inn
Volatile organic compounds	Rochester Property	Travelers Rest

6.5.2 Filtering Data in a Worksheet

Assume you want to look only at a specific portion of the data set and hide all the other rows of data. For example, you might want to look only at Honda vehicles or all vehicles that have an MPG City rating between 10 and 15 MPG. Excel has a built-in filtering capability by which you can conditionally display rows in a data set.

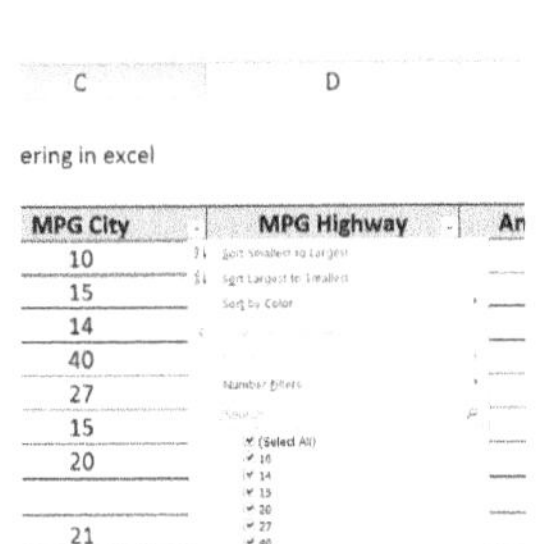

- Select the header row for a data set and click the **Sort & Filter** button in the **Home > Editing** ribbon. Click the **Filter** option to enable filtering for each column of data. Each column label contains a drop-down menu with various sorting options, as well as a number of different approaches for filtering.
    - For data sets that contain a small number of options, use the checkboxes in the drop-down filter to manually check certain options to display.
    - For numerical values, use the Number Filters submenu to filter on certain conditional expressions. The Custom Filter option in the Number Filters submenu lets you combine up to two logical expressions to filter a single column of data.

Assume you want to revisit your fuel economy data set and add in a number of statistical functions to assist in analysis.

	A	B	C	D	E
1	**Fuel Economy of Vehicles**				
2	This worksheet demonstrates the use of sorting and filtering in excel				
3					
4	**Make**	**Model**	**MPG City**	**MPG Highway**	**Annual Fuel Cost**
5	Bentley	Continental GTC	10	17	$2,886
6	BMW	X5 xDrive 30i	15	21	$1,927
7	Ford	Mustang 5.4L	14	20	$2,165
8	Honda	Civic Hybrid	40	45	$743
9	Honda	Fit	27	33	$1,039
10	Jeep	Liberty 4WD	15	21	$1,835
11	Volkswagon	Jetta 2.5L	20	29	$1,301
12					
13		Average:	20	27	$1,700
14		Min:	10	17	$743
15		Max:	40	45	$2,886
16					

Suppose you filter the data set to look only at the Honda vehicles.

	A	B	C	D	E
1	**Fuel Economy of Vehicles**				
2	This worksheet demonstrates the use of sorting and filtering in excel				
3					
4	**Make**	**Model**	**MPG City**	**MPG Highway**	**Annual Fuel Cost**
8	Honda	Civic Hybrid	40	45	$743
9	Honda	Fit	27	33	$1,039
12					
13		Average:	20	27	$1,700
14		Min:	10	17	$743
15		Max:	40	45	$2,886
16					

Notice that the statistical calculations at the bottom are still referencing the entire data set, even though, because of the filter, only a subset of the data is displayed. For data comparisons, this will be a valuable side effect; however, if you want the calculations to apply only to the visible data, you will need to use built-in functions other than the traditional functions (AVERAGE, MIN, MAX).

6.5.3 Using the SUBTOTAL Function

The SUBTOTAL function allows the worksheet to dynamically recalculate expressions generated with a filtered list. In the example where only Honda vehicles are selected, only the two visible vehicles will be used in the calculations, if you modify your worksheet to use the SUBTOTAL function instead of the traditional statistical functions. To use the SUBTOTAL function, pass in two different arguments:

```
= SUBTOTAL (function_num, range)
```

Table 6.7 Available functions in SUBTOTAL

function_num	Function	Definition
1	AVERAGE	Computes the average value of the range
2	COUNT	Counts the number of cells in the range that contain numbers
3	COUNTA	Counts the number of nonempty cells in the range
4	MAX	Calculates the maximum value of the range
5	MIN	Calculates the minimum value of the range
6	PRODUCT	Calculates the product of each number in the range
7	STDEV	Calculates the standard deviation of the numbers in the range ("*n* – 1" method)
8	STDEVP	Calculates the standard deviation of the numbers in the range ("*n*" method)
9	SUM	Calculates the sum of all of the numbers in the range
10	VAR	Calculates the variance of the numbers in the range ("*n*" method)
11	VARP	Calculates the variance of the numbers in the range ("*n* – 1" method)

- The ***function_num*** argument is a number associated to various built-in Excel functions. Table 6.7 lists the available functions for use with the SUBTOTAL function.
- The ***range*** argument is the range of cells to which the function should be applied.

In the example, use the following calculation in cell C13 to calculate the average of MPG City:

= AVERAGE(C5:C11)

The AVERAGE function corresponds to function_num 1, so the resulting calculation in cell C13 using the SUBTOTAL function would appear as follows:

= SUBTOTAL (1, C5:C11)

After you modified all of the statistical calculations in the worksheet to use the SUBTOTAL function, the sheet should appear as shown in the examples below. Note that the values recalculate automatically according to the filtered data.

Filter on Make: Honda Only

	A	B	C	D	E
1	**Fuel Economy of Vehicles**				
2	This worksheet demonstrates the use of sorting and filtering in excel				
3					
4	**Make**	**Model**	**MPG City**	**MPG Highway**	**Annual Fuel Cost**
8	Honda	Civic Hybrid	40	45	$743
9	Honda	Fit	27	33	$1,039
12					
13		Average:	34	39	$891
14		Min:	27	33	$743
15		Max:	40	45	$1,039
16					

Filter on Annual Fuel Cost: Less than $1,500

	A	B	C	D	E
1	**Fuel Economy of Vehicles**				
2	This worksheet demonstrates the use of sorting and filtering in excel				
3					
4	**Make**	**Model**	**MPG City**	**MPG Highway**	**Annual Fuel Cost**
8	Honda	Civic Hybrid	40	45	$743
9	Honda	Fit	27	33	$1,039
11	Volkswagon	Jetta 2.5L	20	29	$1,301
12					
13		Average:	29	36	$1,028
14		Min:	20	29	$743
15		Max:	40	45	$1,301
16					

In-Class Activities

ICA 6-1

You want to set up a worksheet to investigate the oscillatory response of an electrical circuit. Create a worksheet similar to the one shown, including the proper header information.

4			
5			
6			
7	Neper Frequency (α_0)	25	[rad/s]
8	Resonant Frequency (ω_0)	400	[rad/s]
9	Initial Voltage (V_0)	15	[V]
10			
11	Damped Frequency (ω_d)		[rad/s]
12			
13			
14	Time (t) [s]	Voltage (V) [V]	
15			

First, calculate another constant, the damped frequency ω_d, which is a function of the neper frequency (a0) and the resonant frequency (ω_0). This can be calculated with the formula

$$\omega_d = \sqrt{\omega_0^2 - \alpha_0^2}$$

Next, create a column of times (beginning in A15) used to calculate the voltage response, ranging from 0 to 0.002 seconds at an increment of 0.0002 seconds.

In column B, calculate the voltage response with the following equation, formatted to one decimal place:

$$V = V_0 e^{-\alpha_0 t} \cos(\omega_d t)$$

(a) Change neper frequency to 200 radians per second, resonant frequency to 800 radians per second, and initial voltage to 100 volts. At a time of 0.0008 seconds, what is the voltage?

(b) Change neper frequency to 100 radians per second, resonant frequency to 600 radians per second, and initial voltage to 100 volts. At a time of 0.0008 seconds, what is the voltage?

(c) Change neper frequency to 200 radians per second, resonant frequency to 400 radians per second, and initial voltage to 75 volts. At a time value of 0.0008 seconds, what is the voltage?

ICA 6-2

Some alternate energy technologies, such as wind and solar, produce more energy than needed during peak production times (windy and sunny days), but produce insufficient energy at other times (calm days and nighttime). Many schemes have been concocted to store the surplus energy generated during peak times for later use when generation decreases. One scheme is to use the energy to spin a massive flywheel at very high speeds, then use the rotational kinetic energy stored to power an electric generator later.

The worksheet shown below was designed to calculate how much energy is stored in flywheels of various sizes. The speed of the flywheel (revolutions per minute) is to be entered in cell B2, and the density of the flywheel in cell B4. A formula in cell B3 converts the speed into units of radians per second. There are 2π radians per revolution of the wheel.

To simplify the computations, the stored energy was calculated in three steps. The first table calculates the volumes of the flywheels, the second table uses these volumes to calculate the masses of the flywheels, and the third table uses these masses to determine the stored rotational kinetic energy.

Note that in all cases, changing the values in cells B2 and/or B4 should cause all appropriate values to be automatically recalculated.

	A	B	C	D	E	F	G	H	I
1									
2	Speed (v) [rpm]	15000		Volume (V) [m^3]	Height (H) [m]				
3	Speed (ω) [rad / s]	1571		Diameter (D) [m]	0.3	0.6	0.9	1.2	1.5
4	Density (ρ) [kg / m^3]	8000		0.2	0.009	0.019	0.028	0.038	0.047
5				0.4	0.038	0.075	0.113	0.151	0.188
6				0.6	0.085	0.170	0.254	0.339	0.424
7				0.8	0.151	0.302	0.452	0.603	0.754
8				1.0	0.236	0.471	0.707	0.942	1.178
9									
10				Mass (m) [kg]	Height (H) [m]				
11				Diameter (D) [m]	0.3	0.6	0.9	1.2	1.5
12				0.2	75	151	226	302	377
13				0.4	302	603	905	1206	1508
14				0.6	679	1357	2036	2714	3393
15				0.8	1206	2413	3619	4825	6032
16				1.0	1885	3770	5655	7540	9425
17									
18				Kinetic Energy (KE) [J]	Height (H) [m]				
19				Diameter (D) [m]	0.3	0.6	0.9	1.2	1.5
20				0.2	1.9E+06	3.7E+06	5.6E+06	7.4E+06	9.3E+06
21				0.4	3.0E+07	6.0E+07	8.9E+07	1.2E+08	1.5E+08
22				0.6	1.5E+08	3.0E+08	4.5E+08	6.0E+08	7.5E+08
23				0.8	4.8E+08	9.5E+08	1.4E+09	1.9E+09	2.4E+09
24				1.0	1.2E+09	2.3E+09	3.5E+09	4.7E+09	5.8E+09
25				Average KE [J]	3.6E+08	7.3E+08	1.1E+09	1.5E+09	1.8E+09
26				Max KE - Min KE [J]	4.3E+09				

(a) What should be typed in cell B3 to convert revolutions per minute in cell B2 into radians per second?

(b) What should be typed into cell E4 that can then be copied through the rest of the first table to calculate the flywheel volumes? Assume the shape of the flywheel to be a cylinder.

(c) What should be typed into cell E12 that can then be copied through the rest of the second table to calculate the flywheel masses?

(d) What should be typed into cell E20 that can then be copied through the rest of the third table to calculate the kinetic energies stored in the flywheels? The rotational kinetic energy is given by the formula: $KE_{rot} = I\omega^2 = (mr^2)\omega^2$

(e) What should be typed into cell E25 that can then be copied through Row 25 to determine the average kinetic energy at each height (in each column)?

(f) What should be typed into cell E26 to determine the difference between the maximum kinetic energy and 800 times the minimum kinetic energy given in the table?

ICA 6-3

Refer to the following worksheet. The following expressions are typed into the Excel cells indicated. Write the answer that appears in the cell listed. If the cell will be blank, write "BLANK" in the answer space. If the cell will return an error message, write "ERROR" in the answer space.

	A	B	C	D	E	F	G	H
1								
2								
3	Fluid Type	Benzene			Fluid Type	Olive Oil		
4	Density (ρ)	0.879	[g / cm^3]		Density (ρ)	0.703	[g / cm^3]	
5	Viscosity (μ)	6.47E-03	[g / (cm s)]		Viscosity (μ)	1.01	[g / (cm s)]	
6								
7	Velocity (v)	15	[cm / s]		Velocity (v)	50	[cm / s]	
8								
9	Pipe Diameter	Reynolds Number			Pipe Diameter	Reynolds Number		
10	(D) [cm]	(Re) [--]			(D) [cm]	(Re) [--]		
11	1.27	2,588			1.27	44		
12	2.54	5,176			2.54	88		
13	3.81	7,764			3.81	133		
14	5.08	10,352			5.08	177		
15	6.35	12,940			6.35	221		
16	7.62	15,529			7.62	265		

	Expression	Typed into Cell
(a)	= IF (B4 > F4, B3, "F3")	D4
(b)	= IF (B7/2 > F7/10, " ", B7*2)	H7
(c)	= IF (B11 < F11, "B11", IF (B11 > F11, SUM(B11, F11), F11))	D11
(d)	= IF (AND(B4 < F4,B5 < F5), B3, MAX(F11:F16))	D9
(e)	= IF(OR(E16/2^2 > E15*2,E11+E12 < E14),F4*62.4,F4*1000)	H16

ICA 6-4

Use the following worksheet to answer the questions.

	A	B	C
1	Temperature Limit of Phase B	250	
2	Temperature Limit of Phase D	350	
3			
4			
5			
6	Amount of Type S Polymer (S) [wt %]	Temperature (T) [K]	Phase
7	92	387	Phase D
8	86	125	Phase E
9	17	407	Phase D
10	51	323	Phase C
11	12	73	Phase A
12	53	174	Phase B
13	73	79	Phase B
14	75	275	Phase C
15	19	51	Phase B
16	47	300	Phase C
17	45	79	Phase B

(a) If the following is typed into cell C1, what will appear when the statement is executed?

= IF (B1 > 200, IF (B1 < 300, 200 + 50, "High"), MAX(B1, B2))

(b) If the following is typed into cell C2, what will appear when the statement is executed?

= IF (OR(B1 > 200, B2 < 500), "", 300)

(c) The axes for a phase diagram of a polymer blend are shown on the answer sheet. Use the following worksheet to sketch the phase diagram, containing 5 phases A–E, that was used to create the conditional statement that appears in cell C7. The following appears in cell C7, typed on a single line:

= IF (A7 < 15, "Phase A", IF (AND (A7 < 80, B7 < $B$1), "Phase B", IF (B7 > $B$2, "Phase D" IF (A7 > 80, "Phase E", "Phase C"))))

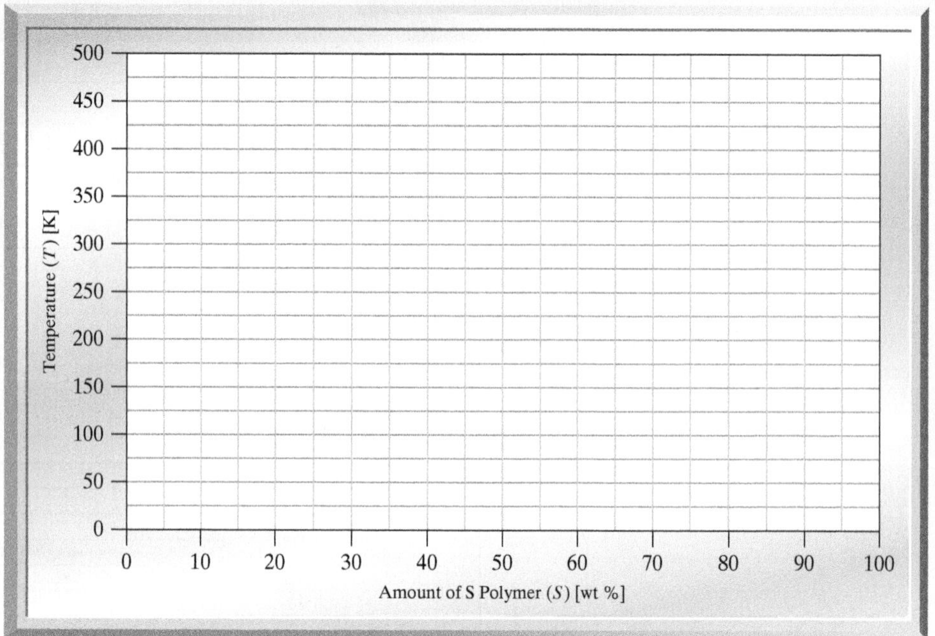

ICA 6-5

A bioengineer conducts clinical trials on stressed-out college students to see if a sleep aid will help them fall asleep faster. She begins the study by having 20 students take a sleep aid for seven days and records through biofeedback the time when they fall asleep. To analyze the data, she sets up the following worksheet. Evaluate the expressions below; state what will appear in the cell when the command is executed. Column I contains the average time each student took to fall asleep during the seven-day trial. Column J contains any adverse reactions the students experienced (H = headache; N = nausea).

(a) Column K will contain the rating of the time it took the student to fall asleep compared with the control group, who did not take the medication. The statement as it appears in cell K14 is given below. What will appear in cell K14 when this statement is executed?

```
= IF > (I14 > $I$2 + $I$3, "MORE", IF (I14 < $I$2 − $I$3, "LESS", ""))
```

(b) Column L groups the participants into three groups according to their reaction to the drug and the time it took them to fall asleep. Assume the statement for part (a) is executed in Column K. The statement as it appears in cell L7 is given below. What will appear in cell L7 when this statement is executed?

```
= IF (AND (K7 = "MORE", J7 = "H"), "MH", IF
                                   (AND (K7 = "MORE", J7 = "N"), "MN", ""))
```

(c) Suppose the formula in Column L was changed to regroup the participants. The statement as it appears in cell L9 is given below. In Excel, this statement would appear as a continuous line, but here it is shown on two lines for space. What will appear in cell L9 when this statement is executed?

```
= IF (AND (K9 = "MORE", OR (J9 = "H", J9 = "N")), "SEVERE",
IF (OR (J9 = "H", J9 = "N"), "MILD", IF (K9 = "LESS", "HELPFUL", "")))
```

(d) Suppose the formula in part (c) was copied into cell L16. What would appear in cell L16 when this statement is executed?

(e) Suppose the formula in part (c) was copied into cell L18. What would appear in cell L18 when this statement is executed?

(f) Does the expression given in part (c) accurately identify all severe reaction conditions? If not, how would you change the expression to include all severe reactions?

	A	B	C	D	E	F	G	H	I	J	K	L
1						Control Group Data						
2						Overall Average			35	[min]		
3						Standard Deviation			4	[min]		
4												
5		Number of Minutes to Fall Asleep										
6	Patient	Day 1	Day 2	Day 3	Day 4	Day 5	Day 6	Day 7	Average	Reaction	Time	Group
7	A	45	39	83	47	39	25	42	46	H		
8	B	35	75	15	36	42	12	29	35			
9	C	42	32	63	45	37	34	31	41	N		
10	D	14	25	65	38	53	33	32	37	H		
11	E	14	71	48	18	29	14	24	31			
12	F	14	25	29	24	18	24	15	21	H N		
13	G	31	14	42	19	28	17	21	25			
14	H	12	24	32	42	51	12	16	27	H N		
15	I	28	29	44	15	43	15	22	28	N		
16	J	21	19	35	41	34	25	18	28	H		
17	K	44	36	51	39	30	26	25	36			
18	L	38	43	36	59	14	34	18	35	N		
19	M	19	15	63	50	55	27	31	37	H		

ICA 6-6

Refer to the worksheet shown, set up to calculate the displacement of a spring. Hooke's law states the force (F, in newtons) applied to a spring is equal to the stiffness of the spring (k, in newtons per meter) times the displacement (x, in meters): $F = kx$.

	A	B	C	D	E	F	G	H
1								
2	Spring Code	Stiffness [N/m]	Maximum Displacement [mm]			Spring Code	Stiffness [N / m]	Maximum Displacement [mm]
3	3-Blue	50	20			1-Blue	10	40
4						1-Black	25	60
5	Mass [g]	Displacement [cm]	Warning			2-Blue	30	25
6	25	0.49				2-Black	40	60
7	50	0.98				2-Red	20	30
8	75	1.47				3-Blue	50	20
9	100	1.96				3-Red	40	30
10	125	2.45	Too Much Mass			3-Green	60	10
11	150	2.94	Too Much Mass					
12	175	3.43	Too Much Mass					
13	200	3.92	Too Much Mass					
14	225	4.41	Too Much Mass					
15	250	4.90	Too Much Mass					
16	275	5.39	Too Much Mass					
17	300	5.88	Too Much Mass					

Cell A3 contains a data validation list of springs. The stiffness (cell B3) and maximum displacement (cell C3) values are found using a VLOOKUP function linked to the table shown at the right side of the worksheet. These data are then used to determine the displacement of the spring at various mass values. A warning is issued if the displacement determined is greater than the maximum displacement for the spring. Use this information to determine the answers to the following questions.

(a) Write the expression, in Excel notation, that you would type into cell B6 to determine the displacement of the spring. Assume you will copy this expression to cells B7 to B17, so be sure and watch your absolute and relative references—and your units!

(b) A LOOKUP function in Excel contains four parts. Fill in the following information in the VLOOKUP function used to determine the maximum displacement in cell C3 based on the choice of spring in cell A3.

= VLOOKUP(___(a)___, ___(b)___, ___(c)___, ___(d)___)

(c) An IF statement in Excel contains three parts. Fill in the following information in the IF function used to determine the warning given in cell C6, using the maximum displacement in cell C3. Assume you will copy this expression to cells C7 to C17, so be sure and watch your absolute and relative references—and your units!

= IF(___(a)___, ___(b)___, ___(c)___)

ICA 6-7

You are interested in analyzing different implant parts being made in a bioengineering production facility. The company has the ability to make 13 different parts from 17 different metal alloys.

	A	B	C
1			
2	MATERIAL	WC-2	
3	Cost / lbm	17	
4	Specific Gravity	11.88	
5			
6	Part Number	JB3	
7	Material Weight [lbm]	0.3	
8	Part Volume [cin]	3.5	
9			
10	Number of Parts	6000	Too Many
11			
12	Amount of Mat'l to Order [lbm]	1800	Check $
13			
14	Size of Shipping Package		OK
15	Length [in]	24	
16	Width [in]	5	
17	Height [in]	2	
18			
19	Amount of Boxes Needed	44	
20			

	D	E	F	G
1		Material	Specific Gravity	Material Cost / lbm
2		AuZn-4	19.8	$ 15.00
3		WC-2	11.88	$ 17.00
4		CuAg-5	6.6	$ 24.00
5		PdSi-3	15.84	$ 18.00
6		PdSi-5	15.84	$ 15.00
7		ZnCd-2	6.6	$ 16.00
8		CoNi-7	7.92	$ 16.00
9		CoAg-12	13.2	$ 24.00
10		CdAl-2	7.92	$ 14.00
11		PtZn-4	7.92	$ 13.00
12		PtC-9	19.8	$ 22.00
13		MnPd-8	14.52	$ 5.00
14		WTi-3	11.88	$ 6.00
15		ScCo-4	6.6	$ 18.00
16		ZrW-8	5.28	$ 18.00
17		MnRh-5	6.6	$ 7.00
18		PdCd-7	7.92	$ 9.00

	H	I	J	K	L	M
1		Part Number	Material Weight [lbm]	Number / Box	Part Volume [cin]	Energy Cost / Part
2		JB2	0.1	12	7.5	0.1
3		JB3	0.3	76	3.5	0.03
4		JB5	0.1	48	7.5	0.08
5		JB6	0.4	66	1	0.1
6		JB8	0.1	96	6.5	0.07
7		KA9	0.1	4	1.5	0.05
8		KA11	0.45	85	4	0.04
9		KA2	0.05	96	7.5	0.01
10		KA5	0.45	5	3.5	0.04
11		DS3	0.3	86	3	0.03
12		DS7	0.5	92	3	0.08
13		DS8	0.05	51	1	0.05
14		DS12	0.1	47	5	0.08

On the worksheet shown, you have created a place for the user to choose the material, linked to Column E, and the part number, linked to Column I, using data validation lists. Once these two values are chosen, the cost per pound, specific gravity, material weight of the part, and part volume all automatically adjust using VLOOKUP functions. LOOKUP functions in Excel contain four parts.

= VLOOKUP(_(a)_,_(b)_,_(c)_,_(d)_)

(a) Fill in the following information in the VLOOKUP function used to determine the cost per pound of material in cell B3 based on the choice of material in cell B2.
(b) Fill in the following information in the VLOOKUP function used to determine the part volume in cell B8 based on the choice of part number in cell B6.

An IF statement in Excel contains three parts. Fill in the following information in the IF function used to determine the following conditions.

= IF(__(a)__,__(b)__,__(c)__)

(c) In cell B10, the user can enter the number of parts needed in production. If this value is more than 2,500 parts, a warning will appear in cell C10 telling the user the quantity is too high; otherwise, the cell remains blank.
(d) In cell B12, the worksheet determines the amount of material to order. If the cost of the materials (determined by the amount in cell B12 times the cost per pound in cell B3) is more than $1,000, a warning will appear in cell C12 telling the user to check with supervision first; otherwise, the cell displays the cost of the material to order.
(e) In cells B15–B17, the user enters the size of the shipping box being used once the pieces have been made and are ready to ship to the hospitals. The worksheet checks to ensure the box dimensions are not larger than 24 inches long by 12 inches wide by 12 inches high. If the user enters values outside this range, the program will warn the user in cell C14 to resize the box; otherwise, the cell will indicate the dimensions are ok.

ICA 6-8

You have a large stock of several values of inductors and capacitors, and are investigating how many possible combinations of a single capacitor and a single inductor chosen from the ones you have in stock will give a resonant frequency between specified limits.

Create two cells to hold a minimum and maximum frequency the user can enter. If the value entered for the maximum frequency (f_{MAX}) is less than the minimum frequency (fMIN), the maximum frequency cell should be shaded dark grey with white, bold text.

Incorrect data:

Allowable Range	
f_{min}[Hz]	f_{max}[Hz]
2500	**1000**

Correct data:

Allowable Range	
f_{min}[Hz]	f_{max}[Hz]
2500	7777

Calculate the resonant frequency (f_R) for all possible combinations of one inductor and one capacitor, rounded to the nearest integer. For a resonant inductor/capacitor circuit, the resonant frequency in hertz [Hz] is calculated by

$$f_R = \frac{1}{2\pi\sqrt{LC}}$$

Here, L is the inductance in units of henry [H] and C is the capacitance in units of microfarads [μF]. Automatically format each result to indicate its relation to the minimum and maximum frequency values as listed below.

- $f_R > f_{MAX}$: The cell should be shaded white with light grey text and no border.f
- $f_R < f_{MIN}$: The cell should be shaded light grey with dark grey text and no border.
- $f_{MIN} < f_R < f_{MAX}$: The cell should be shaded white with bold black text and a black border.

If done properly, the table should appear similar to the table below for f_{MIN} = 2,500 and f_{MAX} = 7,777.

After you have this working properly, modify the frequency input cells to use data validation instead of conditional formatting to warn the user of an invalid value entry.

Resonant Frequency (f_R) [Hz]	Capacitance (C) [μF]							
Inductance (L) [H]	0.0022	0.0082	0.05	0.47	0.82	1.5	3.3	10
0.0005	151748	78601	31831	10382	7860	**5812**	**3918**	2251
0.002	75874	39301	15915	**5191**	**3930**	**2906**	1959	1125
0.01	33932	17576	**7118**	2322	1758	1299	876	503
0.05	15175	7860	**3183**	1038	786	581	392	225
0.068	13012	**6740**	**2729**	890	674	498	336	193
0.22	**7234**	**3747**	1517	495	375	277	187	107
0.75	**3918**	2029	822	268	203	150	101	58

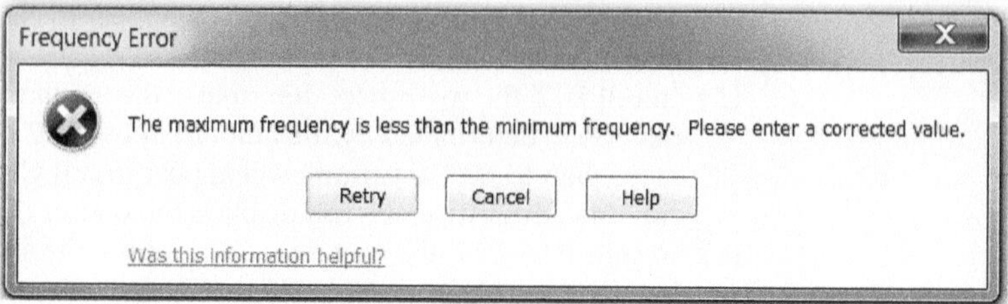
Frequency Error
The maximum frequency is less than the minimum frequency. Please enter a corrected value.
Retry
Cancel
Help
Was this information helpful?

ICA 6-9

We accidentally drop a tomato from the balcony of a high-rise apartment building. As it falls, the tomato has time to ponder some physics and says, "You know, the distance I have fallen equals ½ gravity times the time I have fallen squared." Create a worksheet to solve the question of when the tomato goes splat.

- The user will input the initial balcony height in units of feet. Use data validation to set a limit for the height of 200 feet.
- Place the acceleration due to gravity in a cell under the balcony height and not within the formulas themselves. Be sure to watch the units for this problem!
- Column A will be the distance the tomato falls, starting at a distance of zero up to a distance of 200 feet, in 5-foot increments.
- Column B will show the calculated time elapsed at each distance fallen.
- Column C will display the status of the tomato as it falls.
  - If the tomato is still falling, the cell should display the distance the tomato still has to fall.
  - If the tomato hits the ground, the cell should display "SPLAT" on a red background.
  - SPLAT should appear once; the cells below are blank.

Use the worksheet just created to test the following parameters.

	Balcony Height [ft]
(a)	200
(b)	120
(c)	50
(d)	25

ICA 6-10

You are interested in calculating the best place to stand to look at a statue. Where should you stand so that the angle subtended by the statue is the largest?

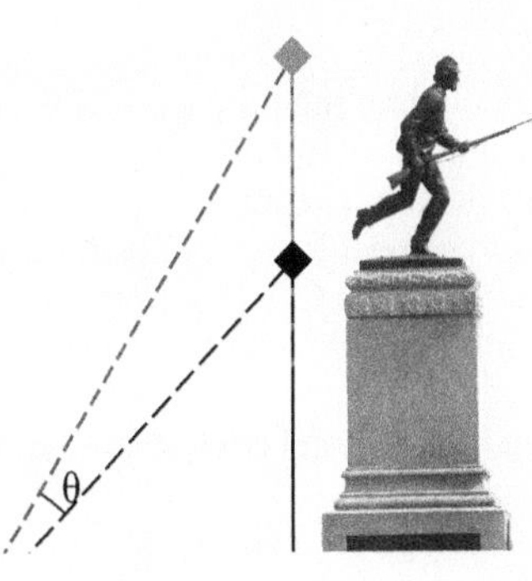

At the top of the worksheet, input the pedestal height (P) and the statue height (S).

In Column A, create a series of distances (d) from the foot of the statue, from 2 feet to 40 feet by 2-foot increments.

In Column B, calculate the subtended angle in radians using the following equation:

$$\theta = \tan^{-1}\left(\frac{P + S}{d}\right) - \tan^{-1}\left(\frac{P}{d}\right)$$

In Column C, write a function to change the angles in Column B from radians to degrees. At the bottom of Column C, insert a function to display the maximum value of all the angles.

In Column D, use a conditional statement whose output is blank except at the single distance where the angle is a maximum; at the maximum, print "Stand Here."

Use the worksheet just created to test the following parameters

	Pedestal Height (P) [ft]	Statue Height (S) [ft]
(a)	20	10
(b)	10	10
(c)	15	20
(d)	30	20

ICA 6-11

Many college students have compact refrigerator-freezers in their dorm room. The data set provided is a partial list of energy efficient models less than 3.6 cubic feet [cft], according to the American Council for an Energy Efficient Economy (www.aceee.org). Complete the analysis below.

(a) We would like to compute the cost to run each model for a year. Assume that it costs $0.086 per kilowatt-hour [kWh]. Create a new column, "Annual Energy Cost [$/year]," that calculates the annual energy cost for each refrigerator.

(b) First, we will sort the first table by energy usage, with the model with the highest kilowatt-hour rating listed first. Which model appears first?

(c) Next, we will sort by the volume in ascending order and the annual energy cost in ascending order. Which model appears first?

(d) Assume we want to restrict our selection to refrigerators that can contain more than 2.5 cubic feet. Which models appear in the list?

(e) Assume we want to restrict our selection to refrigerators that can contain more than 2.5 cubic feet and only require between 0 and 300 kilowatt-hours per year. Which models appear in the list?

ICA 6-12

The complexity of video gaming consoles has evolved over the years. The data set provided is a list of energy usage data on recent video gaming consoles, according to the Sust-It consumer energy report data (www.sust-it.net). Complete the analysis below.

(a) Compute the cost to run each gaming console for a year, including the purchase price. Assume that it costs $0.086 per kilowatt-hour [kWh]. Create a new column, "Cost + Energy [$/yr]," that calculates the total (base + energy) cost for each gaming console.

(b) On average, a consumer will own and operate a video gaming console for four years. Calculate the total carbon emission [kilograms of carbon dioxide, or kg CO_2] for each gaming console over the average lifespan; put the result in a column labeled "Average Life Carbon Emission [kg CO_2]."

(c) First, sort the table by total cost, with the console with the highest total cost listed first. Which console appears first?

(d) Next, sort by the original cost in ascending order and the average life carbon emission in ascending order. Which console appears last?

(e) Restrict your selection to video game consoles that originally cost $300. Which models appear in the list?

(f) Restrict your selection to video game consoles that originally cost less than or equal to $300 and have an average life carbon emission less than or equal to 25 kg CO_2. Which models appear in the list?

CHAPTER 6 REVIEW QUESTIONS

1. With current rocket technology, the cost to lift one kilogram of mass to geosynchronous orbit (GSO) is about $20,000. Several other methods of lifting mass into space for considerably less cost have been envisioned, including the Lofstrom loop, the orbital airship, and the space elevator.

   In space elevators, a cargo compartment (climber) rides up a slender tether attached to the Earth's surface and extending tens of thousands of miles into space. Many designs provide power to the climber by beaming it to a collector on the climber using a laser of maser.

   The leftmost column of the table should contain efficiencies from 0.5% to 2% in 0.25% increments. The top row of the table should list electricity prices from 4 cents to 14 cents per kilowatt-hour with 2 cent increments. Each row of the table thus represents a specific efficiency and each column represents a specific electricity cost. The intersection of each row and column should contain the corresponding total cost of the electricity used to lift one kilogram to GSO.

   Assume that the total change in the potential energy of an object lifted from sea level to GSO is 50 megajoules per kilogram.

   Any constants and conversion factors used should appear as properly labeled constants in individual cells, and your formulae should reference these. Conversions and constants should NOT be directly coded into the formulae. You are expected to use absolute, relative, and mixed cell addressing as appropriate. As an example (not within the table) so you can check your formulae, if electricity costs 18 cents per kilowatt-hour and the conversion efficiency is 3%, the electricity to lift one kilogram to GSO would cost $83.33.

2. A history major of your acquaintance is studying agricultural commerce in nineteenth century Wales. He has encountered many references to "hobbits" of grain, and thinking that this must be some type of unit similar to a bushel (rather than a diminutive inhabitant of Middle Earth), he has sought your advice because he knows you are studying unit conversions in your engineering class.

   He provides a worksheet containing yearly records for the total number of hobbits of three commodities sold by a Mr. Thomas between 1817 and 1824, and has asked you to convert these to not only cubic meters, but also both U.S. and imperial bushels.

   After a little research, you find that the hobbit was equal to two and a half imperial bushels, the imperial bushel equals 2,219 cubic inches, and the U.S. bushel equals 2,150 cubic inches.

   First, you create a table showing the conversion factors from hobbits to the other units, including comments documenting the conversion. You then use these calculated conversion factors to create the rest of the table. (See example, including embedded comment for conversion to cubic meters.)

	A	B	C	D
1	Grain sold by Mr. Thomas			
2				
3		Hobbits Sold		
4	Year	Barley	Wheat	Oats
5	1817	106	154	203
6	1818	118	145	187
7	1819	98	167	167
8	1820	137	124	199
9	1821	102	105	210
10	1822	142	168	147
11	1823	93	132	186
12	1824	117	136	193

Grain sold by Mr. Thomas

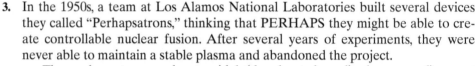

	Barley				Wheat				Oats			
Year	Hobbits	Imp. Bushels	US Bushels	Cubic Meters	Hobbits	Imp. Bushels	US Bushels	Cubic Meters	Hobbits	Imp. Bushels	US Bushels	Cubic Meters
1817	106	265	273.5	9.6	154	385	397.4	14.0	203	507.5	523.8	18.5
1818	118	295	304.5	10.7	145	362.5	374.1	13.2	187	467.5	482.5	17.0
1819	98	245	252.9	8.9	167	417.5	430.9	15.2	167	417.5	430.9	15.2
1820	137	342.5	353.5	12.5	124	310	319.9	11.3	199	497.5	513.5	18.1
1821	102	255	263.2	9.3	105	262.5	270.9	9.5	210	525	541.8	19.1
1822	142	355	366.4	12.9	168	420	433.5	15.3	147	367.5	379.3	13.4
1823	93	232.5	240.0	8.5	132	330	340.6	12.0	186	465	479.9	16.9
1824	117	292.5	301.9	10.6	136	340	350.9	12.4	193	482.5	498.0	17.5

Hobbit	Imp. Bushels	US Bushels	Cubic Meters
1	2.5	2.58023	0.09091

[Imp. Bushel] [2219 cu. In./Imp. Bushel] [2.54 cm/In]^3 [meter/100 cm]^3

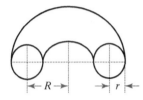

3. In the 1950s, a team at Los Alamos National Laboratories built several devices they called "Perhapsatrons," thinking that PERHAPS they might be able to create controllable nuclear fusion. After several years of experiments, they were never able to maintain a stable plasma and abandoned the project.

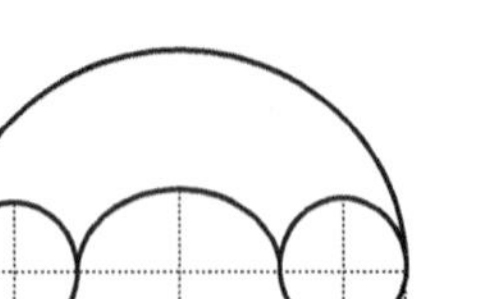

The perhapsatron used a toroidal (doughnut-shaped) plasma confinement chamber, similar to those used in more modern Tokamak fusion devices. You have taken a job at a fusion research lab, and your supervisor asks you to develop a simple spreadsheet to calculate the volume of a torus within which the plasma will be contained in a new experimental reactor.

   (a) Create a simple calculator to allow the user to type in the radius of the tube (r) in meters and the radius of the torus (R) in meters and display the volume in cubic meters.

   (b) Data validation should be used to assure that $R > r$.

   (c) Create a table that calculates the volumes of various toruses with specific values for r and R. The tube radii (r) should range from 5 centimeters to 100 centimeters in increments of 5 centimeters. The torus radii (R) should range from 1.5 meters to 3 meters in increments of 0.1 meters.

The volume of a torus can be determined using $V = 2\pi^2 R r^2$.

4. A phase diagram for carbon and platinum is shown. Assuming the lines shown are linear, we can say the mixture has the following characteristics:

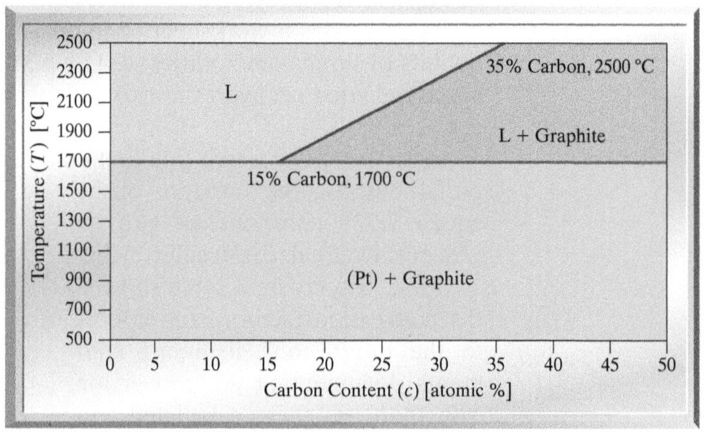

- Below 1,700°C, it is a mixture of solid platinum and graphite.
- Above 1,700°C, there are two possible phases: a liquid (L) phase and a liquid (L) + graphite phase. The endpoints of the division line between these two phases are labeled on the diagram. Develop a worksheet to determine the phase of a mixture, given the temperature and carbon content. A sample worksheet is shown below.

	A	B	C	D	E
1					
2					
3	Maximum Temperature for Pt + G			1700	[°C]
4					
5					
6					
7	Temperature	Carbon Content	Temp between	Phase	
8	(T) [°C]	(c) [%]	L & L+G		
9	1220	30			
10	1300	34			
11	1150	45			
12	1310	56			

(a) Write the equation to describe the temperature of the dividing line between the liquid (L) region and the liquid (L) + graphite region in Column C. Reference the carbon content found in Column B as needed. Add any absolute reference cells you feel are needed to complete this calculation.

(b) Write the conditional statement to determine the phase in Column D. For simplicity, call the phases Pt + G, L, and L + G. For points on the line, YOU can decide which phase they are included in.

(c) Use conditional formatting to indicate each phase. Provide a color key.

5. A simplified phase diagram for cobalt and nickel is shown. Assuming the lines shown are linear, we can say the mixture has the following characteristics:

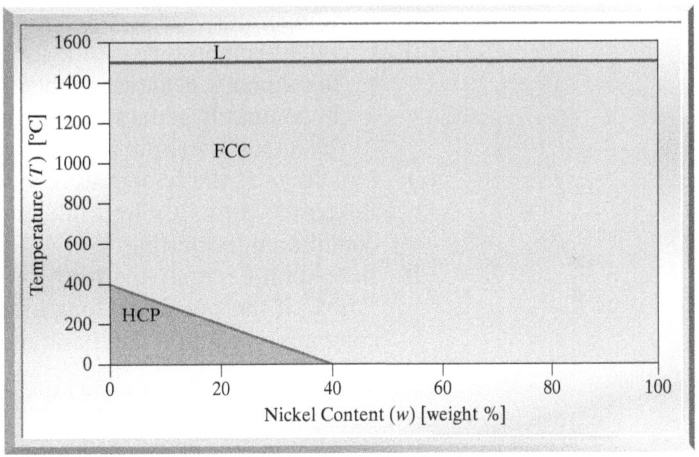

- Above 1,500°C, it is a liquid.
- Below 1,500°C, there are two possible phases: face-centered cubic (FCC) phase and hexagonal close-packed (HCP) phase. Develop a worksheet to determine the phase of a mixture, given the temperature and nickel content. A sample worksheet is shown below.

	A	B	C	D	E	F
1						
2						
3		Minimum Temperature for Liquid			1500	[°C]
4						
5	Temperature	Nickel Content	Temp Between	Phase		
6	(T) [°C]	(w) [%]	HCP & FCC			
7	250	12				
8	1015	43				
9	125	49				
10	360	27				
11	108	68				
12	200	40				

(a) Write the mathematical equation to describe the dividing line between the HCP region and the FCC region in Column C. Reference the nickel content found in Column B as needed. Add any absolute reference cells you feel are needed to complete this calculation.

(b) Write the conditional statement to determine the phase in Column D. For simplicity, call the phases HCP, FCC, and L. For points on the line, YOU can decide which phase they are included in.

(c) Use conditional formatting to indicate each phase. Provide a color key.

6. You enjoy drinking coffee but are particular about the temperature (T) of your coffee. If the temperature is greater than or equal to 70 degrees Celsius [°C], the coffee is too hot to drink; less than or equal to 45°C is too cold by your standards. Your coffee pot produces coffee at the initial temperature (T_0). The cooling of your coffee can be modeled by the equation below, where time (t) and the cooling factor (k) are in units per second:

$$T = T_0 e^{-kt}$$

(a) At the top of the worksheet, create an area where the user can modify four properties of the coffee:

- Initial temperature (T_0); for the initial problem, set to 80°C.
- Cooling factor (k); set to 0.001 per second [s^{-1}].
- Temperature above which coffee is "Too Hot" to drink (T_{hot}); set to 70°C.
- Temperature below which coffee is "Too Cold" to drink (T_{cold}); set to 45°C.

(b) Create a temperature profile for the coffee:

- In column A, generate a time range of 0–300 seconds, in 15-second intervals.
- In column B, generate the temperature of the coffee, using the equation given and the input parameters set by the user (T_0 and k).

(c) In column B, the temperature values should appear on a red background if the coffee is too hot to drink, and a blue background if it is too cold using conditional formatting.

(d) In column C, create a warning next to each temperature that says "Do not Drink" if the calculated temperature in column B is too hot or too cold in comparison with the temperature values the user enters.

7. The phase diagram below for the processing of a polymer relates the applied pressure to the raw material porosity.

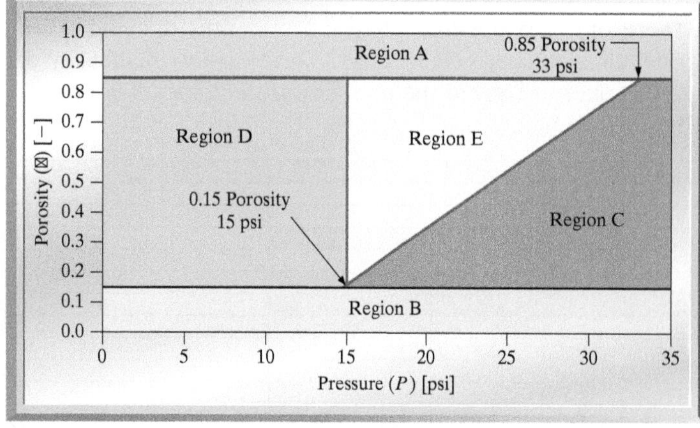

- Region A or B = porosity is too high or too low for the material to be usable.
- Region C = combinations in this region yield material with defects, such as cracking or flaking.
- Region D = below a pressure of 15 pound-force per square inch [psi] the polymer cannot be processed.
- Region E = optimum region to operate.

There are often multiple ways to solve the same problem; here we look a few alternative ways to determine the phase of the material and the processibility of the material.

	A	B	C	D	E
1					
2					
3	Porosity Upper Limit [%]			85	
4	Porosity Lower Limit [%]			15	
5	Pressure Limit [psi]			15	
6					
7	Pressure	Porosity	Porosity between	Phase	Is Material Able
8	(P) [psi]	(ε) [%]	C and E		to be Processed?
9	13	68			
10	26	39			
11	10	43			
12	15	82			
13	22	47			
14	16	84			
15	7	73			
16	25	45			

Method One: Conditional Statements—(a)–(d)

(a) Begin on the worksheet titled Conditionals. In Column C, develop the equation for the line dividing the phases of Region E and Region C. Assume it was written in cell C9 and copied to Column C.

(b) In Column D, write an expression to determine the phase of the material (Phase A–Phase E).

(c) In Column E, write an expression to determine if the material is processible.

(d) When the conditions of Phase E are met, the cell should be highlighted by conditional formatting. Provide a color key.

Method Two: Data Validation—(e)–(i)

(e) Begin on the worksheet titled Validation. In Column A and Column B, use data validation to restrict the user from entering values outside the valid parameter ranges—pressure: 0–35 psi and porosity: 0–100%.

(f) In Column C, develop the equation for the line dividing the phases of Region E and Region C.

(g) In Column D, write an expression to determine the phase of the material (Phase A–Phase E).

(h) In Column E, write an expression to determine if the material is processible.

(i) When the conditions of Phase E are met, the cell should be highlighted by conditional formatting.

(j) Can you write an expression in Column F to tell the user why the material was rejected? For example, under the conditions of pressure = 25 psi and porosity = 40%, the statement might say "Porosity too low."

(k) Can you write an expression in Column F to tell the user why the material was rejected and how to fix the problem to make the product useful? For example, under the conditions of pressure = 25 psi and porosity = 40%, the statement might say "Porosity too low, increase to at least a value of 55%."

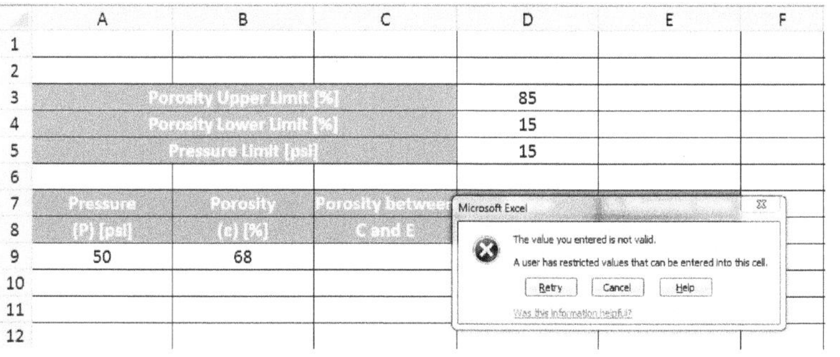

	A	B	C	D	E	F
1						
2						
3	Porosity Upper Limit [%]			85		
4	Porosity Lower Limit [%]			15		
5	Pressure Limit [psi]			15		
6						
7	Pressure	Porosity	Porosity betwee			
8	(P) [psi]	(ε) [%]	C and E			
9	50	68				
10						
11						
12						

Microsoft Excel
The value you entered is not valid.
A user has restricted values that can be entered into this cell.
Retry
Cancel
Help
Was this information helpful?

8. The following phase diagram is for salt water. There are four possible phases, which depend on the temperature and the sodium chloride content (NaCl).

- Ice and SC = Mixed ice and salt crystals.
- Ice and SW = Ice and saltwater.
- SW = Saltwater.
- SW and SC = Saltwater and salt crystals.

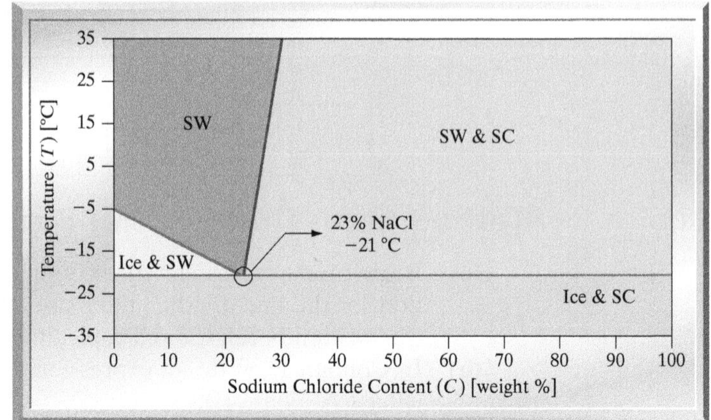

There are often multiple ways to solve the same problem; here we look a few alternative ways to determine the phase of the mixture.

Method One: Conditional Statements—(a)–(d)

(a) Begin on the worksheet titled Conditionals. In Column C, develop the equation for the line dividing the phases of the ice–saltwater mix and the saltwater. Assume it was written in cell C11 and copied down.

(b) In Column D, develop the equation for the line dividing the phases of the saltwater and the saltwater–salt crystals mix. Assume it was written in cell D11 and copied down.

(c) In Column E, write an expression to determine the phase of the mixture.

(d) Use conditional formatting to highlight the various phases. Provide a color key.

	A	B	C	D	E
5					
6					
7	Upper Limit of Mixed Ice and Salt Crystals			-21	[°C]
8					
9			Dividing Temp [°C]		
10	NaCl [%]	Temp [°C]	Ice and SW to SW	SW to SW and SC	Phase
11	83	-25			
12	73	2			
13	30	12			
14	56	-12			
15	90	31			
16	39	23			
17	33	-16			
18	35	5			

Method Two: Data Validation—(e)–(i)

(e) Begin on the worksheet titled Validation. In Column A and Column B, use data validation to restrict the user from entering values outside the valid parameter ranges: NaCl (%): 0–100%; Temp [°C]: −35°C to 35°C.

(f) In Column C, develop the equation for the line dividing the phases of the ice–saltwater mix and the saltwater.

(g) In Column D, develop the equation for the line dividing the phases of the saltwater and the saltwater–salt crystals mix.

(h) In Column E, write an expression to determine the phase of the mixture.

(i) Use conditional formatting to highlight the various phases. Provide a color key.

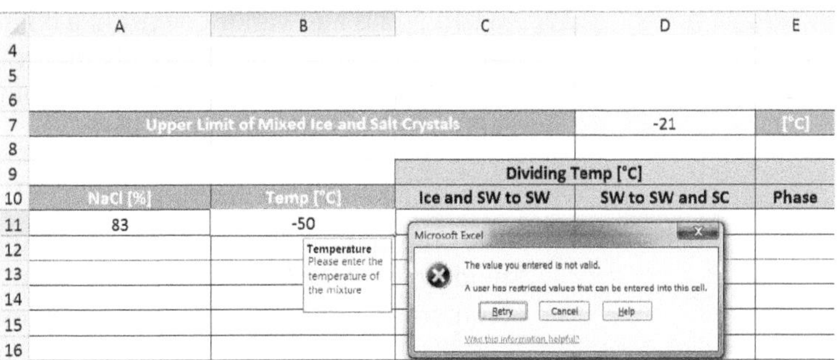

9. Guitars are constructed in a manner to allow musicians to place their fingers on different arrangements of strings to create chords. Chords are arrangements of three or more notes (or pitches) played at the same time. (There is some disagreement among musicologists concerning whether two notes played simultaneously should be classified as a chord.) On a standard electric guitar, there are typically 6 strings strung from the nut down the neck of the guitar with 21 frets set in the neck terminating at the bridge on the guitar. On a 6-string, 21-fret guitar, there are 126 different locations that can generate a pitch plus the 6 pitches generated by playing a string without pressing a fret. However, each fretted string on a guitar can take on 1 of 12 different semitones. As a guitarist moves their finger from lower to higher frets on a string on a guitar, each note changes by increasing 1 semitone.

The 12-tone semitone transitions are shown in the chart below:

From	To	From	To
A	A#/Bb	D#/Eb	E
A#/Bb	B	E	F
B	C	F	F#/Gb
C	C#/Db	F#/Gb	G
C#/Db	D	G	G#/Ab
D	D#/Eb	G#/Ab	A

In other words, if we are on the 5th string playing a B on the 10th fret, moving to the 11th fret would play a C.

Fill in the provided Excel worksheet using LOOKUP statements to the semitone transition table for a standard tuning guitar (E-A-D-G-B-E) to show where each note will be located on the guitar fretboard. The worksheet should be set up so that it can be easily modified for different guitar tunings:

(a) What will the resulting notes on the 5th fret be if an "open tuning," typical of blues and slide guitar music, if the open G tuning were used (G-B-D-G-B-D)?

(b) What will the resulting notes on the 8th fret be if the D-A-D-G-A-D tuning were used (e.g., Led Zeppelin's "Kashmir")?

(c) Use conditional formatting to highlight the sharps and flats (notes with # or b) in light yellow.

(d) Use conditional formatting to highlight all entries with the same note name as one of the base tuning notes within the column by making the text white on a black background. For standard tuning, this would highlight all occurrences of E in the first column, A in the second column, etc.

(e) Use data validation to allow the user to choose the notes from a drop-down list.

10. When liquid and vapor coexist in a container at equilibrium, the pressure is called vapor pressure. Several models predict vapor pressure. One, called the ***Antoine equation***, first introduced by Ch. Antoine in 1888, yields vapor pressure in units of millimeters of mercury [mm Hg].

$$P = 10^{\left(A - \frac{B}{T+C}\right)}$$

The constants A, B, and C are called the *Antoine constants*; they depend on both fluid type and temperature. Note that "B" and "C" must be in the same units as temperature and "A" is a dimensionless number, all determined by experiment.

	A	B	C	D	E	F	G
6							
7		Constants			Validity Range		
8	Compound	A	B [°C]	C [°C]	T_{min}[°C]	T_{max}[°C]	
9	Ethanol	8.204	1642.89	230.3	-57	80	
10							
11							
12							
14							
15	Temperature (T) [°C]	Pressure (P) [mm Hg]					
16	-100						
17	-95						
18	-90						
19	-85						
20	-80						
21	-75						
22	-70						
23	-65						
24	-60						
25	-55	0.0679					
26	-50	0.1236					
27	-45	0.2177					
28	-40	0.3723					

Create a worksheet using the provided template. The Antoine constants should automatically fill in after the user selects one from a drop-down menu in Cell A9 of the compounds shown below. (*Hint:* Use data validation and LOOKUP expressions.) The data in the table below has been provided in the online workbook.

	Constants			Validity Range	
Compound	*A*	*B* [°C]	*C* [°C]	T_{min} [°C]	T_{max} [°C]
Acetic acid	7.5596	1644.05	233.524	17	118
Acetone	7.1327	1219.97	230.653	−64	70
Cyclohexane	6.85146	1206.47	223.136	7	81
Ethanol	8.20417	1642.89	230.3	−57	80
Hexadecane	7.0287	1830.51	154.45	150	321
Methanol	8.08097	1582.27	239.7	15	100
m-Xylene	7.22319	1585.83	226.5	−45	140
Tetrahydrofuran	6.99515	1202.29	226.254	23	100

Next, create a column of temperature (T) beginning at −100 degrees Celsius and increasing in increments of 5 degrees Celsius until a temperature of 400 degrees Celsius.

In column ***B***, calculate the vapor pressure (P, in millimeters of mercury, [mm Hg]) using the Antoine equation, formatted to four decimal places. If the equation is outside the valid temperature range for the compound, the pressure column should be blank.

11. The ideal gas law assumes that molecules bounce around and have negligible volume themselves. This is not always true. To compensate for the simplifying assumptions of the ideal gas law, the Dutch scientist Johannes van der Waals developed a "real" gas law that uses several factors to account for molecular volume and intermolecular attraction. He was awarded the Nobel Prize in 1910 for his work. The ***van der Waals equation*** is as follows:

$$\left(P + \frac{an^2}{V^2}\right)(V - bn) = nRT$$

P, V, n, R, and T are the same quantities as found in the ideal gas law. The constant "a" is a correction for intermolecular forces [atm L^2/mol^2], and the constant "b" accounts for molecular volume [L/mol]. Each of these factors must be determined by experiment.

	A	B	C
1			
2			
3			
4			
5			
6			
7	Type of Gas	Argon	
8	Quantity [g]	4	
9	Temperature (T) [°C]	15	
10			
11			
12	Molecular Weight (MW) [g/mol]	40	
13	vdW Constant "a" [atm L²/mol²]	1.345	
14	vdW Constant "b" [L/mol]	0.0322	
15			
16	Ideal Gas Constant (R) [(atm l)/mol K)]	0.08206	
17			
18			
19		Ideal Gas	van der Waals
20	Volume (V) [L]	Pressure (P) [atm]	
21	0.5	4.73	4.70
22	0.6	3.94	3.92
23	0.7	3.38	3.36
24	0.8	2.95	2.95
25	0.9	2.63	2.62
26	1.0	2.36	2.36

Create a worksheet using the provided template. The molecular weight, "a," and "b" should automatically fill in after the user selects the type of gas in cell B7. (*Hint:* Use data validation and LOOKUP expressions.) The user will also set the quantity of gas and the temperature of the system. The data in the table below has been provided online.

Next, create a column of volume beginning in A21 at 0.5 liters and increasing in increments of 0.1 liters to a volume of 5 liters.

In column B, calculate the pressure (P, in atmospheres [atm]) using the ideal gas law.

In column C, calculate the pressure (P, in atmospheres [atm]) using the van der Waals equation.

Compound	*a* [atm L^2/mol^2]	*b* [L/mol]	MW [g/mol]
Acetic acid	17.587	0.1068	60
Acetone	13.906	0.0994	58
Ammonia	4.170	0.0371	17
Argon	1.345	0.0322	40
Benzene	18.001	0.1154	78
Chlorobenzene	25.433	0.1453	113
Diethyl ether	17.380	0.1344	74
Ethane	5.489	0.0638	30
Ethanol	12.021	0.0841	46
Hexane	24.387	0.1735	86
Methanol	9.523	0.0670	32
Neon	0.211	0.0171	20
Oxygen	1.360	0.0318	32
Pentane	19.008	0.1460	72
Propane	8.664	0.0845	44
Toluene	24.061	0.1463	92
Water	5.464	0.0305	18
Xenon	4.194	0.0511	131

12. One of the NAE Grand Challenges for **Engineering is Engineering the Tools of Scientific Discovery**. According to the NAE website: "Grand experiments and missions of exploration always need engineering expertise to design the tools, instruments, and systems that make it possible to acquire new knowledge about the physical and biological worlds."

Solar sails are a means of interplanetary propulsion using the radiation pressure of the sun to accelerate a spacecraft. The table below shows the radiation pressure at the orbits of the eight planets.

NOTE

The astronomical unit (AU) is he average distance from the Earth to the Sun.

Planet	Distance from Sun (*d*) [AU]	Radiation Pressure (*P*) [mPa]
Mercury	0.46	43.3
Venus	0.72	17.7
Earth	1	9.15
Mars	1.5	3.96
Jupiter	5.2	0.34
Saturn	9.6	0.099
Uranus	19.2	0.025
Neptune	30.1	0.01

Create a table showing the area in units of square meters of a solar sail needed to achieve various accelerations for various spacecraft masses at the distances from the sun of the various planets. Your solution should use data validation and vlookup to select a planet and the corresponding radiation pressure. The columns of your table should list masses of the spacecraft (including the mass of the sail) ranging from 100 to 1,000 kilograms in increments of 100 kilograms. The rows should list accelerations from 0.0001 to 0.001 g in increments of 0.001 g, where "g" is the acceleration of Earth's gravity, 9.81 meters per second squared. All constants and conversion factors should be placed in individual cells using appropriate labels, and all formulae should reference these cells and NOT be directly coded into the formulae. You should use absolute, relative, and mixed addressing as appropriate.

13. A hands-on technology museum has hired you to do background research on the feasibility of a new activity to allow visitors to assemble their own ferrite core memory device—a technology in common use until the 1970s, and in specialized applications after that. The computers onboard the early space shuttle flights used core memory due to their durability, non-volatility, and resistance to radiation—core memory recovered from the wreck of the Challenger still functioned.

Ferrite core memory comprises numerous tiny ferrite rings ("cores") in a grid, each of which has either two or three wires threaded through it in a repeating pattern and can store a single bit, or binary digit—a 0 or a 1. Since the cores were typically on the order of one millimeter in diameter, workers had to assemble these under microscopes.

After investigating ferrite materials, you find several that would be suitable for fabrication of the cores. The museum staff has decided to have the visitors assemble a 4 * 4 array (16 cores—actual devices were MUCH larger) and anticipate that 2,500 people will assemble one of these over the course of the project. Assuming that the cores are each cylindrical rings with a hole diameter half that of the outside diameter of the ring and a thickness one-fourth the outside diameter, you need to know how many grams of ferrite beads you need to purchase with 10% extra beyond the specified amount for various core diameters and ferrite materials. You also wish to know the total cost for the beads.

Using the provided online worksheet that includes a table of different ferrite material densities and costs, use data validation to select one of the materials from the list, then create a table showing the number of pounds of cores for core diameters of 1.2 to 0.7 millimeter in 0.1 millimeter increments as well as the total cost. For cores with a diameter less than 1 millimeter, there is a 50% manufacturing surcharge, thus the smallest cores cost more per gram. Include table entries for individual core volume and total volume of all cores. Your worksheet should resemble the example below.

Cost of Ferrite Cores for Hands-on Museum

Ferrite Compound	Specific Gravity	Cost per Gram [$/g]
CMP C	3.73	$ 32.50

Sets needed	2500
Cores per set	16
Total Cores	40000
Total + 10%	44000

Ferrite Compound	Specific Gravity	Cost per gram [$/g]
CMP A	8.39	$ 39.41
CMP B	7.47	$ 27.32
CMP C	3.73	$ 32.50
CMP D	4.01	$ 27.80
CMP E	7.27	$ 35.56
CMP F	3.92	$ 22.51

	Core Outside Diameter (D) [mm]					
	0.7	0.8	0.9	1	1.1	1.2
Volume of one core [mm^3]	0.0505	0.0754	0.1074	0.1473	0.1960	0.2545
Volume of all Cores [mm^3]	2222	3318	4724	6480	8624	11197
Mass of Cores [g]	8.29	12.37	17.62	24.17	32.17	41.76
Cost of Cores [$]	$ 404.11	$ 603.21	$ 858.87	$ 785.43	$ 1,045.41	$ 1,357.23

Note: Volume of ring: $V = \pi (D/2)^2 H - \pi (0.5 (D/2))^2 H = \pi (3/64) D^3$ assuming that the center hole is half the outside diameter (D) and the thickness (H) is one fourth the outside diameter.

14. A substance used to remove the few remaining molecules from a near vacuum by reacting with them or adsorbing them is called a getter. There are numerous materials used and several ways of deploying them within a system enclosing a vacuum, but here we will look at a common method used in vacuum tubes, once the workhorse of electronics but now relegated to high-end audio systems and other niche markets. In vacuum tubes, after the air is evacuated with a vacuum pump, getters are usually deposited on the inside of the tube, often at the top, by flash deposition.

Assume we are investigating getter materials for use in vacuum tubes with various inside diameters and hemispherical tops. The getter will be flash deposited on this hemispherical area.

We wish to set up a worksheet that will allow the user to select a getter material from a menu using data validation, and produce a table showing the number of moles of that material and the thickness of the deposited film for various masses of material from 20 to 300 milligram with 20 milligram increments and various tube inside diameters from 0.6 to 1.2 inches by 0.1 inch. Your final worksheet should appear similar to the example shown below. A starting worksheet including the table of possible materials and their specific gravities and atomic weights is available online.

Photo courtesy of W. Park

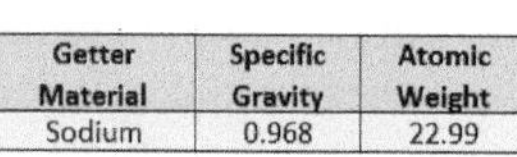

Getter Material	Specific Gravity	Atomic Weight
Sodium	0.968	22.99

Getter Material	Specific Gravity	Atomic Weight
Barium	3.51	137.33
Aluminum	2.7	26.981
Sodium	0.968	22.99
Strontium	2.64	87.62
Calcium	1.55	40.078
Magnesium	1.738	24.305

Getter Thickness [μm]		Vacuum Tube Inside Diameter (D) [in]						
Mass [mg]	Moles	0.6	0.7	0.8	0.9	1	1.1	1.2
20	8.7E-04	56.6	41.6	31.9	25.2	20.4	16.8	14.2
40	1.7E-03	113.3	83.2	63.7	50.3	40.8	33.7	28.3
60	2.6E-03	169.9	124.8	95.6	75.5	61.2	50.5	42.5
80	3.5E-03	226.5	166.4	127.4	100.7	81.6	67.4	56.6
100	4.3E-03	283.2	208.0	159.3	125.8	101.9	84.2	70.8
120	5.2E-03	339.8	249.6	191.1	151.0	122.3	101.1	84.9
140	6.1E-03	396.4	291.3	223.0	176.2	142.7	117.9	99.1
160	7.0E-03	453.1	332.9	254.8	201.4	163.1	134.8	113.3
180	7.8E-03	509.7	374.5	286.7	226.5	183.5	151.6	127.4
200	8.7E-03	566.3	416.1	318.6	251.7	203.9	168.5	141.6
220	9.6E-03	623.0	457.7	350.4	276.9	224.3	185.3	155.7
240	1.0E-02	679.6	499.3	382.3	302.0	244.7	202.2	169.9
260	1.1E-02	736.2	540.9	414.1	327.2	265.0	219.0	184.1
280	1.2E-02	792.9	582.5	446.0	352.4	285.4	235.9	198.2
300	1.3E-02	849.5	624.1	477.8	377.5	305.8	252.7	212.4

15. Create an Excel worksheet that will allow the user to type in the radius of a sphere and the standard abbreviation for the units used.

Standard Unit Abbreviations						
Unit	meter	centimeter	millimeter	yard	foot	inch
Abbreviation	m	cm	mm	yd	ft	in

The volume of the sphere should then be calculated and expressed by the following units: cubic meters, cubic centimeters, cubic millimeters, liters, gallons, cubic yards, cubic feet, and cubic inches. Your worksheet should appear similar to the sample shown below, although you will probably need additional information in the worksheet not shown here.

		Volume							
Enter Radius Value Here	Enter Radius Units Here	m^3	cm^3	mm^3	liters	gallons	yd^3	ft^3	in^3
1.7	in	3.372E-04	3.372E+02	3.372E+05	3.372E-01	8.910E-02	4.416E-04	1.191E-02	2.058E+01

NOTE

Without giving too much awy, try typing **"Round"** into Excel help, click on the link to the ROUND function, then scroll down to the list of related functions. One or more of those might be useful.

16. Most resistors are so small that the actual value would be difficult to read if printed on the resistor. Instead, colored bands denote the value of resistance in ohms. Anyone involved in constructing electronic circuits must become familiar with the color code, and with practice, one can tell at a glance what value a specific set of colors means. For the novice, however, trying to read color codes can be a bit challenging.

You are to design a worksheet similar to the one shown, allowing the user to enter a resistance value and automatically show the color code for that resistance. Note the cells below "First Digit," "Second Digit," and "Number of Zeros" should actually take on the appropriate colors in addition to showing the numerical value. The cells below should use the LOOKUP function to show the color names. The colors assigned to each digit are on the right of the worksheet for convenience.

To enter the resistance, use data validation along with the table on the left. The resistance will be entered in two parts, the first two digits, and a power of 10 by which those digits will be multiplied. Include an appropriate input message when the cell is selected and an appropriate warning if the user enters an invalid number. The user should be able select from a drop-down menu. Note that you must use the two input values to calculate the total resistance, the first digit, the second digit, and the number of zeros.

For example, a resistance of 4,700 ohms [[&|Ome|&]] has first digit 4 (yellow), second digit 7 (violet), and 2 zeros following (red). A resistance of 56 [&|Ome|&] would be 5 (green), 6 (blue), and 0 zeros (black); 1,000,000 [&|Ome|&] is 1 (brown), 0 (black), and 5 zeros (green). Particularly note that if the second digit is zero, it does not count in the multiplier value. There are numerous explanations of the color code on the web if you need further information or examples.

The worksheet shown is available online except for the nine cells in the center containing the desired resistance values and the color code for that resistance.

Resistor Values

	Standard Values	Multipliers
7	10	1
8	12	10
9	15	100
10	18	1,000
11	22	10,000
12	27	100,000
13	33	1,000,000
14	39	
15	47	
16	56	
17	68	
18	82	

Resistor Color Code Calculator

Enter Values Below

First Two Digits	Multiplier	Resistance	First Digit	Second Digit	Number of zeros
68	1,000	68000	6	8	3
			Blue	Grey	Orange

Please enter first two digits of resistance value or

Color Code

Value	Color
0	Black
1	Brown
2	Red
3	Orange
4	Yellow
5	Green
6	Blue
7	Violet
8	Grey
9	White

17. Download the starting file, and complete the following commands using the data provided.

(a) Indicate the following using conditional formatting commands of your choice. Each condition below should appear in a unique format.
- Length shown in Column B is greater than 6 inches or less than 4 inches.
- Width shown in Column C is less than 2.5 inches.
- Inner radius shown in Column D is above average for the inner radius values.
- Outer radius shown in Column E is below average for the outer radius values.
- Volume shown in Column F is less than 10 cubic inches or greater than 20 cubic inches.

(b) For the following conditions, in Column H use an IF statement to indicate the Status:
- If length is less than 4 inches or width is less than 2.5 inches, list the status as "Too Small."
- Otherwise, if twice the inner radius is greater than the outer radius, list the status as "Off Center."
- Otherwise, if the volume is greater than 20 cubic inches or the mass is greater than 3,000 grams, list the status as "Too Large."
- Otherwise, if none of these conditions are true, leave the cell blank.

(c) For the following conditions, in Column J use an IF statement to indicate the Action Code:
- If the status is "Too Small" or "Too Large," list as action code as a numerical value of one.
- If the status is "Off Center," list as action code as a numerical value of two.
- If none of these conditions are met, list as action code as a numerical value of three.

(d) Use a conditional formatting icon set in Column J to indicate the following:
- Status as green for action code 3.
- Status as yellow for action code 2.
- Status as red for action code 1.

(e) Count the following items, showing the results somewhere above the data table. Be sure to indicate each counted item with an appropriate label.
- Indicate the number of items classified as each action code, such as how many items are listed as 1.
- Indicate number of parts that meet the following conditions:
  - Length is greater than 6 inches.
  - Volume is less than 10 cubic inches or greater than 20 cubic inches. As a hint, use two "COUNT" functions and add them together.

(f) Sort the worksheet in the following order: Length, increasing and simultaneously then Outer Radius, decreasing. Be careful to select only the data and not the entire worksheet.

(g) Set the worksheet controls to be filtered in the header row. Filter the worksheet so only parts of length 2.80, 5.20, and 7.15 inches are shown.

CHAPTER 7
BASIC EXCEL GRAPHS FOR WINDOWS

Objectives

By learning the material in this chapter, you should be able to

- describe why and how to create a "Scatter" graph in Excel
- describe why and how to create a "Line" graph in Excel
- describe why and how to create a "Column" graph in Excel
- describe how to plot an equation in Excel

It is strongly recommended that you have Excel running on your computer as you go through this tutorial so you can actually see how things function. Do not be afraid to try things out. The worst thing you can do is to make Excel wander off into LahLahLand (crash), and that is unlikely. You will learn this far more quickly if you treat this tutorial as an interactive exercise.

* In this text, the data needed to create a chart will be shown in rows to efficiently use space. In the worksheets containing the starting data that may be provided for you by your instructor, the data will be shown in columns. When data may be available electronically to begin a question, the problem will be marked with the symbol for Excel Workbook. Please see your instructor for more details.

7.1 AVAILABLE GRAPH TYPES

You can create many types of charts in Excel. Usually you will be concerned with a few main types, shown in Table 7.1.

Taken from *Thinking Like an Engineer: An Active Learning Approach,* by Elizabeth A. Stephan, David R. Bowman, William J. Park, Benjamin L. Sill, and Matthew W. Ohland.

Table 7.1 Common chart types available in Excel

A **scatter plot** is a graph that numerically represents two-dimensional theoretical or experimental data along the abscissa and ordinate of the graph. It is most commonly used with scientific data. To create a scatter plot, you specify each pair in the graph by selecting two identically sized columns or rows of data that represent the (x, y) values of each experimental symbol or point on a theoretical expression.

A scatter plot can be shown as discrete data point (used to show experimental data) or lines only (used to show theoretical expressions). Excel will also show discrete data points connected by lines; the authors of this text do not find this type of chart useful.

The step size of both axes is evenly spaced as determined by the user and can be customized to show all or part of a data set plotted on a graph.

Use a scatter plot to visualize your data when you want to:

- Observe mathematical phenomena and relationships among different data sets
- Interpolate or extrapolate information from data sets
- Determine a mathematical model for a data set, using trendlines.

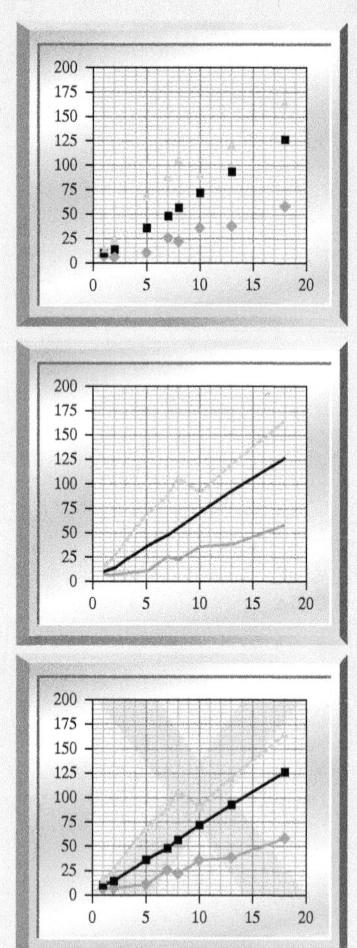

Table 7.1 Common chart types available in Excel (*continued*)

A **line plot** is a graph that visualizes a one-dimensional set of theoretical or experimental data along the abscissa and ordinate of a graph.

A line plot can be shown as points connected by lines, lines only, or in 3-D.

The y-axis values of a line plot are evenly spaced as determined by the user; however, the x-axis of a line plot is not. As shown in the graph to the right, a line plot places each discrete element evenly along the x-axis regardless of the actual step-spacing of the data.

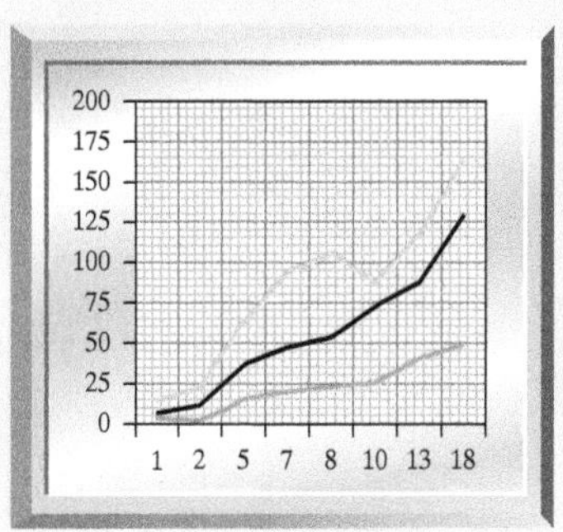

Use a line plot to visualize your data when you want to:

- Display any evenly spaced or sampled data
- Visualize time-series data taken at even intervals
- Display categorical data (e.g., years, profession, colors).

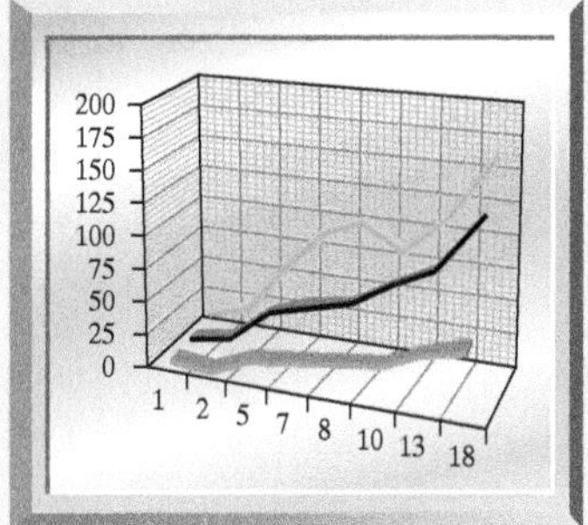

A **column graph** is used for displaying various types of categorical data.

The y-axis increments are spaced evenly, but the x-axis spacing has no meaning since the items are discrete categories. As a rule of thumb, a column graph can be used to represent the same information shown on a line plot.

A column plot can be shown as bars, cylinders, or cones; as a clustered group or stacked; in 1-D or 3-D.

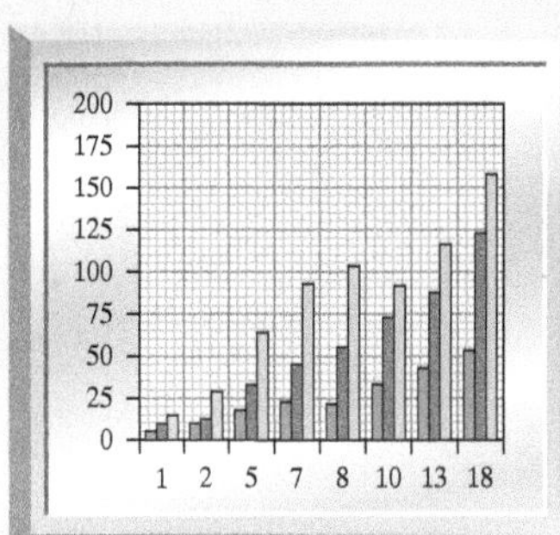

Use a column graph to visualize your data when you want to:

- Display any categorical data
- Observe differences between categories.

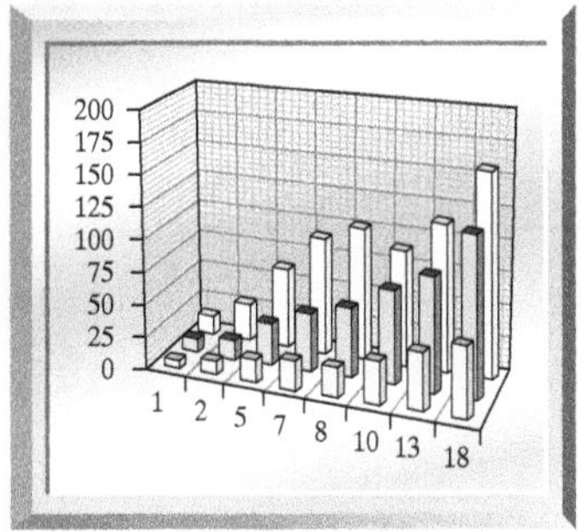

Table 7.1 Common chart types available in Excel (*continued*)

A **bar graph** is identical to a column graph, with the x- and y-categories reversed; the x-category appears on the ordinate and the y-category appears on the abscissa. Because of the similarity, only column graphs are covered in this text.	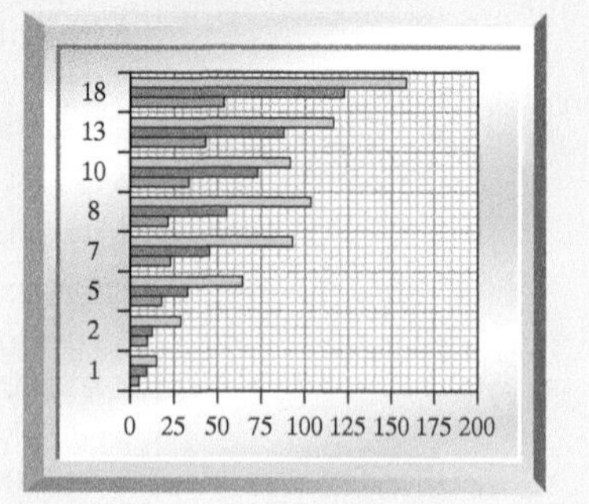
A **pie graph** is used on a single column or row of non-negative numbers, graphed as a percentage of the whole. It is typically used for categorical data, with a maximum of seven categories possible. A pie graph can be shown in 1-D or 3-D, with either the percentages or the raw data displayed with the category names. Use a pie graph to visualize your data when you want to: ■ Display categorical data as part of a whole ■ Observe differences between categories Because pie charts are so simple, they are not covered in this text.	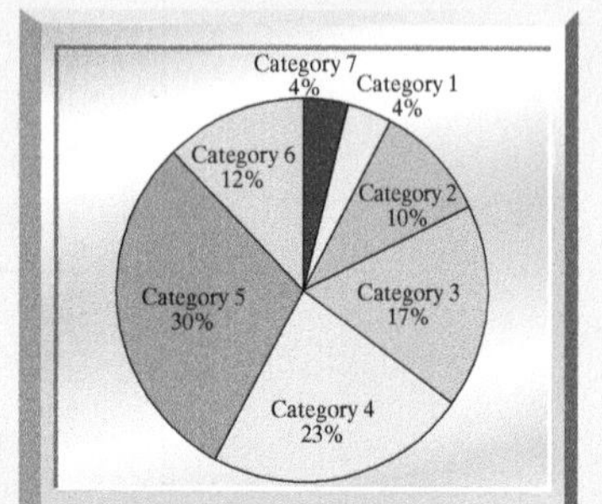

7.2 CREATING A SCATTER GRAPH

EXERCISE 7.1

Use the data below to create a Scatter chart.

Time (t) [h]	0	1	2	3	4	5	6
Distance (d) [mi]	0	60	90	125	200	220	290

Create a Scatter Chart

- Select the data points only for both series. Do not include the column headings.
- **Insert > Charts > Scatter**
- From the pulldown menu, choose the graph illustrating **Scatter with only Markers**

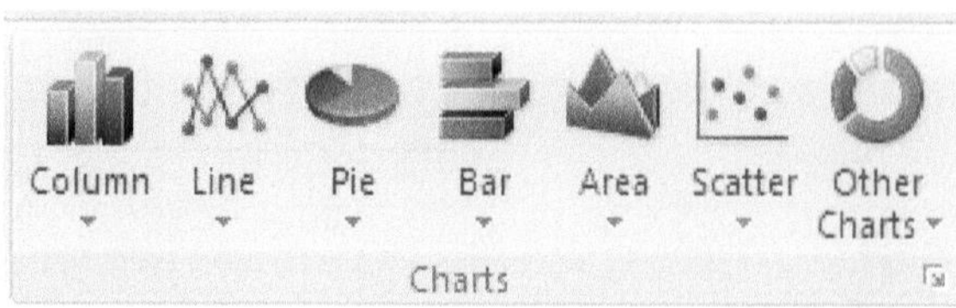

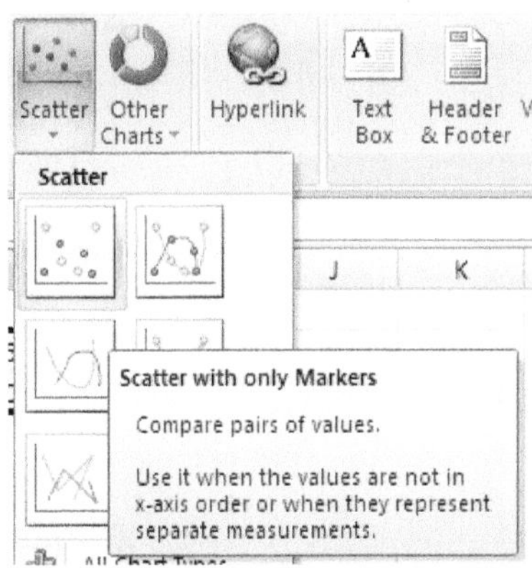

Move the Chart

- Select the chart
- **Design > Location > Move Chart**
- In the Move Chart window, select the **New Sheet** option and type in the title for the new sheet ("7.1 Chart")
- Click **OK.**

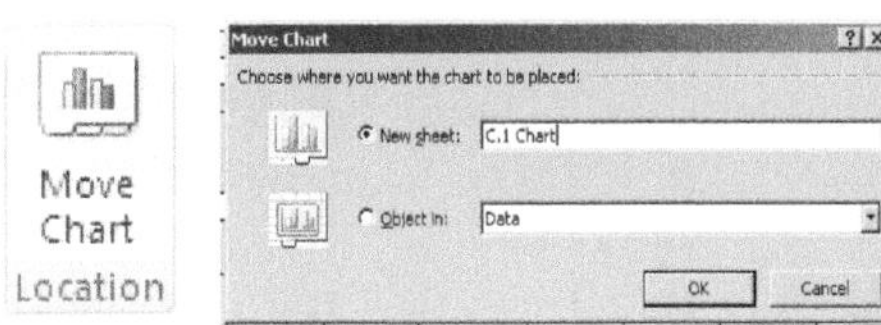

At this point, you should be on a new sheet titled "7.1 Chart", looking at the graph you just created.

With the chart selected, click on the **Layout** ribbon to add or remove different visual attributes to the chart.

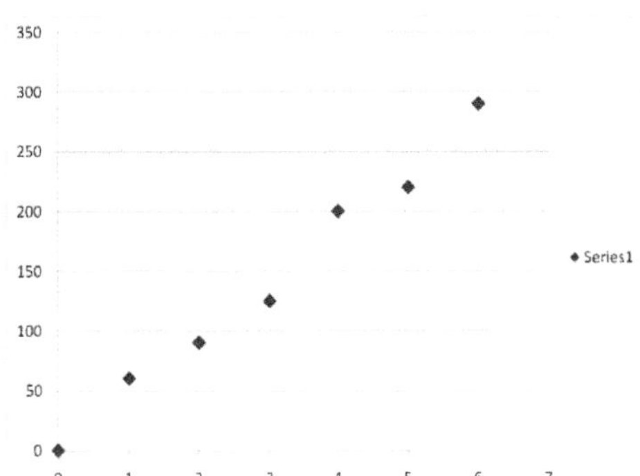

Add a Chart Title

- **Layout > Labels > Chart Title > Above Chart** to place a title above the chart.
- * Do not use the Centered Overlay Title as it may interfere with the data you're displaying on the chart.
- By default, Excel labels the chart as "Chart Title". Highlight the words in the title, press **Delete**, and type in a new title. For example, the chart title may read "Tracking my trip to Tennessee".

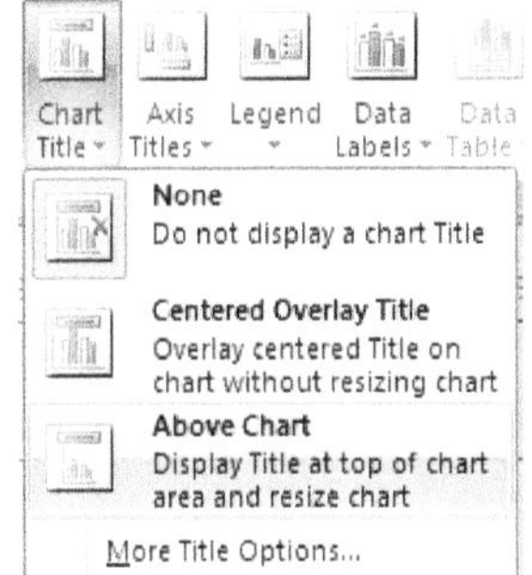

Add X-Axis Labels

- **Layout > Labels > Axis Titles > Primary Horizontal Axis Title > Title Below Axis.**
- By default, Excel labels the x-axis as "Axis Label". Highlight the words in the x-axis label, press **Delete,** and type in a new title. For example, the x-axis label may read "Time (t) [h]".

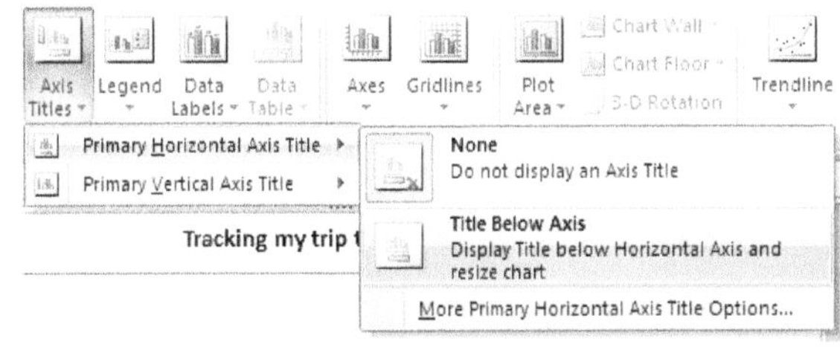

Add Y-Axis Labels

- **Layout > Labels > Axis Titles > Primary Vertical Axis Title > Rotated Title**
- By default, Excel labels the y-axis as "Axis Label". Highlight the words in the y-axis label, press **Delete,** and type in a new title. For example, the y-axis label may read "Distance (d) [mi]".

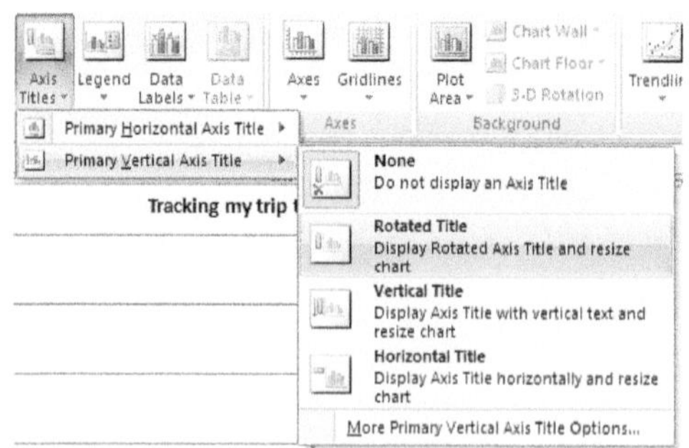

Remove a Legend

* Since we are plotting a single data series, we do not wish to display the legend.
- **Layout > Labels > Legend**
- Choose **None.**

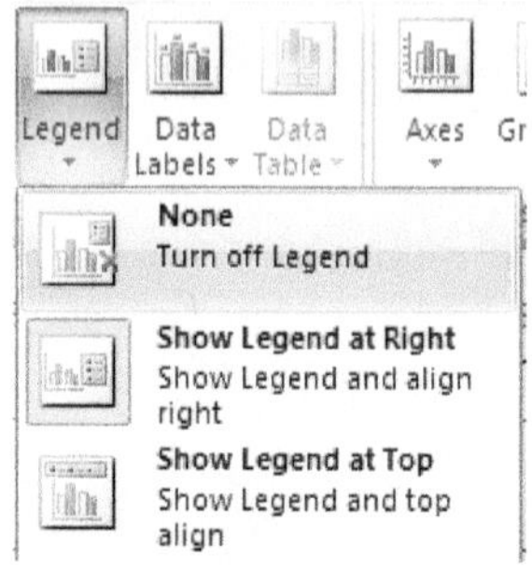

Modify Gridlines

- **Layout > Labels > Gridlines**
* By default, Excel includes the major horizontal gridlines, so we only need to enable the major vertical gridlines.
- Choose **Primary Vertical Gridlines**
- Choose **Major Gridlines.**

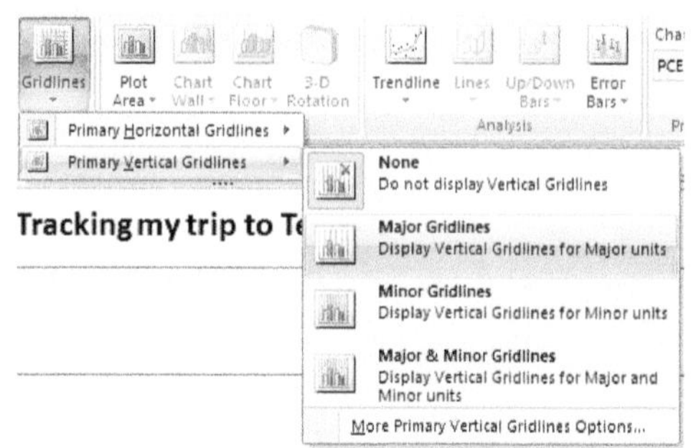

Sometimes Excel's automatic choice for location and range of gridlines is less than ideal, thus you may wish to manually specify the spacing of gridlines.

Change the Grid Spacing on the Axis of a Scatter Chart

- **Layout > Axis > Primary Vertical Axis > More Primary Vertical Axis Options . . .**
- Choose the **Axis Options** tab
- Select the **Fixed** option for **Major unit**
- Enter a value of 100 in the text box
- Click **Close.**

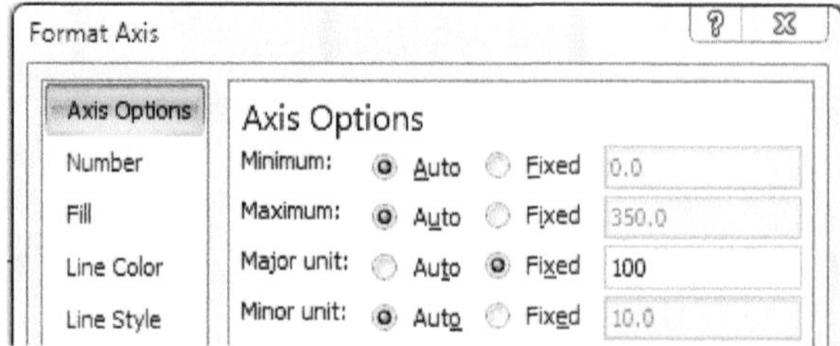

* Notice that Excel automatically changed the upper limit on the axis from 350 to 400

Use a similar procedure to change the horizontal axis to a maximum value of 10.

The completed chart will appear as follows.

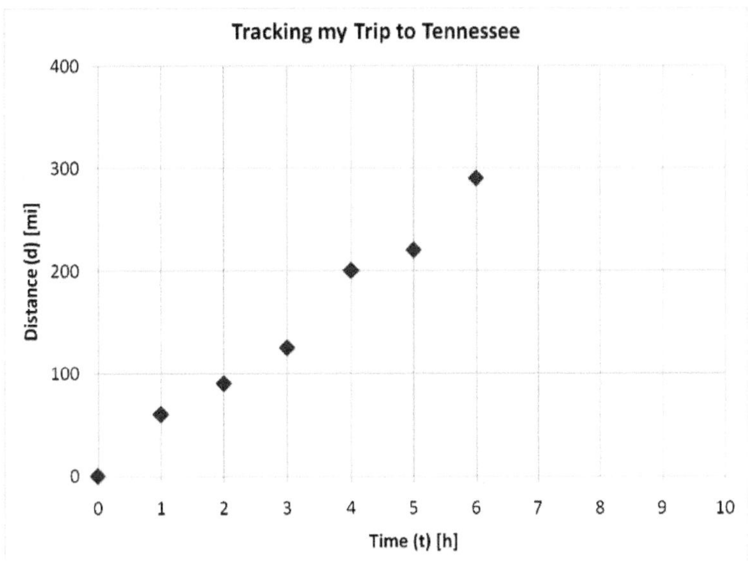

7.3 CREATING A LINE GRAPH

Sometimes it is desirable to plot a dependent variable with respect to discrete categories instead of a numeric independent variable. For example, a civil engineer specializing in transportation systems might want to analyze the average number of traffic fatalities in the United States during each day of the week. In this situation, we would want to include the days of the week on the abscissa, which is a non-numerical value. In such cases, a **Line Graph** is an appropriate choice. Line plots create a sequence of dependent variables with equal horizontal spacing between data points, whether or not the "values" of the "independent variable" have equal spacing or not, and even if "equal spacing" has no real meaning in the context of the categories represented on the horizontal axis. The values plotted on the horizontal axis might be numeric, but are most frequently text descriptors for non-numeric categories, such as color, religious affiliation, chemical composition, ethnic group, type of fastener (nail, screw, etc.), or a host of other possibilities.

EXERCISE 7.2

According to statistics published by the National Highway Traffic Safety Administration (www.nhtsa.dot.gov), the following data reflects the average number of vehicle fatalities from 1998–2002.

Day	Monday	Tuesday	Wednesday	Thursday	Friday	Saturday	Sunday
Average Fatalities	99	96	98	104	129	149	130

* To graph this data, we will use a LINE chart, since the abscissa values are text (days of the week).

Create a Line Chart

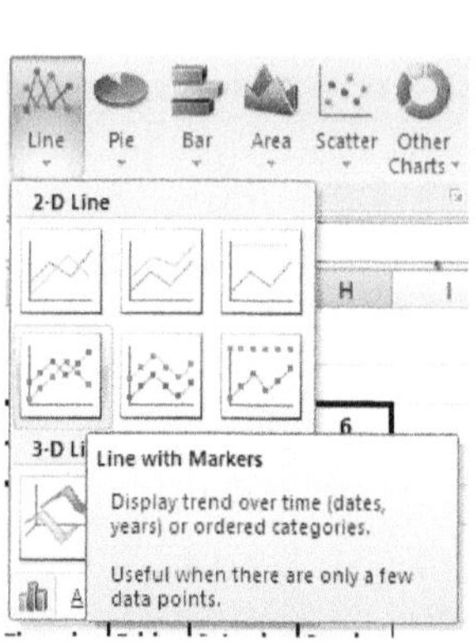

- Select the data for both series
- **Insert > Charts > Line**
- From the pulldown menu, choose the graph illustrating **Line with Markers**

Using the directions found in Exercise 7.1:

- Move the graph to a new sheet ("7.2 Chart")
- Add a chart title above the chart. For this example, the chart title may read "Average Fatalities in Automobile Crashes between 1998–2002"
- Add x-axis labels. For example, the x-axis label may read "Day of the Week". Add y-axis labels. For example, the y-axis label may read "Average Fatalities".
- Remove the legend
- Enable the major vertical gridlines.

When using a line chart, changing the grid spacing on the abscissa is different than when using a Scatter chart.

Change the Grid Spacing on a Line Chart

- **Layout > Axis > Primary Horizontal Axis > More Primary Horizontal Axis Options . . .**
- Choose the **Axis Options** tab
- Select **Interval between tick-marks**
- Enter a value of 2 in the text box
- Select **Specify interval unit**
- Enter a value of 2 in the text box
- Click **Close**

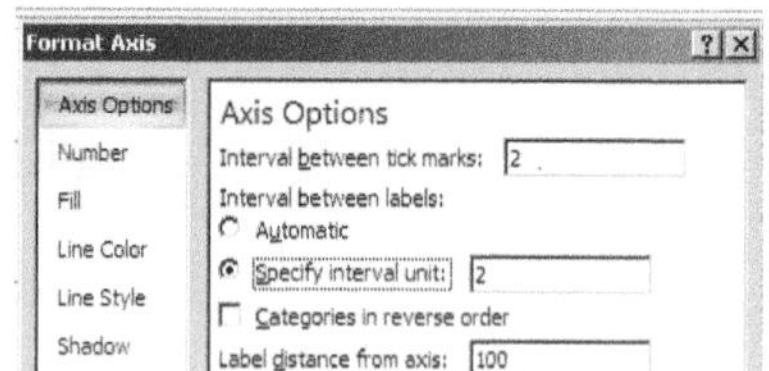

* Notice that Excel removes every other data label and gridline. Since this is NOT what we desire, change the values back to 1.
* Altering the vertical axis will be the same as in the Scatter plot discussed in Exercise 7.1.

The completed chart will appear as follows.

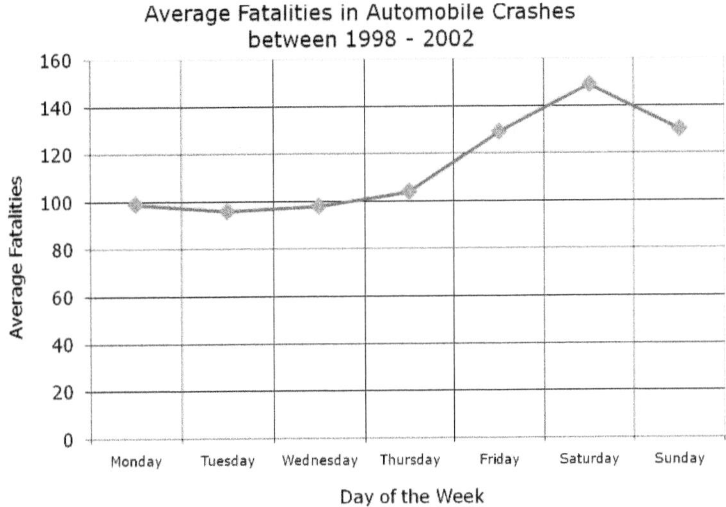

EXERCISE 7.3

A group of students have measured the quantity of water remaining in a tank as it drains as a function of time.

Time (t) [min]	5	9	12	24	47	55	95
Volume (V) [gal]	19.0	17.0	15.5	11.5	8.0	7.0	2.0

Using the directions found in Exercise 7.1:

- Create a Scatter chart, with only markers
- Move the chart to a new sheet
- Add a chart title above the chart
- Add x-axis labels
- Add y-axis labels
- Remove the legend
- Enable the major vertical gridlines.

Let's convert this chart to a Line chart.

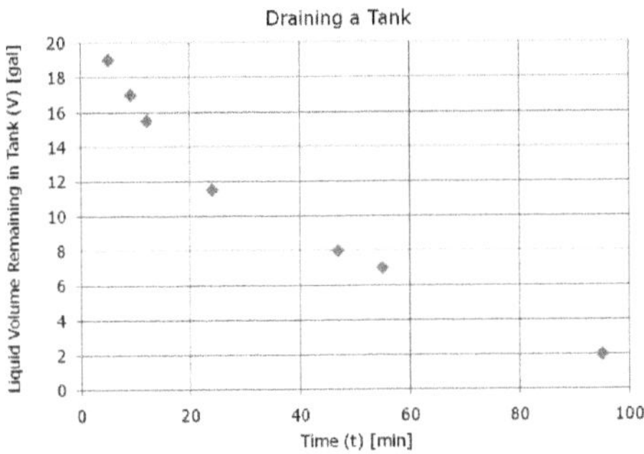

Change the Chart Type

Change Chart Type | Save As Template
Type

- Click somewhere in the chart near the edge to select the entire chart. If you have selected the entire chart, the **Chart Tools** ribbons will appear.
- **Design > Type > Change Chart Type**
- On the **Change Chart Type** window, click the **Line** tab and select the **Line** chart type
- Click **OK**

* Notice the changes in the graph. The Line chart forces the independent variable values to be spaced equally even though the numerical values are not. **The line chart is only occasionally appropriate for engineering applications.**

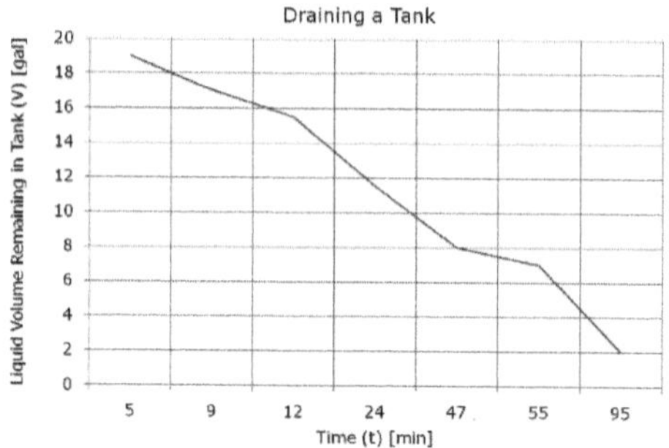

7.4 CREATING A COLUMN GRAPH

It is often useful to express the relationship among data graphically using a column graph. A column graph allows you to compare the values of discrete, unordered items on the ordinate with respect to some category on the abscissa.

EXERCISE 7.4

A company that uses spot-welding robots on its assembly line is planning to expand their operation with the purchase of several dozen more robots. Currently, the factory uses robots manufactured by four different companies. As part of a study to determine which type of robots to purchase, one of the company's industrial engineers compiles data on the number of defective welds produced by each type of robot over twelve months. The data for defective welds is shown in the table. As part of a presentation to the company executives, the engineer plots this data on a column chart.

Company	Defective Welds
Spee-D Weld	386
A-1 Robotics	369
Weld-o-matic	429
RoboWeld	317

Create a Column Chart

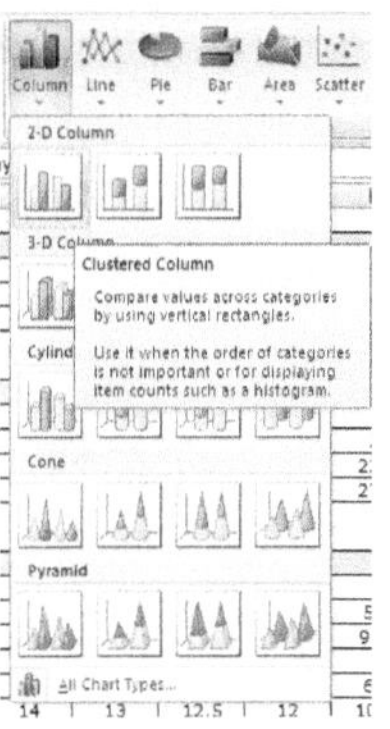

- Select the data, including the column headings
- **Insert > Charts > Column > 2-D Column > Clustered**
- Move the chart to a new sheet
- Add a chart title above the chart
- Add y-axis labels
- Remove the legend.

Modify the Abscissa Labels on a Column Chart

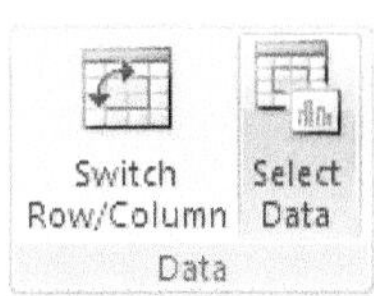

- **Chart Tools > Design > Data > Select Data**.
- By default, there will be a single data series listed (Defective Welds—the title of the dependent variable column).
- In the **Horizontal (Category) Axis Labels** box, the company names appear. If you wish to change the names, click **Edit.**
- When the Axis Labels window appears, select the cells that contain the desired information. Click **OK.**

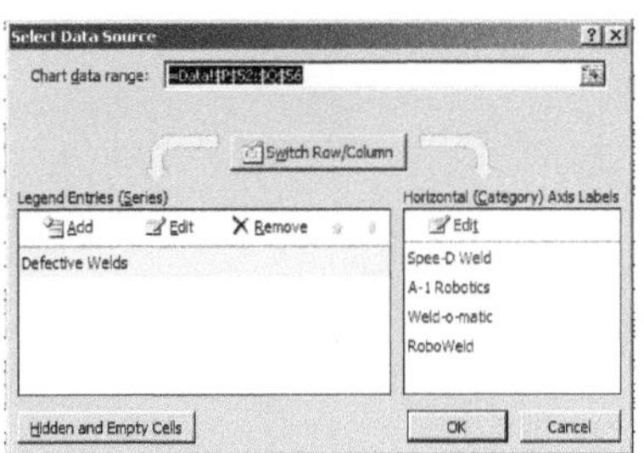

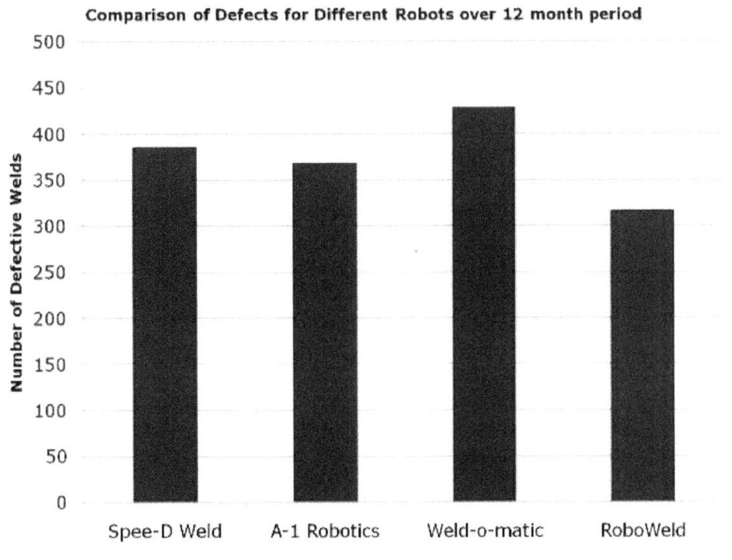

EXERCISE 7.5

In 2005, the average temperature in Clemson, SC was recorded each month (www.wunderground.com).

Month	Temperature (T) [°F]
Jan	50
Feb	55
Mar	61
Apr	65
May	76
Jun	85
Jul	90
Aug	90
Sep	82
Oct	73
Nov	65
Dec	52

Using the directions found in Exercise 7.1:

- Create a Scatter chart, with only markers
- Move the chart to a new sheet
- Add a chart title above the chart
- Add x-axis labels
- Add y-axis labels
- Remove the legend
- Enable the major vertical gridlines

Convert this chart to a Line chart, using the directions found in Exercise 7.2.

Convert this chart to a Column chart, using the directions found in Exercise 7.4.

Which graph do you visually prefer? There is no "right" or "wrong" answer, but often is a choice. When creating graphs of data that is not ordered pairs, experiment with different chart types and decide which one "best" tells the story you are trying to illustrate.

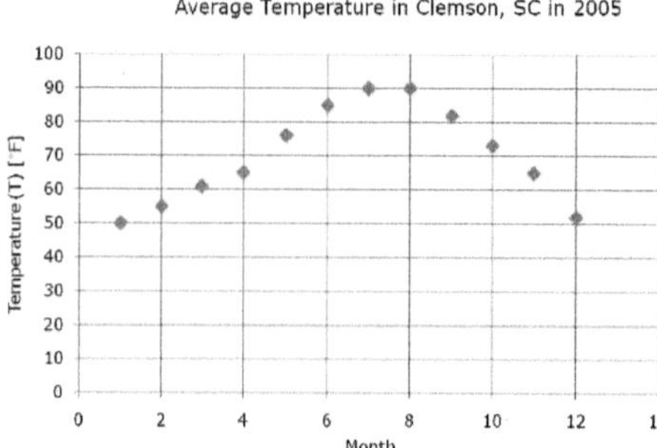

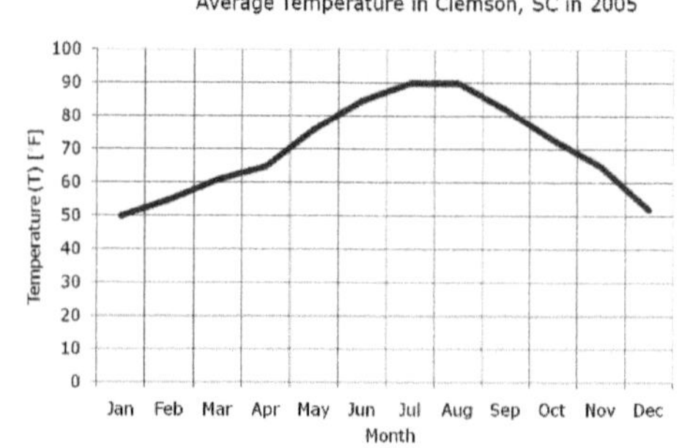

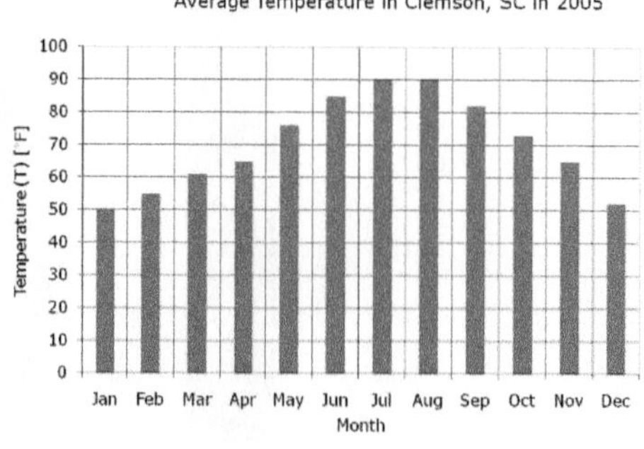

7.5 MULTIPLE DATA SERIES

Sometimes two or more related phenomena depend on the same independent variable. For example, we might wish to consider the distance traveled by two different cars over time. Often it is convenient to plot such information on the same graph with a common abscissa (independent variable values).

EXERCISE 7.6

Begin with the following set of data:

Time (t) [h]	1	2	3	4	5	6
Distance Car #1 (d1) [mi]	60	90	125	200	220	290
Distance Car #2 (d2) [mi]	70	120	170	250	270	325

Using the directions found in Exercise 7.1:

- Select all data, no column headings
- Create a Scatter chart, with only markers
- Move the chart to a new sheet
- Add a chart title above the chart
- Add x-axis labels
- Add y-axis labels
- Enable the major vertical gridlines

* Since there is more than one data set shown, do not remove the legend.

Change the Legend Captions

Many text items on a graph (e.g. titles and axis labels) can be edited directly, just like you can edit the contents of a cell. However, the text of the legend CANNOT be edited in this manner.

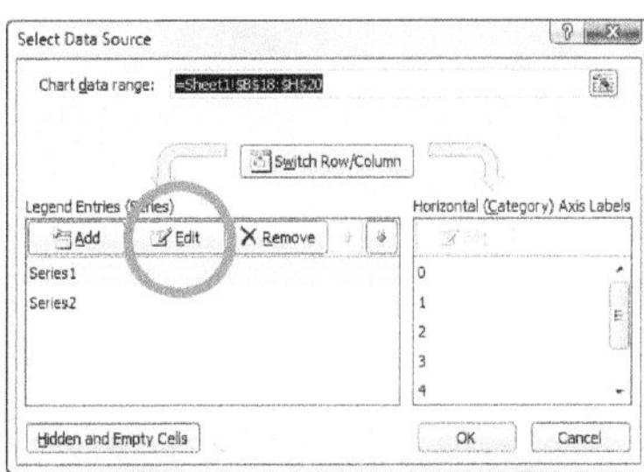

- **Chart Tools > Design > Data > Select Data**
- In the **Select Data Source** window, select **Series1** from the **Legend Entries (Series)** box on the left side and click **Edit.**
- In the **Edit Series** window, type in a caption in the **Series Name** box and click **OK.** For example, "Car #1".
- Repeat for Series 2.
- After naming both data sets, on the **Select Data Source** window, click **OK.**

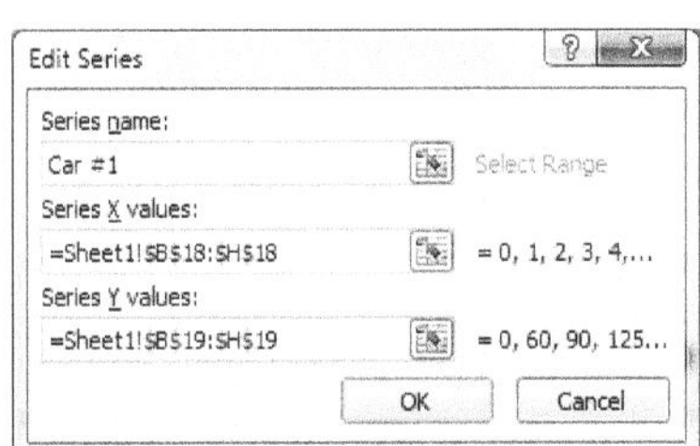

The legend was created by default on the right side, causing the chart to be shrunk to fit.

Move the Legend

- Click once on the legend to select the entire legend box.
- Drag the box to a location on the graph where it is not interfering with the data sets, but is on top of the gridlines.

Format the Legend

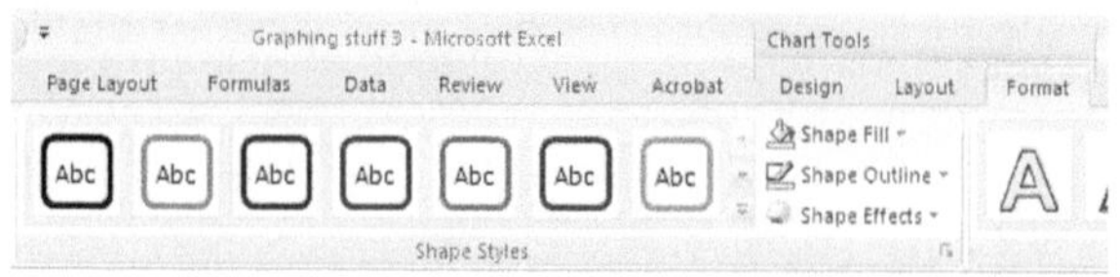

- Click once on the legend to select the entire legend box.
- Select **Chart Tools > Format > Shape Styles** and select a white background with a solid frame.
- To change the color of each text entry, click on the text entry and in the **Home > Font > Text Color** drop-down menu, use the color palette to select a color to match the data series. The legend text font type, size, and formatting (bold, italics) can all be changed from the **Home > Font** ribbon.

This will place a frame around the legend, and make the background opaque so the text can be easily read.

Resize the Grid Area

- Click inside the grid area, but not on a gridline or data series. The outside gridlines will be surrounded by six boxes, called **sizing handles**, one at each corner and one in the center of each side. The corner handles allow you to resize both dimensions simultaneously; the handles at the center of the edges let you resize perpendicular to that edge.
- Select the sizing handle in the center of the far right gridline. When the cursor changes to a double-headed arrow, drag the sizing handle to the right to increase the size of the grid.

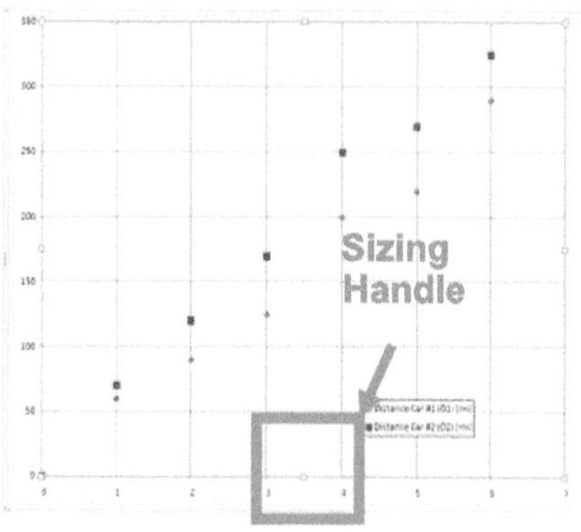

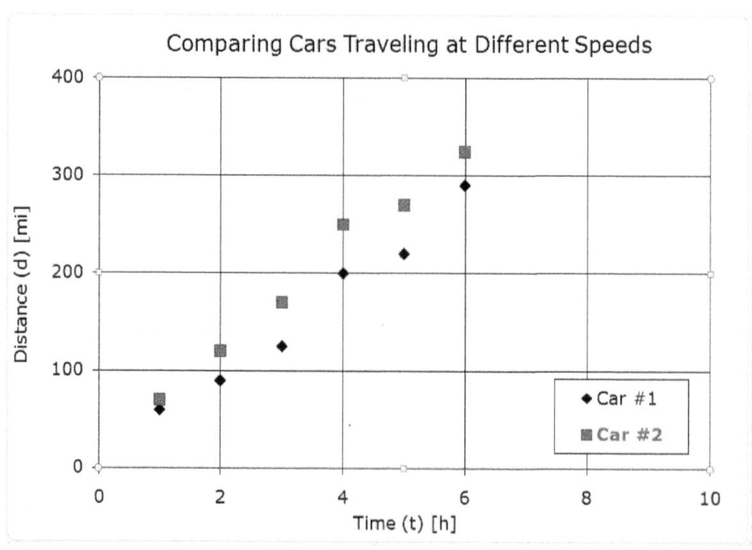

Sometimes we have data that are related and we wish to display these on a single graph, but the data points for the different situations correspond to different values of the independent variable. An example follows:

EXERCISE 7.7

A group of students have measured the quantity of water remaining in two draining tanks. Although each set records the water discharged, the collection time differs from one tank to another.

Time (t) [min]	5	10	15	20	40	55	90
Volume Tank #1 (V1) [gal]	19.0	17.0	15.5	11.5	10.5	9.5	8.0

Time (t) [min]	10	15	20	30	35	40	90
Volume Tank #2 (V2) [gal]	25	21	20	19	17	16	14

- Create a Scatter chart, with only markers, selecting only the data for Tank #1
- Move the chart to a new sheet
- Add a chart title above the chart
- Add x-axis labels
- Add y-axis labels
- Enable the major vertical gridlines
- * Since there will be more than one data set shown, do not remove the legend.
- Move the legend inside the grid and resize the graph
- Format the legend so it is inside a box with a white background
- Change the legend caption to "Tank #1" for Series 1.

Add a Data Series to a Chart

- **Design > Data > Select Data**
- In the **Select Data Source** window, click **Add**
- In the **Series Name** box, type in a series name. For example, "Tank #2".
- In the **Series X values** box:
    - Click on the worksheet icon just to the right of the **Series X values** text box. This will create a new window: **Edit Series.**
    - Change the sheet tabs along the bottom from the 7.7 Chart tab to the Data tab.
    - Select the cells containing the time data for Tank #2. This should change the information in the **Edit Series** window to read something like "=Data! $C$33:$I$33".
    - Click on the worksheet icon at the right side of the **Series X values** window. This should return you to the original **Edit Series** window.

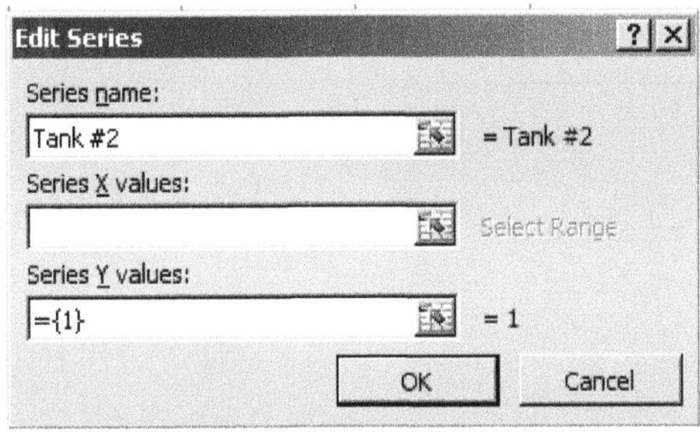

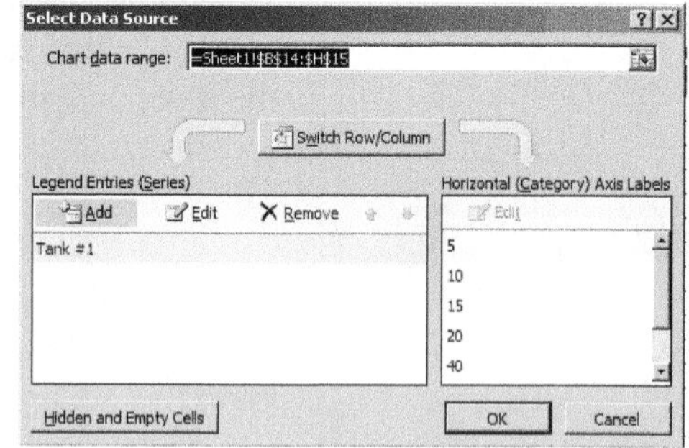

- In the **Series Y Values** box:
  - Click on the worksheet icon just to the right of the **Series Y values** text box. This will create a new window: **Edit Series.**
  - Change the sheet tabs along the bottom from the 7.7 Chart tab to the Data tab.
  - Select the cells containing the volume data for Tank #2. This should change the information in the Source Data window to read something like "=Data! $C$34:$I$34".
  - Click on the worksheet icon at the right side of the **Series Y values** window. This should return you to the original **Edit Series** window.
- Click **OK** to return to the chart.

Your graph should now have two data series: Tank #1 and Tank #2.

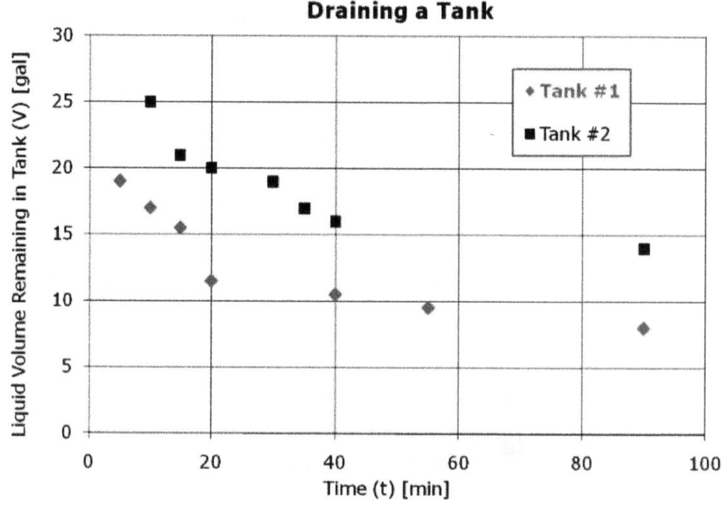

7.6 PLOTTING EQUATIONS

Worksheets have many uses. One of the most useful is plotting equations. For example, we might like to construct plots of:

$$y = 3x^2 + x - 4 \qquad \text{or} \qquad y = 2\sin(6\,\theta) \qquad \text{or} \qquad y = \frac{2 + 4x}{6x^3} \text{ and so on....}$$

At this point, we assume that you have mastered the basics for creating a graph using Excel. We can use this, along with the steps below to create plots of equations.

Create a Table of Function Values

- First, values for the independent variable on the abscissa ("x") will be created in a column. These values are usually equally spaced, and are close enough in value so the resulting plotted line appears smooth. We will discuss "smooth" increments in more detail shortly.
- Next, the values for the dependent variable on the ordinate ("y") will be created in a column adjacent to the abscissa values by typing in the equation and copying it using the fill handle.
- Now that you have two columns of values, you can generate the graph as before.

* Remember when creating a plot of an equation, do not show data points, only a line. This means that you will select **Scatter** plot and the icon for which **lines only and no data points** are shown. You have two choices: the diagram that shows smoothed lines with no data points and the diagram that shows straight lines with no data points. **When initially determining the variable spacing, you should choose straight lines**. Once you have the increment correct, you might be tempted to change this to smooth lines. In general, smooth lines are not recommended for this type of graph. Even with close spacing, sometimes using smooth lines creates artificial end effects.

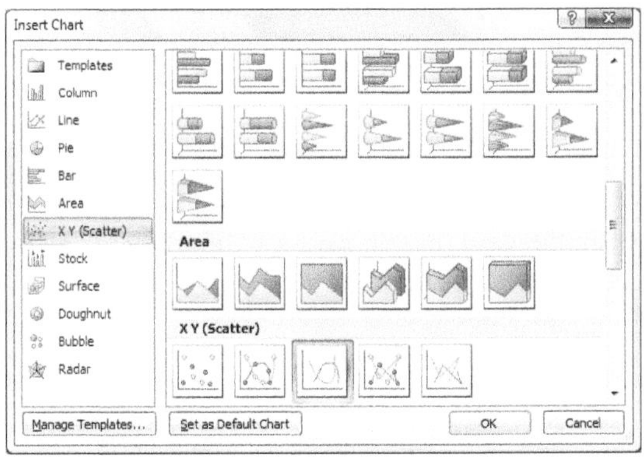

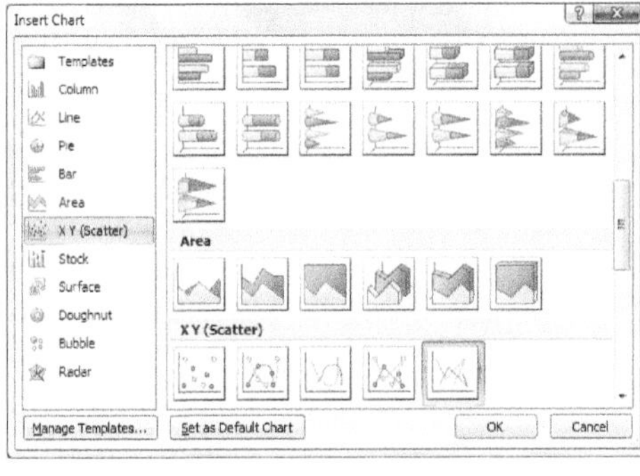

EXERCISE 7.8

We wish to construct a plot of the function: $y = 3\sin(x)$

We will create the data by:

- Using the fill handle, create a series of equally spaced values in Column A from 0–10 radians, by increments of 1 radian, for the first column containing the angle (x).
- In the adjacent Column B, type the equation for the function in the top cell corresponding to the angle of zero. Use the fill handle to copy the equation to the remaining cells.
- Adjust the number format to show two decimal places.

Angle (x) [rad]	Function Value (y)
0	0.00
1	2.52
2	2.73
3	0.42
4	−2.27
5	−2.88
6	−0.84
7	1.97
8	2.97
9	1.24
10	−1.63

Now create a graph from these two columns of data. **Select the option for Scatter with data points connected by straight lines without markers.**

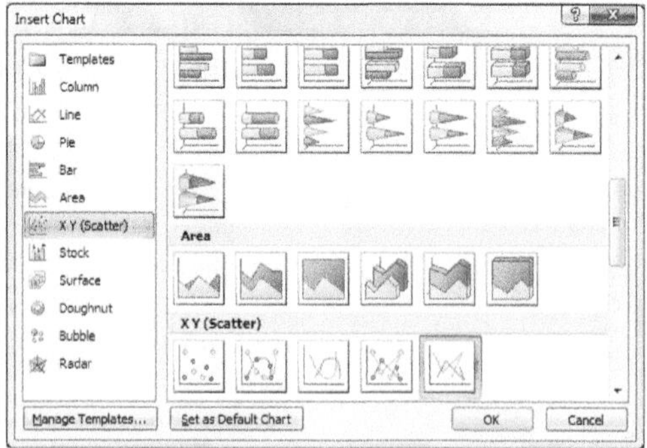

The graph will appear as follows:

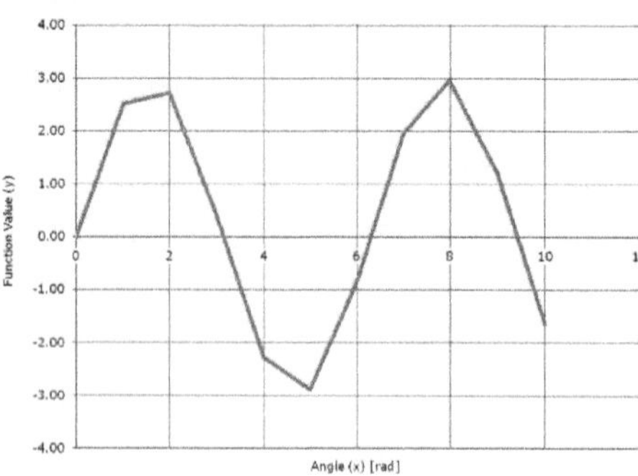

It is obvious that this "jerky" appearance is not satisfactory. This can be improved by reducing the abscissa value increment. For example, reducing the increment from 1 to 0.5 radians gives the following results, which you should duplicate in the worksheet.

Reducing the increment size of the independent variable creates a much smoother plot. It is recommended to select increment sizes sufficiently small to produce a smooth curve when you select the "straight line" option. In this example, the increment should be reduced to about 0.2 or less to produce a smooth curve.

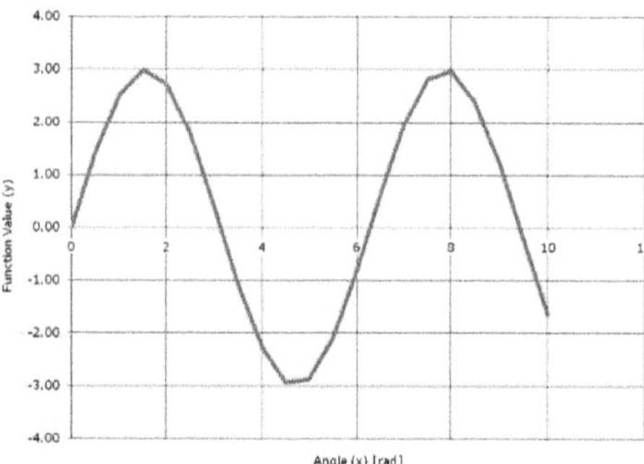

* The option for "Scattered Points with Smooth Lines" will obviously produce a "smooth" curve, but the best judge of increment size is to use the straight line option and select a sufficiently small increment for the independent variable so that the resulting line is smooth. The curve smoothing algorithm used in Excel has no way of knowing what the curve really looks like and simply applies the same mathematical procedure to the data points regardless of the function being implemented. Sometimes this is very close to the true curve, but often it is seriously distorted.
* Note that as the increment size decreases, the total number of data points increases to obtain the same range of independent values.

EXERCISE 7.9

We wish to construct a plot of the function: $Z = A \sin(B\,\theta)$

There are three parameters that we may wish to change: (1) the value of A; (2) the value of B; and (3) the value of the angle increment.

Create a worksheet that appears similar to the one shown.

- Enter 0 as the initial value of the angle (θ) [rad]. Create the remaining angle values using a recursion formula with an absolute reference to the angle increment.
- In the adjacent column, type the equation for Z using absolute references to Parameters A and B.
- Adjust the number format to show two decimal places.

	A	B	C
1			
2			
3			
4			
5	**Parameter A**	**2**	
6	**Parameter B**	**4**	
7	**Angle Increment**	**0.1**	**[rad]**
8			
9	**Angle (θ) [rad]**	**Function Value (Z)**	
10	0.0	0.00	
11	0.1	0.78	
12	0.2	1.43	

Now create a graph from these two columns of date by selecting the option for **Scatter with data points connected by straight lines without markers.**

When entering the axis titles, you will not be able to enter the angle abbreviation as the symbol "θ", but will need to enter it as a "q", then change it using the instructions below.

Change the Axis Label Font or Insert a Symbol (Such as a Degree Sign)

- On the chart, click on the abscissa axis title (Angle (q) [rad])
- Highlight the letter q and right-click.
- When the formatting box appears, click the **Font** menu and choose **Symbol** from the list. This will change the letter q to the symbol θ.

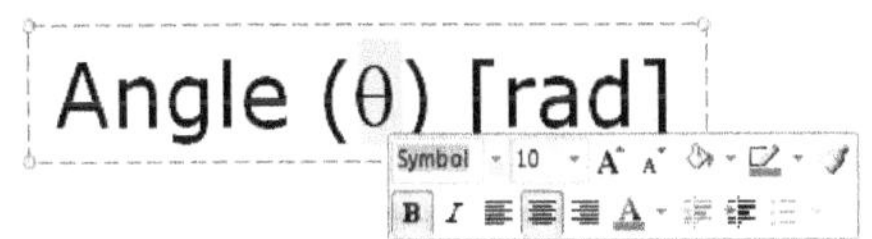

This method works well to adjust letters to a different font. To add a symbol such as a degree sign, use this alternate method:

- On the chart, click on the abscissa axis title (Angle (q) [rad])
- Highlight the letter q
- Go to **Insert > Text > Symbol**

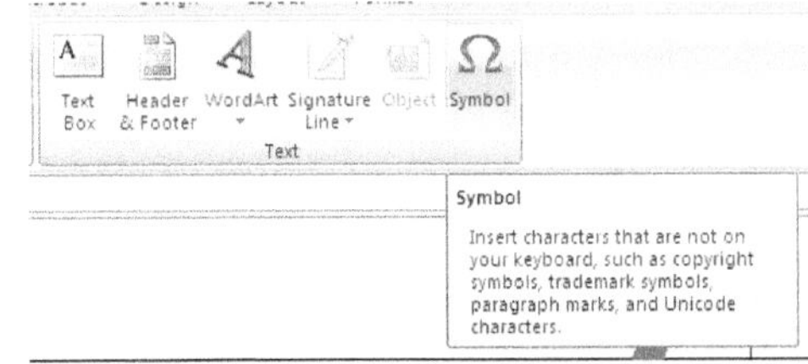

- When the Symbol appears, choose a symbol from the list. This will change the letter q to the symbol θ. Many symbols are available in this palette.
- Click **Insert.**

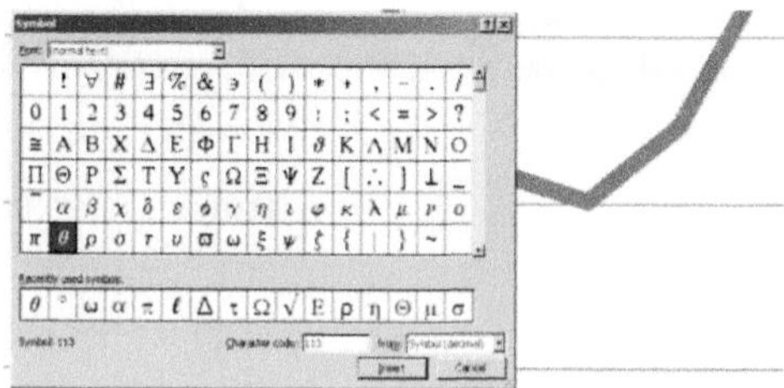

Return to the worksheet and change the parameters: **A = 5 and B = 2.** The graph should now appear as shown to the right.

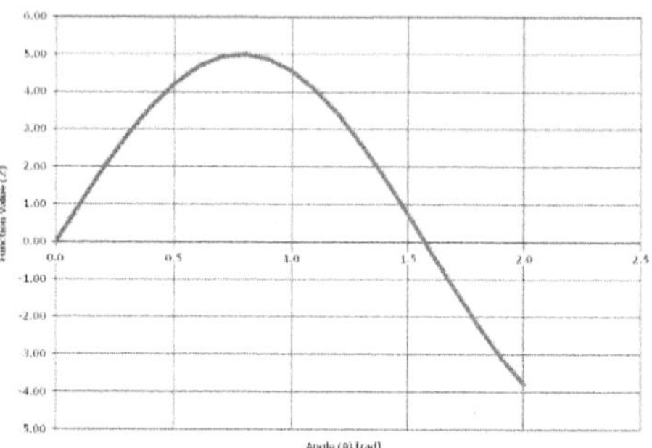

Return to the worksheet and change the parameters: **A = 1 and B = 2 and Increment = 1.** The graph should now appear as shown to the right.

Can you explain why the graph has this jagged appearance?

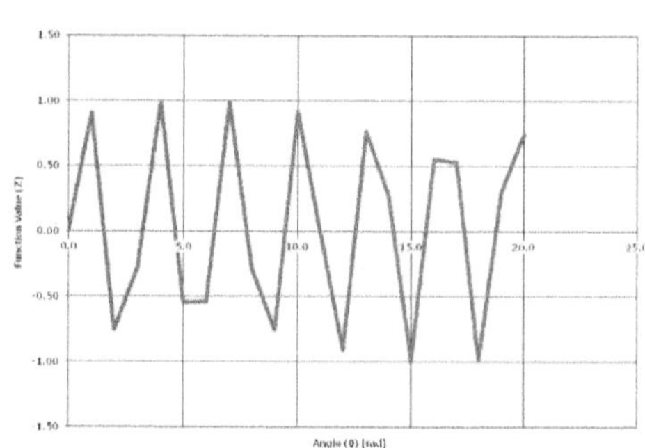

EXERCISE 7.10

We wish to construct a plot of the functions:

$$\alpha = 3 \sin(2\,\theta) \qquad \beta = 5 \cos(\theta) \qquad \lambda = 2 \sin(\theta)$$

These three functions don't require any dynamic parameters in our worksheet, but will require us to recall how to change the symbol type in the worksheet, axis labels, and the legend of our graph.

Inserting Greek symbols:

- When typing each label, if you need a Greek symbol, go to **Insert > Symbol** to bring up the Greek symbol character map.
- Select the Greeks subset of fonts for your current font style (in our example, Calibri) and find your desired Greek symbol and click **Insert.**
- Click **Close.**

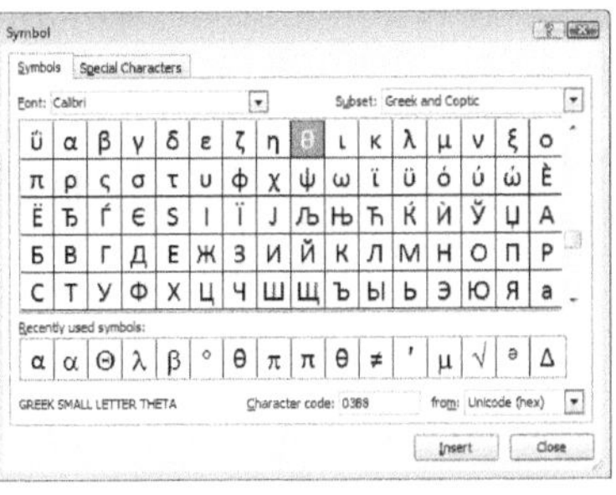

Data Entry for Exercise 7.10

In Column A, enter 0 as the initial value of the angle (θ) [°]. Create a sequence of angles with an increment size of 5 degrees.

In Column B, C and D, type the equations for the three functions. Recall that trigonometric functions must be evaluated in units of radians.

Adjust the number format to show two decimal places in columns B, C, and D.

Now create a graph from these four columns of data by selecting the option for **Scatter with data points connected by lines without markers.** Make the graph a proper plot, following all the previously discussed guidelines.

When entering the axis titles, you will not be able to enter the angle abbreviation as the symbol "θ" and the units as the symbol "°" automatically, but will need to follow the same instructions described on the previous page to insert a special symbol.

The graph should now appear as shown.

Notice the x-axis values appear in the middle of the graph along Y = 0 horizontal line.

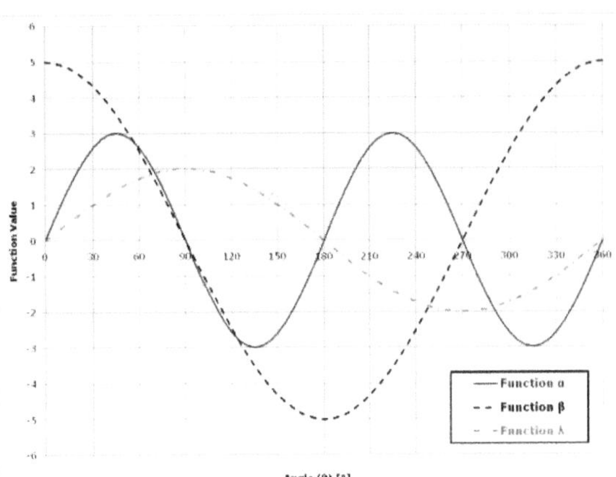

Moving the x-Axis Values

- On the chart, right click on the x-axis values and click **Format Axis.**
- In the Format Axis window under the **Axis Options** tab, click the drop-down menu called **Axis Labels** and select the "Low" option. This will move the x-axis labels below the graph.
- Click **Close.**

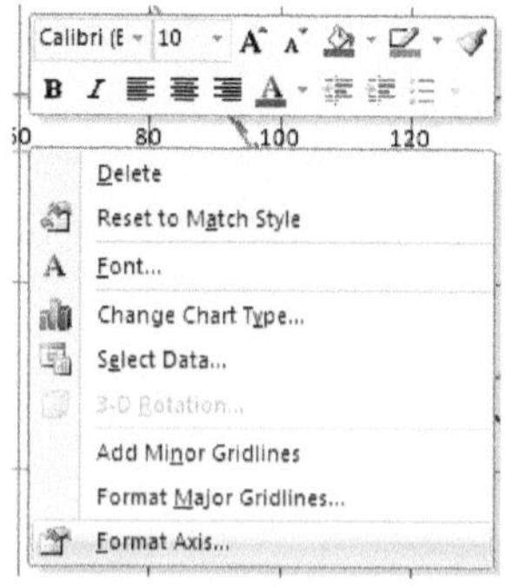

The final graph should appear as shown.

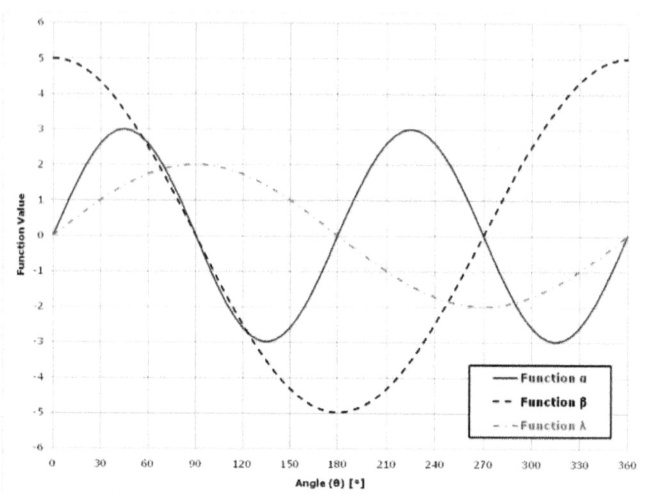

7.7 RIGHT-CLICKING

You are more than likely familiar with the left button on your mouse, but the right button can be very powerful and save you time when you are working with your computer. Generally speaking, whenever you right click on the mouse it will bring up a context or "shortcut" menu. This context menu will contain various actions that you can perform on the item clicked. These actions will vary depending on the type of object you right-click. However, most such menus will usually contain common items such as Copy and Paste.

For example, if you right-click on a graph, the menu that appears is shown at the right. This utility will become very useful to you with experience; you may want to begin to experiment with this function now.

EXERCISES AND ACTIVITIES

7.1 Create a proper plot of the following data set showing the effect of the percent glycerol in water on the viscosity of the solution.

Glycerol	Viscosity
(w) [% by weight]	(μ) [cP]
0	1.01
10	1.31
20	1.77
30	2.50
40	3.75
50	6.05
60	10.96

7.2 Create a proper of the following data set showing the effect of the percent glycerol in water on the freezing temperature of the solution.

Glycerol	Temperature
(w) [% by weight]	(T) [°C]
10	–1.6
30	-9.5
50	–22.0
60	–33.6
70	–37.8
80	–19.2
100	17.0

7.3 **Joule's First Law**, also known as the **Joule effect**, relates the heat generated to current flowing in a conductor. It is named for James Prescott Joule, the same person for whom the unit of Joule is named. The Joule effect states that electric power can be calculated as $P = I^2R$, where R is the resistance in [Ohms, Ω] and I is the electrical current in [Amperes, A]. Use the following data to create a graph of the power (P, on the ordinate) and current (I, on the abscissa).

Current (I) [A]	0.50	1.25	1.50	2.25	3.00	3.20	3.50
Power (P) [W]	1.20	7.50	11.25	25.00	45.00	50.00	65.00

7.4 The following experimental data was collected on the current (symbolized by I) in the positive direction and voltage (symbolized by V) across the terminals of two different thermionic rectifiers. Create a proper plot of the data using the grid provided, placing voltage on the abscissa.

Voltage	Current (I) [milliamperes]	
(V) [volts]	Rectifier A	Rectifier B
18	5	15
30	18	26
40	24	34
45	30	50

7.5 Choose several of the following functions. Plot them, all on the same graph. The independent variable (angle) should vary from 0 to 360 degrees.

(a) sin (θ)
(b) 2 sin (θ)
(c) – 2 sin (θ)
(d) sin (2 θ)
(e) sin (3 θ)
(f) sin (θ) + 2
(g) sin (θ) – 3
(h) sin (θ + 90)
(i) sin (θ – 45)
(j) 2 sin (θ) + 2
(k) sin (2 θ) + 1
(l) 3 sin (2 θ) – 2

7.6 Choose several of the following functions. Plot them, all on the same graph. The independent variable (angle) should vary from 0 to 360 degrees.

(a) cos (θ)
(b) 2 cos (θ)
(c) – 2 cos (θ)
(d) cos (2 θ)
(e) cos (3 θ)
(f) cos (θ) + 2
(g) cos (θ) – 3
(h) cos (θ + 90)
(i) cos (θ – 45)
(j) 2 cos (θ) + 2
(k) cos (2 θ) + 1
(l) 3 cos (2 θ) – 2

7.7 We wish to create a graph showing the relationship of an ideal gas between pressure (P) and temperature (T). Assume the tank has a volume of 12 liters and is filled with nitrogen (formula: N_2, molecular weight: 28 grams per mole). Allow the initial temperature to be 270 kelvin at a pressure of 2.5 atmospheres. Create a graph, showing the temperature on the abscissa from 270 kelvin to 350 kelvin.

7.8 The decay of a radioactive isotope can be modeled using the following equation, where C_0 is the initial amount of the element at time zero and k is the half-life of the isotope. Create a graph of the decay of Isotope A [k = 1.48 hours]. Allow time to vary on the abscissa from 0 to 5 hours with an initial concentration of 10 grams of Isotope A.

$$C = C_0 e^{-\frac{t}{k}}$$

7.9 To compare the popularity of different social networks on the Internet, it's often best to look at what percentage of the global Internet users visit a website. Below is usage data collected from Alexa, a company that collects and reports Internet usage statistics. Create a graph that shows the popularity of three social networks (Facebook, MySpace, Twitter) from July 2008 to May 2009. Experiment with different types of graphs to "best" illustrate the data.

	Jul-08	Aug-08	Sep-08	Oct-08	Nov-08	Dec-08	Jan-09	Feb-09	Mar-09	Apr-09	May-09
Facebook	9.0%	9.5%	10.0%	11.0%	11.5%	12.5%	14.0%	15.0%	15.5%	16.0%	17.0%
MySpace	7.0%	7.0%	6.5%	6.5%	6.0%	6.0%	4.5%	4.5%	5.0%	5.0%	5.0%
Twitter	0.0%	0.0%	0.0%	0.0%	0.0%	0.0%	0.0%	0.5%	1.0%	1.5%	2.0%

7.10 Create a graph to visualize the top 5 major league baseball players for 2008. Below is a chart the top 5 players according to their 2008 batting average (not shown), as well as the number of singles, doubles, triples, and home runs each player hit in 2008 according to ESPN (http://sports.espn.go.com/mlb/stats/batting?league=mlb&season=2008). Experiment with different types of graphs to "best" illustrate the data.

Player	Singles	Doubles	Triples	Home Runs
Chipper Jones	160	24	1	22
Albert Pujols	187	44	0	37
Manny Ramirez	183	36	1	37
Joe Mauer	176	31	4	9
Dustin Pedroia	213	54	2	17

CHAPTER 8
STATISTICS

Objectives

By learning the material in this chapter, you should be able to

- compute descriptive statistics (using Excel)
- interpret the shape of a distribution
- describe a normal distribution and the concept of Six Sigma
- interpret analyzed data and graphical representations to explain relationships or make predictions

Probability is associated with assessing the likelihood that an event will or will not occur. For example:

Airplane crash	Earthquake	Nuclear reactor accident
Tornado	Failure of equipment	Terminal cancer
River breaching a levee	Microprocessor failure	Space probe data reception

Statistics are used for design-concept evaluation because they provide quantitative measures to "things" that behave in a random manner. This evaluation helps us make rational decisions about events and manufactured products. Statistics, as well as probability, use numerical evidence to aid decision making in the face of uncertainty. Roles of statistics in engineering include the following:

- Evaluation of new or alternative designs, concepts, and procedures
- Estimation of amount to bid on projects
- Management (human uncertainty, economic uncertainty, and others)
- Determination of degree of acceptable item-to-item variation (quality control)

Often, the best way to analyze an engineering problem is to conduct an experiment. When we take this approach, we face several questions:

- How many tests do we need?
- How confident are we in the results?
- Can we extrapolate the results to other conditions?
- Can we estimate how often the result will lie within a specified range?

There are many other related issues, but addressing all of them requires a separate book. Many readers will take or have taken an entire course in probability or statistics, so for now we just touch on some of the important fundamentals.

Taken from *Thinking Like an Engineer: An Active Learning Approach,* by Elizabeth A. Stephan, David R. Bowman, William J. Park, Benjamin L. Sill, and Matthew W. Ohland.

- **Repeated tests:** When a test is conducted multiple times, we will not get the same (exact) result each time. For example, use a ruler to measure the length of a particular brand of shoe manufactured by company X. You can produce a table of values, all of which will be nearly, but not exactly, the same. This is because you make slight errors in measurement, so even if every shoe is identical, there will always be some errors in your measurement. Moreover, every shoe is not identical.
- **Differences in a population:** What is the heart rate of all students in a class? Obviously, not everyone will have the same heart rate. We do expect, however, that everyone's rate will lie between, say, 40 and 140 beats per minute. Through measurement, we can determine this variation. In fact, we may find that the average rate for females and males differs. Statistical procedures help us analyze situations such as this.
- **Manufacturing errors:** Suppose you are manufacturing a run of widgets and a buyer wants all of them to be exactly alike. Obviously, this is impossible, but you can make them almost alike and then tell the buyer how much variation to expect. If you measure each widget as it comes off the assembly line, there will certainly be some variation.
- **Design criteria for products:** When you build a house, you would like it to stand safely for some period of time. For example, you might specify that the house be designed to withstand a windstorm that would occur, on average, every 50 years. For that case, you must be able to calculate the wind speeds associated with such a storm. Statistical methods allow you to do this.

8.1 HISTOGRAMS

To illustrate several common statistical concepts, we use data representing the height of several freshman engineering students. Table 8.1 shows the height, to the nearest inch, of each student in a typical class. Table 8.2 shows the same data, summarized by number of students at each height.

When we graph the values shown in Table 8.1, we end up with a scatter plot with data that is exactly the same: scattered, as shown in Figure 8.1.

Instead of using a scatter plot, we can group the data and plot the group values in a chart similar to a column chart, shown in Figure 8.2. Using the summarized data shown

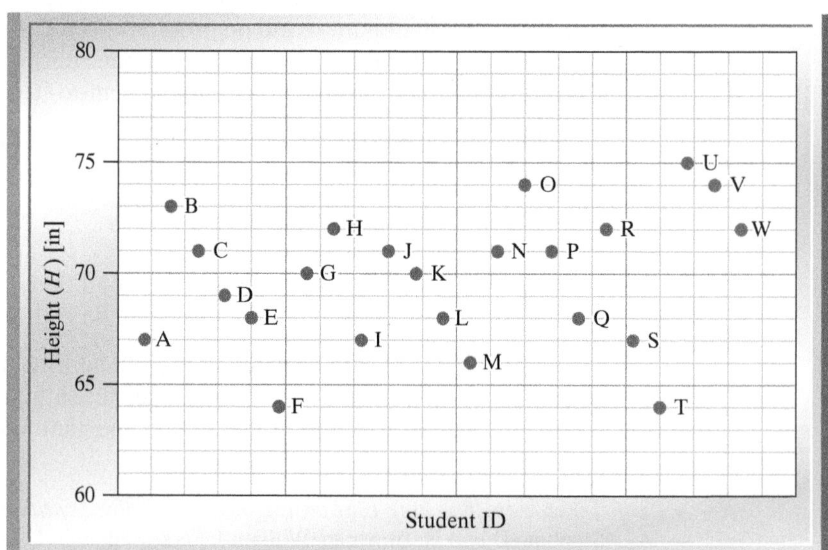

Figure 8.1 Example of student height, shown on scatter plot.

Table 8.1 Student height

Student ID	Height (H) [in]
A	67
B	73
C	71
D	69
E	68
F	64
G	70
H	72
I	67
J	71
K	70
L	68
M	66
N	71
O	74
P	71
Q	68
R	72
S	67
T	64
U	75
V	74
W	72

Table 8.2 Summary of height data

Height (H) [in]	Number of Students
62	0
63	0
64	2
65	0
66	1
67	3
68	3
69	1
70	2
71	4
72	3
73	1
74	2
75	1
76	0
77	0
Total	23

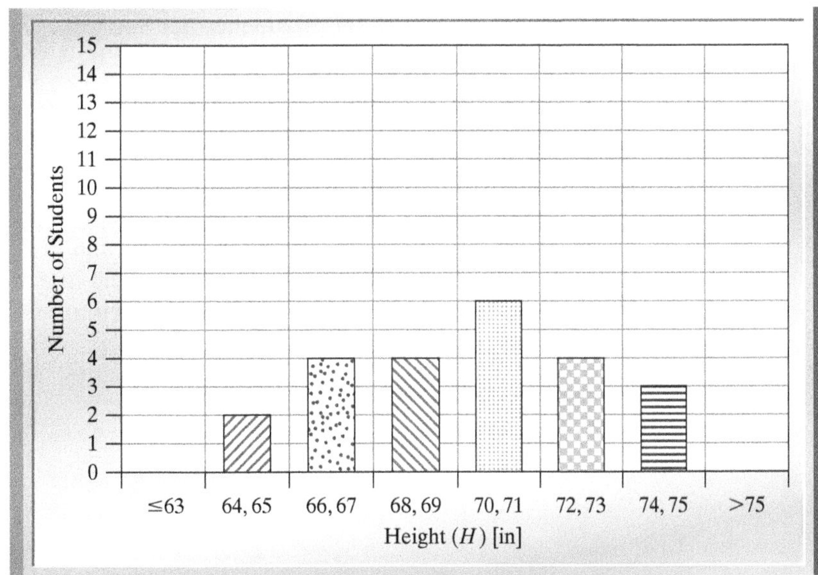

Figure 8.2 Example of student height, shown on a histogram.

in Table 8.2, we will place two height ranges into a single column or **bin**. The first bin will contain all student-height values less than 62 inches. The next bin will contain student-height values of 62 and 63 inches. The next bin will contain student-height values of 64 and 65 inches, and so on. The abscissa of the graph is the height values; the ordinate is the number of students measured. Graphs of this nature are called **histograms**. By counting the number of blocks, we find the area under the curve represents the total number of samples taken, in this case, the total number of students (23) observed.

Technically, before beginning this example we should have mathematically determined a bin size, rather than arbitrarily grouping the measurements in pairs (62 and 63 in one bin, 64 and 65 in the next bin, etc.). There are several ways to calculate the bin size that will best display the information; below is one method.

DETERMINATION OF BIN SIZE

Step One: Determine the number of bins needed.

Number of Bins = Square root of number of data points, rounded to whole number

Step Two: Determine the range of the data.

Range = $X_{max} - X_{min}$

Step Three: Determine the number of items in each bin.

Bin Size = Range divided by Number of Bins, rounded to whole number

Let us apply this to our example.

Step 1: As shown, we have a class of 23 students, so we would need about five bins, since the square root of 23 is about 4.8, which rounds to 5. Four would probably also work fine, as would 6. Remember that this is just a rule of thumb.
Step 2: The shortest person is 64 inches tall and the tallest is 75, so the range is 11 inches.
Step 3: Dividing the range determined in Step 2 by the number of bins determined in Step 1, we get 2.2, or about 2 inches per bin. On the other hand, we might instead decide to have four bins. If we divide the range by 4, we have 2.75 or 3 inches per bin.

Depending on the number of bins, we sometimes get two different, but acceptable, bin sizes. By changing the bin size, we can change the appearance of the data spread, or the data **distribution**.

What happens to the student height data if we alter the bin size? The plot on the preceding page shows a 2-inch bin interval, and Figure 8.3(a) shows a 3-inch interval.

In Figure 8.3(b), we have used a 4-inch bin interval, and while it is not what we obtained from the "rule of thumb" (2- or 3-inch intervals), it is still mathematically correct but not as informative as the other two.

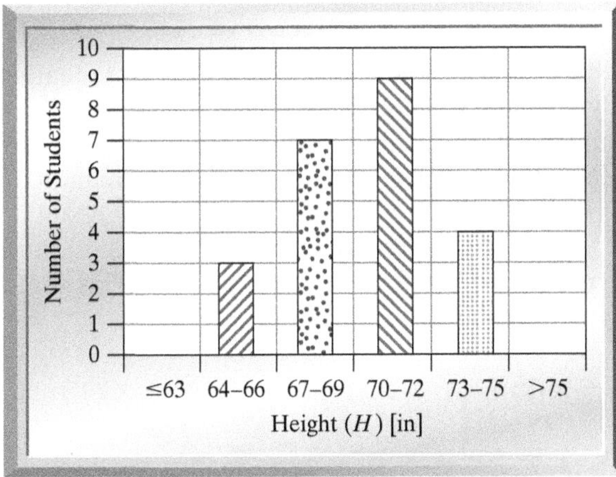

Figure 8.3(a) Bin size of 3.

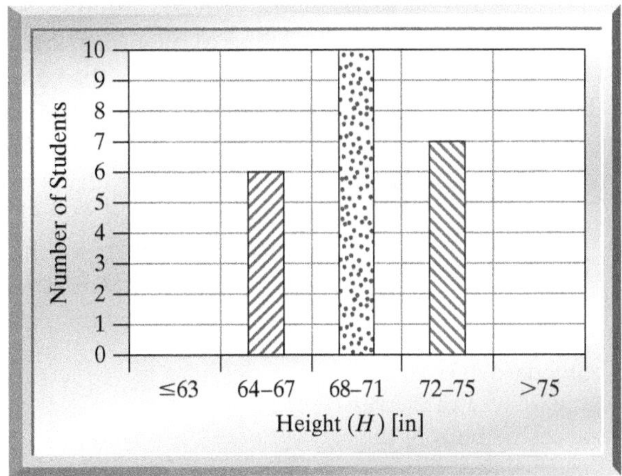

Figure 8.3(b) Bin size of 4.

8.2 STATISTICAL BEHAVIOR

When we have gathered the data and plotted a distribution, the next step is to explain the outcome to others. For convenience, we identify a set of parameters to describe distributions.

NOTE

Average or Mean = typical, expected value of the data set; sensitive to outliers.
Median = value representing the exact middle value of the list; typically unaffected by outliers. Data must be in ascending order to determine!

One parameter of a distribution is the average value. The average, or mean, is an estimate of the value most representative of the population. This is often called the central tendency of the data. The computation of the mean ($\overline{X}$) of a data set containing N values is given in the equation below.

$$Mean = \overline{X} = \frac{1}{N}(X_1 + X_2 + \cdots + X_n) = \frac{1}{N}\sum_{j=1}^{N} Xj$$

In other words, the mean is simply the sum of all of the values divided by the total number of values.

The **median**, another measure of central tendency, is the value between the lower half and the upper half of the population. In other words, if all data points are listed in numerical order, the median is the value exactly in the middle of the list. If the number of data points is odd, the median will be the middle value of the population. If the number of data points is even, however, the median will be the average of the two values at the center. A few examples should clarify this.

Set	Data	Mean	Median
1	1, 2, 3, 4, 5, 6, 7	4	4
2	1, 50, 70, 100	55	60
3	5, 10, 20, 40, 80	31	20
4	50, 50, 50, 50, 50, 1,000	208	50

Review the data shown in set 4. It would seem logical if every data point has a value of 50 except one, the average of the data should be about 50; instead, it is 208! This illustrates the sensitivity of the mean to **extreme values**, or **outliers**. Note that the median is unaffected or only slightly affected. It is for this reason that the mean is insufficient to describe the central tendency of all distributions.

NOTE

Variance = measure of data scatter; has SQUARED UNITS of the original data set.

Standard deviation 5 square root of the variance; has units of the original data set.

Two other terms are useful in describing a distribution: **variance** and **standard deviation**. Both of these terms quantify how widely a set of values is scattered about the mean. To determine the variance (V_x^2), the difference between each point and the mean is determined, and each difference is squared to keep all terms positive. This sum is then divided by one less than the number of data points.

$$\text{Variance} = V_x^2 = \frac{1}{n-1}((\overline{X} - X_1)^2 + (\overline{X} - X_2)^2 + \cdots + (\overline{X} - X_N)^2)$$

$$= \frac{1}{N-1}\sum_{j+1}^{N}(\overline{X} - X_j)^2$$

The standard deviation (SD_X) is found by taking the square root of the variance:

$$\text{Standard deviation} = SD_x = \sqrt{V_x^2}$$

If we again examine the data found in Table 8.2, we can calculate the mean, median, variance, and standard deviation for our height data.

Height (*H*) [in]	Number of Students
62	0
63	0
64	2
65	0
66	1
67	3
68	3
69	1
70	2
71	4
72	3
73	1
74	2
75	1
76	0
77	0
Total	23

Calculation of the Mean:

Total number of points (N)
= 23 students

The sum of all heights
= (2 students * 64 inches/student) + (1 * 66) + (3 * 67) + (3 * 69) + (1 * 69) + (2 * 70) + (4 * 71) + (3 * 72) + (1 * 73) + (2 * 74) + (1 * 75)
= 1,604 inches

Mean
= 1,604 inches/23 students
= 69.7 inches/student

Calculation of the Median:

Put data in order of value, listing each entry once

64, 64, 66, 67, 67, 67, 68, 68, 68, 69, 70, 70, 71, 71, 71, 71, 72, 72, 72, 73, 74, 74, 75

Find the center value since the total number of students is odd

64, 64, 66, 67, 67, 67, 68, 68, 68, 69, **70,** 70, 71, 71, 71, 71, 72, 72, 72, 73, 74, 74, 75

Median = 70 inches

Calculation of Variance: Note that the variance will have the same units as the variable in question squared, in this case, "inches squared."

$$\text{Variance} = \frac{1}{23-1}((69/7 - 64)^2 + (69.7 - 64)^2 + (69.7 - 66)^2 + \cdots + (69.7 - 75)^2) = 9.5\text{ in}^2$$

Calculation of Standard Deviation: The standard deviation has the same units as the variable in question, in this case, "inches."

$$\text{Standard deviation} = \sqrt{9.5} + 3.08 \text{ in}$$

EXAMPLE 8-1

Consider the following velocity data, listed in units of feet per second. Determine the mean, median, variance, and standard deviation of the data.

1	28	14	32	35	25	14	28	5
16	42	35	26	5	33	35	16	14

Calculation of the Mean:

Total number of points (N) = 18

Sum of all data $(\sum X_j) = (1) + (2 * 5) + (3 * 14) + \cdots + (42) = 404$

Mean $= 404/18 = 22.4$ *feet per second*

Calculation of the Median:

Put data in order, listing each entry once.

1, 5, 5, 14, 14, 14, 16, 16, 25, 26, 28, 28, 32, 33, 35, 35, 35, 42

Find the center two values and average them, since total number of entries is even (18).

1, 5, 5, 14, 14, 14, 16, 16, ***25, 26****, 28, 28, 32, 33, 35, 35, 35, 42*

Median = (25 + 26)/2 = 25.5 feet per second

Calculation of Variance:

$$Variance = \frac{1}{18 - 1}((22.4 - 1)^2 + \cdots + (22.4 - 42)^2) = 147 \text{ (ft/s)}^2$$

Calculation of Standard Deviation:

$$Standard\ deviation = \sqrt{147} = 12.1\ feet\ per\ second$$

EXAMPLE 8-2

Consider the following energy data, given in units of joules. Determine the mean, median, variance, and standard deviation of the data.

159	837	618	208	971	571	379	220	31

Calculation of the Mean:

Total number of points (N) = 9

Sum of all data $(\sum X_j) = 159 + 837 + \cdots 31 = 3{,}994$

Mean $= 3{,}994/9 = 443.7 = 444$ joules

Calculation of the Median:

Put data in order, listing each entry once.

31, 159, 208, 220, 379, 571, 618, 837, 971

Find the center value since the total number of students is odd (9; center value at entry 5).

31, 159, 208, 220, ***379****, 571, 618, 837, 971*

Median = 379 joules

Calculation of Variance:

$$Variance = \frac{1}{9-1}\left[(444-31)^2 + \cdots + (444-971)^2\right] = 105{,}059 \text{ joules}^2$$

Calculation of Standard Deviation:

$$Standard\ deviation + \sqrt{105{,}059} = 324 \text{ joules}$$

COMPREHENSION CHECK 8-1

For the following mass data given in units of kilograms, determine the mean, median, variance, and standard deviation.

8	7	9	11	16
12	2	9	10	9

COMPREHENSION CHECK 8-2

For the following temperature data given in units of degrees Celsius [°C], determine the mean, median, variance, and standard deviation.

105	120	110	100	102
103	58	110	100	118

8.3 DISTRIBUTIONS

From the charts on the preceding pages discussing histograms, you can see a similarity in the shape of all three plots. The values start small, increase in size, and then decrease again. In the case of student height, this means that a few people are short, most people have some "average" height, and a few people are tall. This same conclusion is true in many places in our world. For example:

- If we weigh many standard-size watermelons (neither miniature nor giant), we will find that most weigh between 20 and 30 pounds. A few weigh less than 20 pounds, and a few weigh more than 30 pounds.
- As we look through a dictionary, we find that there are many words with between four and six letters. There are a few with one, two, or three letters and a few with more than six, but clearly most have between four and six letters.
- To improve efficiency in the office, we had an expert to monitor the length of phone calls made by the staff. The expert found that most of the time, phone calls lasted between 3 and 5 minutes, but a few were longer than 5 and some others lasted only a minute or 2.

Normal Distributions

We wanted to know how many "flexes" it takes to cause a paper clip to fail, so we asked volunteers to test the bending performance of paper clips by doing the following:

- Unfold the paper clip at the center point so that the resulting wire forms an "S" shape.
- Bend the clip back and forth at the center point until it breaks.
- Record the number of "flexes" required to break the clip.

Using these data, we created Figure 8.4. This is the same as the earlier histogram, but the "boxes" are replaced by a smooth curve through the values.

When you are interested in the *shape* of the curve rather than the exact data values, you can replace the bars of the histogram with a smooth curve and rename the

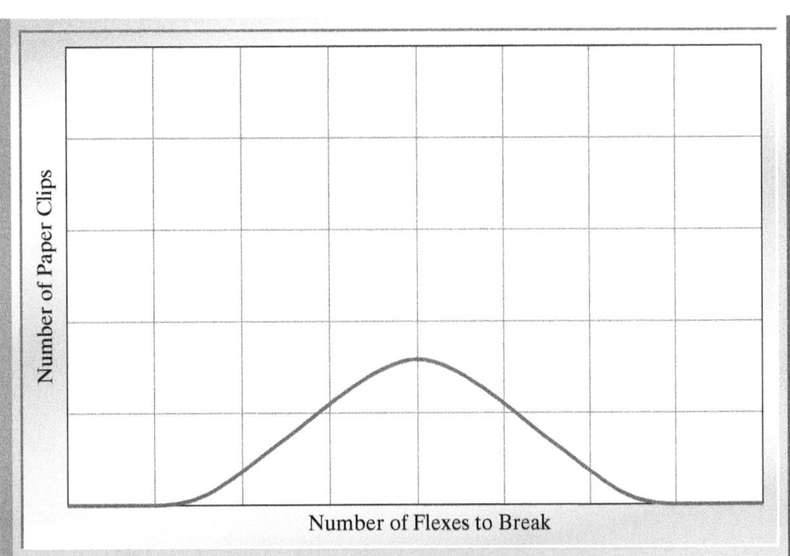

Figure 8.4 Distribution of paper clip failure.

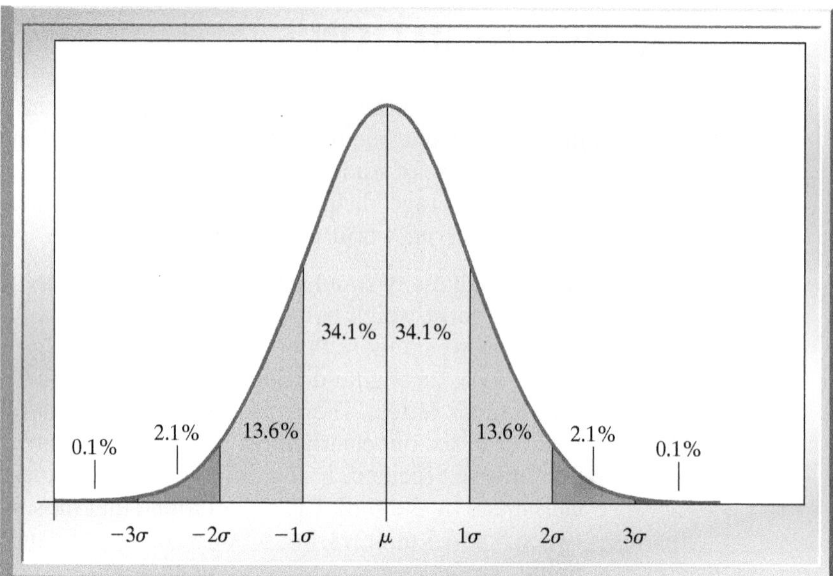

Figure 8.5 "Normal" distribution, showing the 68–95–99.7 rule.

graph *distribution*. A distribution is considered *normal* if the following rules hold true. This is known as the **68-95-99.7 rule**, shown in Figure 8.5.

- 68% of values are within one standard deviation (1s) of the mean (m).
- 95% of values are within two standard deviations (2s).
- 99.7% of values are within three standard deviations (3s).

EXAMPLE 8-3

Suppose we ask a class of students how many states they have visited. The results might appear as shown below.

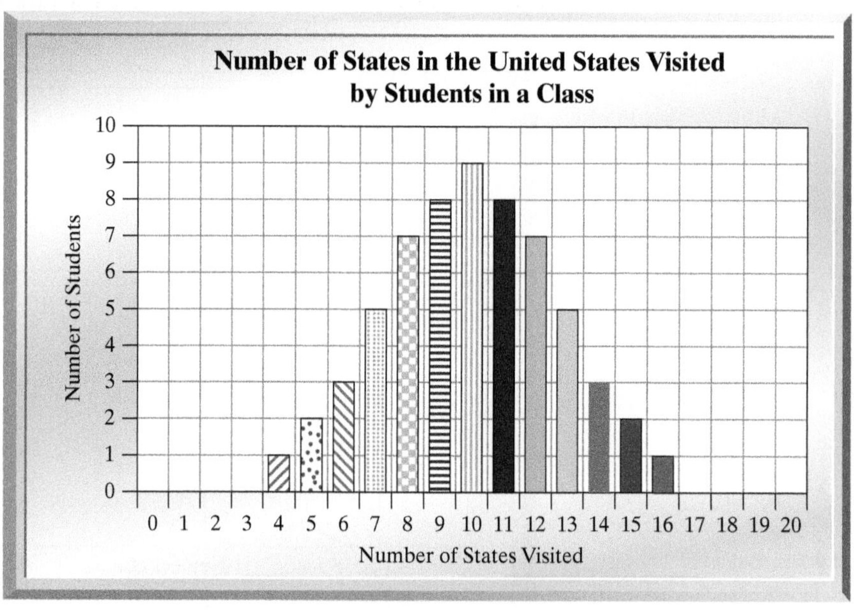

It seems that most have visited between 8 and 12, and that as many have visited more than 10 as have visited fewer than 10. A few have visited as many as 16 states, and all the students have visited at least 4. Let us calculate some values pertinent to this situation.

How many students are there in the class?

To do this we simply add the number of students represented by each bar, or

$$1 + 2 + 3 + 5 + 7 + 8 + 9 + 8 + 7 + 5 + 3 + 2 + 1 = 61$$

What is the cumulative number of state visits?

*We answer this by totaling the product of the bar height with the number of states represented by the bar. For example, 5 students have visited 7 states, so those 5 students have visited a total of 5 * 7 = 35 states. Or, 8 students have visited 11 states, so those students have visited a total of 88 states. We calculate*

$$1*4 + 2*5 + 3*6 + \cdots[+ 2*15 + 1*16 = 610$$

What is the average number of states visited by a student?

Once we have the values from our first two answers, this is straightforward division: the total number of visits divided by the total number of students.

$$610/61 = 10$$

Notice that the value 10 is in the center of the distribution. For distributions that are symmetrical (such as this one), the average value is the one in the center, the one represented by the largest number of occurrences.

Decrease in Variance

Let us examine the shape of the distribution of paper clip failures discussed earlier. How would the distribution change if we brought in a machine that did it "exactly" the same way each time? Both the distribution from the data class and the distribution of the machine are shown below. The same number of clips was tested in each case, so the areas under each curve must be the same. The comparison is shown in Figure 8.6.

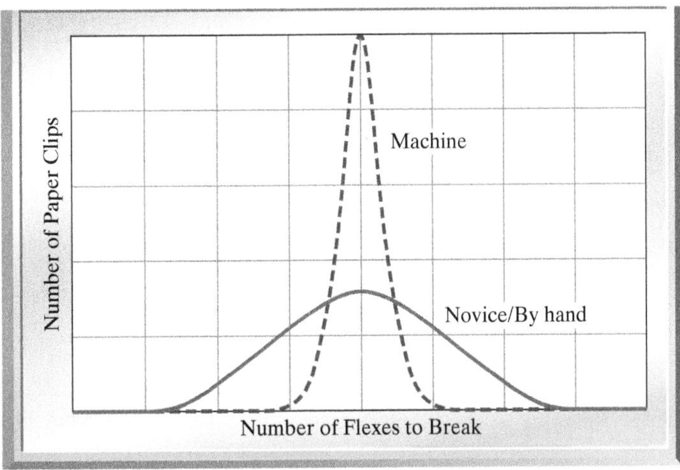

Figure 8.6 Distribution of paper clip failure after a decrease in variance.

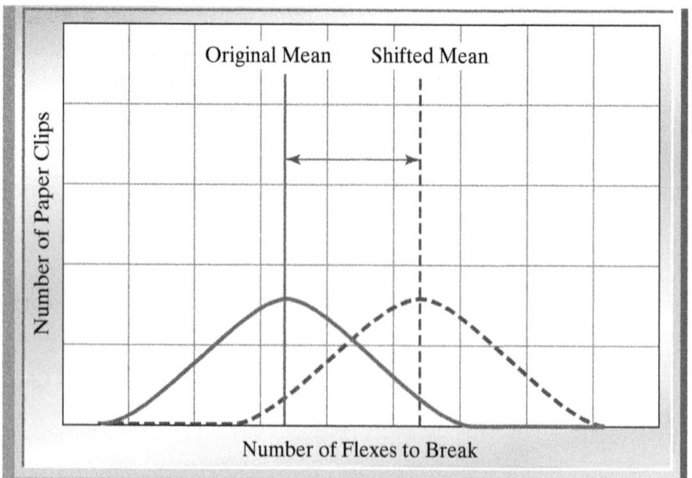

Figure 8.7 Distribution of paper clip failure with a shift.

This exercise illustrates that distributions that have the same mean (and median) can look very different. In this case, the difference between these two distributions is in their "spread," or their variation about the mean.

Shift in Mean

Redraw the paper clip distribution; then on the same plot, sketch the distribution if each volunteer tested clips that were manufactured by the same manufacturer as before but were stronger and typically required 10 more flexes to fail. The result is shown in Figure 8.7.

Skewed Data

It is often easy to place an upper limit on the value of the possible outcome. In these cases, the distribution is no longer symmetric—it is **skewed**. A population is **positively skewed** if the mean has been pulled higher than the median, and **negatively skewed** if the mean has been pulled lower than the median (see Figure 8.8). You have probably

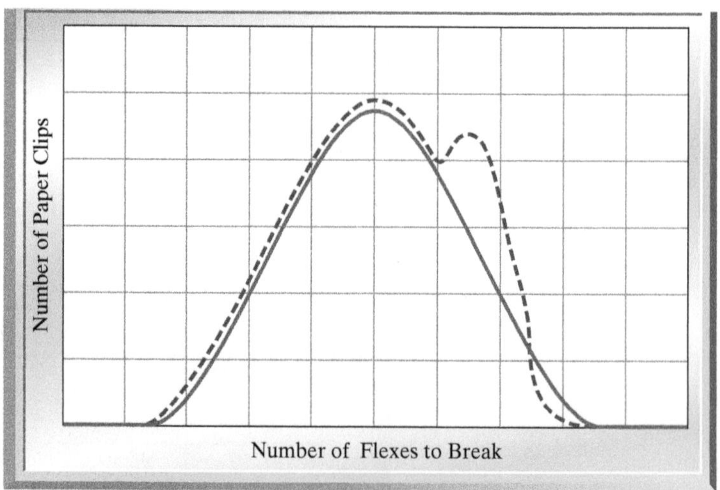

Figure 8.8 Distribution of positively skewed data.

heard news reports that use the median to describe a distribution of income in the United States. The median is used in this case because the distribution is positively skewed. This skew is caused by two factors, the presence of extreme values (millionaires) and the range restriction, the latter because income cannot be lower than $0. The extreme values causing the positive skew are not shown on the graph. Most of these would be far off the page to the right.

COMPREHENSION CHECK 8-3

For each graph shown below, decide if the mean, variance, or population size has changed.

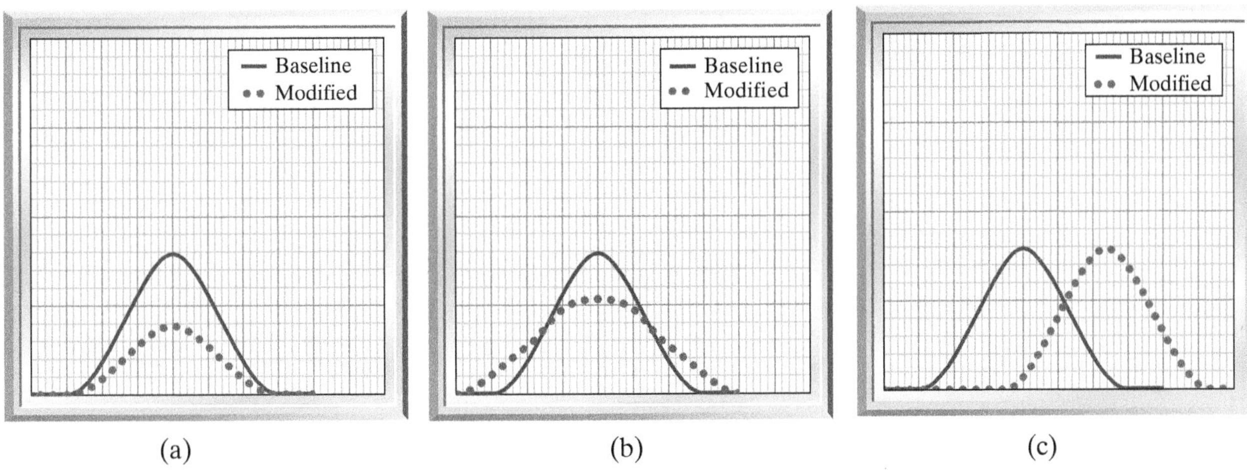

(a) (b) (c)

EXAMPLE 8-4

For each scenario, identify one graph from the following that best illustrates how the baseline curve would change under the conditions of that scenario. Each graph shows the usual distribution (labeled baseline) and the way the distribution would be modified from the baseline shape (labeled modified) under certain conditions.

The graphs show SAT composite (verbal + quantitative) scores, for which 400 is generally considered to be the minimum possible score and 1,600 is considered to be the maximum possible score.

(a) The designers of the SAT inadvertently made the test more difficult.

> *This is shown by Curve (F): Area is the same; mean shifted to left.*

(b) The variability of scores is reduced by switching to true/false questions.

> *This is shown by Curve (D): Area is the same; distribution is narrower.*

(c) A population boom increases the number of students seeking college admission.

> *This is shown by Curve (B): Area increases, distribution stays the same.*

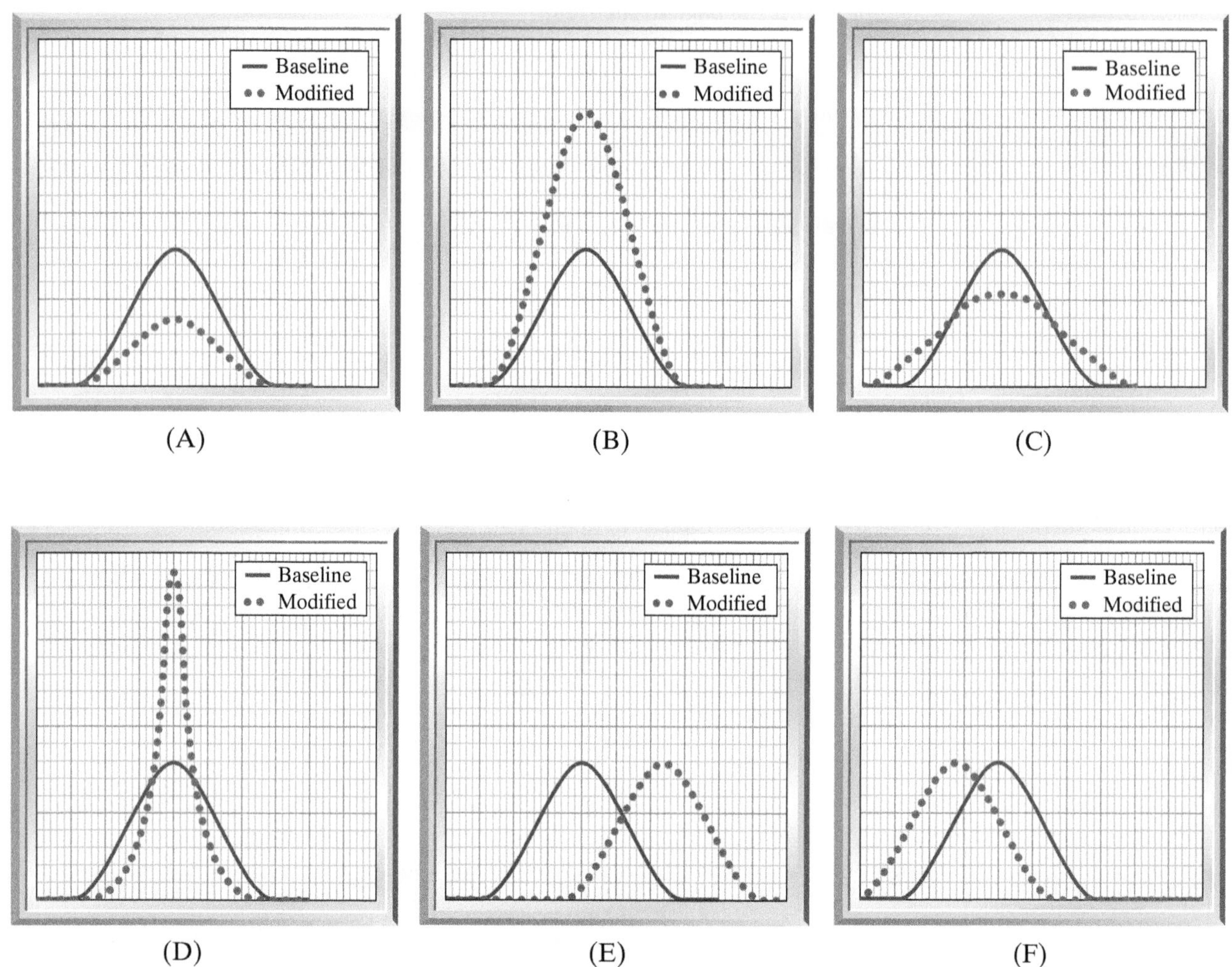

8.4 STATISTICS IN EXCEL

To create **histograms** and **CDFs** with Excel, you need to first activate the Analysis ToolPak in Microsoft Excel.

- In Excel, go to the Office button and click **Excel Options**.
- Choose the **Add-Ins** tab on the left menu of the Excel Options window to display all the active add-in applications in Excel. Notice in our list that the Analysis ToolPak is listed as inactive.

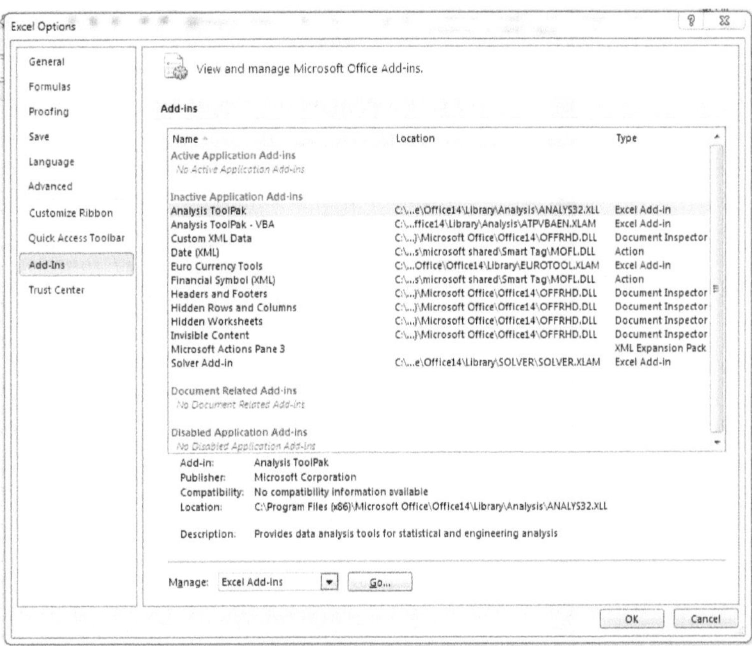

- At the bottom of the Excel Options window, select **Excel Add-Ins** in the **Manage** drop-down menu and click **Go.**
- In the Add-Ins window, check the **Analysis ToolPak** option and click **OK.**
- A prompt might pop up telling you to install the add-in—click **Yes** and finish the installation, using the Office Installer.

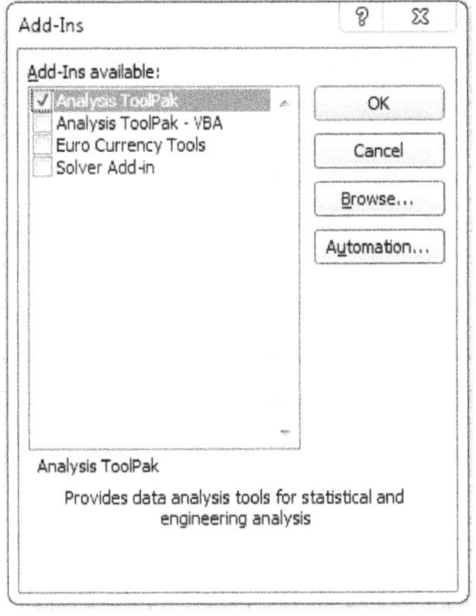

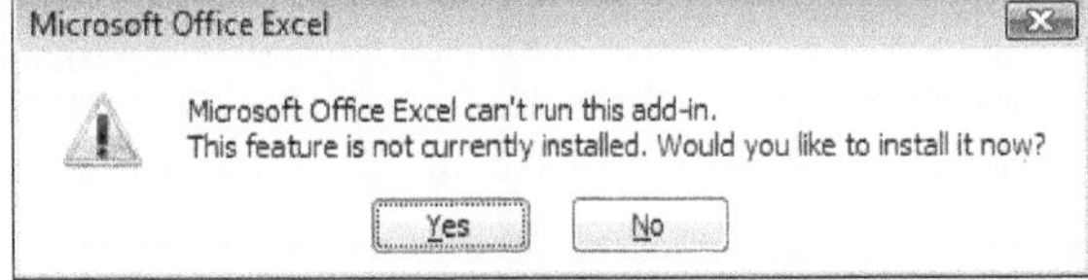

EXAMPLE 8-5

The outline below gives the steps necessary to use the data analysis tool in Excel for basic statistical analysis of a data set. This is presented with an example of the high and low temperatures during the month of October 2006.

- *If necessary, input the data; the data for this example have been provided online. Use Column A to input an identifier for the data point, in this case, the date. Columns B and C will contain the actual high and low temperatures for each day, respectively.*
- *Next, decide on the bin range. This discussion focuses on the high temperatures, but can easily be repeated with the low temperatures.*
  - *A rule of thumb is that the number of bins is approximately equal to the square root of the number of samples. While it is obvious in this example how many total samples are needed, the COUNT function is often very useful. October has 31 days, and the square root of 31 is 5.57; thus, you should choose either 5 or 6 bins.*
  - *Examine your data to determine the range of values. Using the MAX and MIN functions, you can determine that the highest high temperature during October was 86 degrees Fahrenheit and the lowest high temperature was 56 degrees Fahrenheit. Thus, your range is 86 − 56 = 30°F.*
  - *Since 5.57 is closer to 6 than to 5, choose 6 bins. Remember, however, that you might want to try a different number of bins to see if that would result in a clearer representation of the data. With a range of 30 degrees Fahrenheit, 6 bins gives 30°F/6 bins = 5°F per bin.*
- *Type the range of values that will appear in each bin. For example, the first bin will contain temperatures 55, 56, 57, 58, and 59; the second bin will contain temperatures 60–64, and so on.*
- *In the adjacent column, type the corresponding upper value of temperature for each of the bins listed.*

To create histograms and CDF charts:

- *Go to* ***Data > Analysis > Data Analysis*** *and under Analysis Tools choose* ***Histogram****. Click* ***OK****.*

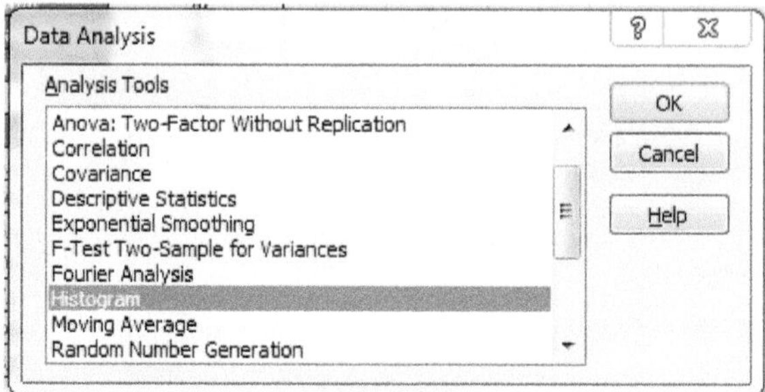

- *In the* ***Input Range****, click the icon at the right end of the blank box. You can then highlight the range (in this case, $B$6:$B$36). Close the box by clicking the icon at the right-hand end of this small box where the range is shown.*
- *Repeat this procedure for the Bin Range, highlighting the cells that contain the upper values.*
- *Next, for the* ***Output Range****, click the circle and identify a single cell to begin the placement of the output data.*
- *Finally, check the boxes to activate the options of* ***Cumulative Percentage*** *calculations and* ***Chart Output****.*
- *Click OK.*

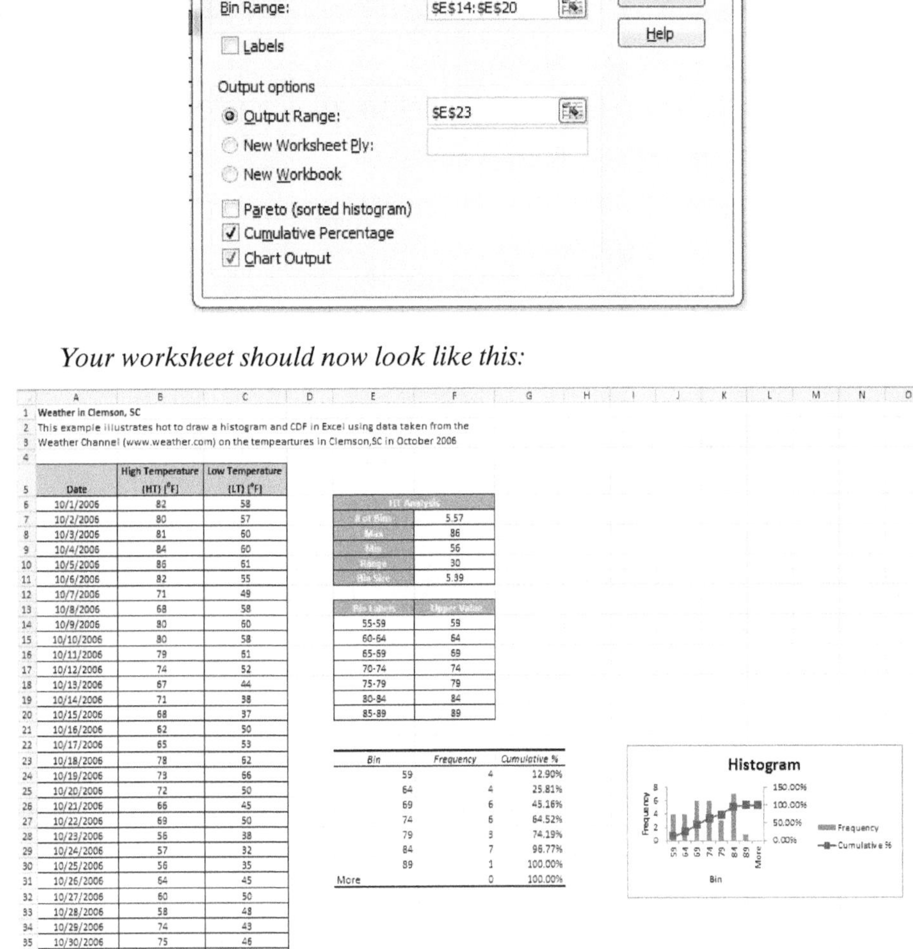

Your worksheet should now look like this:

Weather in Clemson, SC

This example illustrates hot to draw a histogram and CDF in Excel using data taken from the Weather Channel (www.weather.com) on the tempeartures in Clemson,SC in October 2006

Date	High Temperature (HT) [°F]	Low Temperature (LT) [°F]
10/1/2006	82	58
10/2/2006	80	57
10/3/2006	81	60
10/4/2006	84	60
10/5/2006	86	61
10/6/2006	82	55
10/7/2006	71	49
10/8/2006	68	58
10/9/2006	80	60
10/10/2006	80	58
10/11/2006	79	61
10/12/2006	74	52
10/13/2006	67	44
10/14/2006	71	38
10/15/2006	68	37
10/16/2006	62	50
10/17/2006	65	53
10/18/2006	78	62
10/19/2006	73	66
10/20/2006	72	50
10/21/2006	66	45
10/22/2006	69	50
10/23/2006	56	38
10/24/2006	57	32
10/25/2006	56	35
10/26/2006	64	45
10/27/2006	60	50
10/28/2006	58	48
10/29/2006	74	43
10/30/2006	75	46
10/31/2006	64	49

HT Analysis	
# of Bins	5.57
Max	86
Min	56
Range	30
Bin Size	5.39

Bin Labels	Upper Value
55-59	59
60-64	64
65-69	69
70-74	74
75-79	79
80-84	84
85-89	89

Bin	Frequency	Cumulative %
59	4	12.90%
64	4	25.81%
69	6	45.16%
74	6	64.52%
79	3	74.19%
84	7	96.77%
89	1	100.00%
More	0	100.00%

- ***Replace the values in the histogram data table for "Bin" with the "Bin Labels"*** *you entered earlier. This will change the axis labels to the range, rather than the upper value, for each bin.*
- ***Move the histogram location*** *to a new worksheet rather than imbedded in the original worksheet to allow the data to be seen clearly. After selecting the chart, use the* ***Chart > Location*** *option to select "As new sheet."*
- ***Modify the histogram to be a proper plot*** *just as you would with any other chart. The same rules for a "proper plot" apply to a histogram also, so make sure the background is white and alter the series colors, etc., as appropriate. The histogram generated with the directions above is shown below, properly formatted.*
- ***Change the vertical scale on the left axis*** *to be a multiple of 2, 5, or 10 to allow the cumulative percentages on the right axis to line up with the gridlines. This is important to do!*
- ***Change the vertical scale on the right axis*** *to be a maximum value of 100%. This is important to do.The resulting analysis should appear as follows.*

Weather in Clemson, SC

This example illustrates hot to draw a histogram and CDF in Excel using data taken from the Weather Channel (www.weather.com) on the tempeartures in Clemson,SC in October 2006

Date	High Temperature (HT) [°F]	Low Temperature (LT) [°F]
10/1/2006	82	58
10/2/2006	80	57
10/3/2006	81	60
10/4/2006	84	60
10/5/2006	86	61
10/6/2006	82	55
10/7/2006	71	49
10/8/2006	68	58
10/9/2006	80	60
10/10/2006	80	58
10/11/2006	79	61
10/12/2006	74	52
10/13/2006	67	44
10/14/2006	71	38
10/15/2006	68	37
10/16/2006	62	50
10/17/2006	65	53
10/18/2006	78	62
10/19/2006	73	66
10/20/2006	72	50
10/21/2006	66	45
10/22/2006	69	50
10/23/2006	56	38
10/24/2006	57	32
10/25/2006	56	35
10/26/2006	64	45
10/27/2006	60	50
10/28/2006	58	48
10/29/2006	74	43
10/30/2006	75	46
10/31/2006	64	49

HT Analysis	
# of Bins	5.57
Max	86
Min	56
Range	30
Bin Size	5.39

Bin Labels	Upper Value
55-59	59
60-64	64
65-69	69
70-74	74
75-79	79
80-84	84
85-89	89

Bin	Frequency	Cumulative %
55-59	3.00	9.7%
60-64	4.00	22.6%
65-69	7.00	45.2%
70-74	6.00	64.5%
75-79	3.00	74.2%
80-84	7.00	96.8%
85-89	1.00	100.0%
>89	0.00	100.0%

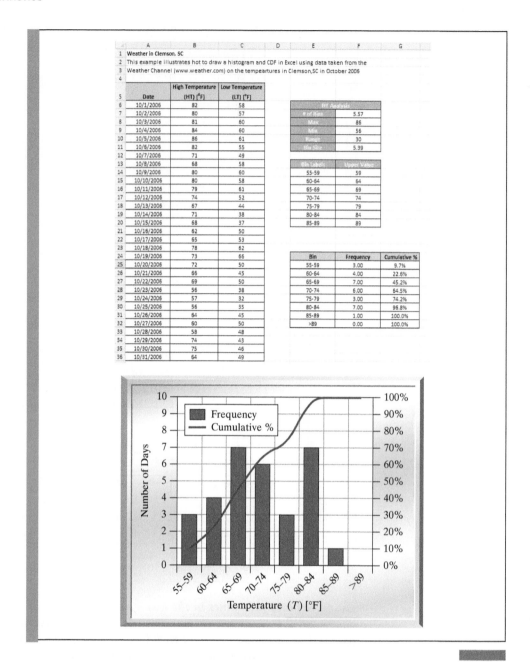

COMPREHENSION CHECK 8-4

Repeat this analysis, using the daily low temperatures during October 2006.

⌘ Statistics on the Mac OS

Unfortunately, as this book goes to press, Microsoft has chosen not to include the histogram tool in Excel 2008 or Excel 2011 for the Mac OS. You have a few options.

- If you have an Intel-based Mac, you can use Excel 2007 or 2010 for Windows. If you do not know how to activate the Windows option on your machine, ask your friendly local Mac guru at your computer center.

- You can use Excel 2004 for the Mac OS, which did include a histogram tool.
- You can create the histogram manually according to the instructions below.

Create columns for the data, bin ranges, and upper value in each bin as described above.

Next, determine the number of data points in each bin. After doing a few, you will find it easy. Use the advanced Excel function, known as an array function, to accomplish this determination. A detailed explanation of array functions is beyond the scope of this book, but if you follow the instructions carefully, you should not have any trouble. The specific function to use is called FREQUENCY.

1. In the cell immediately to the right of the topmost "upper bin value" cell (this would be cell G14 in the example above) enter the formula

   = FREQUENCY (Datarange, UpperbinvalueRange)

   and press return. In the example above, this would be

   = FREQUENCY (B6:B36, F14:F20)

2. Click-and-hold the cell into which you entered the formula, then drag straight down to the cell in the row following the row containing the last "upper bin value." This would be cell G21 in the example above. Release the mouse button. At this point, you will have a vertical group of cells selected (G14:G21 in the example), the top cell will contain the number of data points in the first bin, and the rest of the selected cells will be blank. The formula you entered in the topmost of these cells will appear in the formula bar at the top of the window.
3. Click once in the formula in the formula bar. The top cell of the selected group will be highlighted.
4. Hold down the Command ( ) key and press Return. The selected cells will now contain the number of data points in each bin immediately to the left. The bottommost selected cell will contain the number of data points larger than the upper bin value in the final bin. In the example, this "extra" cell should contain a 0, since no values are larger than those in the final bin. Note the formulae that appear in these cells are all identical—the cell references are exactly the same. This is normal for an array function.

> **NOTE**
>
> *Do not* select these cells by clicking the bottom one and dragging up to the top one—it will not work correctly.
>
> *Do not* use the replicate handle in the lower-right corner of the cell to drag down.

Use these values to create the histogram.

1. Select the cells containing the bin ranges (E14:E20 in our example), then hold down the command ( ) key while you select the cells containing the number of data points per bin. In our example, since the "extra" cell at the bottom contains a 0, you need not include it. If this were nonzero, you might want to add a cell at the bottom of the cell ranges that said something like >89. You should now have the two columns for bin ranges and number per bin selected (E14:E20 and G14:G20 in our example).
2. In the toolbar, select **Gallery > Charts > Column**. A row of column chart icons should appear.
3. Click the first icon, which shows pairs of columns. The chart that appears shows the histogram. Be sure to follow all appropriate proper plot rules for completing the histogram.

   Finally, generate the CDF. If you have survived this far, you should be able to do this with minimal guidance. Create another column of values next to the column containing the number of data points per bin. In the cell next to the topmost bin cell, enter the number of data points in that bin. In the next cell down, enter a formula that will add the cell above to the cell beside it containing the number of data points in that bin. Replicate this formula down to the last bin. Each cell in the new column should now contain the sum of all data points in all bins to that point.

8.5 INTERPRETING DISTRIBUTIONS

Calculating statistics is useful, but interpreting them is also important. Since a wide variety of distributions can yield the same mean, median, and standard deviation, it is important to look at a graph of the distribution. Each baseline curve is a normal distribution of whatever is being measured (to emphasize the generality of the graphs, axis labels and scale are omitted). The question below each graph asks what change would result in the modified curve.

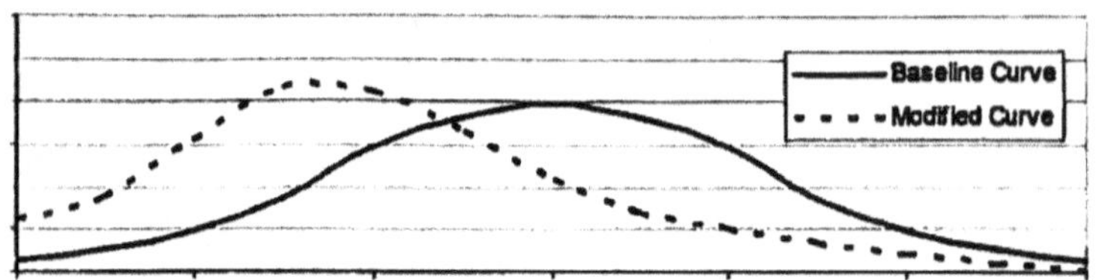

The baseline curve above represents the distribution of growth rates of oil-eating bacteria dropped into an oil spill. The data for the baseline curve were gathered by a single researcher. Another researcher makes independent measurements, and reports the modified curve. What could have caused the disparity in the results of the two researchers?

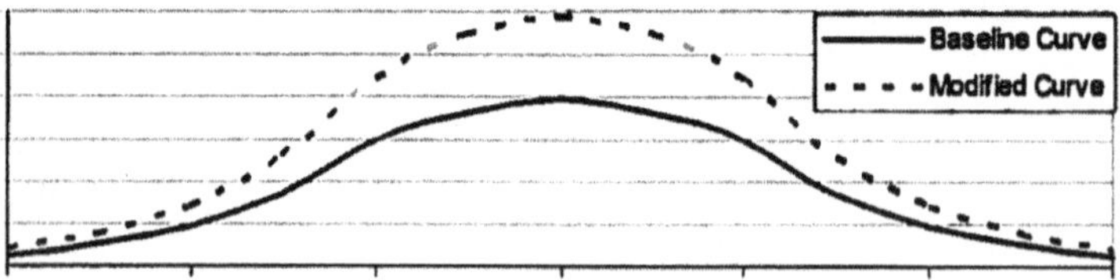

The baseline curve above represents the distribution of tensile strength of knee ligaments harvested from mature rabbits two weeks are a certain type of ligament repair was performed. A second experiment resulted in the modified curve—how was the second experiment different?

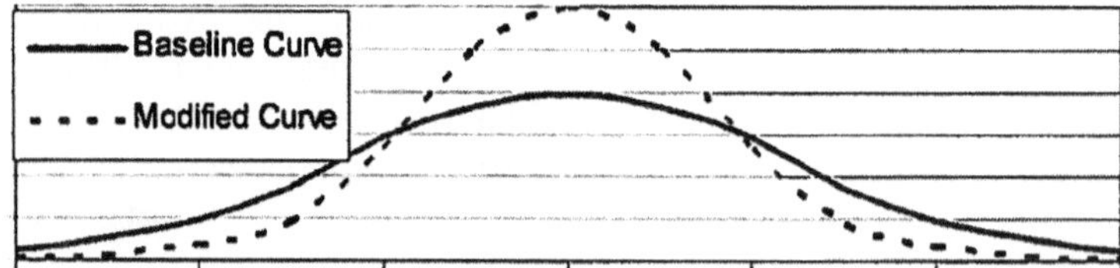

The baseline curve above represents the distribution of the width of bolts produced by manufacturing equipment at an Indiana plant. A second sample resulted in the modified curve—what could have happened to make the second sample different?

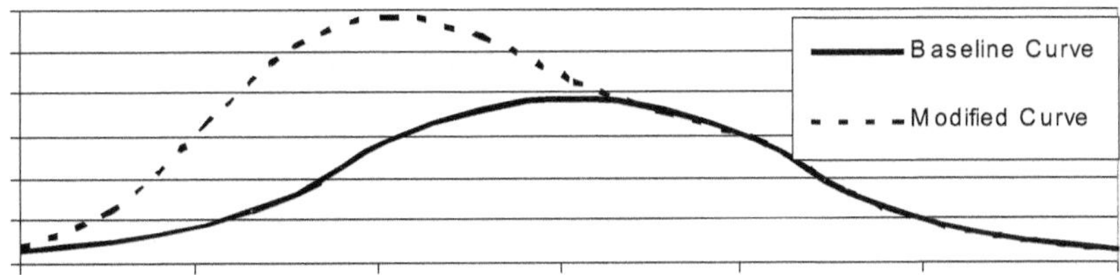

The baseline curve above represents the distribution of neutron energies measured at a particular location in a fusion reactor. A similar measurement at a different location yields the modified curve. What differences between the two locations could cause this?

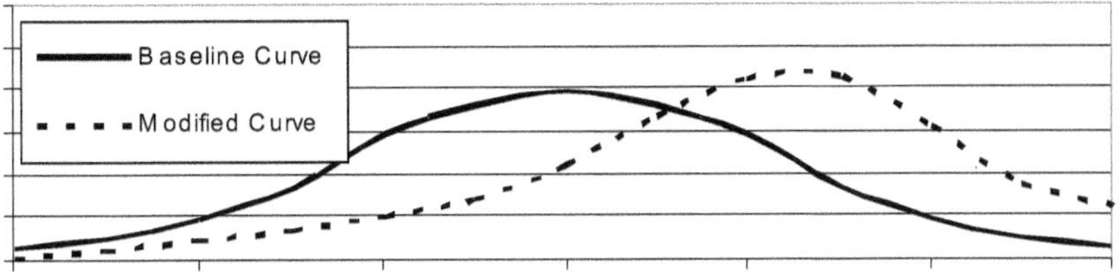

The baseline curve above represents the distribution of size of kernels of feed corn purchased from an Indiana company in 2003. The same company provides feed corn in 2006 with the distribution shown in the modified curve. What changed?

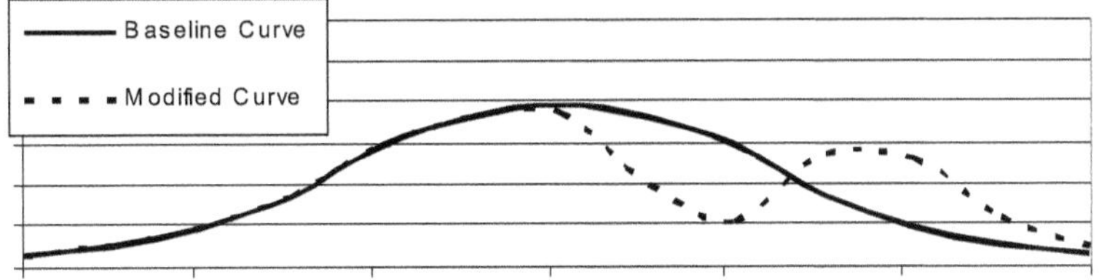

The baseline curve above represents the distribution of lifetimes of a national sample of a particular line of computer equipment. A design change is made, resulting in a lifetime distribution shown in the modified curve. What happened? Did the change improve service life?

In-Class Activities

ICA 8-1

This exercise includes the measurement of a distributed quantity and the graphical presentation of the results. You are to determine how many flexes it takes to cause a paper clip to fail.

Test the bending performance of 20 paper clips by doing the following:

- Unfold the paper clip at the center point so that the resulting wire forms an "S" shape.
- Bend the clip back and forth at the center point until it breaks.
- Record the number of flexes required to break the clip.

On a copy of the table below, record the raw data for the paper clips you break. Then, summarize the data for the team by adding up how many clips broke at each number of flexes. Each team member should contribute 20 data points.

(a) Use the data to plot by hand the following: a histogram with an appropriate bin size, the normalized plot, and CDF.

(b) Use the data to plot using Excel the following: a histogram with an appropriate bin size, and CDF.

Paper clip flexing

Paper Clip	Flexes to Break
1	
2	
3	
4	
5	
6	
7	
8	
9	
10	
11	
12	
13	
14	
15	
16	
17	
18	
19	
20	

Summary of data

No. of Flexes	No. of Clips

ICA 8-2

For the following pressure data, recorded in units of pound-force per square inch, answer the following questions.

1	14	2	15	10
6	3	1	18	

(a) What is the mean of the data?
(b) What is the median of the data?
(c) What is the variance of the data?
(d) What is the standard deviation of the data?

ICA 8-3

The table below lists the number of computer chips rejected for defects during random testing over the course of a week on a manufacturing line. Four samples of 20 parts are pulled each day. Use the following data to generate a histogram and CDF.

1	1	8	0	2	0
0	2	10	1	3	2
0	1	12	0	2	1
1	6	15	0	0	
3	8	1	2	5	

ICA 8-4

One of the NAE Grand Challenges for Engineeering is **Develop Carbon Sequestration Methods**. According to the NAE website: "In pre-industrial times, every million molecules of air contained about 280 molecules of carbon dioxide. Today that proportion exceeds 380 molecules per million, and it continues to climb. Evidence is mounting that carbon dioxide's heat-trapping power has already started to boost average global temperatures. If carbon dioxide levels continue up ward, further warming could have dire consequences, resulting from rising sea levels, agriculture disruptions, and stronger storms (e.g., hurricanes) striking more often."

The Mauna Loa Carbon Dioxide Record is the longest continuous record of atmospheric concentrations of carbon dioxide (CO_2), the chief greenhouse gas responsible for global climate warming. These data are modeled as the Keeling Curve, a graph showing the variation in concentration of atmospheric CO_2 based on measurements taken at the Mauna Loa Observatory in Hawaii under the supervision of Charles David Keeling. It is often called the most important geophysical record on Earth and has been instrumental in showing that mankind is changing the composition of the atmosphere through the combustion of fossil fuels.

The Keeling Curve also shows a cyclic variation in each year corresponding to the seasonal change in the uptake of CO_2 by the world's land vegetation. Most of this vegetation is in the northern hemisphere, where most of the land is located. The level decreases from northern spring onward as new plant growth takes CO_2 out of the atmosphere through photosynthesis and rises again in the northern fall as plants and leaves die off and decay to release the gas back into the atmosphere.

Data and wording for this problem set were obtained from: www.esrl.noaa.gov/gmd/ccgg/trends/. Additional information on the Mauna Loa Observatory can be found at: http://scrippsco2.ucsd.edu/.

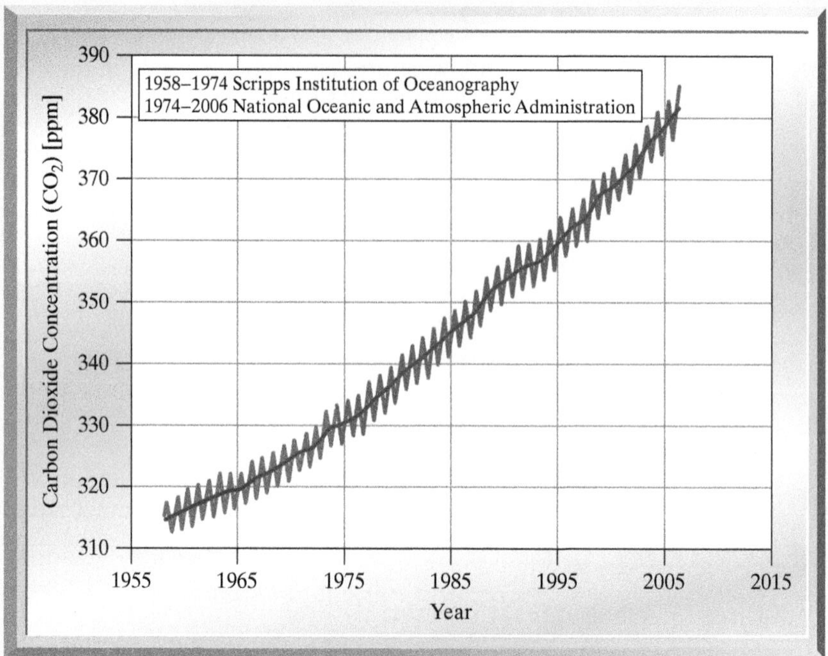

Examine the increase in monthly CO2 emissions for 2009, taken from the Mauna Loa data set. All values given are in parts per million [ppm] CO2 as the difference between the December 2008 and the monthly 2009 reading.

1.38	4.64	–0.77	3.23	2.20	0.45
1.87	3.89	–1.16	3.92	0.37	1.73

(a) What is the mean of these data?

(b) What is the median of these data?

(c) The variance of the data set shown here is 3.5 parts per million squared [ppm^2]. What is the standard deviation of these data?

(d) The estimated annual growth rates for Mauna Loa are close, but not identical, to the global growth rates. The standard deviation of the differences is 0.26 parts per million per year [ppm/year]. What is the variance?

You use the data from the Mauna Loa observatory to create the following histogram and CDF. These data reflect the observed yearly increase in CO_2 emissions for the past 51 years. The annual mean rate of growth of CO_2 in a given year is the difference in concentration between the end of December and the start of January of that year. If used as an average for the globe, it would represent the sum of all CO_2 added to, and removed from, the atmosphere during the year by human activities and by natural processes.

NOTE

In the graph, A and B are *not* drawn to scale, and the locations of C, D, and E are approximate. In other words, you cannot *guess* the value based upon the graph—you must *calculate* the value.

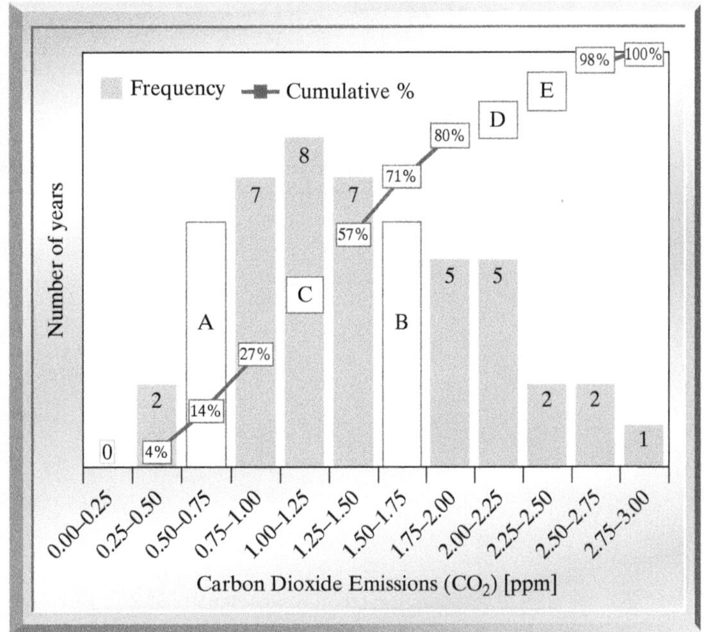

(e) What is the value of point A?
(f) What is the value of point B?
(g) What is the value of point C?
(h) What is the value of point D?
(i) What is the value of point E?

ICA 8-5

An Excel worksheet, titled "Midterm Data," is available online. Use the data provided to determine the following:

(a) Class mean and median.
(b) Class standard deviation.
(c) Often in problems such as this, the bin sizes are preset according to certain constraints. Draw a histogram and CDF, based on the letter grade ranges given below. After the histogram is created, change the bin labels to be the letter grade rather than the numerical value.

Grade	F	D	C	B	A
Minimum	0	60	70	80	90
Maximum	59	69	79	89	100

Use the chart to determine the following:

(d) How many students received a C on the exam?
(e) What percentage of students received an A on the exam?
(f) What percentage of students received a passing grade (C, B, or A) on the exam?

ICA 8-6

From the CDF shown, draw the histogram that was used to create the CDF. Assume there are 20 points, with a minimum of 2 and a maximum of 50.

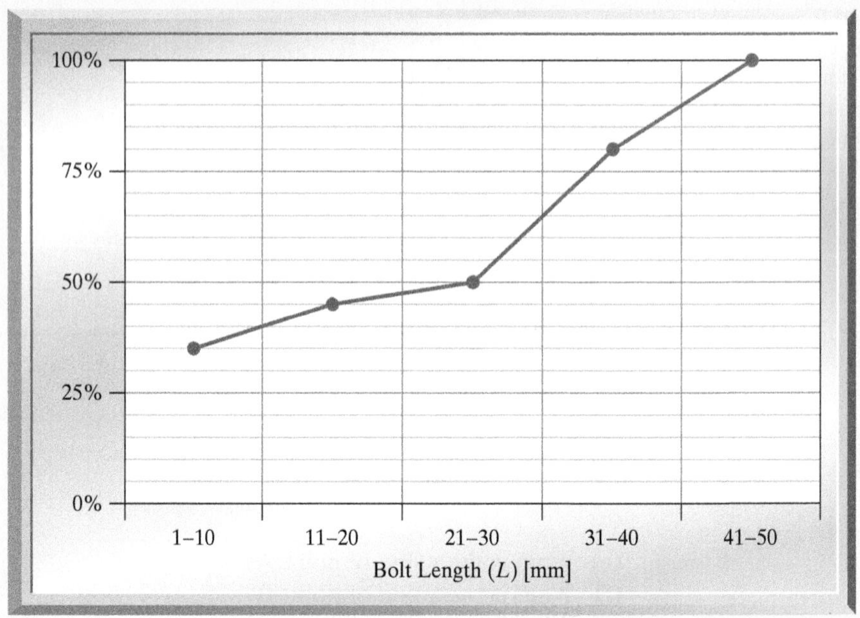

ICA 8-7

A technician tested a temperature probe by inserting it in boiling acetic acid (theoretical boiling point is 118 degrees Fahrenheit), recording the readings, removing and drying the probe, and repeating the process. The data are shown in the following table.

Temperature, Probe 1 (T) [°F]	120	118	105	115	105	120	125
Temperature, Probe 1 (T) [°F]	100	90	95	105	90		

(a) Determine the mean of Probe 1.

(b) Determine the median of Probe 1.

(c) A second probe was tested, yielding a mean of 95 degrees Fahrenheit and a median of 92.5 degrees Fahrenheit. If the data from Probe 2 are as shown above, determine the missing data point.

(d) If a probe has a standard deviation of 8 degrees Fahrenheit, what is the variance of the probe?

ICA 8-8

A technician tested two temperature probes by inserting them in boiling water (theoretical boiling point is 100 degrees Celsius), recording the readings, removing and drying the probe, and repeating the process. The CDF for both probes is shown below.

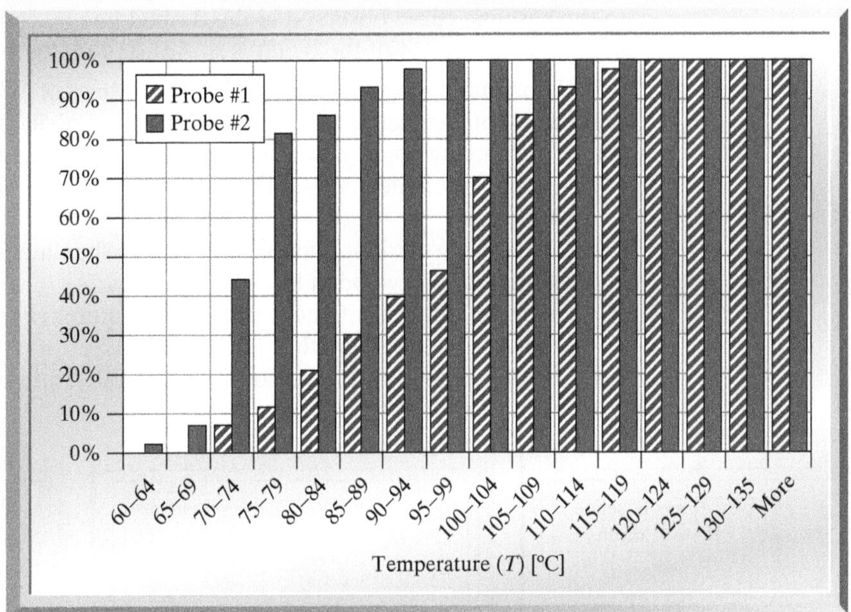

(a) Using this information, which probe would you choose to use?

(b) How would you use the probe you chose above to ensure that you found the correct boiling point?

(c) Which probe has the higher standard deviation?

ICA 8-9

During the month of November, the heating system in your apartment appeared to be broken. To prove this, you record the following daily high temperatures in degrees Fahrenheit, taken every other day:

68	54	60	58	55	55	60	60
86	80	85	85	82	85	91	93

(a) Calculate the mean and median of the data.

(b) Draw the associated histogram and CDF for the data; plot temperature on the abscissa and days on the ordinate.

(c) When you take your complaint to the apartment manager, he fails to see the problem; according to his heating bill, your apartment had an average temperature of 72 degrees Fahrenheit. Show both the mean and the median on the graph drawn for part (b). Which is a better presentation of the data, part (a) or part (b)? Justify.

ICA 8-10

You are assigned to inspect metal-composite beam trusses for a new bridge being built over a nearby lake. The manufacturer has run a prototype set of 500 beams and conducted strength tests, which you consider to be the baseline case, shown by the solid line in all graphs. Examine the graphs on the following page, and explain the changes to the baseline curve observed in the dashed line by choosing a cause from the following list. The strength of the beam is shown on the abscissa.

(a) The manufacturer tested 1,000 beams instead of 500 beams.
(b) The manufacturer tested 200 beams instead of 500 beams.
(c) A reinforcing coating was used on a sample of 500 beams.
(d) An impurity, which caused the beams to weaken, was discovered in a sample of 500 beams.
(e) A data entry clerk accidentally combines the data for 300 metal-composite beams with 200 wooden beams.
(f) The manufacturer upgrades processing equipment to lower the variability of the metal-composite strength.
(g) During a plant strike by union workers, substitute workers manufacture the beams.

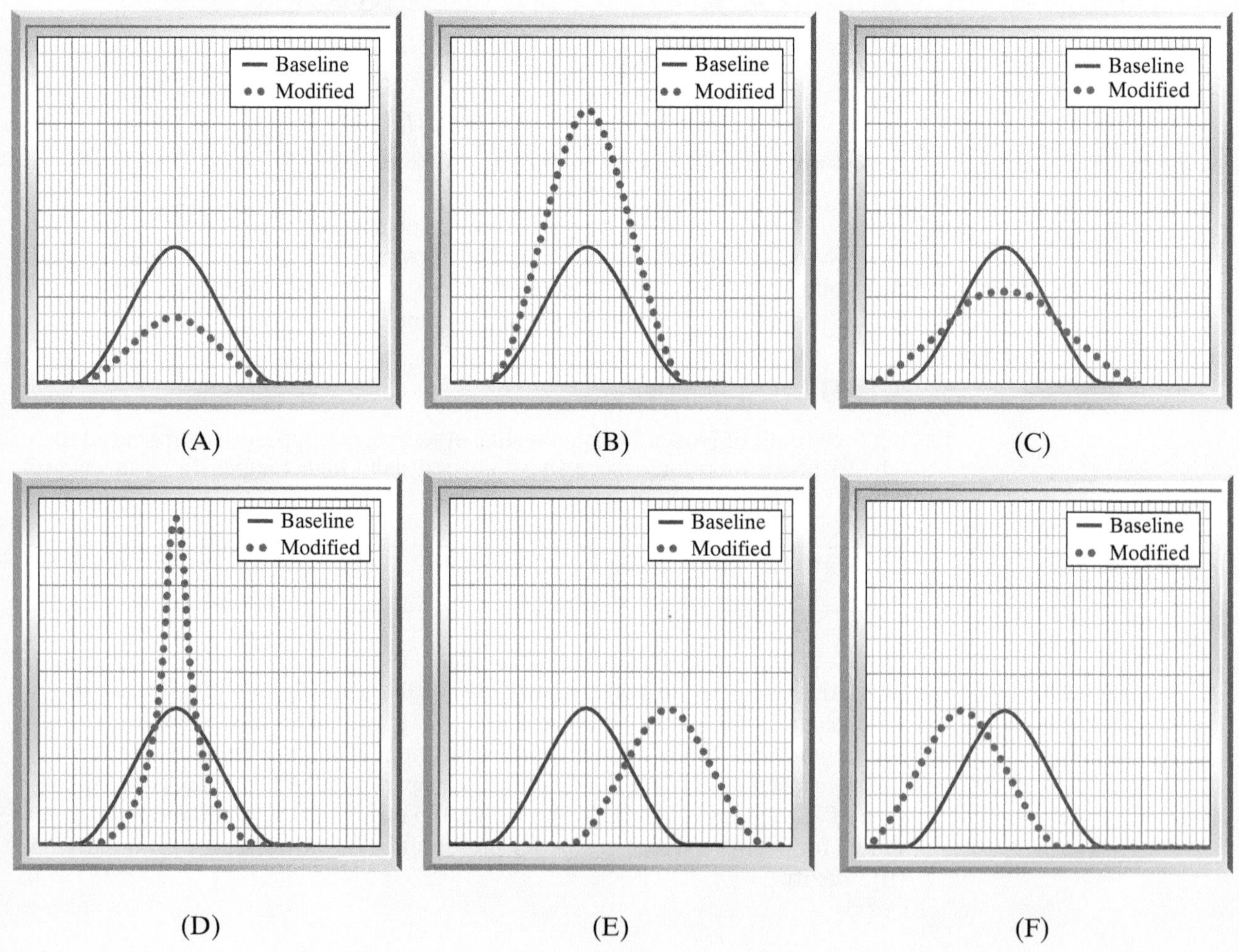

ICA 8-11

The data below were collected from a manufacturing process for making plastic cylinders. According to the specifications, the cylinder diameter should be 100 inches (the average diameter is 100 inches) and the standard deviation is ±5 inches.

Graph the data on a control chart. Be sure to clearly indicate the "Zones" of control.

Using the eight SPC rules, determine whether the process is in statistical control. If it is not in statistical control, indicate which rule or rules are violated.

Part	Diameter (D) [in]
1	100
2	106
3	103
4	99
5	90
6	95
7	105
8	107
9	97
10	96
11	89
12	89
13	87
14	92
15	94
16	87
17	96
18	98

CHAPTER 8 REVIEW QUESTIONS

1. Over 12 school terms, Clemson University recycled the following amount of waste (www.clemson.edu/facilities/recycling). For each set of six academic years (1994 to 1995 through 1999 to 2000 and 2000 to 2001 through 2005 to 2006), determine the mean, median, variance, and standard deviation by hand.

Year	1994–1995	1995–1996	1996–1997	1997–1998	1998–1999	1999–2000
Waste in tons	324.5	204.5	413.7	192.5	280.9	536.9

Year	2000–2001	2001–2002	2002–2003	2003–2004	2004–2005	2005–2006
Waste in tons	671.3	705.9	784.7	681.5	750.7	811.1

2. A technician tested two temperature probes by inserting their probes in boiling water, recording the readings, removing and drying the probes, and repeating the process. The results are shown below, giving temperature reading in degrees Celsius.
For each probe, determine the mean, median, variance, and standard deviation by hand.

Probe 1	87.5	86.5	88	89.5	87	88.5	89
Probe 2	95.5	100	101.5	97.5	90.5	91.5	103.5

3. Ten students are asked to participate in a golf-putting contest. Each student is given five balls, placed at a distance of 60 feet from the hole. They are to try to get each ball in the hole with a single putt. The number of feet that each ball is from the hole when it comes to rest is measured. For simplicity, the assumption is that no students make their putt.
   - **(a)** On a paper, sketch a histogram of this situation (number of students on the ordinate and distance the putt stops from the hole on the abscissa) using the data given.
   - **(b)** In Excel, create a histogram of this situation (number of students on the ordinate and distance the putt stops from the hole on the abscissa), using the data given.

Distance from hole [ft]	0	1	2	3	4	5	6	7	8	9	10	11	12	13	14
Number of balls	0	1	3	2	3	5	4	6	9	7	5	3	2	0	0

4. Metal plates and screws are used to fix complex bone fractures, such as in cases with multiple bone fragments or a large gap in the bone. There are many plate and screw designs with different features, and surgeons need information on how these designs perform in order to choose the correct designs for their cases. For

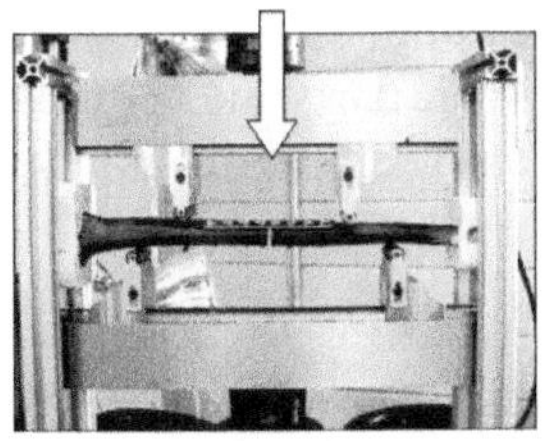

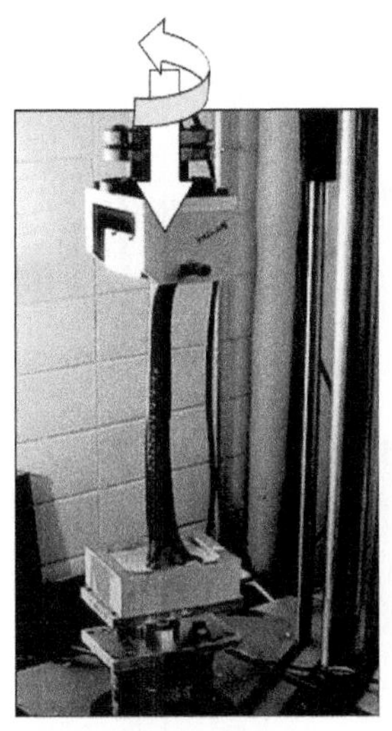

Photos Courtesy of L. Benson

example, Limited Contact Dynamic Compression (LCDC) plates have spherical screwheads that can pivot within the holes in the plate. This allows the bone fragments to compact when they are loaded, which can promote healing. Locking Compression (LC) plates have screws with threaded heads that actually lock into the holes in the plate when they are tightened down. This makes the plate-screw combination stiffer and stronger than the traditional LCDC design and holds the fragments in place when the bone is loaded.

Biomechanical testing mimics the types of loads that are applied to the plates and screws when they are implanted and measures the amount of bending or deformation that a plate undergoes while loaded. The following table shows results from biomechanical testing for the two types of plates described above, under four different types of loading: compression along the long axis of the bone, torsion (or twisting) along the long axis of the bone, four-point bending in the anterior-posterior (A-P, or forward-backward) direction, and four-point bending in the medial-lateral (M-L, or side-to-side) direction. The plates and screws were fastened to composite resin models of the humerus, with a gap between the bone fragments.

The bone plate test setup is the same for loading in compression and torsion, shown in the figure at left. The bone is clamped at both ends in a mechanical testing machine, and loads are applied along the long axis of the bone. The test setup for the four-point bending tests is shown below.

3.5-mm Locking Compression Plate Stiffness				
Test	Compression	Torsion	A-P Bending	M-L Bending
1	400.18	1.05	419.45	587.94
2	863.95	0.96	427.31	435.99
3	526.52	1.03	408.22	533.99
4	596.58	1.03	388.35	543.57

4.5-mm Limited Contact Dynamic Compression Plate Stiffness				
Test	Compression	Torsion	A-P Bending	M-L Bending
1	556.5	1.08	422.27	868.76
2	441.2	1.39	435.63	716.2
3	545.87	1.35	576.77	794.48
4	487.95	1.38	413.1	1,025.75

(a) For each of the four loading conditions, calculate the mean and standard deviation for the stiffness of both plate designs.

(b) The most common mode of fracturing the humerus is a fall where the person puts an arm out to break the fall. This could load the humerus in the medial-lateral direction. Which of these plate designs would you recommend to withstand medial-lateral loading? Justify your answer.

(c) Test results are not considered "significantly different" if the ranges of one standard deviation overlap. For example, if Product A has a mean of 10 and a standard deviation of 5, and Product B has a mean of 14 and a standard deviation of 2, the products are not significantly different since Product A can range from 5 to 15 and Product B from 12 to 16; the two ranges overlap. Compare the two designs in the anterior-posterior bending and in torsional loading. Can one design be considered superior to the other design in these modes of loading?

5. Polyetheretherketone (PEEK)™ are polymers that are resistant to both organic and aqueous environments; they are used in bearings, piston parts, and pumps. Several tests were conducted to determine the ultimate tensile strengths in units of megapascals [MPa]. The following CDF shows results from 320 points.
   (a) What is the frequency value of A on the chart?
   (b) What is the frequency value of B on the chart?
   (c) What is the frequency value of C on the chart?
   (d) What is the frequency value of D on the chart?
   (e) What is the frequency value of E on the chart?

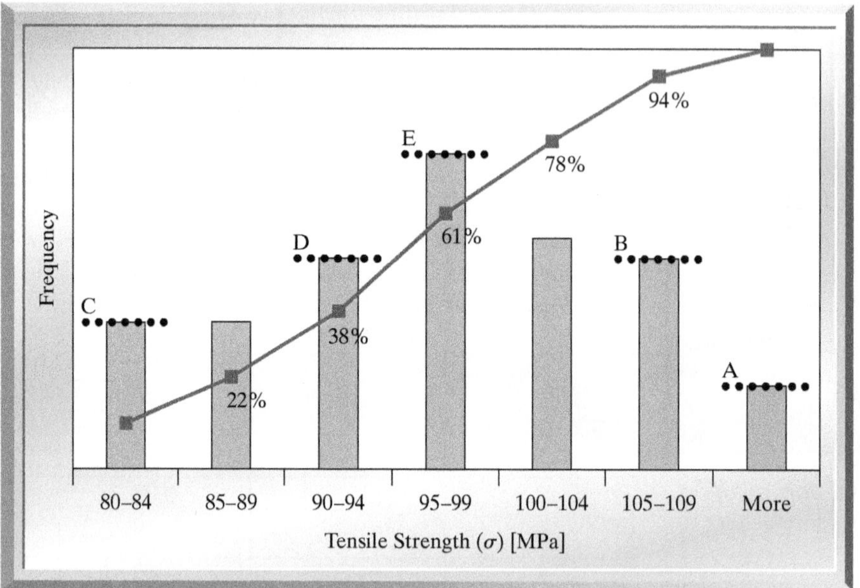

6. A company that fabricates small, custom machines has been asked to generate a machine that throws darts at a dart board as precisely and accurately as possible. To assess the precision and accuracy of each proposed design, the engineers build a model and record the distance from the bullseye of the dart board to the location of each dart thrown—both the straight-line distance (A) and the horizontal (B) and vertical (C) distances are recorded separately with regard to the bullseye, as demonstrated in the figure. The engineers throw 15 darts with their prototype machine and record the three data points for each dart.

   Using the data collected for a design, create a histogram and a CDF for the straight-line distance (A), as well as the horizontal (B) and vertical (C) distances and determine which graph or graphs are better for assessing the performance of the design. Justify your answer with a few sentences about why you selected the graph or graphs.

Dart	Straight Distance (A) [in]	Horizontal Distance (B) [in]	Vertical Distance (C) [in]
1	0.703	0.400	−0.578
2	2.740	1.976	1.898
3	1.555	−.484	0.466
4	0.387	−0.387	0.010
5	1.180	−1.147	−0.278
6	1.424	−1.418	0.132
7	0.899	0.835	0.335
8	2.069	0.330	2.043
9	0.547	0.514	0.187
10	3.451	1.566	3.076
11	2.532	2.361	−0.912
12	3.070	1.602	2.619
13	1.386	0.176	1.375
14	1.637	1.458	−0.744
15	0.888	−0.822	0.337

7. You will be given an Excel spreadsheet, titled "Baseball Data," that contains salary data from major league baseball in 2005. Use the data provided to determine the following:
   (a) Salary mean, median, and standard deviation for all players.
   (b) Salary mean, median, and standard deviation for the Arizona Diamondbacks.
   (c) Salary mean, median, and standard deviation for the Atlanta Braves.
   (d) Salary mean, median, standard deviation for all pitchers. (Hint: Sort first!)
   (e) Salary mean, median, standard deviation for all outfielders. (Hint: Sort first!)
   (f) Which team had the highest average salary?
   (g) Which team had the lowest average salary?
   (h) Which position had the highest average salary? (Hint: Sort first!)
   (i) Which position had the lowest average salary? (Hint: Sort first!)
   (j) Draw a histogram and CDF in Excel for all players.
   (k) What percentage of players earned more than \$1 million?
   (l) What percentage of players earned more than \$5 million?

8. This information was taken from the report of the EPA on the U.S. Greenhouse Gas Inventory (http://www.epa.gov).

"Greenhouse gas emission inventories are developed for a variety of reasons. Scientists use inventories of natural and anthropogenic emissions as tools when developing atmospheric models. Policy makers use inventories to develop strategies and policies for emission reductions and to track the progress of those policies. Regulatory agencies and corporations rely on inventories to establish compliance records with allowable emission rates. Businesses, the public, and other interest groups use inventories to better understand the sources and trends in emissions.

The Inventory of U.S. Greenhouse Gas Emissions and Sinks supplies important information about greenhouse gases, quantifies how much of each gas was emitted into the atmosphere, and describes some of the effects of these emissions on the environment.

In nature, carbon is cycled between various atmospheric, oceanic, biotic, and mineral reservoirs. In the atmosphere, carbon mainly exists in its oxidized form as CO2. CO2 is released into the atmosphere primarily as a result of the burning of fossil fuels (oil, natural gas, and coal) for power generation and in transportation. It is also emitted through various industrial processes, forest clearing, natural gas flaring, and biomass burning."

The EPA website provides data on emissions. The data found in the file "Carbon Dioxide Emissions Data" were taken from this website for the year 2001 for all 50 states and the District of Columbia.

(a) Use the data on all 50 states (+DC) provided in "Carbon Dioxide Emissions Data" to create a histogram with an appropriate bin size; use Excel.

(b) Determine the mean and median of the data. Indicate each of these values on your graph for part (a).

(c) Which value more accurately describes the data? Indicate your choice (mean or median) and the value of your choice. Justify your answer.

9. The Excel data provided online was collected by Ed Fuller of the NIST Ceramics Division in December 1993. The data represent the polished window strength, measured in units of kilopounds per square inch [ksi], and were used to predict the lifetime and confidence of airplane window design. Use the data set to generate a histogram and CDF in Excel (http://www.itl.nist.gov/div898/handbook/eda/section4/eda4291.htm).

10. Choose *one* of the following options and collect the data required. For the data source you select, do the following:
    - Construct a histogram, including justification of bin size.
    - Determine the mean, median, variance, and standard deviation values.
    - Construct a cumulative distribution function.

(a) On a campus sidewalk, mark two locations 50 feet apart. As people walk along, count how many steps they take to go the 50 feet. Do this for 125 individuals.

(b) Select 250 words at random from a book (fiction). Record the number of letters in each word. Alternatively, you can count and record the words in 250 sentences.

(c) Go to one section of the library, and record the number of pages in 125 books in that same section.

(d) Interview 125 people to determine how far their home is, in miles, from the university.

11. You test several temperature probes by inserting them in boiling ethanol (theoretical boiling point is 78.4 degrees Celsius), recording the readings, removing and drying the probe, and repeating the process 20 times. The distribution curves for the probes are shown below. The solid line "baseline" curve in every graph is the same curve, for a previous probe tested 20 times in boiling ethanol.
   (a) Which probe was tested 40 times instead of 20 times?
   (b) Which probe has the highest standard deviation?
   (c) During the testing of one probe, you suspect your assistant of using formic acid (which boils at 101 degrees Celsius) instead of ethanol. Which probe did your assistant incorrectly test?
   (d) Which probe has the lowest standard deviation?
   (e) Which probe was tested 10 times instead of 20 times?
   (f) During the testing of one probe, you suspect your assistant of using chloroform (which boils at 61 degrees Celsius) instead of ethanol. Which probe did your assistant incorrectly test?
   (g) If you could choose between probes C and F, which probe would you choose to use? In a single sentence, describe how you would use the probe you chose to ensure that you found the correct boiling point.

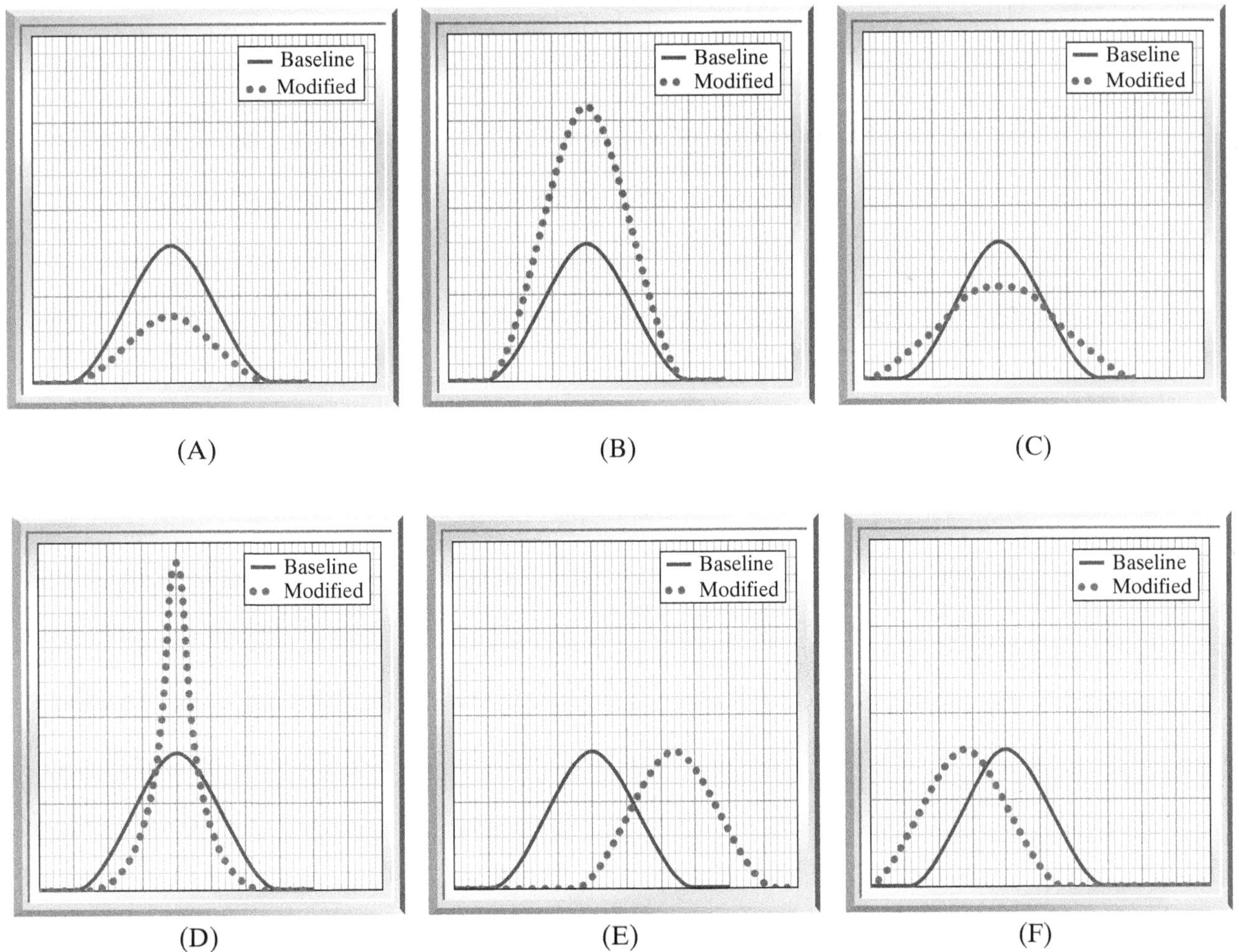

12. You work for a company developing a new hybrid car. Before releasing it to the market, the company has conducted many tests to assess different aspects of the cars' performance. For each characteristic being tested, 500 nonhybrid cars of the same basic design as the new hybrids are tested along with 500 hybrids. The nonhybrid tests are considered the baseline.

You are given six plots (see previous page) showing the results of testing different aspects of the cars' performance. For each type of test described below, determine which plot is most likely to represent the results of that particular test and explain why. Depending on the characteristic being assessed the abscissa variable will vary.

(a) This test assesses gas mileage. The hybrid cars are supposed to have better gas mileage than the nonhybrids.

(b) This test assesses horsepower of the gasoline engine in both hybrid and nonhybrid cars. To ensure engine efficiency, the computer-controlled ignition sequence for the hybrids must have less car-to-car variation than the nonhybrids, thus providing better performance (horsepower).

(c) This test assesses acceleration time. For the nonhybrid cars, the average 0–60 miles per hour acceleration time is 8 seconds. For the hybrid models, it was determined that only 3 of the 500 cars had times of more than 11 seconds. Since the complex manufacturing process for the new hybrids still has some kinks in it, the hybrids do not perform as consistently as the nonhybrid. Assume the hybrids and nonhybrids had the same average acceleration time.

13. The data below were collected from a manufacturing process involving reactor temperature measured in degrees Celsius. The following values are desired: average = 100 degrees Celsius; standard deviation = ±10 degrees Celsius.

Graph the data on a control chart. Be sure to clearly indicate the "Zones" of control.

Using the eight SPC rules, determine whether the process is in statistical control. If it is not in statistical control, indicate which "rule" or "rules" are violated.

Reading No.	Temperature (T) [°C]	Reading No.	Temperature (T) [°C]
1	100	11	103
2	105	12	101
3	106	13	100
4	97	14	98
5	98	15	97
6	95	16	96
7	100	17	104
8	101	18	102
9	96	19	95
10	105	20	101

14. The data below were collected from a manufacturing process involving reactor temperature measured in degrees Celsius. The following values are desired: average = 100 degrees Celsius; standard deviation = ±5 degrees Celsius.

Graph the data on a control chart. Be sure to clearly indicate the "Zones" of control.

Using the eight SPC rules, determine whether the process is in statistical control. If it is not in statistical control, indicate which "rule" or "rules" are violated.

Reading No.	Temperature (*T*) [°C]	Reading No.	Temperature (*T*) [°C]
1	101.0	11	97.5
2	103.5	12	100.0
3	98.5	13	95.0
4	100.5	14	97.0
5	96.5	15	103.0
6	102.5	16	103.0
7	105.0	17	105.5
8	100.0	18	100.5
9	102.0	19	5
10	98.0	20	98.5

CHAPTER 9

DISPLAYING DATA IN WRITTEN DOCUMENTS

Objectives

By learning the material in this chapter, you should be able to

- describe the importance of displaying data;
- design and construct appropriate representations of your data for written documents
- integrate graphical representations into your documents;
- explain in words the significance of each graphic;
- use mathematical and chemical notation.

9.1 INTRODUCTION

A picture is said to be worth a thousand words. And so is a table, a scatter plot, or a bar chart. Figures and tables are often the heart of an engineering document. They display the data, and the exact relationships among data, that will give life and meaning to all interpretation and conclusions. In addition, representing data graphically allows us to show relationships among the data quickly and effectively. For example, it would take far longer to try to explain in words all of the relationships expressed in Figure 9.1.

If you were to explain all parts of Figure 9.1, you would have to write something like this:

> *Air-quality modeling integrates emissions data (from multiple sources), meteorological information, and chemical mechanisms to determine pollutant production over time and space. Emissions are produced by natural organisms as well as by man-made sources such as automobiles. The pollutants produced are many, and the current work is concerned with how these pollutants interact to produce ozone in concentrations greater than current standards deemed safe for human health. This work is concerned primarily with ozone concentrations in the northeastern U.S.*

However, you cannot make the mistake of thinking that a good technical communicator does not need words to describe the significance of these relationships. A picture may be worth a thousand words, but it does not necessarily replace all words. Some people are not used to reading figures and tables, and they need to be oriented to what the figure shows. Other people know how to read figures, but they are reading quickly and could thereby miss the significance of the information revealed by the graphic. Using figures or tables *and* words allows you to communicate very effectively.

Taken from *Engineering Communication,* Second Edition, by Hillary Hart.

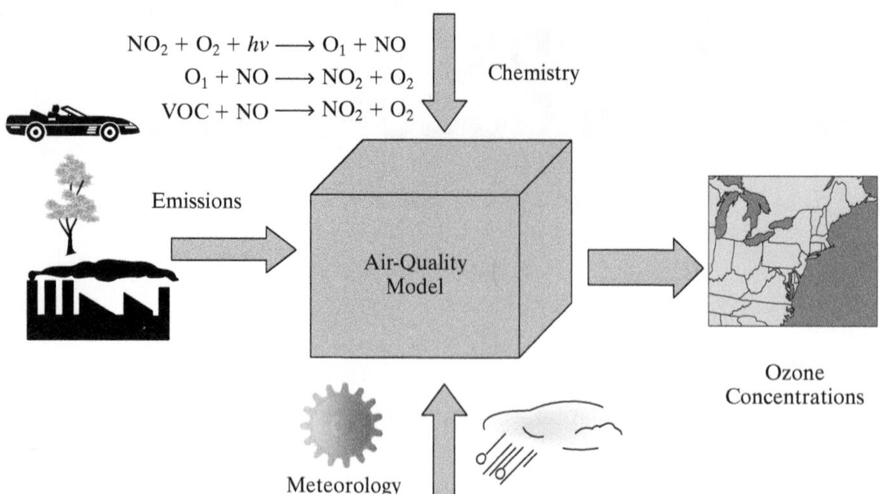

Figure 9.1 A model for ozone concentrations in the northeastern U.S.

By combining modes of delivery, you allow readers to use parallel processing in understanding the importance of your information: They can use both their visual and their verbal understanding. Especially when dealing with complex data, you need the double power of words plus graphics to ensure that readers and listeners will get the total picture. Some people are more visual in their orientation toward learning, and some people are more verbal. Most engineers tend to be visual, but your readers may not be engineers.

WHY USE GRAPHICS IN TECHNICAL DOCUMENTS?

- to show complex data in a simplified form
- to show a lot of data in one place
- to emphasize relationships
- to help the reader remember
- to allow parallel processing of information

Graphics are also a very important part of presenting information verbally. It is difficult to imagine a technical presentation that does not exhibit well-projected, readable figures. The design rules governing presentation graphics, however, are somewhat different from those for graphics in written documents. This chapter deals with how to design and use graphics in *documents*.

9.2 DISPLAYING YOUR DATA

As an engineer, you will collect data in various ways. Sometimes you will model a system or process, providing certain inputs and extracting outputs. Sometimes you will use mathematical calculations to test a hypothesis or prove a theory. And very commonly, you will use experiments, in the lab or in the field, to yield information that helps solve

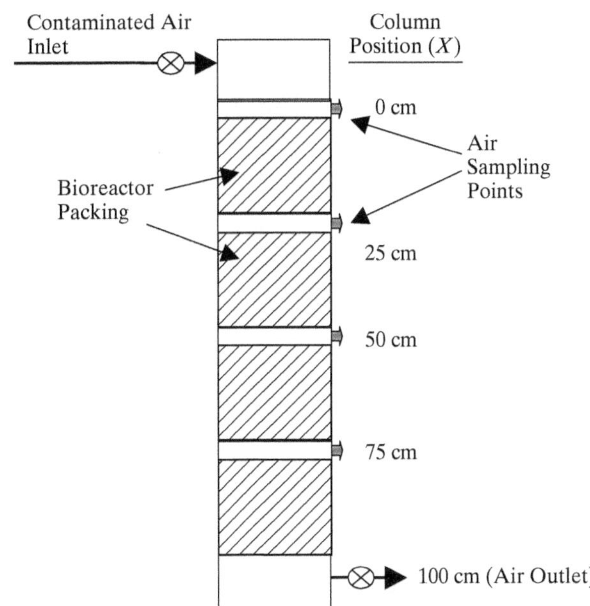

Figure 9.2 Schematic of the experimental bioreactor.

problems. Let us posit a situation in which you work for a manufacturing company as an air-pollution control expert. Your job is to find economical ways of cleaning the gas waste stream produced by the manufacturing process. Biofiltration is a promising technique that uses microorganisms to reduce pollutants in the gas stream, but you need to find out how large a biofiltration system would be needed at the plant and how much it would cost. A typical system uses a packed bed of biological material inside a column through which the gas stream is run for treatment. Figure 9.2 is a schematic identifying key components of the system.

> ***Key Idea:*** You will create different displays of your data for different audiences, and for yourself.

You set about designing and conducting a series of experiments to show the relationship between the size of the system and the amount of pollutants in the gas stream that is destroyed by the microorganisms. You run the experiments, collect the data by taking samples of the gas at various positions within the column, and record the data. At that point, your communication work begins, because you must present the data to various managers within your company and help them come to a decision about what size system to use. You must first display the data for your own benefit, so you can determine at what position in the column enough pollutants are destroyed that the column has done its work and is no longer necessary; a shorter column makes for a cheaper treatment system. Then you must show these data and this relationship (between position in the column and concentration of pollutants) to others in a comprehensible, visual form. But how?

Well, to understand the data yourself, you will use a spreadsheet program such as Microsoft® Excel. You will enter the sampling data (concentration of pollutants) that you recorded, with three samples for each position in the column. Let us say you recorded data in triplicate at the inlet point, at the outlet point, and at 25, 50, and 75 cm from the inlet of the column. Since you will want to take the average of the three readings for each sample, your data sheet would look like Table 9.1 (where pollutant concentration is measured in milligrams per cubic meter).

Once you have entered the data in the spreadsheet, you can create many kinds of graphs to show the relationship between pollutant concentration and position in the

Table 9.1 Excel worksheet containing sample data for an experimental biofiltration system

Position (CM)	0	25	50	75	100
Concentration (mg/m^3)					
sample 1	101.0	68.0	45.5	28.8	15.0
sample 2	98.4	66.5	43.0	27.3	13.1
sample 3	97.7	71.2	46.3	22.3	16.8
Average (mg/m^3)	**99.0**	**68.6**	**44.9**	**26.1**	**15.0**
Standard Deviation	1.74	2.40	1.72	3.40	1.85

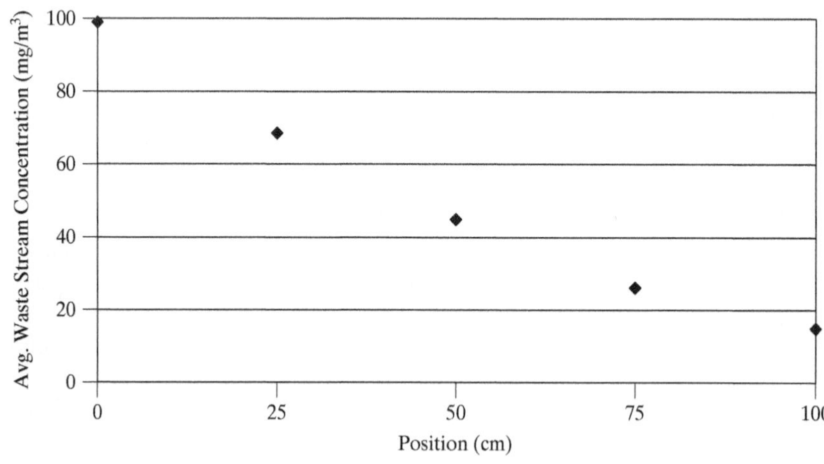

Figure 9.3 Relationship of position in the biofiltration column and pollutant concentration of the gas waste stream [data points only].

column. You could show simply the data points, as in Figure 9.3 (remember that the points on the graph are averages of the three samples taken at each position).

If you want to show more clearly the *trend* in the data, you could connect the data points (as in Figure 9.4a) or fit the data by using a regression model (as in Figure 9.4b). Excel contains a tool called "trendline" that provides various regression models. Be sure to indicate the equation of the trendline on the figure.

If you wanted to show more clearly the *scatter* in your data (emphasizing the fact that not every one of the three samples taken at the same position had exactly the same concentration), you could use error bars, which plot the standard deviation of the data at each point, as in Figure 9.5.

So, now you would be ready to put together a report for a variety of audiences, from the other project engineers to the head of your division, and even the chief financial officer. Of course, your presentation or report should begin with a schematic of the system, showing the column and where the gas stream enters and exits. Remember, we began this discussion about displaying data with a drawing of the treatment column. Be sure to use visuals to orient your reader to as many aspects of your experimental conditions as possible.

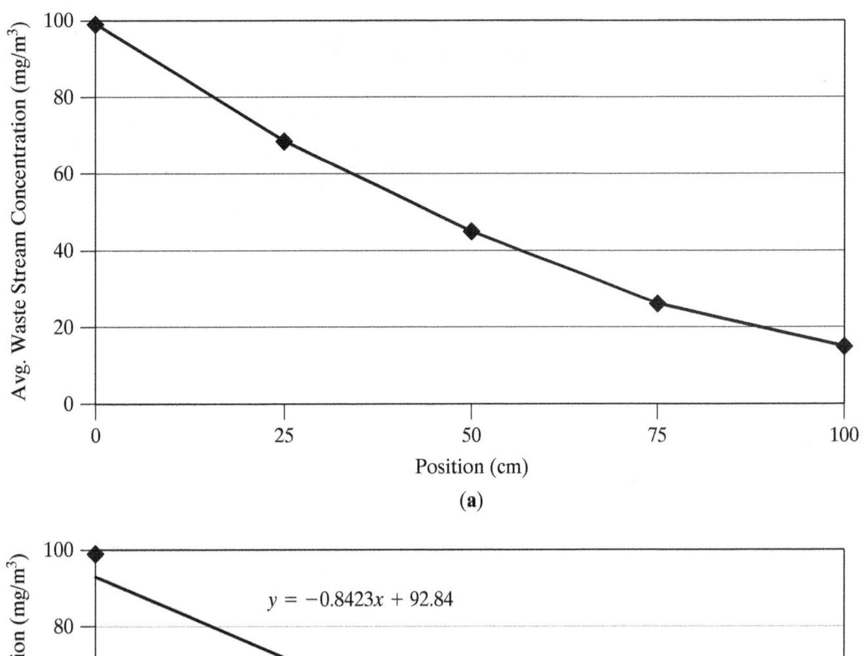

Figure 9.4 (a and b) Relationship of position in the biofiltration column and pollutant concentration in the gas waste stream: (a) data connected from point to point; (b) linear regression fit to the data.

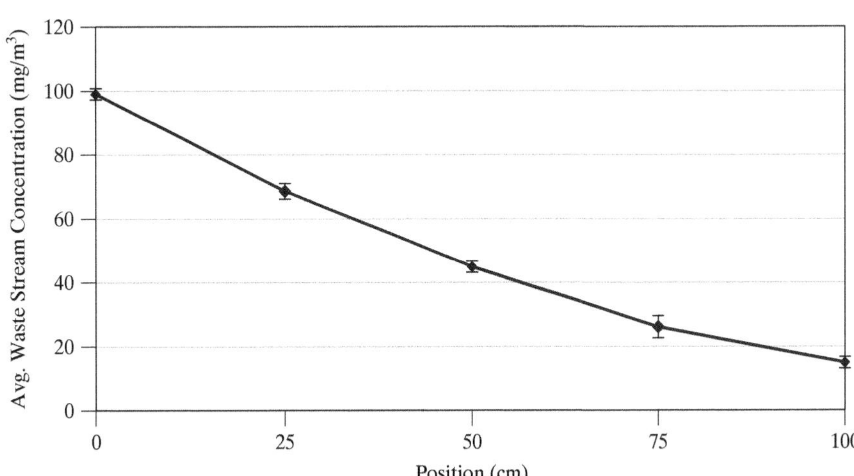

Figure 9.5 Relationship of position in the biofiltration column and pollutant concentration in the gas waste stream [showing standard deviation of data at each point].

9.3 FIGURES AND TABLES: WHICH IS WHICH?

Although there are many different types of graphical display, in engineering documents these types are usually grouped into one of two categories for purposes of labeling and numbering: figures and tables. So, first of all, let us answer the question, "What is a figure and what is a table, and why?"

9.3.1 Tables

Tables are compilations of reference data, usually displaying numbers and/or keywords. The data are listed in columns (vertical elements) and rows (horizontal), with headers clearly delineated. Table 9.2 shows a typically designed table.

Table 9.2 Comparison of three air filters for an aquarium

Filter	Calibration Factor	Flow Rate (gallons/hour)	Efficiency
Power	4–5	1000	Least
Canister	1–2	250	Moderate
Wet/Dry	3–4	700	Highest

Notice that the units of measurement for flow rate are given in the column heading, so that they do not have to be repeated in each row. In written documents, all tables are numbered consecutively—Table 1, Table 2, etc.—and each has an explanatory title and is referred to in the text. Sometimes the numbering of tables is done in Roman numerals (e.g., III, IV, and V) instead of Arabic numerals, to differentiate the tables from figures.

9.3.2 Figures

Figures are what we call every other sort of graphical representation: bar charts, line graphs, scatter plots, schematics, plan views, photographs, pie charts, etc. In written documents, all figures are numbered consecutively and have explanatory labels and titles. A few books and journals still call certain illustrations (especially drawings and photographs) "plates" instead of "figures." All figures (and plates) are also explained and referred to in the text.

Here are descriptions of the more common types of figures.

Figures: Graphs

X–Y graphs are most engineers' favorite way of displaying data. They are particularly useful for showing trends in data over time and changes in the relationship of two variables. The independent variable is usually plotted on the x-axis and the dependent variable on the y-axis. In Figure 9.6, the independent variable is time (in seconds), and the dependent variable is position, measured in meters from the starting point (0). The graph shows how far a ball travels when it is tossed into the air until it starts to fall. In this graph, the slope of the curve mimics the physical reality that the graph expresses; however, graphs do not usually try to look like what they are depicting.

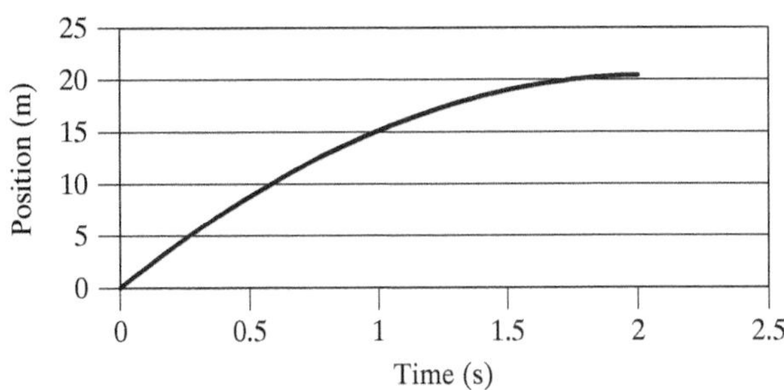

Figure 9.6 Distance a ball travels when tossed into the air.

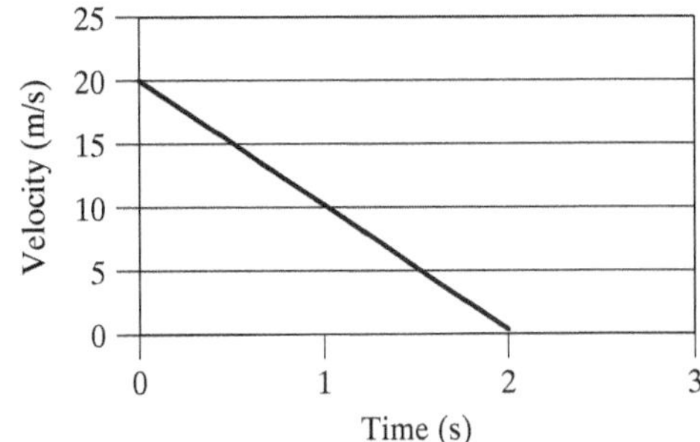

Figure 9.7 Velocity of ball tossed into the air (at constant acceleration of –9.8 meters/second²).

In Figure 9.7, the slope of the curve actually looks like the opposite of what is happening. This figure displays the velocity of a ball as it travels upward through the air to the point where it would start to fall and actually show a negative velocity.

A portion of the data set for Figures 9.6 and 9.7 is shown in Table 9.3. To graph the *distance* the ball travels, you would plot the values for the independent variable in column 1 (time) and the dependent variable in column 2 (position). To graph the *velocity* of the ball over time, you would plot columns 1 (time) and 3 (velocity). These data can be generated by the formulas you enter for velocity and by the ranges you specify for time and position. Since acceleration is a constant governed by gravity (g), you probably would not want to graph it, but you should include it in your explanation of the figure and, whenever possible, show such relevant data on the figure itself.

Line graphs are useful to show changes in one variable over time or differences in values for certain items. You use line graphs when the x-axis is showing labels or increments, not numerical values. Thus, for example, you could show the differences in grades among four students as displayed in Figure 9.8.

Table 9.3 Data set for Figures 9.6 and 9.7

INITIAL POSITION	0		
initial velocity	20		
time (s)	position (m)	velocity (m/s)	acceleration (m/s²)
0	0	20	–9.8
0.5	8.775	15.1	–9.8
1	15.1	10.2	–9.8
1.5	18.975	5.3	–9.8
2	20.4	0.4	–9.8

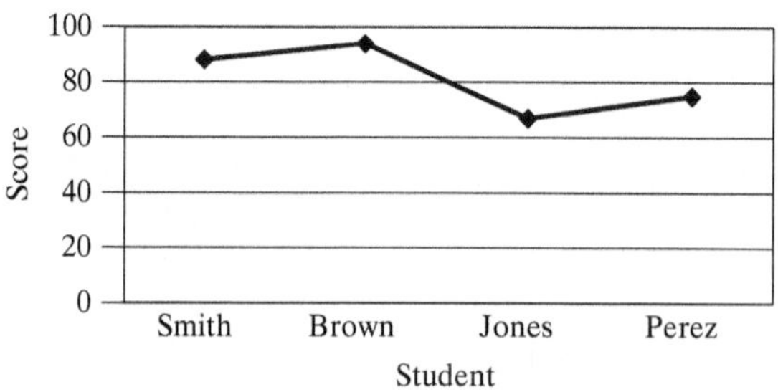

Figure 9.8 Final scores for four students.

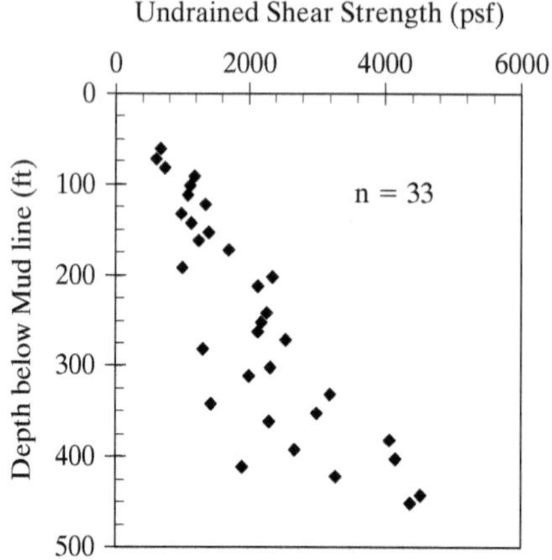

Figure 9.9 Relationship of undrained shear strength and depth for soil samples taken in the Gulf of Mexico, July 2001. *Graph courtesy of Dr. Robert Gilbert, University of Texas at Austin.*

Most line graphs could also be constructed as bar charts. Do not confuse line graphs with scatter plots that have a line drawn through the data points. Engineers do not use line graphs as often as x–y scatter plots because the former do not plot the relationship between two variables. For line graphs to make sense, the increments along the x-axis must be equal.

Scatter plots show a relationship between variables for a particular phenomenon or quality at precise points. For example, Figure 9.9 shows measurements of soil samples from an offshore boring that was drilled from an oil production platform. The measurements are of the undrained shear strength of the soil, which is an indication of how strong the soil is. In the graph, the strength is shown in relation to the depth (below the mud line) of the sample taken. The important conclusions from this plot are twofold:

1. The plot shows a trend wherein the undrained shear strength tends to increase with depth.
2. The amount of scatter about this trend increases with increasing depth.

Notice that the labels for the x-axis are on the top of the figure rather than at the bottom and that the independent variable (depth) is plotted along the ordinate (the y-axis) instead of along the abscissa (the x-axis) as is usual. This exception to the rule governing placement of the dependent and independent variables occurs most commonly for graphs that plot depth. Because the concept of depth is inherently visual, we normally plot depth where it makes visual sense—along the vertical axis. Note also that the number n of data points is indicated on the figure. Whenever possible, place such helpful information right on the figure itself. If the information is more complex, it may be more appropriate to put it in a caption. If not, you will want to discuss it in your text, along with any other information about the experimental, modeling, or mathematical procedure behind the graphic.

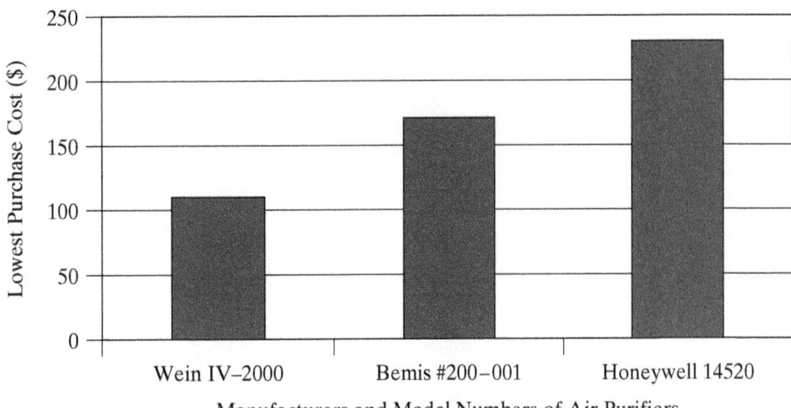

Figure 9.10 Lowest purchase costs found for Bemis, Honeywell, and Wein air purifiers.

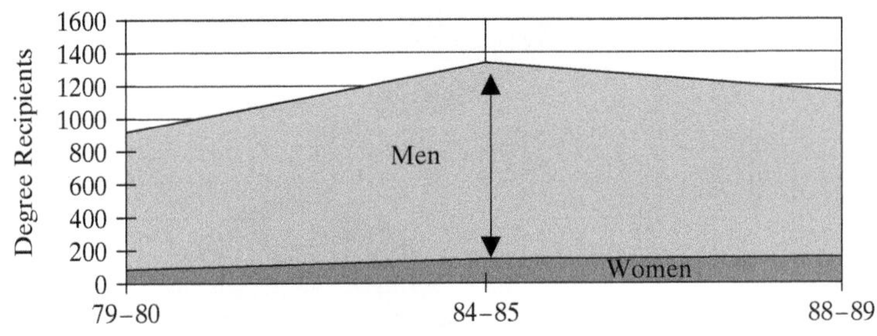

Figure 9.11 University of Malibu degree recipients by gender [hard to read].

Figures: Charts

Bar charts are probably the most widely used graphic in the popular press, if not in engineering reports, because they are easy to understand and multifunctional. They come in many varieties, too, including histograms and Gantt charts. Comparing the sizes of bars is an easy way to compare differences in values or amounts of particular items. The prevalence of bar charts in annual reports suggests that cost comparisons are a natural subject for these kinds of charts. Figure 9.10 compares the costs of various air purifiers.

Area charts, or stacked charts, are really a series of line graphs piled on top of each other. They are tricky to read because, beyond the bottom line, you do not read from the beginning of the scale: You separate out the "chunk" that is bounded by two lines and figure out the values within that chunk. Most nontechnical people, and even a lot of engineers, tend to read stacked charts improperly. Consequently, this type of chart should be used only rarely in technical documents. Consider Figure 9.11 and ask yourself how to determine the number of men who got degrees from this university in 1984–1985. In order to figure out the number of men receiving degrees in 1984–1985, you have to estimate how many are indicated in the chunk delineated by the arrows. Such an estimate is not very precise, and many people would be tempted to estimate the number by starting at the very bottom of the graph instead of at the line at the top of the "Women" chunk, adding about 100 to the correct number. The correct number is 1,240.

Pie charts are often used to depict constituents of a whole. These kinds of charts are seen everywhere, especially in magazines and newspapers, because they are ostensibly easy to read. They *are* easy to read, but only if they are designed and used well. Figure 9.12 displays the cost breakdown for the air purifiers (discussed previously) as a pie chart. Designing this chart in three dimensions doesn't make much sense, however, and

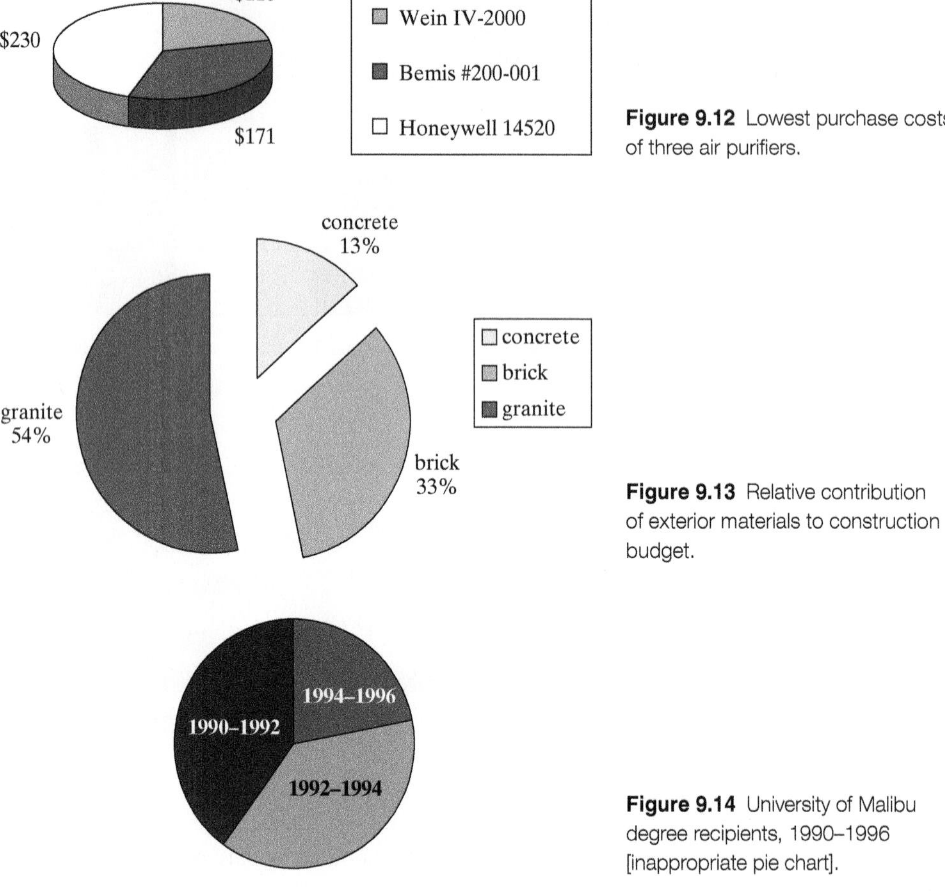

Figure 9.12 Lowest purchase costs of three air purifiers.

Figure 9.13 Relative contribution of exterior materials to construction budget.

Figure 9.14 University of Malibu degree recipients, 1990–1996 [inappropriate pie chart].

lends a bit of distortion to the figure. The slices facing toward us seem proportionately larger than they are because they (seemingly) show a third dimension.

Pie charts really come into their own when you display the values as percentages of a whole, as in Figure 9.13. The reader can easily see the pieces as representative of the portion each material contributes to the total construction budget. In this figure, the pieces are "exploded," which emphasizes their relative size (and therefore value) even more.

Be sure that when you use a pie chart, your goal is to focus on the whole of something: a whole year, a whole graduating class, etc. In the pie chart in Figure 9.14, the importance of the whole—the total number of graduates from this university in the years 1990–1996 is not immediately clear. Why is that number important, especially when it is not even given? It might be important for some analysis of recent alumni, for example, *but the graphic does not clarify this information.*

Flowcharts make visual a process that otherwise would be more difficult to conceptualize and understand. They can depict processes as simple as activities in a workday, or they can depict more complicated processes, rendering them simpler to understand. Figure 9.15 shows a flowchart depicting the performance-review process in a company.

Figures: Drawings and Schematics

Drawings and schematics simplify reality and thereby show the essential elements necessary to understand a particular problem or phenomenon. Figure 9.16 is a schematic

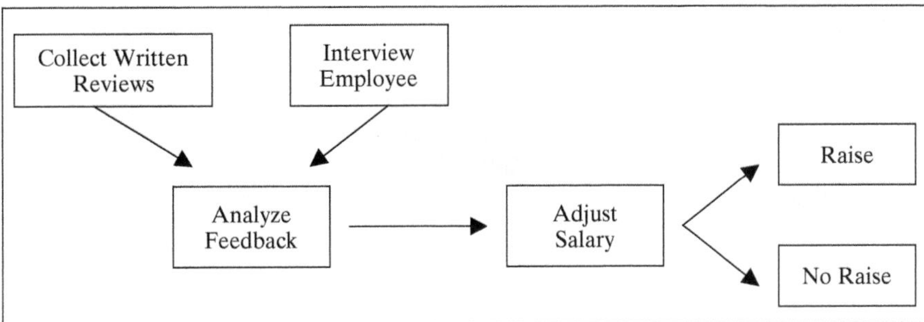

Figure 9.15 Performance-review process for Integrated Documentation, Inc.

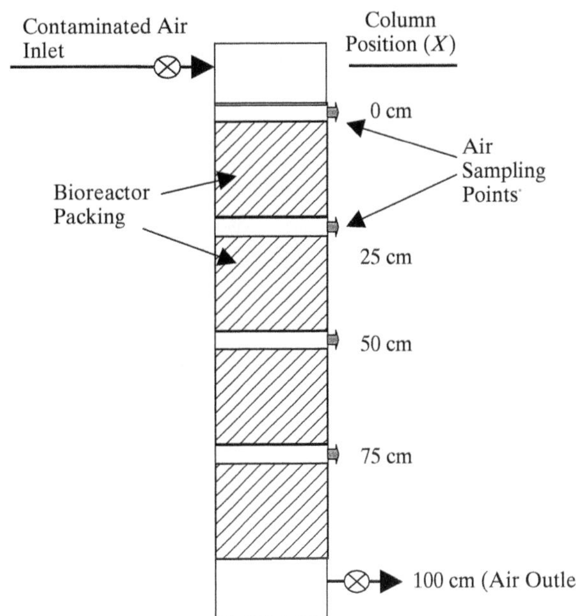

Figure 9.16 Schematic of an experimental bioreactor.

of a bioreactor. The actual column, made from stainless steel, does not look exactly like the schematic in Figure 9.16, but the drawing shows all that is essential to understand how the experimental work was accomplished using this bioreactor. We see that the contaminated air stream was fed into the column at the top, that samples of air were taken every 25 centimeters, and that the column is 100 cm long. The figure also establishes that, for purposes of graphs showing results of the sampling, "0" is the top of the column, where the air is first fed in.

Figures: Combinations

Some figures artfully combine the attributes of several types of figures, as in Figure 9.17, a drawing and flowchart depicting the process of pollution in an aquarium. Be careful of trying to combine too many types of figures and thereby failing to help the reader understand information quickly. Figure 9.17 works because of its elegant simplicity.

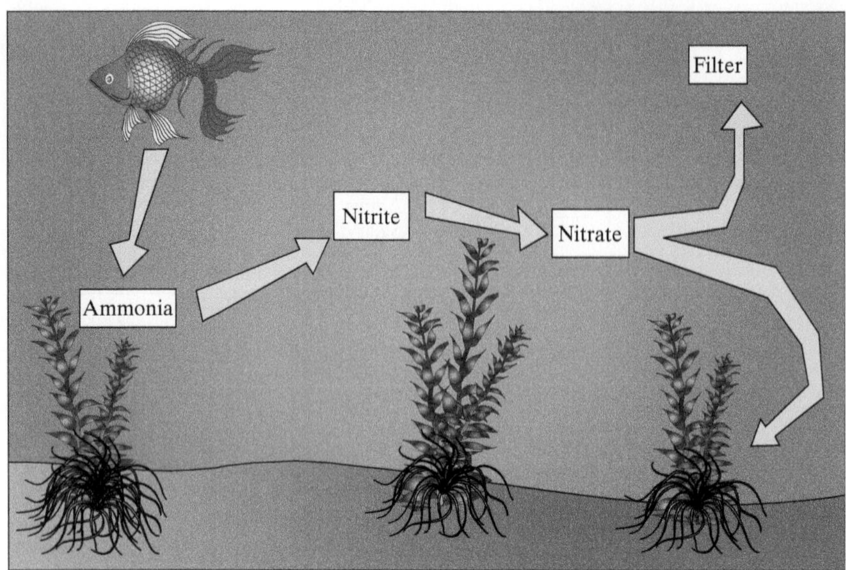

Figure 9.17 Process of pollution in an aquarium.

GUIDELINES FOR GRAPHICS: ENGINEERING CONVENTIONS

- In graphs, use lines to illustrate predictions of models, and points to indicate data values found through experiment, especially when comparing the two types of information.
- Follow the convention for direction: When tables or figures are printed sideways on a piece of paper, the paper should be turned clockwise for the table or figure to be read.

9.4 GUIDELINES FOR DESIGNING FIGURES AND TABLES

Because figures and tables are often the heart of an engineering document, your figures must be clear and correct. If they are not, your methodology begins to seem questionable to the reader, and the foundation for your interpretive judgments crumbles. A picture may be worth a thousand words, but a graphic will be worth less than nothing if it represents the data inaccurately or confusingly. How do you construct useful and readable figures and tables?

9.4.1 Graphs

Here are some instructions for constructing a clear, readable graph. The abscissa is the horizontal axis, which typically displays values for the independent variable. The ordinate is the vertical axis, which typically displays values for the dependent variable. The point of origin of both the ordinate and the abscissa is generally zero, although there is a lot of disagreement about the importance of adhering to this guideline. In displaying certain data, zero may not be a meaningful value, and having to begin the ordinate with zero may

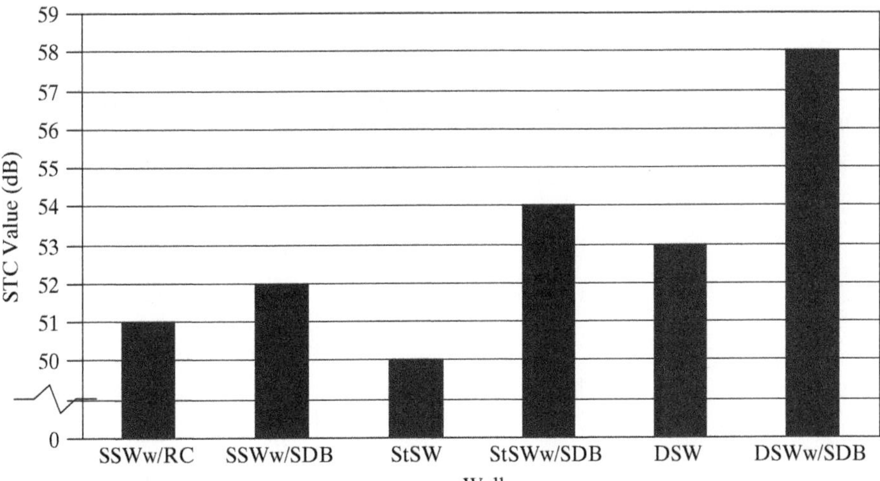

Figure 9.18 Performance measured as Sound Transmission Class (STC) values for each wall design. *Source:* Simmons, Leslie. *Construction: Principles, Materials, and Methods.* 2001.

mean creating a scale that does not capture the relevant data. To ensure that your audience will not misunderstand the graph for such a case (especially when you are unsure about the audience's technical background), consider starting the ordinate values at zero and then inserting a zig-zag break mark to indicate that the scale is being broken for the sake of displaying the relevant data. In Figure 9.18, all of the relevant values for the dependent variable (the STC values) were between 50 and 58 decibels, so the author started the *y*-axis at zero but then jumped to 50 to begin the next interval. The break mark indicates this jump. Unfortunately, Excel does not contain a feature that will insert a break mark. Other programs, such as SigmaGraph, do contain such a feature.

Both axes should be properly labeled. These labels should use words and symbols whenever possible and include the units of measurement; using both words and symbols can tie the figure well to the text. Common abbreviations may be used; when in doubt, however, spell out the word. In Figure 9.18, dB is the common abbreviation for "decibels."

9.4.2 Tables

Tables can be useful for showing comparisons of and changes in data, but they can easily become overcrowded and hard to read. Be sure to highlight important information in tables, such as totals or especially significant numbers or words. Color is effective as a highlighter, but remember that someone may make black-and-white copies of your table. For example, the original version of Table 9.4 had red numbers indicating unacceptable settlement. But in a black-and-white copy those numbers are lost in a sea of other black-and-white numbers, and thus the point of this table (that certain sizes of piles allow too much settlement of a structure) is not as clear. Also, the caption has to be rewritten, since red will not show up in the black-and-white copy. You can use shading to differentiate.

Tables often give a more compete "story" than a line graph (e.g., tables give specific numbers, while graphs typically present only approximate numbers), but generally they are not as effective as more pictorial forms. Consider including tables in appendices and creating line or bar graphs to summarize the same data in the body of your document.

Table 9.4 Comparison of settling for various types of piles

Piles that exceed 0.25 inches of settlement are shown in red. Piles that are shaded in gray were discarded. *[Author's note: Red cannot be seen in black-and-white reproduction.]*

Concrete Pile			Hollow Steel Pile			Concrete-Filled Pile		
Diam (in)	Len (ft)	Sett (in)	Diam (in)	Len (ft)	Sett (in)	Diam (in)	Len (ft)	Sett (in)
12	50	0.19	12	50	0.07	12	50	0.19
12	55	0.37	12	55	0.18	12	55	0.37
12	60	0.36	12	60	0.17	12	60	0.36
12	65	0.61	12	65	0.28	12	65	0.61
14	50	0.20	14	50	0.10	14	50	0.20
14	55	0.33	14	55	0.16	14	55	0.33
14	60	0.43	14	60	0.21	14	60	0.43
14	65	0.68	14	65	0.26	14	65	0.58
16	50	0.23	16	50	0.10	16	50	0.23
16	55	0.32	16	55	0.20	16	55	0.32
16	60	0.41	16	60	0.42	16	60	0.41
16	65	0.43	16	65	0.43	16	65	0.43

9.4.3 Taking Control of the Design

The default parameters used in standard software for generating figures are not always the best choice for conveying technical information. Figures 9.19 and 9.20 contain the same data; however, Figure 9.20 is much easier to read.

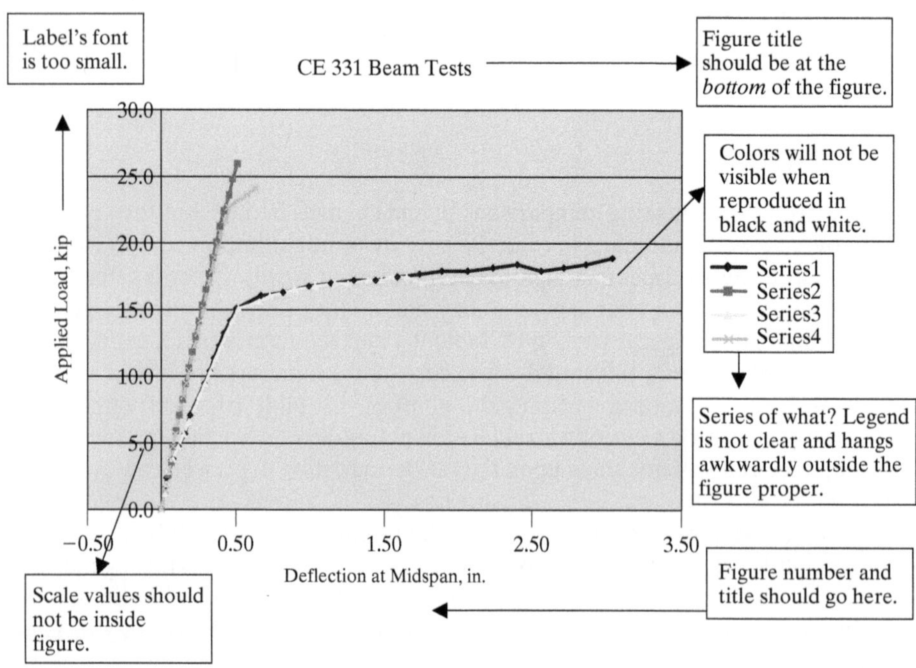
Label's font is too small.
CE 331 Beam Tests
Figure title should be at the *bottom* of the figure.
Colors will not be visible when reproduced in black and white.
Series1
Series2
Series3
Series4
Series of what? Legend is not clear and hangs awkwardly outside the figure proper.
Applied Load, kip
30.0
25.0
20.0
15.0
10.0
5.0
0.0
−0.50
0.50
1.50
2.50
3.50
Deflection at Midspan, in.
Figure number and title should go here.
Scale values should not be inside figure.

Figure 9.19 Concrete beam deflections at various loads [badly formatted graph].

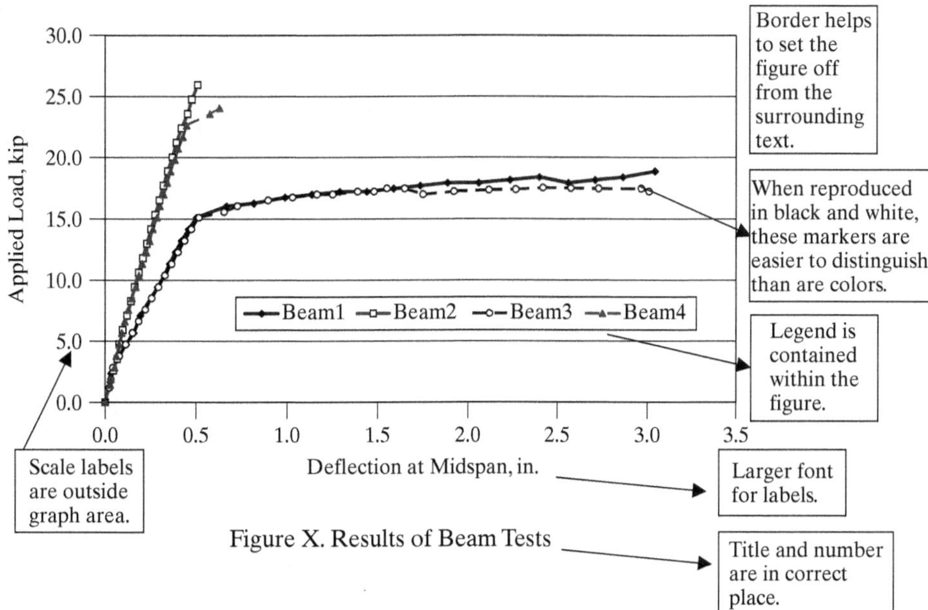

Figure 9.20 Concrete beam deflections at various loads [well formatted].

The modified graph is easier to read because it uses a larger font and has a larger area in which to display the data. The modified graph also has a figure number and a meaningful title in the proper place.

Note that Figures 9.19 and 9.20 seem to flout the rule that the independent variable is plotted on the abscissa: Deflection, or strain, is dependent on the load (or stress) applied in the experiment. In structural engineering, however, stress–strain curves are always plotted such that strain is plotted horizontally and stress is plotted vertically. Be sure to become familiar with the conventions of your particular branch of engineering. A good way to obtain this familiarity is by reading around in the journals in your field. Notice how figures and tables are presented. Do the axes always cross at zero? Are units of measurement always abbreviated? Is the independent variable always plotted on the *x*-axis? Are tables numbered with a different style than are figures?

Consider the following items when preparing your figures:

- Gray backgrounds, such as that in Figure 9.19, look nice on the screen, but the technical information tends to be lost when the figure is plotted in black and white.
- Whenever possible, select scales so that the axes cross at (0,0). In all cases, position the axis labels outside the graph area.
- It is not always easy to distinguish among the default colors and symbols when graphs are printed in black and white. Selecting open and filled markers is one way to distinguish one data set from another.
- Default text sizes from graphing programs are typically too small when graphs are imported into a word processor.
- Default line widths from graphing programs are often too thin when graphs are imported into a word processor.
- The location of the legend may decrease the available area for displaying technical information.
- A figure should have a number and a meaningful title placed below, not above, the figure.

Key Idea: Keep every graphic as simple and uncluttered as the complexity of your data allows.

When designing tables, remember that the default parameters used in standard software are not always the best choice for conveying technical information. Tables 9.5 and 9.6 contain the same data; however, Table 9.6 is much easier to read.

All of these changes create a graphically simpler table that lets us focus on the data it presents rather than distracting us with meaningless lines and too much white space. Notice that the number and title of tables are placed on top.

Table 9.5 Example of table that uses default parameters

Column heads are not spaced sensibly and are not in boldface.

Sieve Size	Weight Retained (g)	Percent Retained	Cumulative Percent Retained	Percent Passing
#4	54	10.2	10.2	89.9
#8	78	14.7	24.9	75.1
#16	125	23.5	48.4	51.6
#30	116	21.8	70.2	29.8
#50	88	16.6	86.8	13.2
#100	60	11.3	98.1	1.9
#200	5	0.9	99.0	1.0
Pan	5	0.9	100.0	0.0
Total	531	100.0		

Too many horizontal lines. Our eyes become distracted from the data.

Numbers and text are not centered.

Ponder This

PRACTICE QUESTION: DESIGNING TABLES

What changes make Table 9.6 easier and faster to read than Table 9.5?

SUGGESTED ANSWER

- Text and labels are centered.
- Unnecessary horizontal lines are removed.
- Column and row headings are in boldface and single spaced.

9.4.4 A Word about Titles

Key Idea: Position each graphic as near as possible to the text it supports, but always after the first reference to it.

Titles for graphics are often slapped on at the last minute without much thought. As such, in engineering documents, they are far too often superficial and do not help the reader understand the significant relationships or phenomena displayed by the graphic. A title that simply repeats the labels of the *x*-and *y*-axes adds nothing to the knowledge of the reader. Figure 9.21 depicts the decreasing velocity of a ball tossed into the air and has the title, "Velocity vs. Time." With this inadequate title as a guide,

Table 9.6 Example of table with modified parameters

Sieve Size	Weight Retained (g)	Percent Retained	Cumulative Percent Retained	Percent Passing
#4	54	10.2	10.2	89.9
#8	78	14.7	24.9	75.1
#16	125	23.5	48.4	51.6
#30	116	21.8	70.2	29.8
#50	88	16.6	86.8	13.2
#100	60	11.3	98.1	1.9
#200	5	0.9	99.0	1.0
Pan	5	0.9	100.0	0.0
Total	531	100.0		

PONDER THIS

PRACTICE QUESTION: LABELING GRAPHICS

What is wrong with this title for a graph?

"Time vs. Temperature"

SUGGESTED ANSWER

The title gives no more information than can be found by reading the axes of the graph. That information is already on the figure, so the title should add more information, such as the material involved (e.g., the temperature of what?).

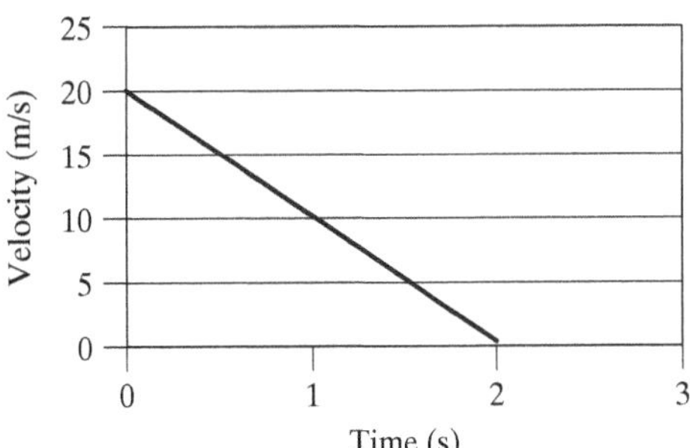

Figure 9.21 Velocity vs. Time [bad title].

we cannot understand why velocity is decreasing, because we have no idea as to what object's velocity is being measured. Here is a better, more descriptive title:

> **Figure 9.21. Velocity of ball tossed into the air** (at constant acceleration of -9.8 meters/sec^2).

Another example of an inadequate title is shown in Figure 9.22, which depicts a graph showing air density as a prediction of the ideal-gas law. This *x*-vs.-*y* title simply

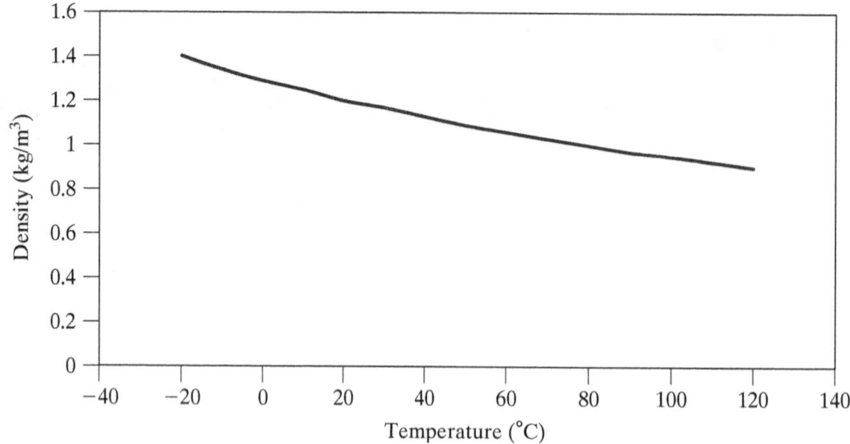

Figure 9.22 Density vs. Temperature [bad title].

repeats the labels on the figure without *interpreting* the data at all. A much better title would be the following:

> **Figure 9.22. Predicted relationship of density and temperature of air at standard atmospheric pressure**

If any of your readers are likely to be nontechnical, you might want to add a caption after the title, such as the following:

> **Figure 9.22. Predicted inverse relationship of density and temperature of air at standard atmospheric pressure.** Note that density tends to decrease with increasing temperature.

Captions are sometimes used in addition to titles. Captions can help the reader understand the data being presented; they often refer either to the way the data have been shown or to the conditions under which the data were collected. Let us look again at the title and caption from Table 9.4, which shows settlement data for piles. The caption tells us how to read the table for the greatest understanding. But, of course, this particular caption works only if the table is presented in color. Remember that *you cannot rely on your work always being reproduced in color in hard copy*.

> **Table 9.4. Comparison of settling for various types of piles.**
> Piles that exceed 0.25 inches of settlement are shown in red. Piles that are shaded in gray were discarded.

The punctuation of titles and captions has not been standardized across all engineering and scientific fields. Even the venerable *Chicago Manual of Style* does not indicate a preference for capitalization of titles and captions. Thus, you may either capitalize the first letter in all the words in your figure and table titles (not counting articles such as "a" and "the") or capitalize only the first letter of the initial word. If the figure has a title *and* a caption, the caption is most often treated as a sentence. You may have noticed that, in this chapter, all the figure and table titles have only the first letter of the initial word capitalized. In addition, the table titles in this chapter have no period, even if a caption follows, but figure titles have a period at the end, even if no caption follows. These decisions were made by the publisher, not by me. Most journals use the same format for both figure and table titles—the position (below vs. above the graphic), not the title's format, is what distinguishes a figure from a table. I suggest using periods only

GUIDELINES FOR GRAPHICS: *LABELS*

- Label each figure or table clearly with a number and a title. For tables, the number and title are centered or left justified above the table. For figures, the number and title go beneath the figure. Your graphics program might have different defaults, but override them, unless your instructor says otherwise.
- Give pertinent details about the experiment either on the figure itself or in parentheses after the title.
- Create a title that draws attention to significant aspects of the illustration. Be more creative than using a simple "*y* vs. *x*" title.

after the figure number (to separate it from the title) and not at the end of the title, unless it is followed by a caption. If there is a caption, then use a period to separate the title from the caption for both figures and tables. This latter treatment is recommended by the *Chicago Manual.* The best way for you to find out what to do is to read the journals in your field and notice how they handle figure titles and captions. Also, ask your instructor for guidance.

9.5 INTEGRATING TEXT WITH FIGURES AND TABLES

The most important point to remember when integrating your text with your figures and tables is this: Each figure or table should be explained and interpreted in your text, and yet each should be able to stand by itself, to make sense even out of context. Your explanation of a figure or table should answer two questions sequentially:

1. What information does the figure or table contain, and (in many cases) how were those results obtained?
2. What does this information mean?

First orient the reader to the particulars shown in the figure or table (experimental details, values obtained, etc.); then fully interpret and discuss all changes, relationships, processes, or phenomena indicated by these data. If your figure or table is partially a repetition of information shown in earlier figures or tables, simply remind the reader of that information; do not repeat all of it. If the previous writing up to the point of any particular figure or table is good, very little new information should be necessary in order to answer the first question. You should focus instead on the meaning or interpretation of the information in the figure or table.

Key Idea: Make your figures and tables right the first time, including the labeling and titling. It is easier to write and rewrite the text when you have final figures.

9.5.1 Using Graphics Designed by Others

Sometimes, the graphic you want to use already exists, because the data it depicts did not originate with you. Sketches and photographs especially fall into this category, and they are readily available on the Internet. May you use a drawing created and published by someone else? For educational purposes (a report for class, for instance), the answer is a qualified "yes," as long as you acknowledge the source of the graphic. Figure 9.23 is an example of a picture used in a report comparing rocket engines. This drawing already existed on the NASA website and became an important

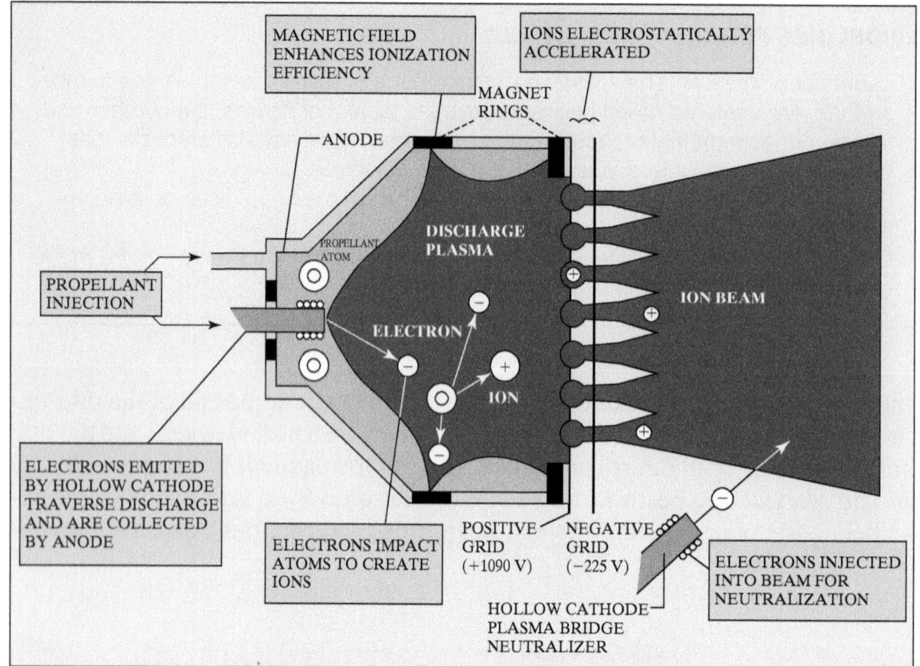

Figure 9.23 An internal schematic of the Xenon Ion engine. *Source:* NASA Glenn Research Center.

WHEN DISCUSSING TECHNICAL GRAPHICS, HERE ARE SOME GUIDELINES:

- Do not repeat in the text *all* of the data represented in the graphic (especially a table).
- Do not continually say, "The figure shows. . . ." The emphasis should be on the information, not on the word "figure."
- Do not fail to interpret the graphic and explain its significance.
- Do not use "data" as a singular word. "Data" is a plural word; "datum" is the singular version.

tool in this student's research. There was no point in redesigning this visual depiction of the process by which a rocket engine produces thrust. So, the student provided the source of the drawing directly underneath the title.

It is a good idea to provide at least author information in the source citation. In this case, the author is the research center rather than an individual. The full citation should then go in the list of references at the end of the document. In this case, the full citation would include the URL (http://www.lerc.nasa.gov/www/pao/html/ipsworks.htm) and the date the student accessed the site, since the date of publication is not available on the Web page from which this picture came.

The site from which the Xenon Ion engine picture came is maintained by a public agency, so the images are usually considered to be public and therefore usable by the public, especially for educational purposes. The safest plan in borrowing an image, however, is to write to the authors or sponsors of the site (in this case, NASA) for permission to use the picture.

If you have designed your own graphical depiction of some data, but the data themselves came from another source, you do have an obligation to indicate the source

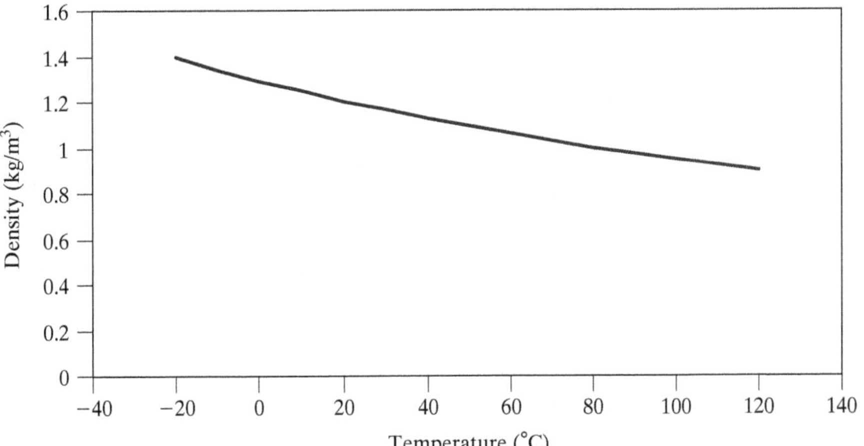

Figure 9.24 Relationship between density and temperature of air at standard atmospheric pressure. *Source of data:* Crowe, C.T., et al. 2001. *Engineering Fluid Mechanics,* 7th ed.

of those data. For example, if you create an x–y plot to show the correlation between density of air and temperature at successive measurements, and the values for the plot came from a textbook, you should cite that book right under the title of your figure, as in Figure 9.24.

You do not have to cite all of the publication details under the title if those details are included in a reference list in your document.

9.6 MATHEMATICAL AND CHEMICAL NOTATION

Representing mathematical and chemical formulas and equations is easier today than ever before. MS Word has an Equation Editor that will render fractions and special relationships and offers a variety of special characters and Greek letters for equations. There are certain conventions for incorporating mathematical or chemical formulas into your writing. All equations are numbered sequentially in your text, and can thereafter be referred to in your text by the number:

$$Y = X^{2/3} + X \tag{1}$$

$$E = mc^2 \tag{2}$$

Einstein's simple equation is justly famous because it posits that two almost opposite entities, mass and energy, are related by a simple equation, and that the factor for converting one to the other is numerically enormous—the square of an already large number, the speed of light. For even simple equations, however, you must define all your variables and, if possible, give dimensions, either generally or specifically:

E = energy (in joules)
m = mass (in kilograms)
c = speed of light in a vacuum (in meters/second; approximately 300,000,000 m/s)

In the case of Equation (1), you could define Y as the density of water in either general or specific terms:

Y = density of water (M/L^3) [mass divided by Liters cubed]

OR

Y = density of water (g/c^3)

There is, of course, an International System of Units (SI) that defines many variables. This system is worldwide and is published by various organizations such as the National Institute for Standards and Technology (NIST): http://physics.nist.gov/cuu/Units/units.html. Consult the tables for notation of standard units, but, again, remember that not all of your readers or listeners will be familiar with all of the standard notations. It is safest to define all your variables somewhere in your document; for those variables that are used in several of your equations in a longer document (a technical report, for instance), define the variables in a Glossary or somewhere up front.

Be careful of using programming conventions to represent mathematical formulas in place of standard conventions; such use may lead to confusion. Consider, for instance, this formula generated from a spreadsheet application such as Excel:

$$Y = X\hat{}2/3 + X \tag{3}$$

This notation could be misinterpreted to mean any of these three versions of the equation using conventional mathematical notation:

$$Y = \frac{X^2}{3 + X} \tag{4}$$

OR

$$Y = \frac{X^2}{3} + X \tag{5}$$

OR

$$Y = X^{2/3} + X \tag{6}$$

Those familiar with programming languages will know that Equation (5) is the correct translation into conventional notation, but not all of your readers will interpret Equation (3) properly.

These same comments apply to chemical notation. Number the chemical reactions you represent. Define all symbols (even elements), unless you are writing for a technically advanced audience, and even then define symbols with any complexity;

As	Should be familiar to scientists and environmental engineers as "Arsenic"
CH_4	Might or might not be familiar to all engineers as a "molecule of methane"
CH_3COOH	Most likely needs defining as "acetic acid"

A courteous way to write the chemical formula for the breakdown of acetic acid would be:

CH_3COOH (acetic acid) $\longrightarrow$ CH_4 (methane) + CO_2 (carbon dioxide)

Greek letters should generally be defined, even those that are very common in chemical notation. If units are measured in μg/L, it is helpful to define the terms as micrograms/liter. And for some readers, it may be wise to define micro: $\mu = 10^{-6}$

Spreadsheet programs such as Excel generally follow the rule held by many engineering journals: use italic type for all letters representing variables except uppercase Greek letters, which should be in upright type.

SUMMARY

- Spreadsheet programs help you organize and synthesize numerical and other data that you collect. Use such programs to perform calculations on your data and, ultimately, to represent the data in chart form as a table or figure.
- If you experiment with the different chart forms available in Excel and other spreadsheet or graphing programs, you will learn which forms represent different kinds of data best. Bar charts and line graphs are good for showing changes in one variable over time; *x–y* and scatter plots are the best choices for showing changes in the relationship between two variables. Engineers use the latter types of graph most of the time.
- Readers need help in understanding the significance of the information in your graphics. Interpret and explain your graphics in words.
- Give proper credit when you use a graphic created by someone else. If possible, ask permission first.
- Use an equation editor and SI units to express mathematical and chemical formulae and equations. Define all variables.

EXERCISES AND ACTIVITIES

9.1 Record the temperature in your bedroom over a 48-hour period. Then, make an *x–y* graph showing relationship between time of day/night and temperature. Answer these questions, and justify your choices:

What decisions do you have to make about displaying the data and labeling the axes?

Which kind of *x–y* graph did you choose (with line, with trendline, etc.)?

9.2 Take the same data on temperature of your bedroom as in Problem 9.1 and make another kind of graph or chart (other than an *x–y* graph). Try at least two types, such as these: a line graph, a pie chart, a bar chart, an area chart. Experiment to see which type of visual display looks best and displays the information best. Which type(s) do you think do *not* work well?

9.3 Test the graphs you produced in Problem 9.1 and/or Problem 9.2 on at least one friend. Which type of visual display works best and why? Ask your friends to explain their preferences.

9.4 Read an engineering article on a topic you are studying for one of your classes. Study the graphics and write a brief description of their effectiveness by answering the following questions:

Are the graphics easy to decipher and understand? Why or why not?

Do the graphics convey the information discussed in the text of the article, or do they introduce new data/information not completely discussed in the text?

Does each graphic contain enough details such that it could stand alone, without the accompanying discussion?

9.5 Look again at the graphics in the article you read in Problem 9.4. Which single graphic (figure or table) seems the best to you, and why? Discuss its virtues—what makes it clear and full of useful information? Can you point to design elements that help make this figure or table clear and useful?

9.6 Looking at the graphic of the Xenon Ion engine in Figure 9.23, write a paragraph or two of description of how the engine works. Does the graphic give you enough information to do this, or do you have to fill in some gaps?

9.7 True or false? Area charts (stacked charts) are the easiest to read of all types of charts.

9.8 True or false? Using color is always an effective way to highlight numbers on a table.

9.9 True or false? An acceptable strategy for presenting a set of data in reports is to include a selection of the data in a graphic in the body of the report and the full set of data in a table in the appendix.

9.10 Write at least one paragraph defending *one* of these positions:

(a) The *y* axis should always start at zero.

(b) Under certain circumstances, the *y* axis does not have to start at zero.

FURTHER READING

Cleveland, W.S. 1994. *The Elements of Graphing Data*. Hobart Press: Summit, NJ.

This comprehensive work covers every aspect of understanding how best to graph data. The discussion is high level, but easy to follow. There is more information here than most undergraduates will need, but everyone from beginning students to working engineers will benefit from the substantive discussions of how to make your data stand out and how to avoid ambiguity. Use the index to target answers to any questions you have about specific graphical elements. Error bars, for instance, can actually be ambiguous if the graph does not make clear whether they show the sample standard deviation (one use of error bars) or an estimate of the standard deviation of the standard mean (another use of error bars; see pp. 60–61).

Tufte, E.R. 1983. *The Visual Display of Quantitative Information*. Graphics Press: Cheshire, CT.

This beautifully produced book revolutionized the study of information display and raised the level of awareness of how important graphics are in understanding scientific and technical concepts. When Tufte could not get this book printed properly, he started his own publishing firm in Connecticut. Every page of this book has nuggets of gold, but you should look especially at Part I and the "Chartjunk" chapter in Part II.

Tufte, E.R. 1990. *Envisioning Information*. Graphics Press: Cheshire, CT.

This second major work by Tufte expands the variety of graphics examined, looking at every type of information display, including words themselves. There is a wonderful reproduction of a three-dimensional model published by Euclid in 1570.

Valiela, I. 2001. *Doing Science: Design, Analysis, and Communication of Scientific Research*. Oxford University Press: Oxford, U.K.

The first four chapters of this much-needed book cover how to obtain and analyze scientific information, as well as how to design one's research. Chapters 5–11 offer good guidance and examples for communicating those data effectively and accurately so that everyone, even the general public, can think critically about scientific information and make well-founded decisions.

CHAPTER 10
SUSTAINABILITY IN ENGINEERING DESIGN

Objectives

By learning the material in this chapter, you should be able to

- define sustainability in at least two ways
- define the ideas of footprint, life cycle analysis, and systems design
- complete a Graedel analysis and justify calculation
- read a McKinsey curve
- describe why sustainable designs are art of good engineering

10.1 INTRODUCTION

10.1.1 Introduction to Sustainable Design

Over the past decade, the term *sustainable design* has increasingly entered the language of engineering; all indications are that sustainability will become central to good engineering in the next decades. While the term "sustainability" is relatively new, its principles are not (although they have not always been followed well). Most common definitions of sustainable design involve using resources, defined broadly, in a way that does not impair the ability of future generations to live with a similar quality of life. It is, quite simply, long-term and broad-scale planning. In terms that even Purdue's earliest engineering students would have understood, sustainability is the old admonition, "don't eat your seed corn."

Brainstorming: in groups of four, name as many "resources" as you can in one minute.

In this context, sustainable design is not merely a special interest, the buzzword of "treehuggers," or a topic to be handled only by a specialist. Sustainability is remarkably broad; the "seed corn" can take many forms. It can be any resource—natural, ecological, social, political, economic—that people will need to continue to function efficiently in the future. Making sure that all aspects of a design solution fit the framework of

---

Courtesy of Purdue University.

long-term sustainability is fundamental to all design work and all engineers. Environmental science teaches us that everything is connected—that every aspect of any system affects all other aspects of that system. More importantly, there are no truly isolated systems—every aspect of a system affects all other aspects of *all other* systems.

Therefore, design requires consideration of where materials come from, where they will continue to come from, how much waste will be produced and what will happen to it, how much energy is needed and in what forms, what long-term maintenance costs will incur, what the lifetime expectation are, what public health implications are, and what neighboring systems will be affected and how, etc. These are the considerations of sustainability, and design without these considerations is, simply, bad design.

Unsustainability of Current Practices

The first step toward assessing and defining what sustainable engineering would look like is the identification of current practices that are not sustainable. In the current industrial and engineering system, which social and industrial practices can not continue at the current rate without imperiling the future ability of the system to function effectively?

Unsustainable practices can take several forms, including resource depletion, ecosystem impairment, and exceedance of pollution assimilation abilities.

Resource depletion is a straightforward problem, with straightforward sustainability designs: use less, recycle, develop alternatives, increase efficiency of use, etc. A prime example of important resource depletion concerns petroleum, and the concept of "peak oil." The peak oil concept assumes that resource extraction rates follow a defined peak-shaped pattern; the point where the extraction rate is at its maximum is the time point of peak oil.

Oil production in the US peaked in 1974, and is currently more than 40% lower than the peak value (see figure). It is less clear where the world is relative to its eventual peak oil point. Estimates of world peak oil time range from immediate to a few decades away—it is likely that world oil production will begin drop in your professional lifetime, and all engineers will need to adjust their designs to compensate for a lower-oil economy. It is important to note that US oil *consumption* has not seen a similar peak and decline: over the past three decades, US demand has increased steadily at a rate of about 80–90 million barrels per year.

> Think-Pair-Share: Consider a field of engineering that particularly interests you. How will the activities and designs of engineers in that field need to change if oil (and the products derived from oil, including both energy and petrochemicals) become less available?

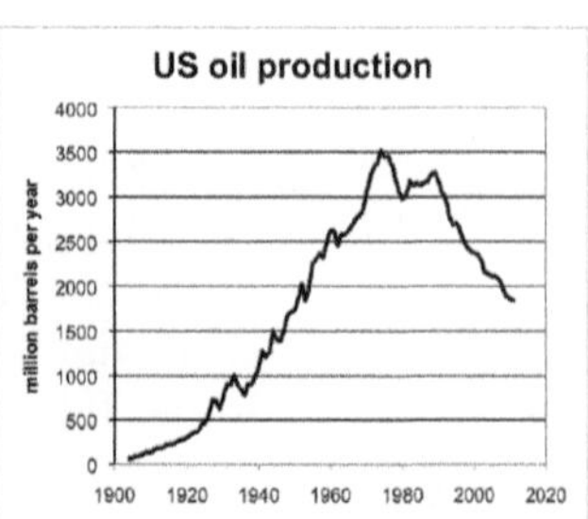

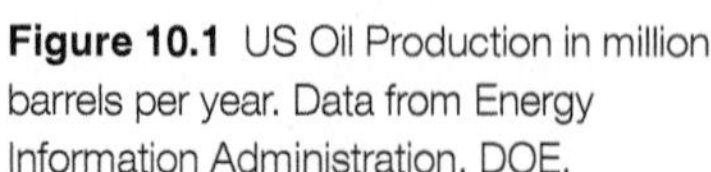
Figure 10.1 US Oil Production in million barrels per year. Data from Energy Information Administration, DOE.

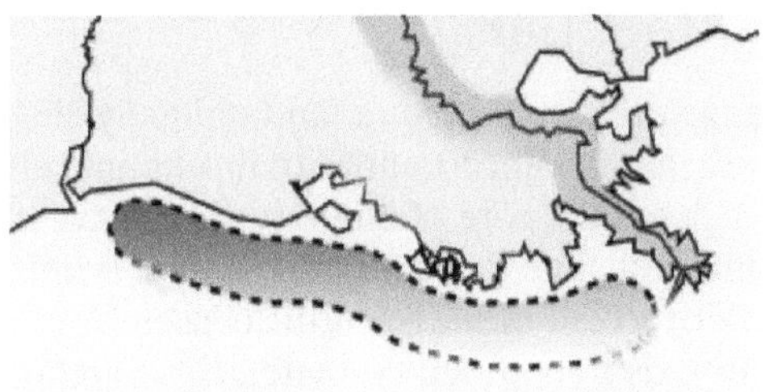

Figure 10.2 Approximate extent of deep water hypoxia in late summer, Gulf of Mexico. Map from Louisiana Sea Grant.

Some current practices may be unsustainable because they degrade environmental or ecological systems that we rely on. Consider the "hypoxia zone" in the Gulf of Mexico, an area off the shore of Louisiana, near the mouth of the Mississippi River. In late summer every year, the deep water in this area becomes "hypoxic" (low oxygen), presenting a danger to fish and, therefore, fisheries. The oxygen decreases because of decomposition of sinking algae, which were overabundant because of excess nutrients in the water, which came from agricultural fertilizers in the Midwest. The actions in the Midwest negatively affected ecosystems and industry elsewhere. Often, this is a hallmark of sustainable thinking—actions and processes need to be designed not only for the long-term success of the particular system, but also for all other connected systems, including those that may be far removed in both space and time.

Fortunately, natural systems do have an ability to incorporate pollution without permanent adverse impacts; unfortunately, this ability is not infinite. The earliest wastewater schemes involved dumping sewage directly into a nearby river with little or no treatment; this sounds like a horrible idea, but, to a point, it may have some merit. A main goal in wastewater treatment is the removal and decomposition of organic matter, something accomplished in modern wastewater treatment plants with the help of bacteria and other microbes. But these microbes exist in rivers as well—a small amount of waste dumped directly into a river could effectively be treated *in situ* in the river. This effect is easily measurable by tracking the dissolved oxygen level of the river downstream from a dumping point (because decomposition consumes oxygen, a decrease in oxygen can be interpreted as evidence of decomposition activity). Dissolved oxygen is the regenerated through algae photosynthesis and movement of atmospheric oxygen into the water. As long as the rate of decomposition use of oxygen is slow relative to rates of regeneration, the total oxygen level can be relatively stable. This is an example of a sustainable use of the river (and an example of the fact that sustainable use does not necessarily mean zero use)—small amounts of waste can be assimilated; larger (unsustainable) amounts of waste would cause hypoxia and fish kills in the river.

(It should be noted, however, that wastewater treatment may be needed for other reasons—small direct discharges of sewage may be sustainable with regard to dissolved oxygen effects, yet unsustainable with regard to pathogens, synthetic chemicals, or high nutrient levels in the waste.)

Brainstorming: In groups of four, in one minute, identify ways of determining the extent of air pollution emissions (smog, smoke, carbon dioxide, etc.) that might be considered sustainable?

10.1.2 Climate Change

Global climate change presents a unique (and uniquely challenging) sustainability issue because of its global scale, the uncertainties of its ultimate effects, and the close link with energy systems (which are the core of industry). You have likely heard much about carbon dioxide and climate change in the media and in previous courses. There is room here for only a very quick overview of the scientific consensus of global climate change:

First, uncertainty exists about the ultimate effects and time scales of climate change, but the uncertainty exists in a very different place than many public media reports would suggest. The following are parts of the story that we know with significant certainty:

1. *The greenhouse effect is real and important.* Climate scientists have understood for more than a century that carbon dioxide and other trace gases play a special role in climate regulation through infrared absorption: this is the "greenhouse effect." The physics and thermodynamics are well understood, and the geological record indicates a strong correlation between climate and greenhouse gas concentration, (both of which have varied considerably, but varied together, through the earth's history). The greenhouse effect is unequivocally real, and makes the surface of the earth much warmer than it would be otherwise—and it is not, by itself, a bad thing.
2. *Concentrations of carbon dioxide (CO_2) and other greenhouse gases (GHGs) are increasing* due to human activities. We have the data to show the increase (see figure), and in the case of carbon dioxide, we have the invoices to prove it (CO_2 comes from fuel combustion—we know how much fuel we have burned, and therefore can calculate how much CO_2 we are responsible for emitting).

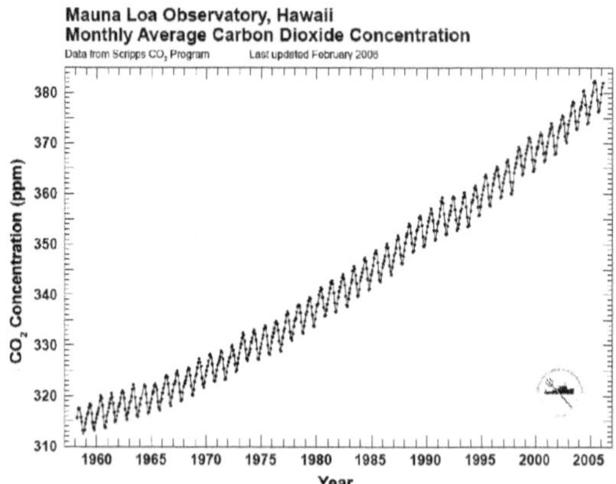

Figure 10.3 The "Keeling curve" of atmospheric carbon dioxide at the Mauna Loa Observatory, Hawaii. Data from NOAA and Scripps Institute of Oceanography.

The annual variation results from the annual photosynthesis and decomposition cycle in Northern Hemisphere forests.

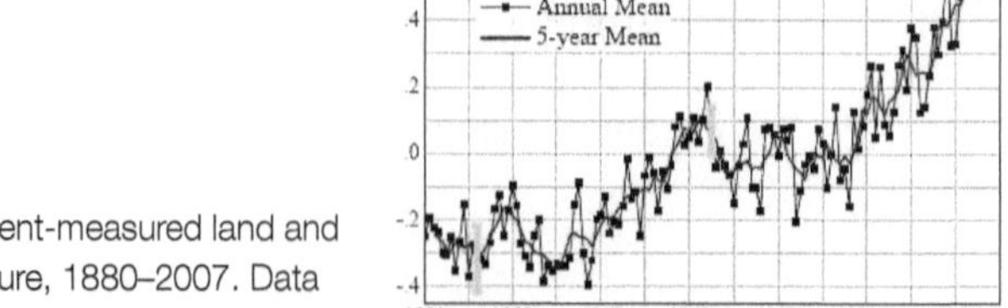

Figure 10.4 Instrument-measured land and sea surface temperature, 1880–2007. Data from NASA Goddard Institute.

3. The *temperature has increased* over the past 150 years, and particularly in the past 30 years. The eight or nine warmest years on record (the data are not yet complete for 2008), worldwide, have all occurred since 1998. This temperature change is reflected in a multitude of other environmental changes, from lowered summer ice cover in the Arctic to species distributional changes. These changes are moderately small compared to temperature changes in earth history, but the rate of change is unprecedented, and we have no experience of major climate changes in the age of industrial agriculture.
4. The exact relationship between GHG concentration and climate is confounded by the presence of many complex and slow-acting "feedback loops," or causal connection loops where, for example, a change in temperature causes a change in extent of biological, physical, or chemical processes that in turn exert temperature control back, either causing an enhanced change (a "positive feedback") or negating the initial change (a "negative feedback").

The major questions about global climate change that remain include:

1. The extent of changes in the future, both in response to the feedback loops (not all of which are well understood), and the potential changes in social behavior and policy.
2. The ability to respond to change. The current systems (e.g., agricultural, urban, manufacturing, transportation) have been engineered to maximize efficiency in the current working environment—if the environment changes even slightly, will these systems still be able to function? This is a fundamental question of sustainability—and planning for flexibility is a fundamental tenet of sustainable design. Our current susceptibility to relatively small climatic changes is a consequence of previous unsustainable design.

Brainstorming: In groups of four, in one minute, identify ways engineering will need to respond to climate change, and how the practice of engineering might be different.

ENERGY BASICS:

Many sustainability issues have their roots in **energy** and all of the questions surrounding energy: how much do we have? how much are we using? what are the best sources? what are the negative impacts of each source? what energy is renewable? how are energy costs going to change?

Some familiarity with the basics of energy use and production in the US, especially the scale, is therefore helpful in considering sustainable design. Consider the following data:

Total amount of energy used in US in 2007 (all sources, all uses): about 100 billion gigajoules. Percent used for:

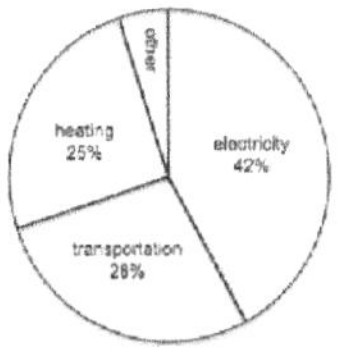

Electricity: 42%
Transportation: 28%
Heating: 25%

Current US sources of energy, normalized to joules, excluding sources with <0.5% of total production:

Petroleum: 40%	Nuclear: 8%
Coal: 23%	Hydroelectric: 3%
Natural gas: 23%	Biomass: 3%

Connection of sources to uses:

Petroleum → primarily (>70%) used for transportation
Natural gas → primarily (>70%) used for heating
Coal → almost exclusively (>97%) used for electricity
Nuclear and hydro → exclusively (100%) used for electricity

QUESTIONS:

- What percentage of energy comes from non-renewable resources?
- What are some other energy sources that might be developed in the future? For which of the three primary categories of uses are they most appropriate?
- List "solutions" to the energy crisis that you have thought about or heard of in the media.
- What are some of the engineering constraints that might not allow using all energy sources for all energy uses? What implications do these constraints have for some of the "solutions" you listed in the previous question?

10.1.3 Resource Availability and a "Graedel Analysis"

One way to determine sustainable patterns quantitatively is to perform a simple analysis based on the method of Graedel and Klee (2002, *Environmental Science and Technology*, vol. 36, p. 523). The results of this analysis indicate whether the current rate of resource use can be sustained over a defined time period using certain assumptions. The analysis includes four steps:

i. Estimate the total current resource availability.
ii. Allocate that supply to the estimated number of people who will use it and the assumed time frame, to derive a need per person per year.
iii. Estimate resource recovery and recycling rates—how much of the material can be recovered and used to meet needs without drawing on initial sources.
iv. Combine results from ii and iii to determine "sustainable limiting rate," and compare to current actual use rate.

Consider the case of zinc as an example, taken from the 2002 Graedel and Klee article. Zinc is a commonly used industrial metal (e.g., galvanization of steel, which retards corrosion, is the most common use). A quick analysis would have the following results:

i. The reserve (unmined) zinc resource is 430 Tg (430×10^{12} g).
ii. Allocating over the next 50 years (the time horizon used by Graedel and Klee) and equally to all people (estimated average population over this time frame = 7.5 billion) gives the annual personal allocation:

$$430 \text{ Tg} / 7.5 \text{ billion people} / 50 \text{ years} = 1.15 \text{ kg/person/yr.}$$

iii. The current recovery/recycling rate of zinc is 30%, so additional recycled supply would be 1.15 × 30% = 0.35 kg/person/yr, for a sustainable limiting rate of **1.50 kg/person/yr**.

iv. The current US per capita consumption is 6.2 kg/person/yr (more than four times the sustainable allocation).

> Brainstorming: In groups of four, in one minute, identify the implicit (or explicit) assumptions included in this analysis. What opportunities are available for developing a more sustainable zinc use plan?

10.2 ASPECTS OF SUSTAINABLE DESIGN

1. Natural resources and energy.

   A focus of sustainable design is the full consideration of costs of natural resources and energy. The supply of fossil fuels (coal, petroleum, and natural gas), metals and minerals, fresh water, wood, soil, and food crops is large, but not inexhaustible. Sustainable design seeks to limit the use of natural resources, both as a cost-saving measure and as a guarantee that these resources will be available and not degraded in the future. Sustainable design requires the assessment of resource needs for *all* aspects of the project, including those required by subcontractors, suppliers and consumers, with explicit consideration of the tradeoffs between energy costs of production and energy costs of use.

Some indications that our current national use of resources is not sustainable:

- Proven US oil reserves in Dec. 2006 (the most recent data available) were less than 21 billion barrels, the lowest since 1946 (US DoE Energy Information Administration).
- More than 50% of the available freshwater in the US is currently being used for irrigation, industry, domestic use, in-stream use (i.e., waste dilution). This demand tripled between 1950 and 2000, and is expected to double again by 2025 (deVilliers, 2000, "Water: the fate of our most precious resource").
- Estimated economically viable US copper reserves in Jan 2008 were about 35 million metric tons; current annual extraction is 2 million metric tons (data from USGS).
- Groundwater aquifers including the Illinoisan-Wisconsinan Sandstone (source for Chicago and Milwaukee suburbs) and the Ogallala (in US high plains from Texas to South Dakota and source for most of the irrigated agriculture in five states) may be depleted within 25–50 years (data from USGS).

These indicators may not affect the design projects of individual engineers directly, but engineers still need to know about potential future changes and make decisions to allow the project to continue to succeed in different conditions.

> Discussion: How would engineering change if an important resource like copper were to be economically unavailable?

2. Waste disposal, repurposing, and recycling.

   Produced waste represents a loss of efficiency: waste removal is expensive (and sometimes dangerous), landfill space is limited, and potential resource material in the waste stream is a lost opportunity. Reducing waste saves money, and design that reduces waste production through the useful life of the project potentially saves a significant amount of money and effort. Recycling, or refining old materials into new uses, is not simply virtuous—it is an increasingly necessary option for waste handling. It reduces the cost of disposal for one entity, and reduces the need for use of exhaustible natural resources for another entity. Furthermore, energy costs of material production from virgin sources are frequently much larger than for production from recycled material.
3. Public health.

   Health and safety have always been critical parts of the responsibilities of an engineer. In the broader context suggested by sustainable design, this extends to concern for public health and environmental health. Does the design cause adverse impacts to people who will be using the product? What are the health impacts to others, perhaps through increased pollution caused by the design? Are materials required that are hazardous or toxic to handle, and is there a design choice that would allow you to avoid these materials? These questions, and others like them, are all part of sustainable design.

Brainstorm: In teams of four, identify as many ways an engineering design might affect public health as you can in one minute. Consider the health of users, consumers, or the general public.

4. Upfront vs. long-term costs.

   As you know, a primary driver in design is often simple cost—how much will the addition of each new feature add to the total cost of the project or the product? Conventional design often asks only the costs of construction and production; sustainable design requires consideration of long-term costs—those felt as the product is used. As an example, geothermal heating and cooling of buildings typically requires only 20–30% of the energy required for conventional heating and AC, with a concurrent decrease in continuing energy cost. However, the initial cost of installation of a geothermal system can be significantly more than a conventional system, so geothermal is still rarely used. But the "payoff" time (the time required for the additional upfront costs to be offset by continuing savings) for geothermal systems is often less than a decade; after that, the user is saving both money *and* natural resources. Good sustainable design absolutely requires the consideration of lifetime costs (both money and resource) rather than simply upfront costs.

Discussion: Who is responsible for the long-term costs of a project? What ethical responsibilities does an engineer have to advise the user about costs far in the future?

5. Triple bottom line.

   You have probably heard of the "bottom line" of business: the number at the end, after all expenses are subtracted from all revenues, that determines whether a particular business has been profitable. This bottom line model has considerable significance, as success or failure is determined by this one figure.

   Today, many large companies are beginning to calculate and report a "triple bottom line," adding costs and benefits in social and environmental terms to the traditional economic accounting. This is recognition of sustainable thinking, as these social and environmental factors determine if the viability of future generations has been affected. With this thinking, a positive economic bottom line with negative (unsustainable) social and environmental impacts may not be considered a success. As engineers, you may have responsibilities toward understanding your user's needs for the triple bottom line.

10.2.1 Tools and Terms Related to Sustainable Design

The following terms, ideas, and tools may be helpful as you consider sustainability in designs.

1. Footprint analysis.

   A *footprint analysis* is simply the measurement and estimation of the entirety of the impact of a person, object, or process. In the original idea, the "footprint" measured an actual physical area—how much land is required to produce all of the materials (water, food, minerals, oil, etc.) for an individual. A comparison of the size of the footprint to the average area available per person then provided a measurement of relative impacts.

   The key aspect of footprint analysis, however, is not that it measures land area; the key is that the analysis includes all aspects of resource use that can be assigned to an individual. This has allowed the metaphor of the footprint to be broadened to "carbon footprints" (how much carbon dioxide is formed due to all activities and consumption of an individual), "energy footprints" (how much energy is used, in all of its forms), and "water footprints" (how much water is used in total to produce an object), among others.

Think-Pair-Share: For one minute, consider your own personal energy footprint. What forms of energy do you use on a daily basis? What data would you collect to sum them all into a single analysis? How would you collect these data? With a partner, try to think of more.

2. Embedded energy.

   Central to an energy footprint analysis is the idea of *embedded energy*, or the energy required to produce materials used in a process. This is different from the direct-use energy, or that used *by* the materials. For example, the complete analysis of the energy footprint of two types of lightbulbs includes not only the comparison of each bulb's operating wattage (perhaps normalized to luminosity), but also the energy required to produce the bulbs, and the energy required to transport the bulbs from their production location, the energy required to extract the metals in the bulbs from their ores, and the energy required to dig up the ores in the first place! These last four energy terms are all part of the embedded energy in the bulb. As you might guess, this is often a very difficult part of a footprint analysis.

Think-Pair-Share: Identify at least one source of embedded energy you didn't consider in your footprint earlier. Talk with a partner about it.

3. Life cycle analysis and cradle-to-cradle design.

   Complete footprint analyses also require consideration of the entire lifetime of the object, or a *life cycle analysis*, in addition to the resource needs of production and use, what are the resource requirements and pollution implications of decommissioning and waste? This has long been ignored as part of design, as most engineers move on to other projects long before the objects they design complete their useful lifetime. While this sort of "cradle-to-grave" analysis was at one time considered forward-thinking, today's leaders in sustainability think about impact from *cradle-to-cradle*. (This idea was made famous by McDonough and Braungart's 2002 book by that name.) Cradle-to-cradle design takes the final step, asking for an analysis of how the material will be converted to another use after the end of the original design's useful lifetime. Asking this question early can have profound effects on the initial design process, as engineers strive to make sure materials and parts will not be degraded beyond recyclability or reusability.
4. Systems design and boundary-drawing.

   The consideration of a large interconnected system is the basis of sustainable thinking. If an engineer defines the process narrowly, it may be possible to design what appears to be the optimal process—lowest cost, lowest energy use, lowest environmental impact, etc., yet the process will be felt outside of the system. The challenge for an engineer then, is to draw the boundaries around the system as widely as reasonably possible, look for unexpected connections and consequences, and include them in analyses and design decisions. Applying *systems design* will naturally cause you to consider these concepts of sustainability, including footprints, embedded energy, and cradle-to-cradle.
5. Economic analysis of costs of changes.

   Increasing the sustainability of current industrial practices will certainly have cost implications (both cost savings and increased expenses), and the performance of a cost analysis over a long time scale will be a critical part of a sustainability plan. As an example, look at Exhibit 10.1, which estimates the total costs or savings (to all people, institutions, governments, and corporations) of various greenhouse gas abatement practices. This figure was prepared by McKinsey and Company, a consulting firm, in 2007 and published in *McKinsey Quarterly*, their journal releasing results of company research to the public.

The current total emission of greenhouse gases is about 40 Gt (gigatons, or 10^{15}g) of carbon dioxide equivalent, or CO_2e (the "equivalent" means that other greenhouse gases are included, scaled to their relative greenhouse impact); by 2030 under the "business as usual" scenario, this is expected to grow to 58 Gt CO_2e. Stabilizing atmospheric GHG levels at 400 ppm (slightly above the current value) will require a reduction in emissions to 25 Gt CO_2e by 2030. Exhibit 10.1 shows the cost associated with abatement practices, organized from those that will actually save money to those that cost more. The *y*-axis depicts the abatement cost in Euro (€) per ton CO_2e (negative is a cost savings), and the width of each bar in the *x* dimension indicates the worldwide amount of abatement potential. For example, increasing building insulation could save between € 100–150 per ton, and could remove (in total) about 1 Gt CO_2e by 2030. "Industrial CCS" (carbon capture and sequestration), near the right end of the figure, would cost about € 40 per ton, and could remove about one half of a Gt. It is important to note that some potential technologies or practices that cost more than €40 per ton were not included in the analysis; this includes widespread adoption of photovoltaic (solar) electricity generation.

10.2.2 Reading the Cost Curves

The cost curves we developed show estimates of the prospective annual abatement cost[1] in euros per ton of avoided emissions of greenhouse gases,[2] as well as the abatement potential of these approaches in gigatons of emissions. The abatement cost for wind power, for example, should be understood as the additional cost of producing electricity with this zero-emission technology instead of the cheaper fossil fuel–based power production it would replace. The abatement potential of wind power is our estimate of the feasible volume of emissions it could eliminate at a cost of 40 euros a ton or less. Looked at another way, these costs can be understood as the price—ultimately, to the global economy—of making any approach to abatement cost competitive or otherwise viable through policy decisions. A wide range of assumptions about the future cost and feasible deployment rates of available abatement measures underlie the estimates of their cost and significance. For example, the significance of wind power assumes that actions to abate greenhouse gases will have already begun across regions by 2008. The volumes in our model (and this article) should be seen as potential abatement, not as forecasts.

Our model for the "supply" of abatement can be compared with any politically determined target ("demand") for abatement in the years 2010, 2020, and 2030. The science of climate change is beyond the scope of our study and our expertise, however. We thus compare, for illustrative purposes, our findings on supply with three emissions targets discussed in the debate—targets that would, respectively, cap the long-term

[1]Calculated as the annual additional operating cost (including depreciation) less potential cost savings (for example, from reduced energy consumption) divided by the amount of emissions avoided. This formula means that costs can be negative if the cost savings are considerable. Possible costs for implementing a system to realize the abatement approaches are not included.

[2]Such as carbon dioxide, methane, nitrous oxide, and sulfur hexafluoride.

What might it cost?

Global cost curve for greenhouse gas abatement measures beyond 'business as usual'; greenhouse gases measured in $GtCO_2e$[1]

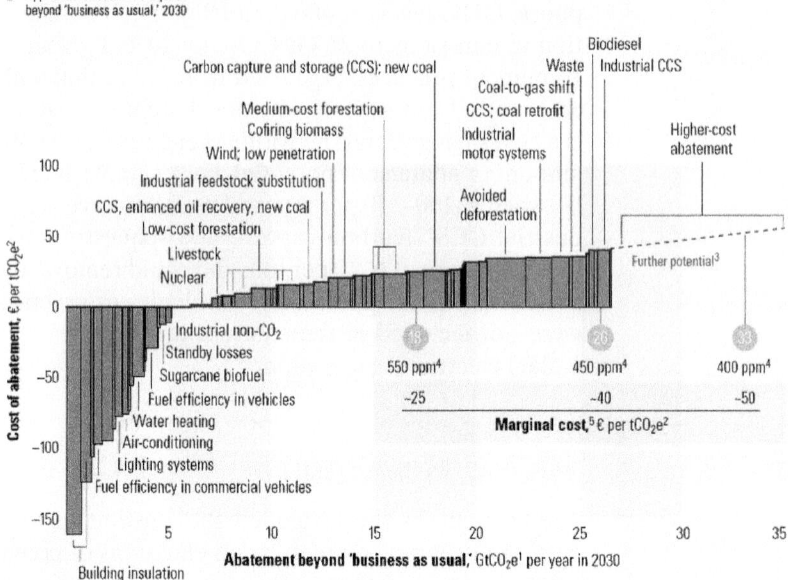

[1] $GtCO_2e$ = gigaton of carbon dioxide equivalent; "business as usual" based on emissions growth driven mainly by increasing demand for energy and transport around the world and by tropical deforestation.
[2] tCO_2e = ton of carbon dioxide equivalent.
[3] Measures costing more than €40 a ton were not the focus of this study.
[4] Atmospheric concentration of all greenhouse gases recalculated into CO_2 equivalents; ppm = parts per million.
[5] Marginal cost of avoiding emissions of 1 ton of CO_2 equivalents in each abatement demand scenario.

Figure 10.5 Global cost curve for greenhouse gas abatement measures beyond "business as usual" in the year 2030.

http://www.mckinsey.com/clientservice/sustainability/costcurves.asp

For an updated version of the greenhouse global gas abatement cost curve, including the effects of the economic crisis that began in 2008, see version 2.1 on McKinsey's Web site.

concentration of greenhouse gases in the atmosphere at 550, 450, or 400 parts per million (a measure of the share of greenhouse gas molecules in the atmosphere). The goal of each target, according to its advocates, is to prevent the average global temperature from rising by more than 2 degrees Celsius. Any of these emissions targets would be challenging to reach by 2030, for they would all require at least a 50 percent improvement in the global economy's greenhouse gas efficiency (its volume of emissions relative to the size of GDP) compared with business-as-usual trends.

A simplified version of the global cost curve (Figure 10.5) shows our estimates of the significance and cost of feasible abatement measures in 2030—the end year of a period long enough for us to draw meaningful conclusions but short enough to let us make reasonably factual assumptions. We have developed similar cost curves for each sector in each region and for each of the three time frames.

At the low end of the curve are, for the most part, measures that improve energy efficiency. These measures, such as better insulation in new buildings (see "Making the most of the world's energy resources," in the current issue), thus reduce emissions by

Three Scenarios

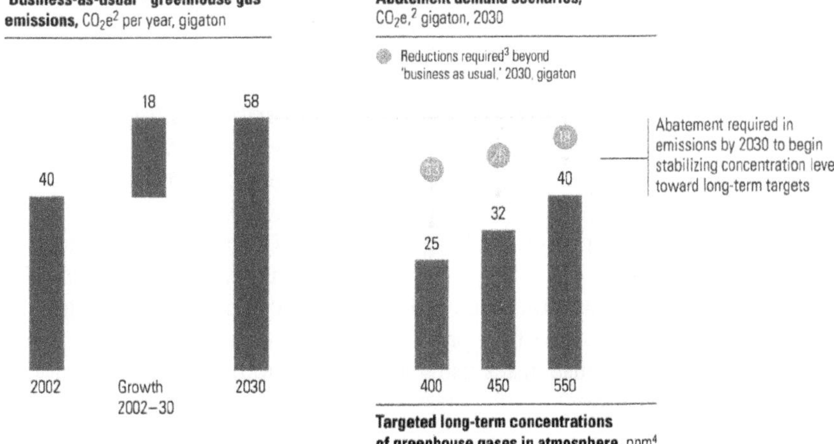

[1]"Business as usual" based on emissions growth driven mainly by increasing demand for energy and transport around the world and by tropical deforestation.
[2]CO_2c = carbon dioxide equivalent.
[3]Reduction requirements = midpoints with uncertainty of +/– several gigatons.
[4]Parts per million.

Source: International Energy Agency (IEA); US Environmental Protection Agency (EPA); McKinsey analysis

Figure 10.6 Calculation of "business as usual," abatement demand, and targeted long-term concentrations of greenhouse gas emissions.

lowering demand for power. Higher up the cost curve are approaches for adopting more greenhouse gas–efficient technologies (such as wind power and carbon capture and storage[3]) in power generation and manufacturing industry and for shifting to cleaner industrial processes. The curve also represents ways to reduce emissions by protecting, planting, or replanting tropical forests and by switching to agricultural practices with greater greenhouse gas efficiency.

We have no opinion about the demand for abatement or the probability of concerted global action to pursue any specific goal. But the application of our supply-side research to specific abatement targets can help policy makers and business leaders to understand the economic implications of abatement approaches by region and sector, as well as some of the repercussions for companies and the global economy. Our analysis assumes that the focus would be to capture all of the cheapest forms of abatement around the world but makes no judgment about what ought to be the ultimate distribution of costs. Of course, the ability to pay for reducing emissions varies greatly between developed and developing economies and among individual countries in each group.

For simplicity's sake, we compared our cost curve with the 450-parts-per-million scenario—in the midrange of the targets put forward by advocates. This scenario would require greenhouse gases to abate by 26 gigatons a year by 2030 (Figure 10.6). Under

[3]A technology for separating greenhouse gases from the combustion gases of fossil fuels and industrial processes and then storing the greenhouse gases in natural underground cavities.

that scenario, and assuming that measures are implemented in order of increasing cost, the marginal cost per ton of emissions avoided would be 40 euros. (As a point of reference, since trading under the EU ETS began, in 2005, the price of greenhouse gas emissions has ranged from 6 to 31 euros a ton.)

We had to make many assumptions about future cost developments for these measures and the practical possibilities for realizing them. We assumed, for instance, that the cost of carbon capture and storage will fall to 20 to 30 euros per ton of emissions in 2030 and that 85 percent of all coal-fired power plants built after 2020 will be equipped with this technology. These assumptions in turn underpin our estimate that it represents 3.1 gigatons of feasible abatement potential.

In a 25-year perspective, such assumptions are clearly debatable, and we make no claim that we are better than others at making them. We believe that the value of our work comes primarily from an integrated view across all sectors, regions, and greenhouse gases using a uniform methodology. This model allows us to assess the relative weight of different approaches, sectors, and regions from a global perspective.

Discussion: In your group, make sure that you understand the meaning of Figure 10.5. What is the meaning of the area under the curve (both below and above the *x* axis)? What do you think are the main barriers to implementation of these actions, particularly those that save both money and CO_2e?

10.3 THE BUILT ENVIRONMENT AND SUSTAINABILITY*

The engineering of buildings and building systems is a critical place to start in the discussion of sustainability, for several reasons:

- A large percentage of resources currently goes to cities and built environments: 40% of the energy, 25% of water, and 30% of raw materials are used in buildings.
- The earth's population is growing, but even more so, the *urban* population is growing. The population today is about 6.2 billion, with 50% living in urban environments; this is expected to grow to almost 9 billion with 80% living in urban locations by 2050.
- Many of the most cost-effective carbon abatement practices in Figure 10.5 deal with buildings and building efficiency.
- Engineering designs that go into buildings and cities are likely to be the most long-term (and therefore design decisions today are likely to be the most important for the next century), compared to all engineering decisions.

*Courtesy of Purdue University.

10.3.1 LEED Building as an Example

Purdue's upcoming addition to the Mechanical Engineering Building will attempt to achieve certification by LEED (Leadership in Energy and Environmental Design, a program of the US Green Building Council). This is an indication that the design of the building will include many of these sustainable ideas, but what does it mean in practice? To achieve LEED certification (at standard, silver, gold, or platinum levels), a building must meet a certain ***number*** of criteria (the ones that best fit the design). While some of these criteria are specific to building construction, they stem from wider sustainability ideals, and can be applied to other forms of engineering and design. Some of the LEED criteria for large commercial buildings include:

LEED Criterion	Sustainability Ideal Exemplified
Construction waste management: >50% of waste recycled or diverted from landfill stream	Encourages recycling and reuse, consideration of lifetime and eventual fate of materials.
Regional materials: >20% of construction materials originate regionally.	Reduces embedded energy of transportation.
Water use reduction: >20% reduction from "standard" water fixtures and systems	Reduces water use, encourages long-term reduction, even if it is at the expense of increased upfront costs.
Stormwater design: Inclusion of stormwater quality design features	Shows larger system thinking (how stormwater runoff from the property will affect neighboring properties)
Low emitting materials: Use of adhesives and sealants that do not emit volatile irritating chemicals	Consideration of human health and consideration of effects of construction materials on the lifetime of the building.
Daylight views: >75% of the building space has outside windows/daylight views	Reduces energy requirements for lighting—considers long-term energy use.
Alternative transportation: Building includes bike-commuting friendly features, like indoor bike room/racks and showers for commuters.	Shows system thinking, and how the impact of the location of the building and how the people who will work there will get there sustainably can be managed.

CHAPTER 11
ETHICS

Objectives

By learning the material in this chapter, you should be able to

- list and apply the steps of an ethical decision-making process
- identify sources of ethical codes in the engineering profession

Every day, we make numerous ethical decisions, although most are so minor that we do not even view them as such.

- When you drive your car, do you knowingly violate the posted speed limit?
- When you unload the supermarket cart at your car, do you leave it in the middle of the parking lot, or spend the extra time to return it to the cart corral?
- You know that another student has plagiarized an assignment; do you rat him or her out?
- A person with a mental disability tries to converse with you while waiting in a public queue. Do you treat him or her with respect or pretend he or she does not exist?
- In the grocery, a teenager's mother tells her to put back the package of ice cream she brought to the cart. The teenager walks around the corner and places the ice cream on the shelf with the soft drinks and returns to the buggy. Do you ignore this or approach the teenager and politely explain that leaving a package of ice cream in that location will cause it to melt thus increasing the cost of groceries for everyone else, or do you replace it in the freezer yourself?
- When going through a public door, do you make a habit of looking back to see if releasing the door will cause it to slam in someone's face?
- You notice a highway patrolman lying in wait for speeders. Do you flash your lights at other cars to warn them?
- A cashier gives you too much change for a purchase. Do you correct the cashier?
- You are on the lake in your boat and notice a person on a JetSki chasing a great blue heron across the lake. The skier stops at a nearby pier. Do you pilot your craft over to the dock and reprimand him for harassing the wildlife?

> Good people do not need laws to tell them to act responsibly, while bad people will find a way around the laws.
>
> Plato

On a grand scale, none of these decisions is particularly important, although some might lead to undesirable consequences. However, as an aspiring engineer, you may face numerous decisions in your career that could affect the lives and well-being of thousands of people. Just like almost everything else, practice makes perfect, or at least better. The more you practice analyzing day-to-day decisions from an ethical standpoint, the easier it will be for you to make good decisions when the results of a poor choice may be catastrophic.

In very general terms, there are two reasons people try to make ethical decisions.

- They wish to make the world a better place for everyone—in a single word, altruism.
- They wish to avoid unpleasant consequences, such as fines, incarceration, or loss of job.

EXCERPTS FROM THE CODE OF UR-NAMMU

- If a man commits a murder, he must be killed.
- If a man commits a robbery, he will be killed.
- If a man commits a kidnapping, he is to be imprisoned and pay 15 shekels of silver.
- If a man knocks out the eye of another man, he shall weigh out half a mina of silver.
- If a man has cut off another man's foot, he is to pay 10 shekels of silver.
- If someone severed the nose of another man with a copper knife, he must pay two-thirds of a mina of silver.
- If a man knocks out a tooth of another man, he shall pay 2 shekels of silver.

In an ideal society, the second reason would not exist. However, history is replete with examples of people, and even nations, who do not base their decisions solely on whether or not they are acting ethically. Because of the common occurrence of unethical behavior and the negative impact it has on others, almost all societies have developed rules, codes, and laws to specify what is and is not acceptable behavior, and the punishments that will be meted out when violations occur.

The major religions all have fairly brief codes summarizing how one should conduct their life. Some examples are given below; other examples exist as well.

- Judaism, Christianity, and derivatives thereof have the Decalogue, or Ten Commandments.
- Islam has the Five Pillars in addition to a slightly modified and reorganized form of the Decalogue.
- Buddhism has the Noble Eightfold Path.
- Bahá'í has 12 social principles.
- In Hinduism, Grihastha dharma has four goals.

Secular codes of conduct go back more than four millennia to the Code of Ur-Nammu. Although by today's standards, some of the punishments in the earliest codes seem harsh or even barbaric, it was one of the earliest known attempts to codify crimes and corresponding punishments.

Admittedly, although not specifically religious in nature, these codes are usually firmly rooted in the prevailing religious thought of the time and location. Through the centuries, such codes and laws have been expanded, modified, and refined so that most forms of serious antisocial behavior are addressed and consequences for violations specified. These codes exist from a local to a global level. Several examples are given below.

- Most countries purport to abide by the Geneva Conventions, which govern certain types of conduct on an international scale.
- Most countries have national laws concerning murder, rape, theft, etc.
- In the United States, it is illegal to purchase alcohol unless you are 21 years of age. In England, the legal age is 18.
- In North and South Dakota, you can obtain a driver's license at age $14\frac{1}{2}$. In most other states, the legal age is 16.
- It is illegal to say "Oh boy!" in Jonesboro, Georgia.
- Many cities, such as Santa Fe, New Mexico, have ordinances prohibiting use of cell phones while driving.

11.1 ETHICAL DECISION MAKING

Some ethical decisions are clear-cut. For example, essentially everyone (excluding psychopaths) would agree that it is unethical to kill someone because you do not like his or her hat. Unfortunately, many real-world decisions that we must make are far from "black and white" issues, instead having many subtle nuances that must be considered to arrive at what one believes is the "best" decision.

There is no proven algorithm or set of rules that one can follow to guarantee that the most ethical decision possible is being made in any particular situation. However, numerous people have developed procedures that can guide us in considering questions with ethical ramifications. A four-step procedure is discussed here, although there are various other approaches.

Step 1: Determine *What* the issues are and *Who* might be affected by the various alternative courses of action that might be implemented.

We will refer to the *Who* as **stakeholders**. Note that at this point, we are not trying to determine how the stakeholders will be affected by any particular plan of action.

- The issues (What) can refer to a wide variety of things, including, for example, personal freedom, national security, quality of life, economic issues, fairness, and equality.
- The term stakeholders (Who) does not necessarily refer to people, but might be an individual, a group of people, an institution, or a natural system, among other things.

EXAMPLE 11-1

Consider the question of whether to allow further drilling for oil in the Alaska National Wildlife Refuge (ANWR). List several issues and stakeholders.

Issues:

- Oil independence
- The price of gasoline
- Possible impacts on the ecosystem

Stakeholders:

- Oil companies
- The general population of the United States
- Other countries from whom we purchase oil
- The flora and fauna in ANWR
- The native people in Alaska

Step 2: Consider the effects of alternative courses of action from different perspectives.

Here, we look at three perspectives: consequences, intent, and character.

Perspective 1: Consequences

When considering this perspective, ask how the various stakeholders will be affected by each alternative plan being contemplated. In addition, attempt to assign a relative level of importance (weight) to each effect on each stakeholder. For instance, an action that might affect millions of people adversely is almost always more important than an action that would cause an equivalent level of harm to a dozen people.

EXAMPLE 11-2

Should all U.S. children be fingerprinted when entering kindergarten and again each third year of grade school (3, 6, 9, 12)? Identify the stakeholders and consequences.

Stakeholders:

- All U.S. children
- All U.S. citizens
- Law enforcement
- The judicial system
- The U.S. Constitution

Consequences:

- Provides a record to help identify or trace missing children (not common, but possibly very important in some cases)
- Affords an opportunity for malicious use of the fingerprint records for false accusation of crime or for identity theft (probability unknown, but potentially devastating to affected individuals)
- Could help identify perpetrators of crimes, thus improving the safety of law-abiding citizens (importance varies with type of crime)
- Raises serious questions concerning personal freedoms, possibly unconstitutional (importance, as well as constitutionality, largely dependent on the philosophy of the person doing the analysis)

This list could easily be continued.

Fingerprint technology has advanced in recent years with the implementation of computer recognition for identification. Originally in the United States, the Henry Classification System was used to manually match fingerprints based on three main patterns: arches, loops, and whorls (shown below from left to right).

Today, the Automated Fingerprint Identification System (AFIS) uses algorithmic matching to compare images. Future work of AFIS systems is in the adoption and creation of secure multitouch devices like mobile computers and tablets, which can identify different security levels for the operator of the device. For example, a multitouch computer owner might be able to issue permissions to an administrator that might not be available to a 5-year old, all without providing a single password!

Perspective 2: Intent

The intentions of the person doing the acting or deciding are considered in this perspective, sometimes called the "rights" perspective. Since actions based on good intentions can sometimes yield bad results, and vice versa, the intent perspective avoids this possible pitfall by not considering the outcome at all, only the intentions.

It may be helpful when considering this perspective to recall Immanuel Kant's Categorical Imperative: "Act only according to that maxim whereby you can at the same time will that it should become a universal law." To pull this out of the eighteenth century, ask yourself the following questions:

(a) Is the action I am taking something that I believe everyone should do?

(b) Do I believe that this sort of behavior should be codified in law?

(c) Would I like to be on the receiving end (the victim) of this action?

EXAMPLE 11-3

Should you download music illegally over the Internet?

Rephrasing this question using the suggestions above yields:

(a) Should everyone illegally download the music they want if it is there for the taking?

(b) Should the laws be changed so that anyone who obtains a song by any means can post it on the web for everyone to get for free?

(c) If you were a struggling musician trying to pay the bills, would you like your revenue stream to dry up because everyone who wanted your music got it for free?

Perspective 3: Character

Character is the inherent complex of attributes that determines a person's moral and ethical actions and reactions. This perspective considers the character of a person who takes the action under consideration. There are different ways of thinking about this. One is to simply ask: Would a person of good character do this? Another is to ask: If I do this, does it enhance or degrade my character? Yet another way is to ask yourself if a person you revere as a person of unimpeachable character (whoever that might be) would take this action.

EXAMPLE 11-4

Your friends are deriding another student behind her back because she comes from a poor family and does not have good clothes.

Do you:

(a) Join in the criticism?

(b) Ignore it, pretend it is not happening, or simply walk away?

(c) Tell your friends that they are behaving badly and insist that they desist?

- Which of these actions would a person of good character take?
- Which of these actions would enhance your character and which would damage it?
- What would the founder of your religion do? (Moses or Jesus or Buddha or Mohammed or Bahá'u'lláh or Vishnu or whoever.) If you are not religious, what would the person who, in your opinion, has the highest moral character do?

Step 3: Correlate perspectives.

Now look back at the results of considering the issues from the three perspectives. In many cases, all three perspectives will lead to the same or a similar conclusion. When this occurs, you have a high level of confidence that the indicated action is the best choice from an ethical standpoint.

If the three perspectives do not agree, you may wish to reconsider the question. It may be helpful to discuss the issue with people whom you have not previously consulted in this matter. Did you omit any factors? For complicated issues, it is difficult to make sure you have included all possible stakeholders and consequences. Did you properly assign weights to the various aspects? Upon reconsideration, all three perspectives may converge.

If you cannot obtain convergence of all three perspectives, no matter how hard you try to make sure you left nothing out, then go with two out of three.

Step 4: Act.

This is often the hardest step of all to take, since ethical action often requires courage. The whistle-blower who risks losing his or her job, Harriet Tubman repeatedly risking her life to lead slaves to freedom via the Underground Railroad, the elected official standing up for what she knows to be right even though it will probably cost her the next election, or even something as mundane as risking the ridicule of your friends because you refuse to go along with whatever questionable activities they are engaging in for "fun." Ask yourself the question: "Do *I* have the courage to do what I know is right?"

EXAMPLE 11-5

Your company has been granted a contract to develop the next generation of electronic cigarette, also known as a "nicotine delivery system," and you have been assigned to the design team. Can you in good conscience contribute your expertise to this project?

> **NOTE**
>
> In the interest of brevity, this is not an exhaustive analysis but shows the general procedure.

Step 1: Identify the issues (What) and the stakeholders (Who).

Issues:

- Nicotine is poisonous and addictive
- These devices eliminate many of the harmful components of tobacco smoke
- Laws concerning these devices range from completely legal, to classification as a medical device, to banned, depending on country
- There are claims that such devices can help wean tobacco addicts off nicotine
- The World Health Organization does not consider this an effective means to stop smoking
- Whether an individual chooses to use nicotine should be a personal decision, since its use does not generally degrade a person's function in society
- The carrier of the nicotine (80–90% of the total inhaled product) is propylene glycol, which is relatively safe, but can cause skin and eye irritation, as well as other adverse effects in doses much larger than would be obtained from this device
- A profit can be made from nicotine products or anti-smoking devices

Stakeholders:

- You (your job and promotions)
- Your company and stockholders (profit)
- Cigarette manufacturers and their employees and stockholders (lost revenue)
- Tobacco farmers (less demand)
- The public (less second-hand smoke)
- The user (various health effects, possibly positive or negative)

Step 2: Analyze alternative courses of action from different perspectives.

1. Consequences
   - You may lose your job or promotion if you refuse

- If you convince management to abandon the project, the company may lose money
- If you succeed brilliantly, your company may make money hand over fist, and you receive a promotion
- If the project goes ahead, the possibility of future lawsuits exists
- Users' health may be damaged
- Users' dependence on nicotine may either increase or decrease

2. Intent

- Should everyone use electronic cigarettes, or at least condone their use?
- Should use of electronic cigarettes be unrestricted by law?
- Would I like to risk nicotine addiction because of using these devices?
- Would I be able to kick my tobacco habit by using these devices?

3. Character

- Would a person of good character develop this device, use it, or condone its use?
- Would work on this project (thus implicitly condoning its use) or use of the device itself enhance or degrade my character?
- Would my personal spiritual leader, or other person I revere, condone development or use of this product?

Step 3: Correlate perspectives.

Here we enter the realm of subjective judgment. The individual author responsible for this example has a definite personal answer, but it is in the nature of ethical decision making that different people will often arrive at different results in good conscience. You would have to weigh the various factors (including any that have been overlooked or knowingly omitted) to arrive at your own conclusion. We refuse to dictate a decision to you.

Step 4: Act on your decision.

If your decision was that working on this project poses no threat to your soul (if you happen to believe in such), probably little courage is required to follow through, since your career may blossom, or at least not be curtailed.

On the other hand, if you believe that the project is unethical, you need to have the intestinal fortitude to either attempt to change the minds of management or refuse to work on the project, both of which may put your career at risk.

11.2 PLAGIARISM

> Did you know? There are Internet services available that will accept a document and search the web for exact or similar content. Also, there are programs that will scan multiple documents and search for exact or similar content.
>
> ---
>
> Did you know? Prior to the romantic movement of the eighteenth century, European writers were encouraged not to be inventive without good reason and to carefully imitate the work of the great masters of previous centuries.

You probably know what plagiarism is—claiming someone else's work as your own. This is most often used in reference to written words, but may be extended to other media as well. From a legal standpoint, plagiarism per se is not illegal, although it is widely considered unethical. However, if the plagiarism also involves copyright infringement, then this would be a violation of the law. Certainly, in the context of your role as a student, plagiarism is almost universally regarded as academic dishonesty, and subject to whatever punitive actions your school deems appropriate.

In some cases, plagiarism is obvious, as when an essay submitted by a student is almost identical to one found on the Internet, or is the same as that submitted by another student. It is amazing how frequently students are caught cheating because they copied verbatim from another student's work, complete with strange mistakes and bizarre phrasing that grab the grader's attention like an 18-wheeler loaded with live pigs locking its brakes at 80 miles per hour. (Thanks to Gilbert Shelton for that image.)

In other cases, things are far less clear. For example, if you were writing a short story for your English class and used the simile "her lips were like faded tulips, dull and wrinkled," can you (or the professor) really be sure whether that was an original phrase or if you had read it at some time in the past, and your brain dragged it up from your subconscious memory as though it were your own?

We all hear or read things during our lives that hang around in our brains whether we are consciously aware of them or not. We cannot go through life in fear of being accused of plagiarism because our brain might drag up old data masquerading as our own original thought, or even worrying about whether our own original thoughts have ever been concocted by another person completely independently.

Any reasonable person (although admittedly, there is a surfeit of unreasonable people) will take the work as a whole into account. If there is simply a single phrase or a couple of instances of wordings that are similar to another source, this is most likely an innocent coincidence. On the other hand, if a work has many such occurrences, the probability that the infractions are innocent is quite low.

We arrive here at intent. Did you knowingly copy part of someone else's work and submit it as your own without giving proper credit? If you did not, stop worrying about it. If you did, Big Brother, also known as your professor, is watching, possibly with the assistance of high-tech plagiarism detection tools. (A tip of the hat to George Orwell.)

11.3 ENGINEERING CREED

Ethical decisions in engineering have, in general, a narrow focus specific to the problems that arise when designing and producing products or services of a technical nature. Engineers and scientists have, by the very nature of their profession, a body of specialized knowledge that is understood only vaguely, if at all, by most of the population. This knowledge can be used for tremendous good in society, but can also cause untold mischief when used by unscrupulous practitioners. Various engineering organizations have thus developed codes of conduct specific to the profession. Perhaps the most well known is the Code of Ethics for Engineers developed by the National Society of Professional Engineers (NSPE). The entire NSPE Code of Ethics is rather long, so we list only the Engineer's Creed and the Fundamental Canons of the Code here.

Engineer's Creed

As a Professional Engineer, I dedicate my professional knowledge and skill to the advancement and betterment of human welfare. I pledge:

- To give the utmost of performance
- To participate in none but honest enterprise
- To live and work according to the laws of man and the highest standards of professional conduct
- To place service before profit, the honor and standing of the profession before personal advantage, and the public welfare above all other considerations

In humility and with need for Divine Guidance, I make this pledge.

Fundamental Canons

Engineers, in the fulfillment of their professional duties, shall

- Hold paramount the safety, health, and welfare of the public
- Perform services only in areas of their competence
- Issue public statements only in an objective and truthful manner
- Act for each employer or client as faithful agents or trustees
- Avoid deceptive acts
- Conduct themselves honorably, responsibly, ethically, and lawfully so as to enhance the honor, reputation, and usefulness of the profession

The complete code can easily be found online at a variety of sites. When this book went to press, the URL for the Code of Ethics on the NSPE site was http://www.nspe.org/Ethics/CodeofEthics/index.html.

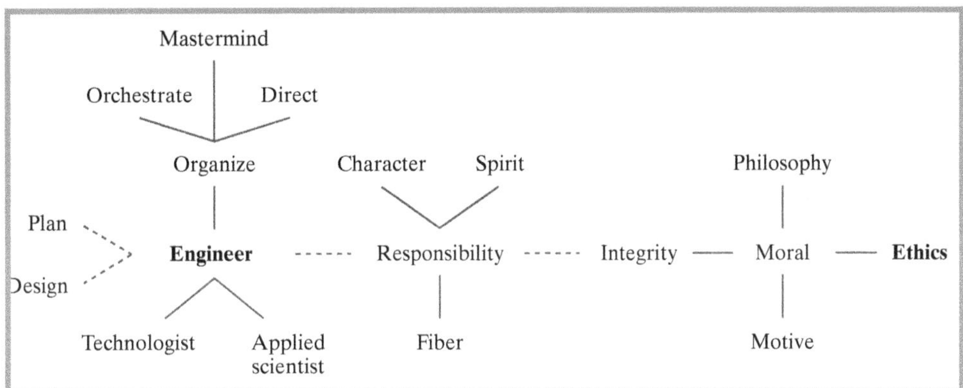

11.4 SOCIAL RESPONSIBILITY

Contributed by: Jason Huggins, P.E., Executive Councilor for Tau Beta Pi, the National Engineering Honor Society, 2006–2014.

NOTE

Social responsibility is the ideology that an individual has an obligation to act to benefit society at large.

As a freshman engineering student, you are just beginning your journey to join the Engineering Profession. Have you thought about what it will mean to be a part of a profession? Being a professional means we hold the public's trust and confidence in our training, skills, and knowledge of engineering. As a profession, we recognize the importance of this trust in the Engineering Canons and the Engineering Creed that define our standards for ethics, integrity, and regard for public welfare. So, does adherence to the Engineering Canons and the Engineering Creed fulfill our social responsibilities as engineers?

Traditionally, professions have always been held in very high regard by society, largely due to the extensive amount of training, education, and dedication required for membership. With this come high expectations of how the members of a profession conduct themselves both in their professional and private lives: doctors save lives, lawyers protect people's rights, and engineers make people's lives better. I did not really make this connection or understand what it meant until I was initiated into Tau Beta Pi, the National Engineering Honor Society. The Tau Beta Pi initiation ceremony has remained largely unchanged for over 100 years, and emphasizes the obligation as engineers and members of Tau Beta Pi to society that extends beyond the services we offer to our employers and our clients.

Over the years, I have taken these obligations to mean that as a profession we are not elevated above anyone else in society. We are affected by the same problems as the general public and we must have an equal part in addressing them. In your lifetime, you will be impacted by issues such as the strength of the economy, the effectiveness of the public educational system, unemployment, the increasing national debt, national security, and environmental sustainability. You cannot focus your talents as an engineer on solving only technical issues and assume the rest of society will address the nontechnical issues. The same skill sets you are currently developing to solve technical issues can be applied to solve issues outside the field of engineering. Your ability as an engineer to effectively examine and organize facts and information in a logical manner and then present our conclusions in an unbiased fashion allows others to more fully understand complex issues and in turn help develop better solutions.

This does not mean that as an engineering profession, we are going to solve all of the world's problems. It simply means that it is our responsibility to use our skills and talents as engineers in helping to solve them. It is our obligation to actively use our skills and talents to act upon issues impacting our local, national, and global communities, not merely watching as passive observers.

I challenge you to pick one issue or problem facing society that you feel passionate about and get involved. Once you do, you will be surprised at the impact you can have, even if on a small scale. By adhering to the Engineering Canon and Creed in your professional life and getting actively involved trying to solve societal issues in your personal life, you will be fulfilling your social responsibility.

In-Class Activities

ICA 11-1

For each of the following situations, indicate whether you think the action is ethical or unethical or you are unsure. Do not read ahead; do not go back and change your answers.

Situation	Ethical	Unethical	Unsure
1. Not leaving a tip after a meal because your steak was not cooked to your liking			
2. Speeding 5 miles per hour over the limit			
3. Killing a roach			
4. Speeding 15 miles per hour over the limit			
5. Having plastic surgery after an accident			

Situation *(continued)*	Ethical	Unethical	Unsure
6. Killing a mouse			
7. Driving 90 miles per hour			
8. Using Botox			
9. Not leaving a tip after a meal because the waiter was inattentive			
10. Killing a healthy cat			
11. Driving 90 miles per hour taking an injured child to the hospital			
12. Killing a healthy horse			
13. Dyeing your hair			
14. Killing a person			
15. Having liposuction			

ICA 11-2

For each of the following situations, indicate whether you think the action is ethical or unethical or you are unsure. Do not read ahead; do not go back and change your answers.

Situation	Ethical	Unethical	Unsure
1. Using time at work to IM your roommate			
2. Accepting a pen and pad of paper from a company trying to sell a new computer system to your company			
3. Obtaining a fake ID to purchase alcohol			
4. Using time at work to plan your friend's surprise party			
5. Accepting a wedge of cheese from a company trying to sell a new computer system to your company			
6. Taking a company pen home from work			
7. Taking extra time at lunch once a month to run a personal errand			
8. Accepting a set of golf clubs from a company trying to sell a new computer system to your company			
9. Drinking a beer while underage at a party in your dorm			
10. Using the company copier to copy your tax return			
11. Drinking a beer when underage at a party, knowing you will need to drive yourself and your roommate home			
12. Taking extra time at lunch once a week to run a personal errand			
13. Borrowing company tools			
14. Going to an NC-17 rated movie when underage			
15. Accepting a Hawaiian vacation from a company trying to sell a new computer system to your company			

ICA 11-3

For each of the following situations, indicate whether you think the action is ethical or unethical or you are unsure. Do not read ahead; do not go back and change your answers.

Situation	Ethical	Unethical	Unsure
1. Acting happy to see an acquaintance who is spreading rumors about you			
2. Letting a friend who has been sick copy your homework			
3. Shortcutting by walking across the grass on campus			
4. "Mooning" your friends as you drive by their apartment			
5. Registering as a Democrat even though you are a Republican			
6. Cheating on a test			
7. Shortcutting by walking across the grass behind a house			
8 . Saying that you lunched with a coworker, rather than your high school sweetheart, when your spouse asks who you ate lunch with			
9. Helping people with their homework			
10. Shortcutting by walking through a building on campus			
11. Not telling your professor that you accidentally saw several of the final exam problems when you visited his or her office			
12. Suppressing derogatory comments about the college because the dean has asked you not to say anything negative when he or she invited you to meet with an external board evaluating the college			
13. Letting somebody copy your homework			
14. Shortcutting by walking through a house			
15. Not telling your professor that your score on a test was incorrectly totaled as 78 instead of the correct 58			

ICA 11-4

For each of the following situations, indicate how great you feel the need is in the world to solve the problem listed. Do not read ahead; do not go back and change your answers.

Situation	Ethical	Unethical	Unsure
1. Teaching those who cannot read or write			
2. Helping starving children in poor nations			
3. Helping people locked in prisons			
4. Helping to slow population growth			
5. Helping to reduce dependence on foreign oil			
6. Helping to reduce greenhouse gas emissions			
7. Helping people persecuted for sexual orientation			
8. Helping to reduce gun ownership			
9. Helping those who are mentally disabled			
10. Helping to supply laptops to poor children			
11. Helping prevent prosecution of "victimless" crimes			
12. Helping to end bigotry			
13. Helping to prevent development of WMD (weapons of mass destruction)			
14. Helping prosecute "hate" crimes			
15. Helping to eliminate violence in movies			
16. Helping homeless people in your community			
17. Helping people with AIDS			
18. Helping people in warring countries			
19. Helping endangered species			

ICA 11-5

Discuss the possible actions, if any, that you would take in each of the following situations. In each case, use the four-step analysis procedure presented in Section 2.1 to help determine an appropriate answer.

(a) Your roommate purchased a theme over the Internet and submitted it as his or her own work in English class.

(b) Your project team has been trying to get your design to work reliably for 2 weeks, but it still fails about 20% of the time. Your teammate notices another team's design that is much simpler, that is easy to build, and that works almost every time. Your teammate wants your group to build a replica of the other team's project at the last minute.

(c) You notice that your professor forgot to log off the computer in lab. You are the only person left in the room.

(d) The best student in the class, who consistently wrecks the "curve" by making 15–20 points higher than anyone else on every test, accidentally left her notes for the course in the classroom.

(e) You have already accepted and signed the paperwork for a position as an intern at ENGR-R-US. You then get an invitation to interview for an intern position (all expenses paid) at another company in a city you have always wanted to visit. What would you do? Would you behave differently if the agreement was verbal, but the papers had not been signed?

(f) One of your professors has posted a political cartoon with which both you and your friend vehemently disagree. The friend removes the cartoon from the bulletin board and tears it up.

ICA 11-6

Discuss the possible actions, if any, that you would take in each of the following situations. In each case, use the four-step analysis procedure presented in Section 11.1 to help determine an appropriate answer.

(a) You witness several students eating lunch on a bench on campus. When they finish, they leave their trash on the ground.
(b) You see a student carving his initials in one of the largest beech trees on campus.
(c) You see a student writing graffiti on a trash dumpster.
(d) There is a squirrel in the road ahead of a car you are driving. You know that a squirrel's instinct is to dart back and forth rather than run in a straight line away from a predator (in this case a vehicle) making it quite likely it will dart back into the road at the last instant.
(e) You find a wallet containing twenty-three $100 bills. The owner's contact information is quite clear. Does your answer change if the wallet contained three $1 bills?

ICA 11-7

Read the Engineer's Creed section of this chapter.

If you are planning to pursue a career in engineering: Type the creed word for word, then write a paragraph (100–200 words) on what the creed means to you, in your own words, and how the creed make you feel about your chosen profession (engineering).

If you are planning to pursue a career other than engineering, does your future discipline have such a creed? If so, look this up and type it, then write a paragraph (100–200 words) on what the creed means to you, in your own words, and how the creed makes you feel about your chosen profession. If not, write a paragraph (100–200 words) on what items should be included in a creed if your profession had one and how the lack of a creed makes you feel about your chosen profession.

ICA 11-8

Engineers often face workplace situations in which the ethical aspects of the job should be -considered.

Table 11.1 lists a variety of types of organizations that hire engineers, and one or more possibly ethical issues that might arise.

Pick several of the organizations from the table that interest you (or those assigned by your professor) and answer the following:

(a) Can you think of other ethical problems that might arise at each of these organizations?
(b) Apply the four-step ethical decision-making procedure to gain insight into the nature of the decision to be made. In some cases, you may decide that an ethical issue is not really involved, but you should be able to justify why it is not.
(c) List 10 other types of organizations at which engineers would confront ethical problems, and explain the nature of the ethical decisions to be made.
(d) How does one find a balance between profit and environmental concerns?
(e) Under what circumstances should an engineer be held liable for personal injury or property damage caused by the products of his or her labor?
(f) Under what situations would you blow the whistle on your superior or your company?
(g) Should attorneys specializing in personal injury and property damage litigation be allowed to advertise, and if so, in what venues?

Table 11.1 Industries and Issues for ICA 11-8

Organization/Occupation	Possible Issues
Alternative energy providers	Use of heavy metals in photovoltaic systems Effect of wind generators on bird populations Aesthetic considerations (e.g., NIMBY) Environmental concerns (e.g., Three Gorges project)
Environmental projects	Fertile floodplains inundated by dams/lakes Safety compromised for cost (e.g., New Orleans levees) Habitat destruction by projects Habitat renovation versus cost (e.g., Everglades)
Chemical engineers	Toxic effluents from manufacturing process Pesticide effect on ecosystem (e.g., artificial estrogens) Insufficient longitudinal studies of pharmaceuticals Non-biodegradable products (e.g., plastics)
Civil engineers	Runoff/erosion at large projects Disruption of migration routes (freeways) Quality of urban environments Failure modes of structures
Computer engineers	Vulnerability of software to malware Intellectual property rights (e.g., illegal downloads) Safety issues (e.g., programmed medical devices, computer-controlled transportation)
Electrical engineers	Toxic materials in batteries Cell phone safety concerns Power grid safety and quick restoration in crises Possible use to break the law (e.g., radar detectors)
Electric power industry	Shipment of high sulfur coal to China Disposal of nuclear waste Environmental issues (e.g., spraying power-line corridors)
Food processing industry	Health possibly compromised by high fat/sugar/salt products Use of genetically engineered organisms Sanitation (e.g., Escherichia coli, Salmonella) Use of artificial preservatives
Manufacturing companies	Manufacturing in countries with poor labor practices Lax safety standards in some countries Domestic jobs lost Environmental pollution due to shipping distances Trade imbalance
Industrial engineers	Quality/safety compromised by cost Efficiency versus quality of working environment Management of dangerous tools and materials
Mechanical engineers	Automotive safety versus cost Environmental impact of fossil fuels Robot failsafe mechanisms

CHAPTER 12
USER-CENTERED DESIGN AND NEEDFINDING

Objectives

By learning the material in this chapter, you should be able to

- describe principles of user-centered design
- identify needs
- name and describe the stages of an interview
- interview a user to gather information that is important to the design process
- describe the role of and tools for needfinding in the design process

12.1 USER-CENTERED DESIGN

There are many different criteria and constraints that you take into account when you are engaged in design. You will probably take into account cost, safety, time, sustainability, and many other factors as you are considering different solutions; an additional criterion to consider is the user of your design. For example, imagine that you are asked to design a car. Your final design will differ quite a bit if you are designing the car for a mother of five children versus a single male in his twenties. In engaging in user-centered design, you consider two key things: **who is the user?** and **how will they use the product (or process) I am designing?**

12.1.1 Basic Principles of User-Centered Design

- Taking the user into account early, instead of only testing at the end
- Designing a product for a specific group of users; sometimes involving users as designers
- Gathering information about the user though data collection and evaluation, not just guessing what the user would like based on your own experiences
- Iteration—continuing to gather more information about the user and the way that the product will be used and testing your design with users

12.1.2 Benefits of Engaging in User-Centered Design

- The user will be more satisfied and will be happier with the product/process, leading to improved acceptance and market share
- The product/process will help the user increase productivity and make fewer errors—this is especially relevant for products/processes for your own company
- You can reduce time and money spent on training and user support

---

- You can reduce time and money spent on re-developing the product/process
- You/your company will enjoy an enhanced reputation, loyalty, and branding
- The process also facilitates product extension—recognition of other ways to market the product and other similar products that will benefit the user
- You may also be able to identify ways to promote sustainability as you identify areas of waste associated with the user(s)

12.1.3 How Do I Go About User-Centered Design?

There are many ways to consider your user. Generally, you will follow five steps:

1. **Plan the user-centered design process:** Choose your methods.
2. **Specify the context of use:** Describe the intended user (and others who may also use the design or be affected by it), what they will do with your product or process, the context of use (Where will it be used? How? Why?), and problems the design might address.
   [*This step is also related to Needfinding, a separate section in the text*]
3. **Specify requirements:** Based on what you have learned about the user(s), what are the requirements for your design? These are statements about what the design should fulfill.
4. **Produce design solutions:** Initially, design solutions might be a list of requirements; later, you will likely have different prototypes. Some prototypes are very rough versions of the solution; this allows you to get feedback on the concept rather than on the appearance (such as the color). After testing your design(s) with users, you will make final decisions.
5. **Evaluate your design:** Evaluate your solution (whether it is a prototype or final solution) based on your requirements and based on data collected from users.

12.1.4 Methods

Although this process is listed as five steps, you will likely cycle through these steps (and may go through the steps "out of order" at times).

1. Planning	2. Context of Use	3. Requirements	4. Design	5. Evaluation
▪ Usability planning and scoping ▪ Usability cost/benefit analysis	▪ Identify stakeholders ▪ Context of use analysis ▪ Literature Review ▪ Survey of existing users (using questionnaires or interviews) ▪ Field study/user observation ▪ Diary keeping ▪ Task analysis	▪ Stakeholder analysis ▪ User cost-benefit analysis ▪ User rqmt interview ▪ Focus groups ▪ Scenarios of use ▪ Personas ▪ Existing system/competitor analysis ▪ Allocation of function	▪ Brainstorming ▪ Parallel design ▪ Design guidelines and standards ▪ Design Patterns ▪ Storyboarding ▪ Affinity diagrams ▪ Card sorting ▪ Paper prototyping ▪ Software prototyping ▪ Organizational prototyping	▪ Participatory evaluation ▪ Assisted evaluation ▪ Heuristic or expert eval. ▪ Controlled user testing ▪ Satisfaction questionnaires ▪ Assessing cognitive workload ▪ Critical incidents ▪ Post experience interviews

Based on your experiences, you probably know something about interviews, questionnaires, focus groups (an interview with multiple people at the same time) and conducting observations of people (think about "people watching"). Some of the methods in the table are probably less familiar. There are many books and websites on user-centered design and human-computer interaction if you want to learn more. Two methods that we focus on here are generating a persona and generating scenarios of use. Both methods will help you synthesize the information that you accumulated about your user group and how the user(s) will use the product or process you are designing, and use the information to identify specific requirements for the design.

12.1.5 Generating a Persona

A persona is a fictional prototypical user that you create to represent the data that you have collected though interviews, questionnaires and/ or observations as well as information you gain from reading about others' studies. As you create the persona, it is important to describe this prototypical user with details—details that help you to understand the user's life as a whole as well as details that are specifically relevant to your product/process. Generally, you will have one primary persona representing your primary user group, but you may also have 1–3 secondary persona representing other important users or stakeholders.

TRY CREATING A PERSONA:

Persona

Name:

Age:

Occupation:

Family:

Hobbies:

Other key background information:

How/when/where/why might he use this product? :

Image Courtesy of PhotoDisc, Inc.

12.1.6 Scenarios

You can think of scenarios as "before and after" stories of your persona using the product or process you are designing. In creating the scenario, you focus on potential problems or needs that the user has, and how their life might be improved. The scenarios often take the form of short "vignettes"—1–3 paragraph stories—as well as sketches and/or storyboards.

Try creating a scenario (write about a paragraph and draw some sketches):

Before

After

12.1.7 Usability Testing

After you have created a prototype of your design (even if it is a sketch or a play-dough model) you can begin collecting feedback from people who represent your user group—**people with demographic characteristics that match your user's**. You can simply ask these users to respond to your idea; you can interview them about their impressions of your design; you can ask them to try to accomplish a series of tasks with your prototype and watch to see what tasks are difficult or lead to errors. Generally, you are trying to find out if your design is appealing, usable, appropriate for the users' needs, fun, and/or educational.

You will want to try to have *7 users* test your design. After this, you will make changes to your design (and the prototype representing your design) and repeat this cycle. Sometimes the feedback you get from users will lead to a major re-design; other times a small tweak. You will probably need to repeat this process many times before you have uncovered all of the areas for improvement—but remember, the more effort you put into understanding the user in the beginning of the process (2. Context of User) the less effort and expense you will need to invest in fixing the design after testing!

Wrap-Up

List something that is a good example of a user-centered design:

Why is it a good example?

*User-centered design is a process of **understanding users' needs** before designing a product or process, and ensuring that you are addressing those needs as you design the product or process.*

12.2 NEEDFINDING

Needfinding is a term coined by Robert McKim at Stanford approximately 40 years ago. As you engage in needfinding, you are looking for the **underlying** needs that people have—this is very different from brainstorming products that you can try to convince people they want, or basing designs based on what you yourself want or need! A need is something that is missing or wrong or unfulfilled.

Needfinding is also different from bug listing. You aren't looking for the little things that bother people or the quick fixes, but instead the underlying need. If you look only at the immediate need you might miss an innovative solution that could have much greater impact.

Sometimes needs are obvious or spoken (explicit), some are less well-known (implicit). Sometimes you are able to identify needs based on work-arounds—ways that people use things in ways that were not intended. For example, people often use the plastic photo holders in their wallets for their credit cards instead of photographs; people need a way to organize and protect their credit cards. Using the photo holder is one solution that people have come up with, but now that we have identified this need, we can brainstorm a multitude of other possible solutions.

Remember: Needs are not solutions! People don't necessarily need cell phones (a solution)—people do need a way to talk to each other (need). Needs last longer than specific solutions.

There are some needs that are **common** to everyone, such as food and shelter. There are some needs that are **context-dependent**; they are common to everyone in the same situation (for example, all students need to learn). There are other needs that are very **specific** to a group of people who have something in common and are engaged in the same activity (for example, 18-year old college students have different needs than 5-year old kindergarten students). As a designer, you may find that narrowing your focus to a specific group of people will help you discover a real need, and then an innovative solution for addressing that need.

Needs spur action. They give you a roadmap for how to proceed. Also, once you identify a need, you may find it hard to ignore! Needfinding is a very human endeavor. An underlying goal of needfinding is to relate to human need. As a designer, you can bring your sensitivity, awareness and intelligence to the needfinding process as you look at needs from flexible points of view. To identify and understand needs, it is also helpful to consider the rich context of the need: history, cultural patterns, current events, ideas and values all contribute to the need and the experience associated with the need, as well as potential ways to address the need.

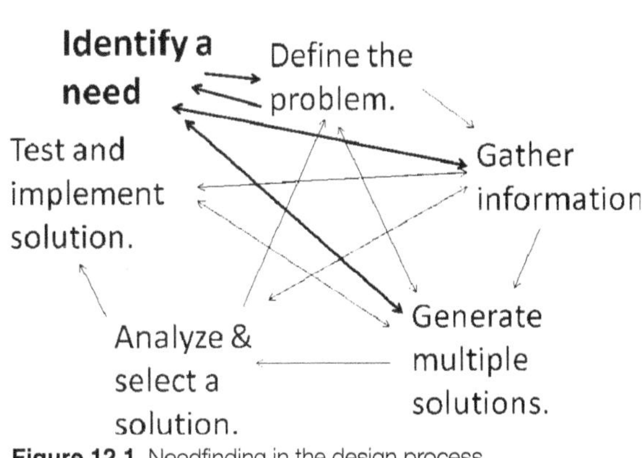

Figure 12.1 Needfinding in the design process

Needfinding changes a typical model of the design process. As with most representations of design, the process is iterative and cyclic. Needfinding influences the earlier part of the process—problem definition—and uses information from and feeds information to other parts of the process as shown.

12.2.1 Needfinding Tools

There are two basic approaches to needfinding: interviews and observations. Each can be used separately, but it can be very effective to combine the two. Regardless of approach (interview, observation, or combination) it is important that you have:

- good subjects (represent the type of person you are trying to learn more about; interesting)
- good environments
- structure and flexibility (have a plan but also a back-up plan and back-up back-up plan)
- good stories
- ways to get past the immediate or surface needs or drivers
- ways to avoid the Hawthorne effect (this is when people change their behavior because they are being observed)
- room for silence (time for them to reflect and then speak)
- respect for your subject

Observations

Viewing users and their behavior in their natural environment can provide insights into needs, as you learn about their experiences. There are several approaches to observations: "people-watching" by spending extended periods of time in an area where you can expect to see your target user group engaging in their normal behavior, "walking in their shoes" by assuming the role of the subject, asking for a tour from an insider, observing (and perhaps photographing) anonymously. Each of these approaches have trade-offs. You will need to decide how much time you can spend on your observations, the extent to which you want the subject to be aware of your observations, and the extent to which you want the subject to provide an explanation of their behavior. One of the key things to remember to do is to look without presupposing that you know what you are looking for. You will need to trust your ability to recognize the problem when you see it, rather than having a guess of what it is you are looking for.

Interviews

There are six major stages to an interview: 1) Introduction, 2) Kick-off, 3) Building rapport, 4) Grand tour 5) Reflection and 6) Wrap-up

1. Introduction: During this phase, you introduce yourself and the purpose of the interview.
   a. The informant (the person you are interviewing) may not understand what is happening
   b. Be direct—give them directions to get going. "Why don't we sit down here?"
   c. Find a good place for the interview: adequate light, low noise, comfortable, few distractions
   d. Describe your purpose
      "Hi, I'm a Purdue student studying coffee. I'm interested in hearing about your experiences with coffee. There are no right or wrong answers, I just want to hear what you have to say."
   e. Outline the interview
      "I'd like to talk with you about your experiences with three things: choosing coffee, making coffee and drinking coffee."
2. Kick-off: At the end of the introduction, make a clear transition to the interview respondent.
      "So first off, do you drink coffee?"
   Clarify with lots of follow-up questions. This helps the respondent to get comfortable with talking to you.
3. Build rapport: Respondents may provide only short answers at first. Be patient, and continue to ask descriptive questions to build trust.
      "Have you had any coffee today? How was it? Do you normally make it at home, or buy it from a particular store?"

Reassure the respondent that they are doing well

"I don't know; is this the kind of information you are looking for?"

"Absolutely, this is exactly what we need."

4. Grand tour: This may be a walk around a kitchen, factory, or calculator. It may be in person, literal walk around, or narrative description. The goal is to elicit incredible detail, including things you would never think to ask.

   "Tell me about the texture on the coffee cup you used this morning"

   You may ask your informant to act out interactions or open up hidden areas

   "Think about your most memorable coffee experience. Why was it so unique? Where was it? Who were the other people involved? What happened?"
5. Reflection: During this phase you review what you have learned and you also provide your informant with another opportunity to add more information.
   a. Take a break and review what you have learned: check to make sure your respondent agrees with your summary of the interview

      "So it sounds like music and lighting are important for your coffee shop experience. Is this right?"
   b. Then encourage personal insights and discussions of why

      "If you were designing the perfect coffee shop, based on your ideal experience . . ."
6. Wrap up: Thank them and tell them how helpful they have been. Ask for any final thoughts, or if they have any questions for you. Knowing that the interview is over (or ending) can jar loose additional comments and insights, so keep the tape recorder rolling.

12.2.2 Additional Tips

1. Cast aside your biases, listen and observe
2. Note the contradictions between what people say and what they do
3. Watch for "work arounds" (people often make do, and "work around" the shortcomings of products and situations) (these might be unintended uses of products)
4. Distinguish between needs and solutions
5. Look beyond the obvious

Try it Out: Try interviewing someone in order to identify a potential need. If possible, interview someone you don't already know well.

1. What did you learn?

2. What surprises came out?

3. To what extent is this related to what engineers do?

12.2.3 Other Methods

- Lead user interviews
- Expert interviews
- History interviews
- Laddering interviews
- Cultural context interviews
- Camera studies
- Surveys
- Process mapping
- Intercepts

Next Step: Maintaining an Idea Log

If you would like to further develop your needfinding skills, you will find that keeping an idea log can help you. Keep notes of things that you notice while waiting in line, riding the bus or walking across campus. Draw sketches that capture problems people encounter or possible solutions (even if they don't seem feasible with today's technology). Drawing concepts maps may also help, as you make a list of ideas or concepts that are related to each other and identify the ways that they are connected.

RESOURCES

Kemper, J.D., *Engineers and Their Profession,* 4th Edition, Oxford University Press.

D. Patnaik & R. Becker, "Needfinding: the Why and How of Uncovering People's Needs," *Design Management Journal,* 1999.

Hasso Plattner Institute of Design at Stanford http://hci.stanford.edu/cs447/docs/NeedFindingCribSheet.pdf

CHAPTER 13
SELECTING A MODEL AND REGRESSION

Objectives

By learning the material in this chapter, you should be able to

- describe the PERIOD process of experimental design
- list different mathematical models that describe system behavior
- explain how linear regression results in a "best-fit" model
- describe possible sources of differences between a model and actual data
- find the best-fit line for a set of data and describe the quality of the model
- select and justify a choice of trendline to model a set of data (linear, power, exponential)

13.1 EXPERIMENTAL DESIGN: PERIOD ANALYSIS

Experiments enable engineers to come up with a creative solution to a problem and test the validity of the proposed idea. An experiment is a test of a proposed explanation of a problem. A good design of an experiment is a critical part of the scientific method.

13.1.1 What Constitutes the Scientific Method?

1. Observation: Observe the problem and note items of interest.
2. Hypothesis: Search for a known explanation of the phenomenon or attempt to formulate a new explanation.
3. Prediction: Create a model or prediction of behavior based on that hypothesis.
4. Experiment: Test your predictions. If necessary, modify your hypothesis and retest.

13.1.2 Why Is Experimental Design Important?

As you move through your college career, you will be inundated with many equations and theories. These are useful in solving a wide variety of problems. However, as you will see, often the equations are really only useful in solving the most basic type of problems.

As an example, suppose you are interested in the speed of a ball as it rolls across the floor after rolling down a ramp. In physics, you will learn the equations of motion for bodies moving under the influence of gravity. If you are good, you can use these to examine rolling balls. What you will quickly find, however, is that numerous complicating factors make it difficult to apply the basic equations to obtain an adequate answer. Let us suppose you are interested in smooth balls (such as racquetballs), rough balls (tennis balls), heavy balls (bowling balls), and lightweight balls (ping-pong balls). The simplified equations of

---

Taken from *Thinking Like an Engineer: An Active Learning Approach,* by Elizabeth A. Stephan, David R. Bowman, William J. Park, Benjamin L. Sill, and Matthew W. Ohland.

Do you know what these unique measurement instruments do?

- Durometer
- Dynamometer
- Euidometer
- Galvanometer
- Gyroscope
- Manometer
- Opisometer
- Pycnometer
- Tachymeter
- Thiele tube

motion predict that all these will behave in essentially the same way. You will discover, however, that the drag of the air affects the ping-pong ball, the fuzz affects the tennis ball, and the flexible nature of the racquetball will allow it to bounce at steep ramp angles. It is difficult to predict the behavior analytically. Often, one of the quickest ways to learn about the performance of such complex situations is to conduct experiments.

13.1.3 What Are Experimental Measurements?

Most scientific experiments involve measuring the effect of variability of an attribute of an object. In an experiment, the **independent variable** is the variable that is controlled. The **dependent variable** is a variable that reacts to a change in the independent variable. A **control variable** is part of the experiment that can vary but is held constant to let the experimenter observe the influence of the independent variable on the dependent variable. Keeping control variables constant throughout an experiment eliminates any confounding effects resulting from excess variability.

Any measurement acquired in an experiment contains two important pieces of information. First, the measurement contains the actual value measured from the instrument. In general, a measurement is some physical dimension that is acquired with some man-made data-collection instrument. As with any man-made device, there may be some imperfection that can cause adverse effects during data collection. Thus, the second piece of information that goes along with any measurement is the level of uncertainty.

Any uncertainty in measurement is not strictly by instrumentation error. Systematic error is any error resulting from human or instrumentation malfunction. Random error is caused by the limits of the precision of the data-collection device. It is possible to minimize the systematic error in an experiment, but random error cannot be completely eliminated.

13.1.4 What Measurements Do You Need to Make?

You need to develop a coherent experimental program. You should make enough measurements to answer any anticipated questions, but you do not usually have the time or money to test every possible condition. Points to consider:

- What are the parameters of interest?
- What is the range of these parameters—minimum values, maximum values?
- What increments are reasonable for testing (every 10 degrees, every 30 seconds, etc.)?
- What order is best to vary the parameters? Which should be tested first, next, etc.?

Here is an acronym (PERIOD) that can help you remember these important steps. As an example, it is applied to the problem of the ramp and rolling balls, described above.

P–Parameters of interest determined

- Parameter 1 is the ramp angle.
- Parameter 2 is the distance up the ramp that we release the ball.
- Parameter 3 is the type of ball.

E–Establish the range of parameters

- Ramp angle can vary between 0 and 90 degrees in theory, but in reality can only vary between 10 degrees (if too shallow, ball would not move) and 45 degrees (if too steep, ball will bounce).
- The distance we release the ball up the ramp can vary between 0 and 3 feet in theory, assuming that the ramp is 3 feet long. We cannot release the ball too close to the bottom of the ramp or it would not move. In reality, we can only vary between 0.5 feet and 3 feet.
- We will test as many types of balls as we have interest in.

R–Repetition of each test specified

- The ramp angle will be set according to the height of the ramp from the floor, so there is not much room for error in this measurement; only one measurement is needed for such geometry.
- Each placement of the ball before release will vary slightly and may cause the ball to roll slightly differently down the ramp; this is probably the most important factor in determining the speed, so three measurements at each location are needed.
- We will assume that every ball is the same, and the actual ball used will not change the outcome of the experiment; only one ball of each type is needed.

I–Increments of each parameter specified

- We will test every 10 degrees of ramp angle, starting at 10 degrees and ending at 40 degrees.
- We will release the balls at a height of 0.5, 1, 1.5, 2, 2.5 and 3 feet up the ramp.
- We will test five types of balls: racquetball, baseball, tennis ball, ping-pong ball, and bowling ball.

O–Order to vary the parameters determined

- We will set the ramp angle and then test one ball type by releasing it at each of the four different distances up the ramp.
- We will repeat this process three times for each ball.
- We will then repeat this process for each type of ball.
- We will then change the ramp angle by 10 degrees and repeat the process.
- This process is repeated until all conditions have been tested.

D–Determine number of measurements needed and Do the experiment

It is always important to determine before you start how many measurements that you need to make. Sometimes you can be too ambitious and end up developing an experimental program that will take too much effort or cost too much money. If this is the case, then you need to decide which increments can be relaxed, to reduce the number of overall measurements.

The number of measurements (N) you will need to make can be easily calculated by the following equation for a total of n parameters:

$$N = (\text{\# increments parameter 1} * \text{number of repetitions for parameter 1}) * \\ (\text{\# increments parameter 2} * \text{number of repetitions for parameter 2}) * \ldots \\ (\text{\# increments parameter } n * \text{number of repetitions for parameter } n) * \ldots$$

Continuing the examples given above, the number of actual measurements that we need to make is calculated as

$$N = (4 \text{ angles})*(6 \text{ distances} * 3 \text{ repetitions})*(5 \text{ types of balls}) = 360 \text{ measurements}$$

In this example, 360 measurements may be extreme. If we examine our plan, we can probably make the following changes without losing experimental information:

- We decide to test every 10 degrees of ramp angle, starting at 20 degrees and ending at 40 degrees. This will lower the angle testing from four angles to three angles.
- We will release the balls at a height of 1, 2, 2.5 and 3 feet up the ramp. This will lower the distances from 6 to 4.
- We will test three types of balls: racquetball, ping-pong ball, and bowling ball. This will lower the type of balls from five to three.

The number of actual measurements that we now need to make is calculated as

$$N = (3 \text{ angles})*(4 \text{ distances} * 3 \text{ repetitions})*(3 \text{ types of balls}) = 108 \text{ measurements}$$

This result seems much more manageable to complete than 360!

13.2 MODELS AND SYSTEMS

A **model** is an abstract description of the relationship between variables in a system. A model allows the categorization of different types of mathematical phenomena so that general observations about the variables can be made for use in any number of applications.

For example, if we know that $t = v + 5$ and $M = z + 5$, any observations we make about v with respect to t also apply to z with respect to M. A specific model describes a *system* or *function* that has the same *trend* or *behavior* as a generalized model. In engineering, many specific models within different subdisciplines behave according to the same generalized model.

This section covers three general models of importance to engineers: **linear**, **power**, and **exponential**. It is worth noting that many applications of models within these three categories contain identical math but apply to significantly different disciplines.

Linear models occur when the dependent variable changes in direct relationship to changes in the independent variable. We discuss such systems, including springs, resistive circuits, fluid flow, and elastic materials, in this chapter by relating each model to Newton's generalized law of motion.

Power law systems occur when the independent variable has an exponent not equal to 1 or 0. We discuss these models by addressing integer and rational real exponents.

Exponential models are used in all engineering disciplines in a variety of applications. We discuss these models by examining the similarities between growth and decay models.

The following is an example of the level of knowledge of Excel needed to proceed. *If you are not able to quickly recreate the following exercise in Excel, including trendlines and formatting, please review trendline basics in appendix materials before proceeding.*

Energy (E) stored in an **inductor** is related to its inductance (L) and the current (I) passing through it by the following equation.

$$E = \frac{1}{2}LI^2$$

The SI unit of inductance, the **henry** [H], is named for Joseph Henry (1797–1878), credited with the discovery of self-inductance of electromagnets.

Three inductors were tested and the results are given here. Create a proper plot of the data and add a properly formatted power law trendline to each data set.

Current (*I*) [A]	2	6	10	14	16
Energy of Inductor #1 (E1) [J]	0.002	0.016	0.050	0.095	0.125
Energy of Inductor #2 (*E*2) [J]	0.010	0.085	0.250	0.510	0.675
Energy of Inductor #3 (*E*3) [J]	0.005	0.045	0.125	0.250	0.310

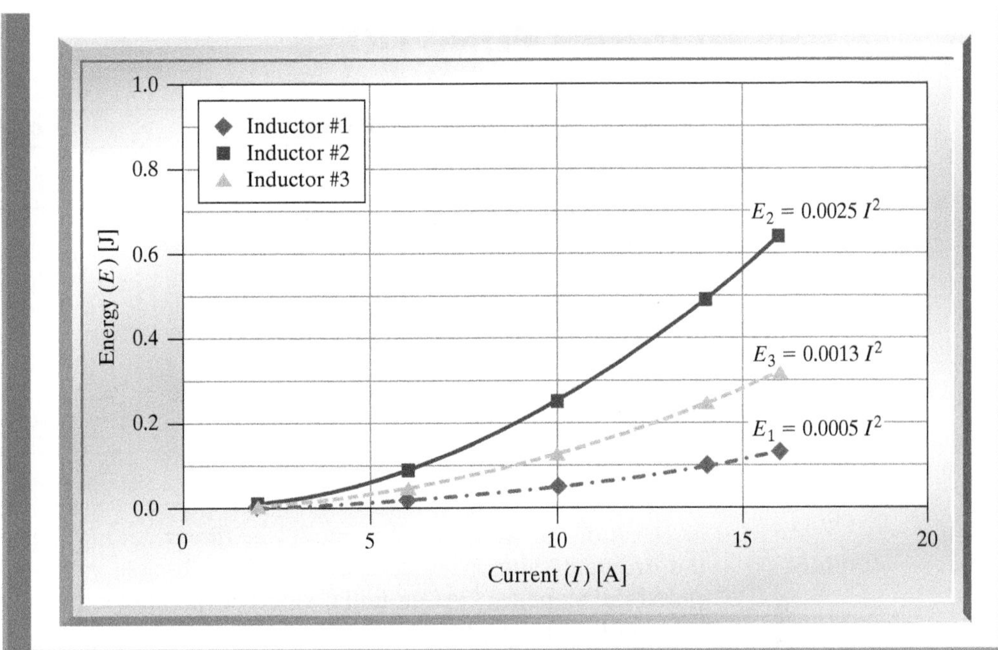

Figure 13.1 is an example of a properly formatted graph, showing an experimental data series with linear trendlines.

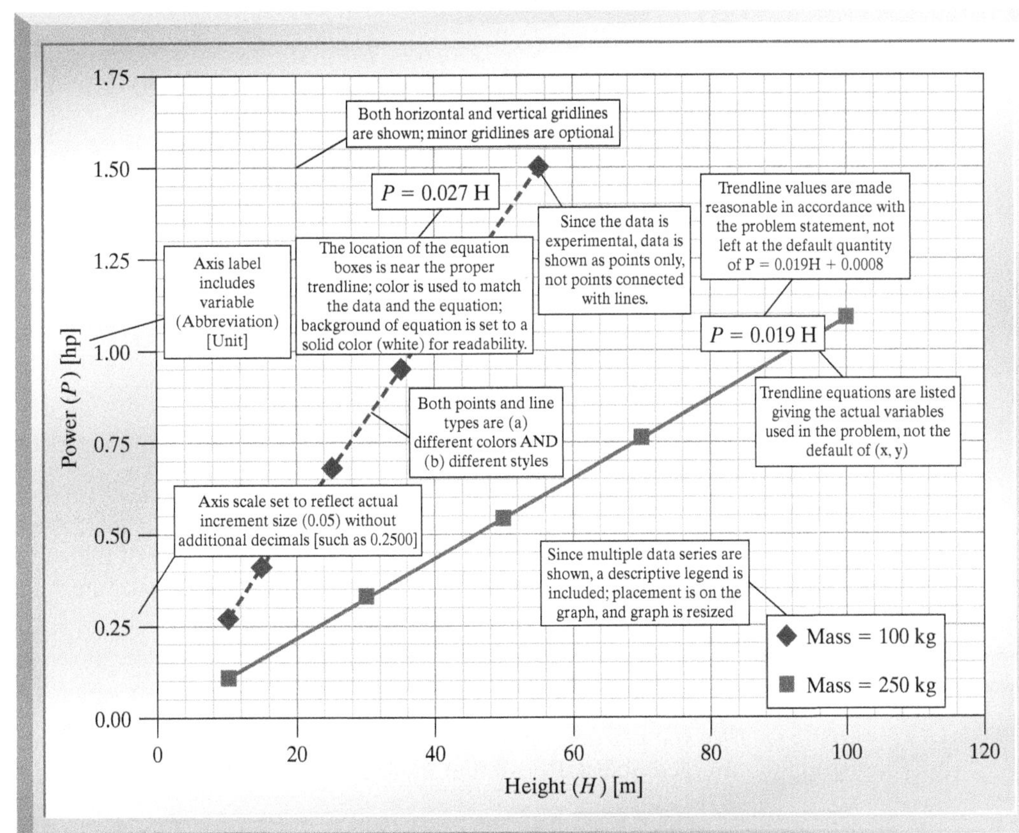

Figure 13.1 Example of a proper plot, showing multiple experimental data sets with linear trendlines

13.3 LINEAR FUNCTIONS

Trend	Equation	Data Form	Graphical Example
Linear	$y = mx + c$	Defined value (c) at x = 0 Data appears as a linear (straight) line	— Positive value of *m* -- Negative value of *m*

One of the most common models is **linear**, taking the form $y = mx + c$, where the ordinate value (y) is a function of the abscissa value (x) and a constant factor called the **slope** (m). At an initial value of the abscissa ($x = 0$), the ordinate value is equal to the **intercept** (c). Examples include

- Distance (d) traveled at constant velocity (v) over time (t) from initial position (d_0):

$$d = vt + d_0$$

- Rate of rotation (ω) as a function of time (t) and angular acceleration (α) from initial rotational rate (ω_i):

$$\omega = \alpha t + \omega_i$$

- Total pressure (P_{total}), relating density (ρ), gravity (g), liquid height (H), and the pressure above the surface ($P_{surface}$):

$$P_{total} = \rho g H + P_{surface}$$

- Newton's second law, relating force (F), mass (m), and acceleration (a):

$$F = ma$$

Note that the intercept value (c) is zero in the last example.

13.3.1 General Model Rules

Given a linear system of the form $y = mx + c$ and assuming $x \geq 0$:

- When $m = 1$, the function is equal to $x + c$.
- When $m = 0$, $y = c$, regardless of the value of x (y never changes).
- When $m > 0$, as x increases, y increases, regardless of the value of c.
- When $m < 0$, as x increases, y decreases, regardless of the value of c.

EXAMPLE 13-1

We want to determine the effect of depth of a fluid on the total pressure felt by a submerged object. Recall that the total pressure is

$$P_{total} = P_{surface} + P_{hydro} = P_{surface} + \rho g H$$

where P_{total} = total pressure [atm]; $P_{surface}$ = pressure at the surface [atm]; ρ = density [kg/m^3]; g = gravity [m/s^2]; H = depth [m]. We enter the lab, take data, and create the following chart.

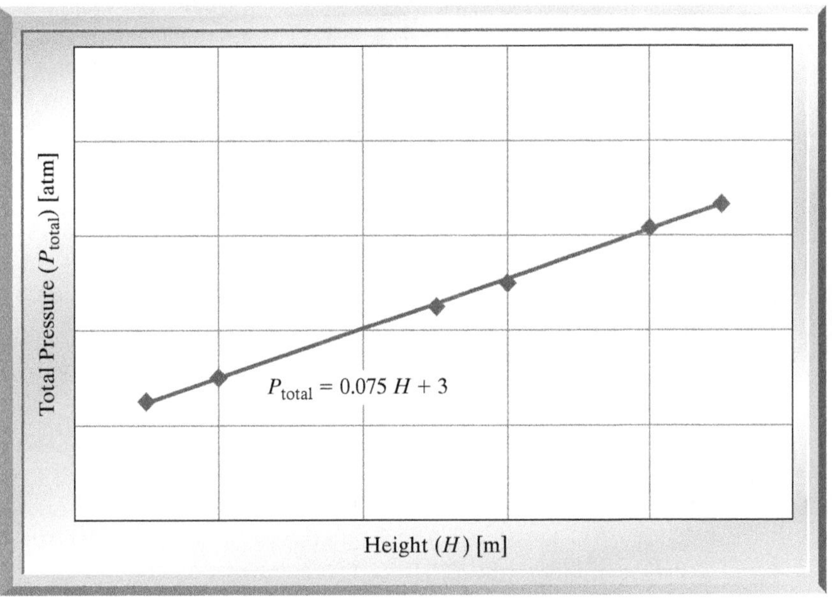

Determine the density of the fluid, in units of kilograms per cubic meter.

We can determine the parameters by matching the trendline generated in Excel with the theoretical expression. In theory: total pressure = density * gravity * height of fluid + pressure on top of the fluid

From graph: total pressure = 0.075 * height + 3

By comparison: density * gravity = 0.075 [atm/m]

$$\frac{0.075 \text{ atm}}{\text{m}} \left| \frac{101{,}325 \text{ Pa}}{1 \text{ atm}} \right| \frac{1 \text{ kg/(ms}^2)}{1 \text{ Pa}} = \rho(9.8 \text{ m/s}^2)$$

$$7{,}600 \text{ kg/(m}^2\text{s}^2) = \rho(9.8 \text{ m/s}^2)$$

$$\rho = 7{,}600 \text{ kg/m}^2\text{s}^2) \left| \frac{\text{s}^2}{9.8 \text{ m}} \right. = 775 \text{ kg/m}^3$$

Determine if the tank is open to the atmosphere or pressurized, and determine the pressure on the top of the fluid in units of atmospheres.

Once again, we can compare the Excel trendline to the theoretical expression. In theory: total pressure = density * gravity * height of fluid + pressure on top of the fluid

From graph: total pressure = 0.075 * height + 3

By comparison, the top of the tank is pressurized at 3 atm.

Increasingly, engineers are working at smaller and smaller scales. Tiny beads made of glass are on the order of 50 micrometers in diameter. They are manufactured so that they become hollow, allowing the wall thickness to be a few nanometers. The compositions of the glass were engineered, so when processed correctly, they would sustain a hollow structure and the glass walls would be infiltrated with hundreds of thousands of nanometer-sized pores. These beads can possibly revolutionize the way fluids and gases are stored for use. The pores are small enough that fluids and even gases could be contained under normal conditions. However, if activated properly, the pores would allow a path for a gas to exit the "container" when it is ready to be used.

Photo courtesy of K. Richardson

COMPREHENSION CHECK 13-1

The graph shows the ideal gas law relationship ($PV = nRT$) between pressure (P) and temperature (T).

(a) What are the units of the slope (0.0087)?

(b) If the tank has a volume of 12 liters and is filled with nitrogen (formula, N_2; molecular weight, 28 grams per mole), what is the amount of gas in the tank (n) in units of grams?

(c) If the tank is filled with 48 grams of oxygen (formula, O_2; molecular weight, 32 grams per mole), what is the volume of the tank (V) in units of liters?

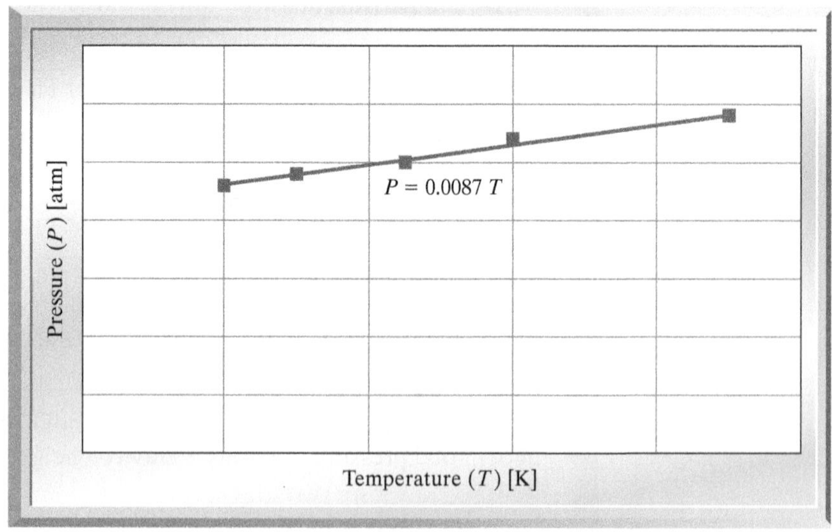

13.4 POWER FUNCTIONS

Trend	Equation	Data Form	Graphical Example
Power	$y = bx^m$	Positive *m* Value of zero at $x = 0$ Negative *m* Value of infinity at $x = 0$	Positive value of *m* Negative value of *m*

Power models take the form $y = bx^m$. Examples include

- Many geometric formulae involving areas, volumes, etc., such as the volume of a sphere (V) as a function of radius (r):

$$V = 4/3\pi r^3$$

- Distance (d) traveled by a body undergoing constant acceleration (a) over time (t), starting from rest:

$$d = at^2$$

- Energy calculations in a variety of contexts, both mechanical and electrical, such as the kinetic energy (KE) of an object as a function of the object's velocity (v), where the constant (k) depends upon the object shape and type of motion:

$$KE = kmv^2$$

- Ideal gas law relationships, such as Boyle's law, relating volume (V) and pressure (P) of an ideal gas, holding temperature (T) and quantity of gas (n) constant:

$$V = (nRT)P^{-1}$$

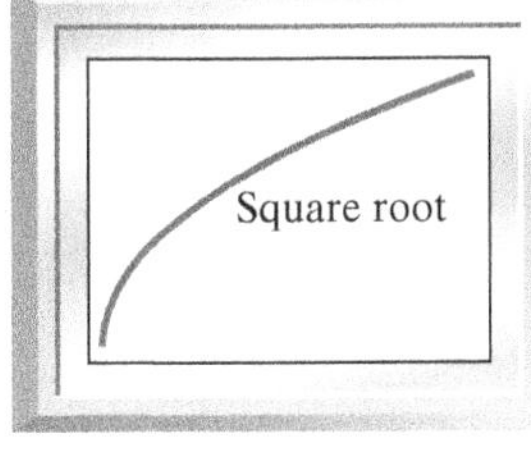

Squared

13.4.1 General Model Rules

Given a power system of the form $y = bx^m = c$, assuming $x \leq 0$::

- When $m = 1$, the model is a linear function.
- When $m = 0$, $y = b + c$, regardless of the value of x.
- When m is rational, the function will contain a rational exponent or may be described with a radical symbol ($\sqrt{\ }$). Certain rational exponents have special names ($1/2$ is "square root," $1/3$ is "cube root").
- When m is an integer, the function will contain an integer exponent on the independent variable. Certain exponents have special names (2 is "squared," 3 is "cubed").
- When $0 < |m| < 1$ and $x < 0$, the function may contain complex values. In this chapter, we will only consider power law models, where c is zero. In the next chapter we will discuss ways of dealing with data when the value of c is non-zero.

EXAMPLE 13-2

NOTE

With a positive integer exponent, the volume of the cone increases as the independent variable (radius) increases. This observation is true with any power model with a positive integer exponent.

The volume (V) of a cone is calculated in terms of the radius (r) and height (H) of the cone. The relationship is described by the following equation:

$$V = \frac{\pi r^2 H}{3}$$

Given a height of 10 centimeters, calculate the volume of the cone when the radius is 3 centimeters.

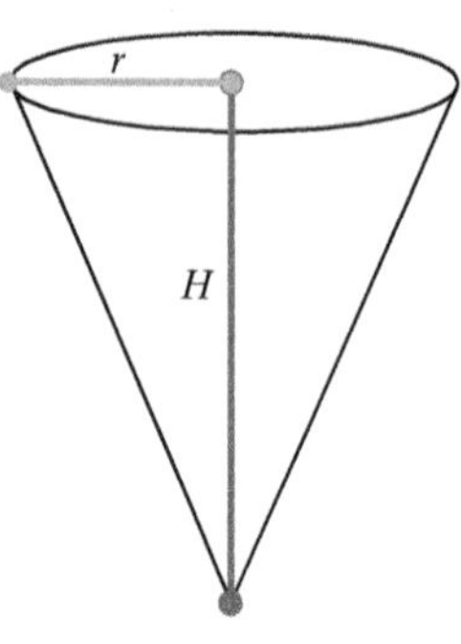

$$V = \frac{\pi(3\text{ cm})^2(10\text{ cm})}{3} \approx 94.2\text{ cm}^3$$

What is the volume of the cone when the radius is 8 centimeters?

$$V = \frac{\pi(8\text{ cm})^2(10\text{ cm})}{3} \approx 670\text{ cm}^3$$

EXAMPLE 13-3

The resistance (R [g/(cm^{4}s)]) of blood flow in an artery or vein depends upon the radius (r [cm]), as described by **Poiseuille's equation**:

$$R = \frac{8\mu L}{\pi} r^{-4}$$

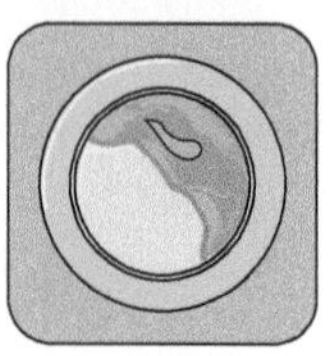

The viscosity of blood (μ [g/(cm s)]) and length of the artery or vein (L [cm]) are constants in the system. In studying the effects of a cholesterol-lowering drug, you mimic the constricting of an artery being clogged with cholesterol. You use the data you collect to create the following graph.

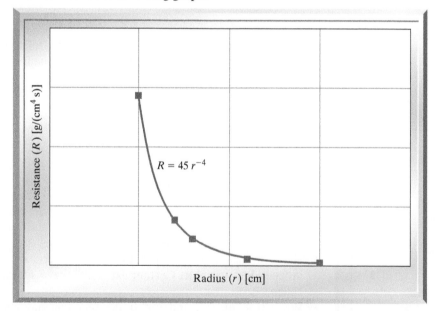

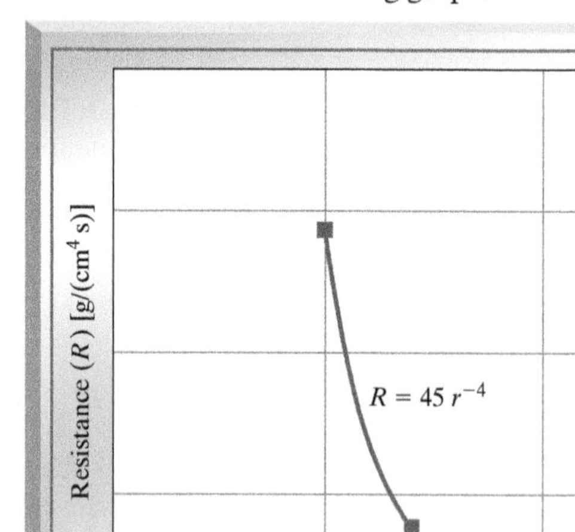

NOTE

Wih a negative integer exponent, the dependent variable (resistance) decreases as the independent variable (radius) increases. This trend is true for any power model with a negative integer exponent.

If the length of the artificial artery tested was 505 centimeters, what is the viscosity of the sample used to mimic blood, in units of grams per centimeter second [g/(cm s)]?

The constant "45" has physical meaning, found by comparison to the theoretical expression. In theory: $R = \frac{8\mu L}{\pi} r^{-4}$ and from graph: $R = 45 r^{-4}$

By comparison:

$$45 \frac{g}{s} = \frac{8\mu L}{\pi} = \frac{8\mu(505 \text{ cm})}{\pi}$$

$$\mu = 0.035 \text{ g/(cm s)}$$

COMPREHENSION CHECK 13-2

The graph shows the ideal gas law relationship ($PV = nRT$) between pressure (P) and volume (V). If the tank is at a temperature of 300 kelvin and is filled with nitrogen (formula, N_2; molecular weight, 28 grams per mole), what is the amount of gas in the tank (n) in units of grams?

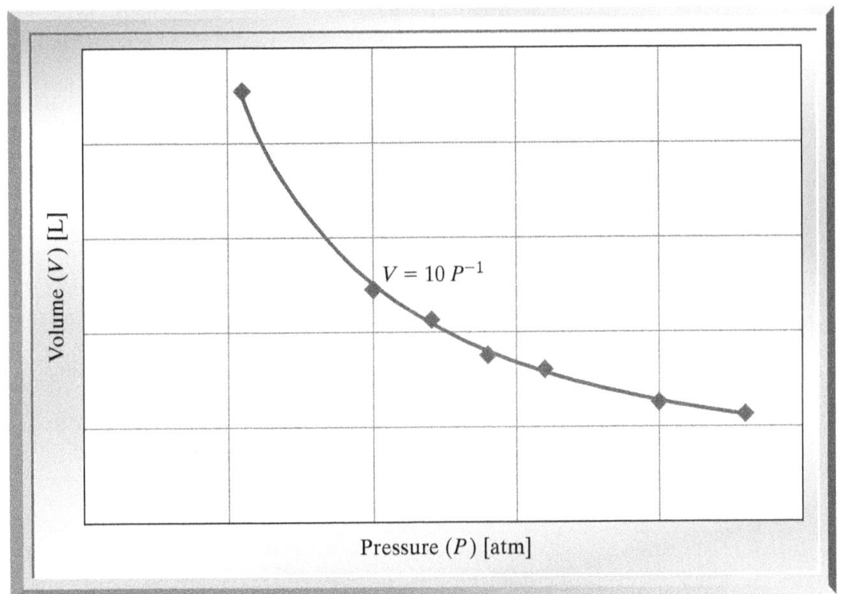

COMPREHENSION CHECK 13-3

The graph above shows the ideal gas law relationship ($PV = nRT$) between pressure (P) and volume (V). If the tank is filled with 10 grams of oxygen (formula, O_2; molecular weight, 32 grams per mole), what is the temperature of the tank in units of degrees Celsius?

13.5 EXPONENTIAL FUNCTIONS

Trend	Equation	Data Form	Graphical Example
Exponential	$y = be^{mx}$	Defined value b ($b \neq 0$) at $x = 0$ Positive m: asymptotic to 0 for large negative values of x Negative m: asymptotic to 0 at large positive values of x	Positive value of m Negative value of m

Exponential models take the form $y = be^{mx} + c$. Examples include

- The voltage (V) across a capacitor (C) as a function of time (t), with initial voltage (V_0) discharging its stored charge through resistance (R):

$$V = V_0 e^{-t/(RC)}$$

- The number (N) of people infected with a virus such as smallpox or H1N1 flu as a function of time (t), given the following: an initial number of infected individuals (N_0), no artificial immunization available and dependence on contact conditions between species (C):

$$N = N_0 e^{Ct}$$

- The transmissivity (T) of light through a gas as a function of path length (L), given an absorption cross-section (s) and density of absorbers (N):

$$T = e^{-sNL}$$

- The growth of bacteria (C) as a function of time (t), given an initial concentration of bacteria (C_0) and depending on growth conditions (g):

$$C = C_0 e^{gt}$$

Note that all exponents must be dimensionless, and thus unitless. For example, in the first equation, the quantity RC must have units of time.

Note that the intercept value (c) is zero in all of the above examples.

13.5.1 General Model Rules

Given an exponential system of the form $y = be^{mx} + c$:

- When $m = 0$, $y = b + c$ regardless of the value of x.
- When $m > 0$, the model is a **growth function**. The minimum value of the growth model for $x \geq 0$ is $b + c$. As x approaches infinity, y approaches infinity.
- When $m < 0$, the model is a **decay function**. The value of the decay model approaches c as x approaches infinity. When $x = 0$, $y = b + c$.

NOTE

An irrational number is a real number that cannot be expressed as the ratio of two integers. Pi (π) is an example.

13.5.2 What Is "e"?

The **exponential constant** "e" is a transcendental number, thus also an irrational number, that can be rounded to 2.71828. It is defined as the base of the natural logarithm function. Sometimes, e is referred to as **Euler's number** or the **Napier constant.** The reference to Euler comes from the Swiss mathematician Leonhard Euler (pronounced "oiler," 1707–1783), who made vast contributions to calculus, including the notation and terminology used today. John Napier (1550–1617) was a Scottish mathematician credited with inventing logarithms and popularizing the use of the decimal point.

13.5.3 Growth Functions

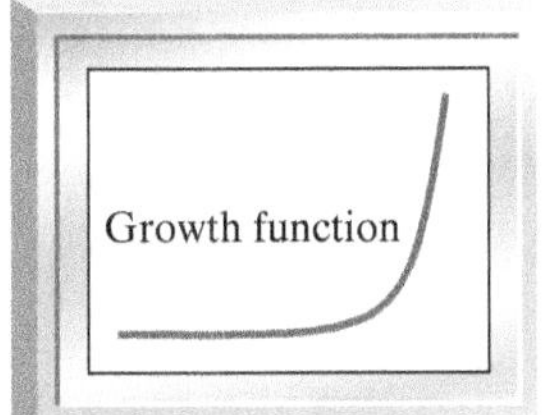

An exponential *growth function* is a type of function that increases without bound with respect to an independent variable. For a system to be considered an exponential growth function, the exponential growth model ($y = be^{mx} + c$) requires that m be greater than zero.

A more general exponential growth function can be formed by replacing the Napier constant with an arbitrary constant, or $y = be^{mx} + c$ In the general growth function, a must be greater than 1 for the system to be a growth function. The value of a is referred to as the base, m is the *growth rate*, b is the *initial value*, and c is a *vertical shift*. Note that when $a = 1$ or $m = 0$, the system is reduced to $y = be + c$, which is a constant.

EXAMPLE 13-4

In 1965, Gordon E. Moore, co-founder of Intel Corporation, claimed in a paper that the number of transistors on an integrated circuit will double every 2 years. This idea by Moore was later referred to as Moore's law. The Intel 4004 CPU was released in 1971 as the first commercially available microprocessor. The Intel 4004 CPU contained 2,300 transistors. This system can be modeled with the following growth function.

$$T = T_0 2^{t/2}$$

In the equation, T_0 represents the initial number of transistors, and t is the number of years since T_0 transistors were observed on an integrated circuit. Predict the number of transistors on an integrated circuit in 1974 using the Intel 4004 CPU as the initial condition.

$$t = 1974 - 1971 = 3 \text{ years}$$

$$T = T_0 2^{1/2} = 2{,}300\left(2^{3/2}\right) = 2{,}300\left(2^{1.5}\right) \approx 6{,}505 \text{ transistors}$$

In 1974, the Intel 8080 processor came out with 4,500 transistors on the circuit.

Predict the number of transistors on integrated circuits in 1982 using the Intel 4004 CPU as the initial condition.

$$t = 1982 - 1971 = 11 \text{ years}$$

$$T = T_0 2^{t/2} = 2{,}300\left(2^{11/2}\right) = 2{,}300\left(2^{5.5}\right) \approx 104{,}087 \text{ transistors}$$

In 1982, the Intel 286 microprocessor came out with 134,000 transistors in the CPU.

Predict the number of transistors on integrated circuits in 2007 using the Intel 4004 CPU as the initial condition.

$$t = 2007 - 1971 = 36 \text{ years}$$

$$T = T_0 2^{t/2} = 2{,}300\left(2^{36/2}\right) = 2{,}300\left(2^{18}\right) \approx 603{,}000{,}000 \text{ transistors}$$

In 2007, the NVIDIA G80 came out with 681,000,000 transistors in the CPU.

No one really knows how long Moore's law will hold up. It is perhaps interesting to note that claims have consistently been made for the past 30 years that Moore's law will only hold up for another 10 years. Although many prognosticators are still saying this, some are not. There is, however, a limit to how small a transistor can be made. Any structure has to be at least one atom wide, for example, and as they become ever smaller, quantum effects will probably wreak havoc. Of course, chips can be made larger, multilayer structures can be built, new technologies may be developed (the first functional memristor was demonstrated in 2008), and so forth.

EXAMPLE 13-5

An environmental engineer has obtained a bacteria culture from a municipal water sample and allowed the bacteria to grow. After several hours of data collection, the following graph is created.

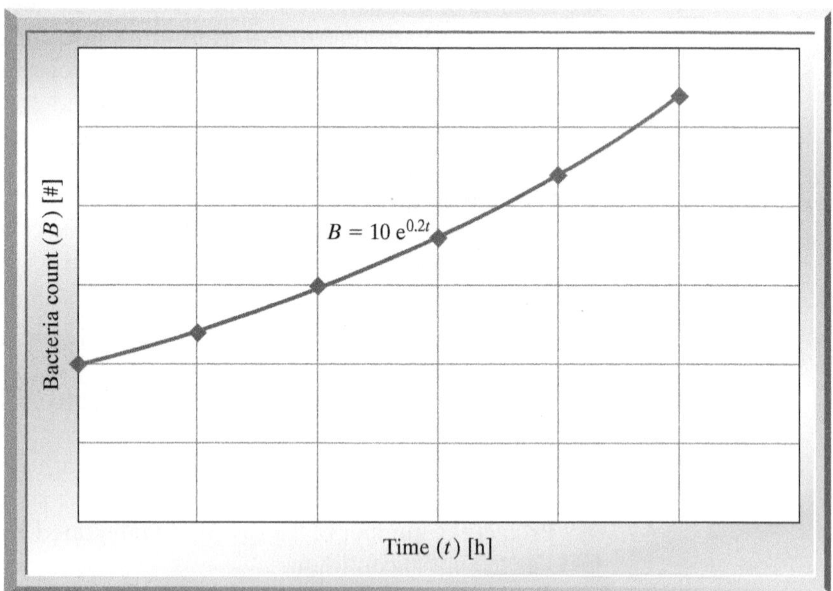

What was the initial concentration of bacteria?

In theory: $B = B_0 e^{gt}$ and from graph: $B = 10e^{0.2t}$

By comparison: $B_0 = 10$ bacteria

What was the growth constant (g) of this bacteria strain?

In theory: $B = B_{0_T} e^{gt}$ and from graph: $B = 10e^{0.2t}$

By comparison: $g = 0.2$ per hour. Recall that exponents must be unitless, so the quantity of ($g\ t$) must be a unitless group. To be unitless, g must have units of inverse time.

The engineer wants to know how long it will take for the bacteria culture population to grow to 30,000.

To calculate the amount of time, plug in 30,000 for B and solve for t:

$$30{,}000 = 10e^{0.2t}$$

$$3{,}000 = e^{0.2t}$$

$$\ln(3{,}000) = \ln(e^{0.2t}) = 0.2t$$

$$t = \frac{\ln(3{,}000)}{0.2\left[\frac{1}{h}\right]} = 40 \text{ h}$$

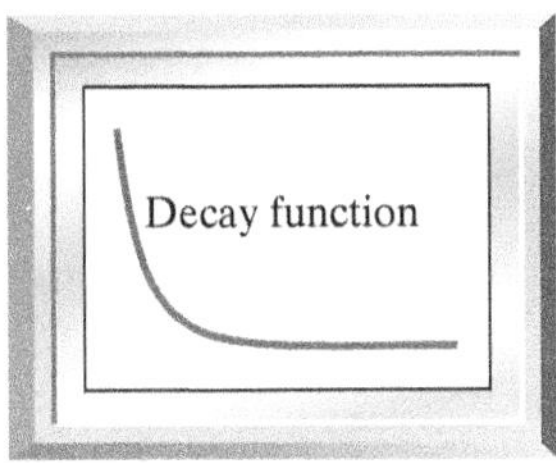

13.5.4 Decay Functions

A *decay function* is a type of function that decreases and asymptotically approaches a value. In the exponential decay model ($y = be^{-mx} + c$), m is a positive value that represents the **decay rate**.

EXAMPLE 13-6

An electrical engineer wants to determine how long it will take for a particular capacitor in a circuit to discharge. The engineer wired a voltage source across a capacitor (C, farads) and a resistor (R, ohms) connected in series. After the capacitor is fully charged, the circuit is completed between the capacitor and resistor, and the voltage source is removed from the circuit. The product of R and C in a circuit like this is called the "time constant" and is usually denoted by the Greek letter tau ($\tau = RC$).

$$\tau = \frac{1}{RC}$$

The following equation can be used to calculate the voltage across a discharging capacitor at a particular time.

$$V = V_0 e^{-\tau} = V_0 e^{-\frac{t}{RC}}$$

NOTE

Exponential models are often given in the form $Y = be^{-t/\tau} + C$, where t is time; thus τ also has units of time. In this case, the constant τ is often called the **time constant**.

Basically, the time constant is a measure of the time required for the response of the system to go approximately two-thirds of the way from its initial value to its final value, as t approaches infinity. The exct value is not $^2/_3$, but $1 - e^{-1} \approx 0.632$ or 63.2%.

Assuming a resistance of 100 kiloohms [k|], a capacitance of 100 microfarads [mF], and an initial voltage (V_0) of 20 volts [V], determine the voltage across the capacitor after 10 seconds.

$$V = 20[\text{V}]\, e^{-\frac{10\text{ s}}{(100\text{ k}\Omega)(100\,\mu\text{F})}}$$

$$= 20\,[\text{V}]\, e^{-\frac{10\text{ s}}{(100\times10^{3}\Omega)(100\times10^{-6}\text{F})}} \approx 7.36\text{ V}$$

Assuming a resistance of 200 kiloohms [k|], a capacitance of 100 microfarads [μF], and an initial voltage (V_0) of 20 volts [V], determine the voltage across the capacitor after 20 seconds. w

$$V = 20\, e^{-\frac{20\text{ s}}{(200\text{ k}\Omega)(100\,\mu\text{F})}} \approx 7.36\text{ V}$$

Note that doubling the resistance in the circuit doubles the amount of time required to discharge the capacitor. In RC circuits, it is easy to increase the discharge time of a capacitor by increasing the resistance in the circuit.

COMPREHENSION CHECK 13-4

The decay of a radioactive isotope was tracked over a number of hours, resulting in the following data. The decay of a radioactive element is modeled by the following equation, where C_0 is the initial amount of the element at time zero, and k is the decay constant of the isotope.

$$C = C_0 e^{-kt}$$

Determine the initial concentration and decay constant of the isotope, including value and units.

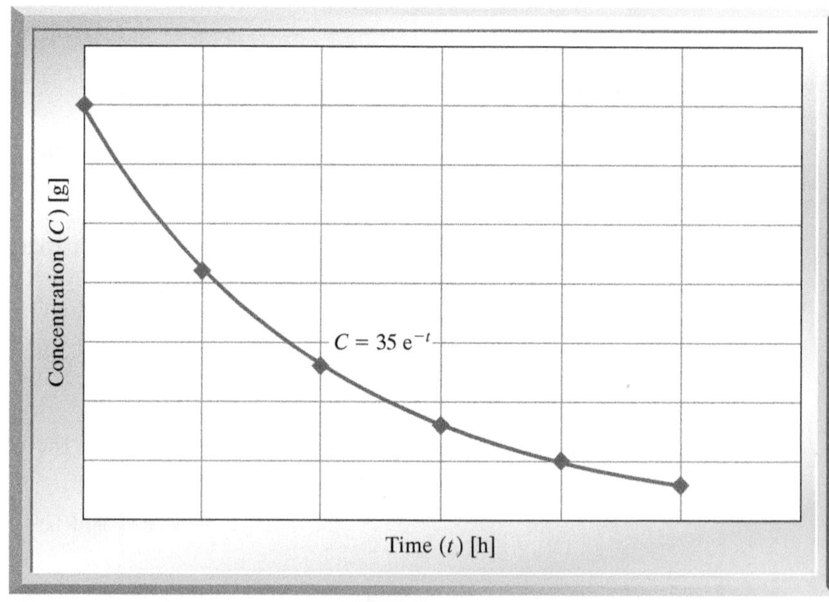

Picture of a single motar shot. The creation of fireworks involves knowledge of chemistry (what materials to include to get the desired colors), physics and dynamics (what amounts of combustible charge should be included to launch the object properly),k and artistry (what colors, shapes, patterns, and sounds the firework should emit such that it is enjoyable to watch). This pictures is a closeup of the instant when a firework is detonating.

Photo courtesy of E. Fenimore

13.6 SELECTING A TRENDLINE TYPE

When you determine a trendline to fit a set of data, in general you want the line, which may be straight or curved, to be as close as is reasonable to most of the data points.

The objective is not to ensure that the curve passes through every point.

To determine an appropriate model for a given situation, we use five guidelines, presented in general order of importance:

1. Do we already know the model type that the data will fit?
2. What do we know about the behavior of the process under consideration, including initial and final conditions?
3. What do the data look like when plotted on graphs with logarithmic scales?
4. How well does the model fit the data?
5. Can we consider other model types?

Guideline 1: Determine if the Model Type Is Known

If you are investigating a phenomenon that has already been studied by others, you may already know which model is correct or perhaps you can learn how the system behaves by looking in appropriate technical literature. In this case, all you need are the specific values for the model parameters since you already know the form of the equation. As we have seen, Excel is quite adept at churning out the numerical values for trendline equations.

If you are certain you know the proper model type, you can probably skip guidelines 2 and 3, although it might be a good idea to quantify how well the model fits the data as discussed in guideline 4. For example, at this point you should know that the extension of simple springs has a linear relationship to the force applied. As another example, from your study of the ideal gas law, you should know that pressure is related to volume by a power law model (exponent $= -1$).

At other times, you may be investigating situations for which the correct model type is unknown. If you cannot determine the model type from experience or references, continue to Guideline 2.

Guideline 2: Evaluate What Is Known About the System Behavior

The most important thing to consider when selecting a model type is whether the model makes sense in light of your understanding of the physical system being investigated. Since there may still be innumerable things with which you are unfamiliar, this may seem like an unreasonable expectation. However, by applying what you do know to the problem at hand, you can often make an appropriate choice without difficulty.

When investigating an unknown phenomenon, we typically know the answer to at least one of three questions:

1. How does the process behave in the initial state?
2. How does the process behave in the final state?
3. What happens to the process between the initial and the final states—if we sketch the process, what does it look like? Does the parameter of interest increase or decrease? Is the parameter asymptotic to some value horizontally or vertically?

EXAMPLE 13-7

Suppose we do not know Hooke's law and would like to study the behavior of a spring. We hang the spring from a hook, pull downward on the bottom of the spring with varying forces, and observe its behavior. We know initially the spring will stretch a little under its own weight even before we start pulling on it, although in most cases this is small or negligible. As an extreme case, however, consider what would happen if you hang one end of a Slinky® from the ceiling, letting the other end fall as it will.

As we pull on the spring, we realize the harder we pull, the more the spring stretches. In fact, we might assume that in a simple world, if we pull twice as hard, the spring will stretch twice as far, although that might not be as obvious. In words we might say,

The distance the spring stretches (x) is directly proportional to the pulling force (F), or we might express the behavior as an equation:

$$x = kF + b$$

where b is the amount of stretch when the spring is hanging under its own weight. This is what we mean by using an "expected" form. Always remember, however, that what you "expect" to happen may be in error.

In addition, suppose we had tested this spring by hanging five different weights on it and measuring the stretch each time. After plotting the data, we realize there is a general trend that as the weight (force) increases, the stretch increases, but the data points do not lie exactly on a straight line. We have two options:

- If we think our assumption of linear behavior may be in error, we can try nonlinear models.
- Or we can use a linear model, although the fit may not be as good as one or more of the nonlinear models.

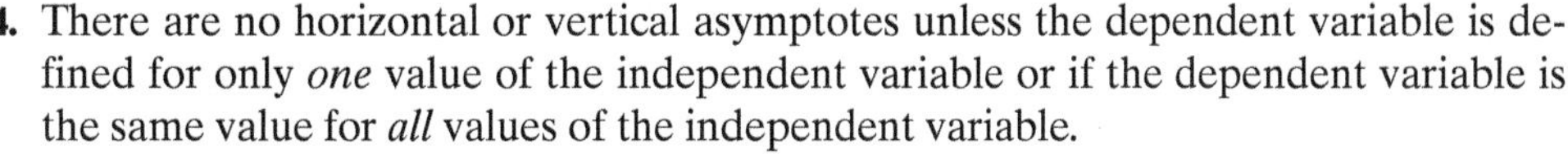

To bring order to these questions, we should ask the following sequence of questions:

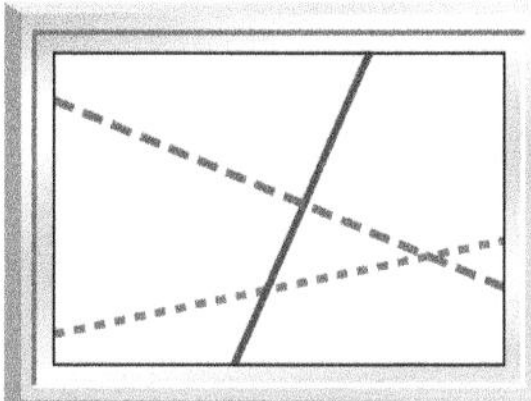

Is the system linear?

Linear systems have the following characteristics. If any of these is not true, then the system is not linear.

1. As the independent variable gets larger, the dependent variable continues to increase (positive slope) or decrease (negative slope) without limit. (See item 4 below.)
2. If the independent variable becomes negative, as it continues negative, the dependent variable continues to decrease (positive slope) or increase (negative slope) without limit unless one of the variables is constant. (See item 4 below.)
3. The rate of increase or decrease is constant; in other words, it will not curve upward or downward, but is a straight line.
4. There are no horizontal or vertical asymptotes unless the dependent variable is defined for only *one* value of the independent variable or if the dependent variable is the same value for *all* values of the independent variable.

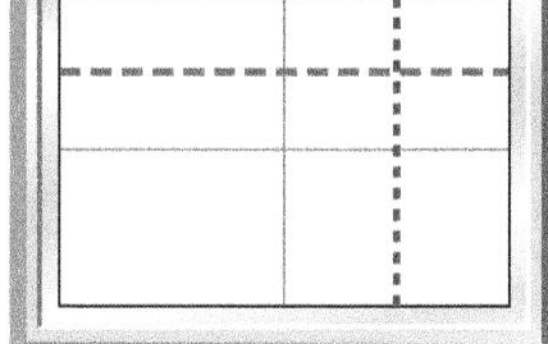

Examples illustrating if a system is linear:

- You are driving your car at a constant speed of 45 miles per hour [mph]. The longer you drive, the farther you go, without limit. In addition, your distance increases by the same amount each hour, regardless of total time elapsed. This is a linear system.
- You observe the temperature of the brake disks on your car to be slowly decreasing. If it continued to decrease without limit, the temperature would eventually be less than absolute zero (an impossibility); thus, it is not linear. Also, it seems reasonable that the temperature will eventually approach the surrounding air temperature; thus, there is a horizontal asymptote.

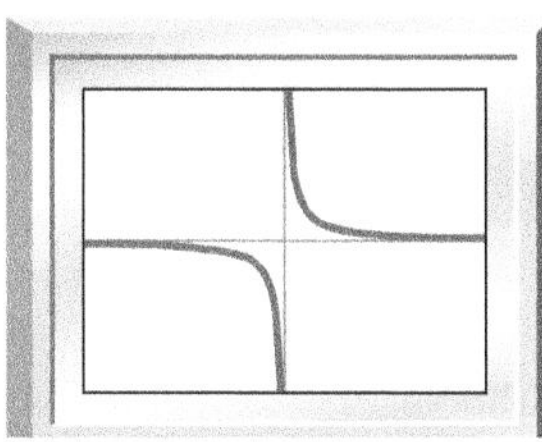

If the system is not linear, is there a vertical asymptote?

If there is a vertical asymptote, it will also have a horizontal asymptote. This is a power law model with a negative exponent. REMEMBER: We are assuming that our data fit one of the three models being considered here, and the previous statement is certainly not true for all other models. For example, $y = \tan x$ has multiple vertical asymptotes, but no horizontal asymptote.

If there is not a vertical asymptote, is there a horizontal asymptote?

If there is a horizontal asymptote (but not a vertical one), then the model is exponential. If the horizontal asymptote occurs for positive values of the independent variable, then the exponent is negative. If the horizontal asymptote occurs for negative values of the independent variable, then the exponent is positive.

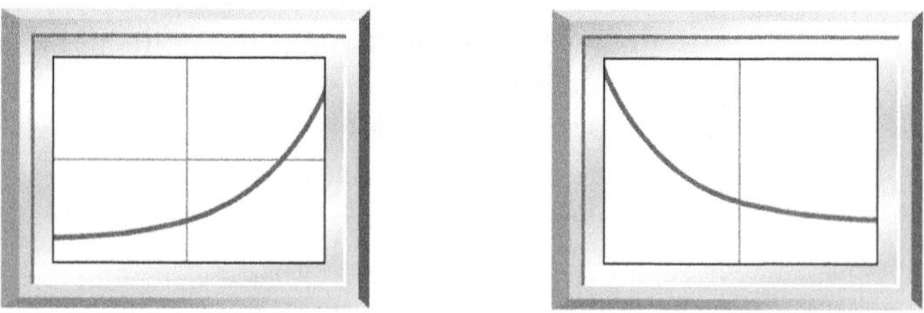

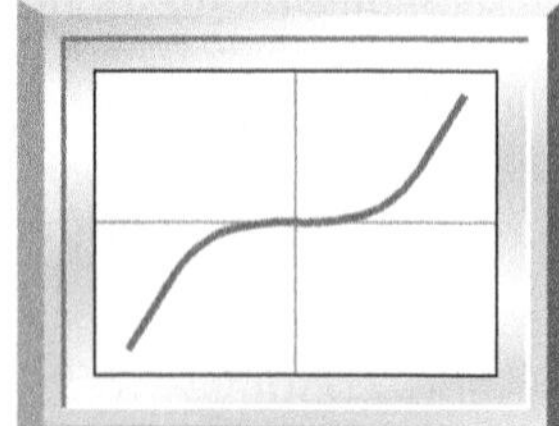

What if there is not a horizontal asymptote or a vertical asymptote?

It is a power law model with a positive exponent. Such models can have a variety of shapes.

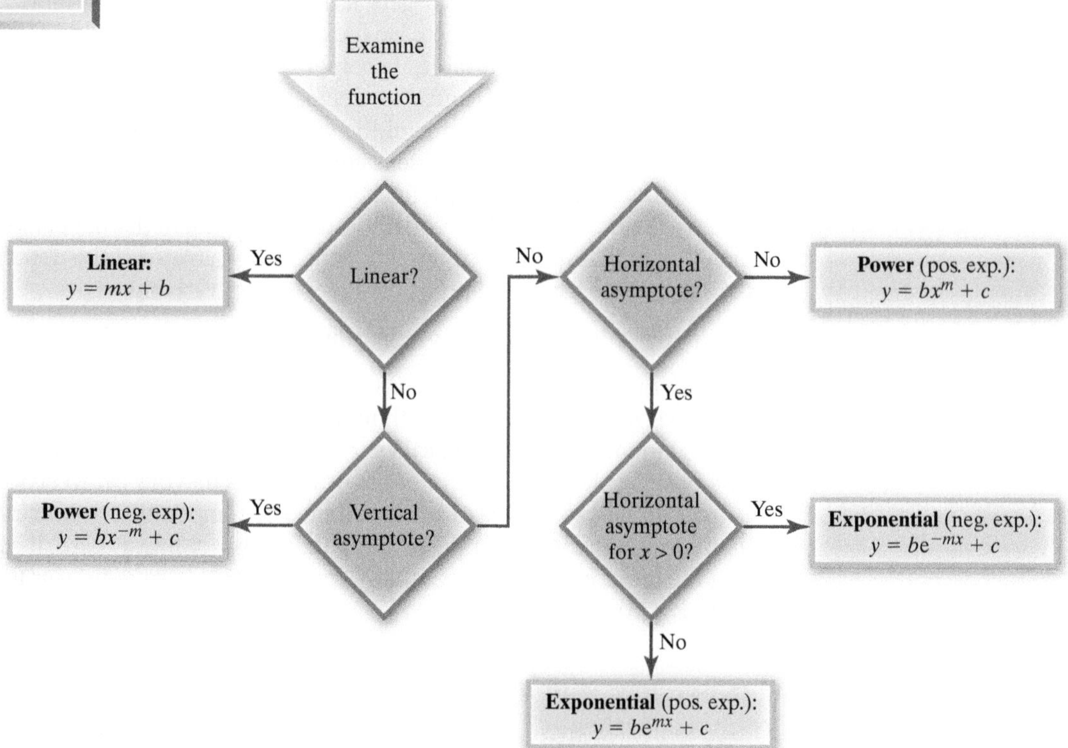

This sequence of questions can be represented pictorially as shown above. Remember, this is only valid if we assume the data fits one of the three models being discussed.

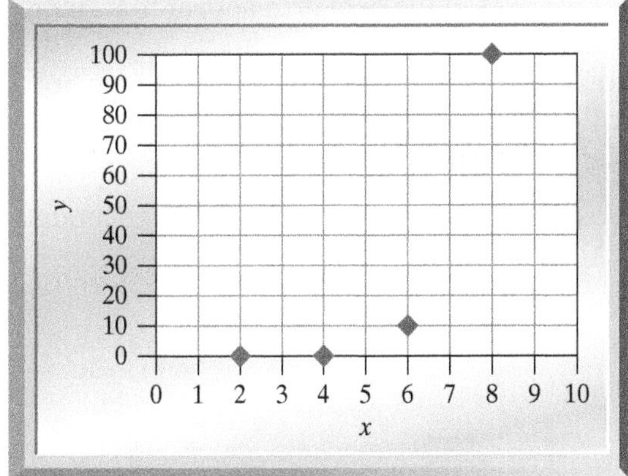

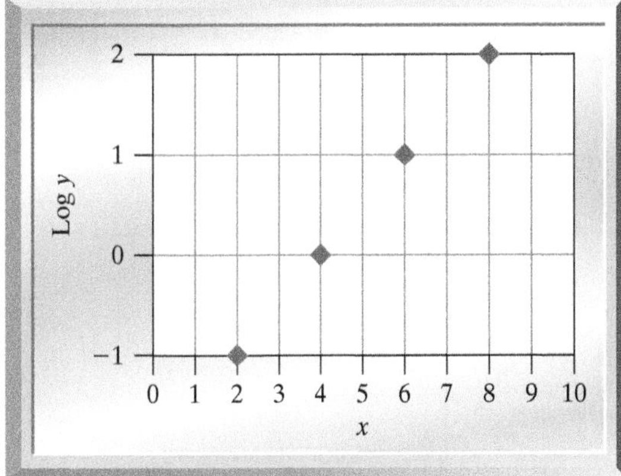

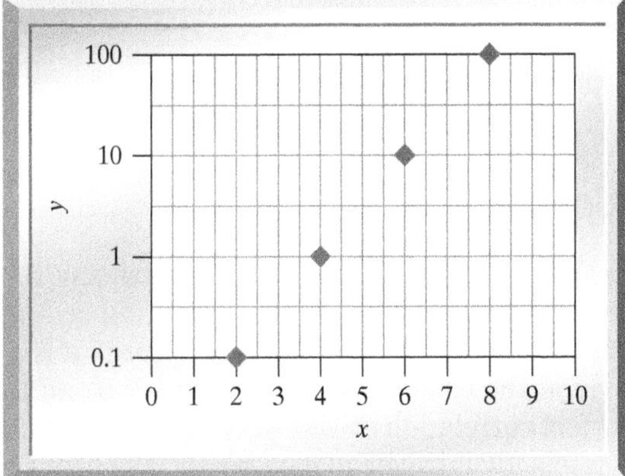

Guideline 3: Convert Axes to a Logarithmic Scale

If the logarithm of the dependent or independent variable is plotted instead of the variable itself, do the modified data points appear to lie on a straight line?

To see how logarithmic axes are constructed, let us consider a simple case. Plotting the data points below gives the graph shown to the left.

x	2	4	6	8
y	0.1	1	10	100

Now let us take the logarithm (base 10) of the independent (vertical) variable and plot.

x	2	4	6	8
y	0.1	1	10	100
log y	−1	0	1	2

Finally, we simply change the labels on the vertical axis of the second chart back to the original values of *y* from which each logarithmic value was obtained.

Note that the vertical positions of the data points are determined by the logarithms of the values, but the numeric scale uses the actual data values.

A note about the use of logarithmic scales:

- The original data would fit an exponential model ($y = 0.01e^{1.15x}$), and when plotted on a logarithmic vertical axis, the data points appear in a straight line.
- The logarithmic axis allows us to more easily distinguish between the values of the two lowest data points, even though the data range over three orders of magnitude. On the original graph, 0.1 and 1 were almost in the same vertical position.
- Note that you *do not* have to calculate the logarithms of the data points. You simply plot the actual values on a logarithmic scale.

Logarithm graphs are discussed in more detail in Section 13.2. How does this help us determine an appropriate model type?

- Plot the data using normal (linear) scales for both axes. If the data appear to lie more or less in a straight line, a linear model is likely to be a good choice.
- Plot the data on a logarithmic vertical scale and a normal (linear) horizontal scale. If the data then appear to lie more or less in a straight line, an exponential model is likely to be a good choice.

- Plot the data with logarithmic scales for *both* axes. If the data then appear to lie more or less in a straight line, a power law model is likely to be a good choice.
- Although not covered in this course, you could plot the data on a logarithmic horizontal scale and a normal (linear) vertical scale. If the data then appear to lie more or less in a straight line, a logarithmic model is likely to be a good choice.

REMEMBER, this is only valid if we assume the data fits one of the three models being discussed.

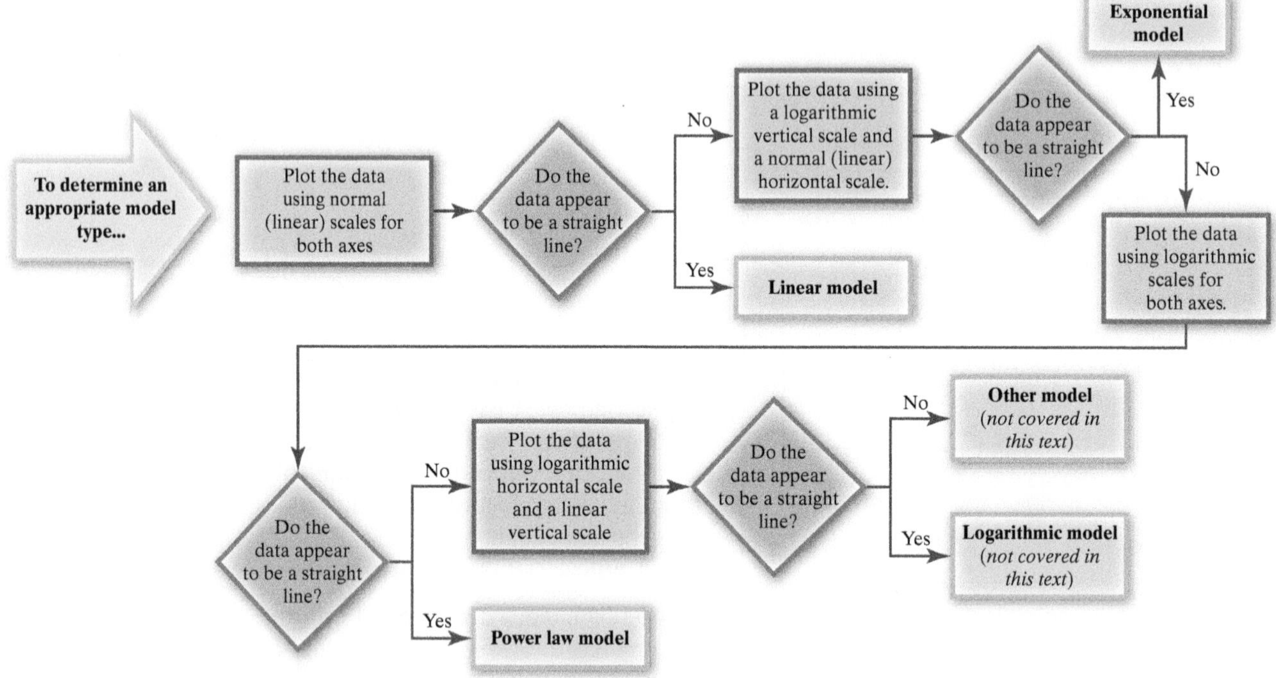

Guideline 4: Consider the R^2 Value

When a trendline is generated in Excel, the program can automatically calculate an $\mathbf{R^2}$ **value**, sometimes called the **coefficient of determination**. The R^2 value is an indication of the variation of the actual data from the equation generated—in other words, it is a measure of how well the trendline fits the data. The value of R^2 varies between 0 and 1. If the value of R^2 is exactly equal to 1, a perfect correlation exists between the data and the trendline, meaning that the curve passes exactly through all data points. The farther R^2 is from 1, the less confidence we have in the accuracy of the model generated. When fitting a trendline to a data set, we always report the R^2 value to indicate how well the fit correlates with the data.

In reality, a fit of $R^2 = 1$ is rare, since experimental data are imprecise in nature. Human error, imprecision in instrumentation, fluctuations in testing conditions, and natural specimen variation are among the factors that contribute to a less-than-perfect fit. **The best R^2 value is not necessarily associated with the best model and should be used as a guide only.** Once again, making such decisions becomes easier with experience.

When displaying the equation corresponding to a trendline, you may have already noticed how to display the R^2 value.

To display an R^2 value:

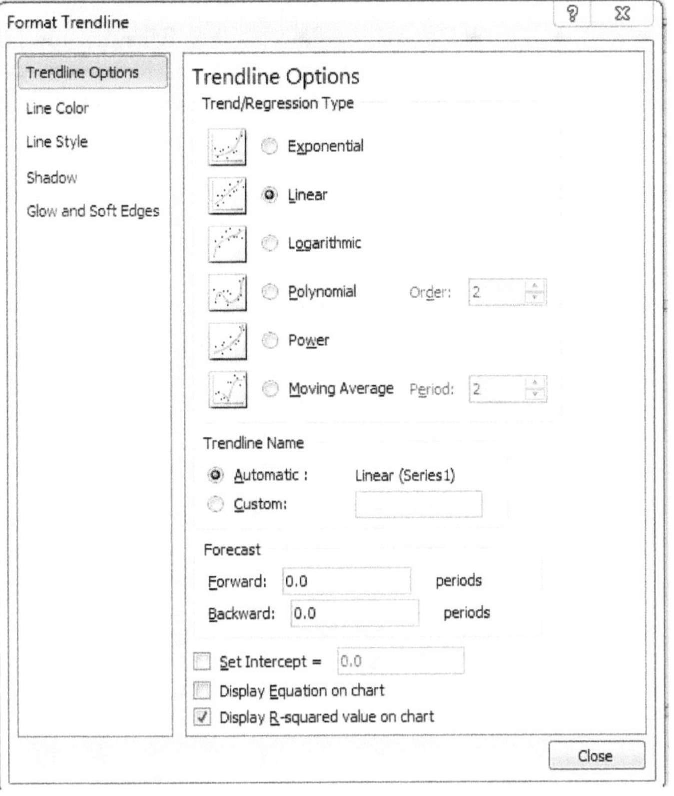

- Right-click the trendline or choose the trendline, then choose **Format > Format Selection.**
- In the **Format Trendline** window that opens, from the **Trendline** Options tab, check the box for **Display *R*-squared value on chart**. Click **Close.**

⌘ **Mac OS:** To show the R^2 value on a Mac, double-click the trendline. In the window that opens, click **Options** and select **Display *R*-squared value**. Click **OK**.

Format Trendline
Line
Shadow
Type
Options
Trendline name
Automatic: Log. (Series1)
Custom:
Forecast
Forward: 0 Periods
Backward: 0 Periods
Set intercept = 0
Display equation on chart
Display R-squared value on chart
Cancel
OK

Try different models and compare the R^2 values.

- If one of the R^2 values is considerably smaller than the others, say, more than 0.2 less, then that model very likely can be eliminated.
- If one of the R^2 values is considerably larger than the others, say, more than 0.2 greater, then that model very likely is the correct one.

In any case, you should always consider Guidelines 1 through 3 above to minimize the likelihood of error.

WARNING!

While practicing with trendlines in the preceding chapters, you may have noticed a choice for polynomial models. Only rarely would this be the proper choice, but we mention it here for one specific reason—a polynomial model can always be found that will perfectly fit any data set. In general, if there are N data points, a polynomial of order $N - 1$ can be found that goes exactly through all N points. Excel can only calculate polynomials up to sixth order. For example, a data set with five data points is plotted below. A fourth-order polynomial can be found that perfectly fits the data. Let us consider a simple spring stretching example to illustrate why a perfect fit to the data is not necessarily the correct model.

The graph shows the five data points for spring displacement as a function of force. As force increases, displacement increases, but the points are certainly not in a straight line. Also shown is a fourth-order polynomial model that goes through every point—a perfect fit. This, however, is a terrible model.

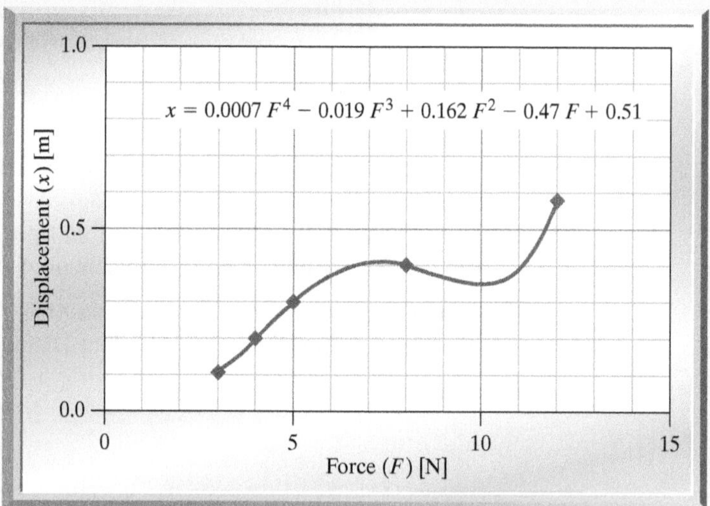

Presumably you agree that as force increases, displacement must increase as well. The polynomial trendline, however, suggests that as force increases from about 7 to 10 newtons, the displacement decreases.

Always ask yourself if the model you have chosen is obviously incorrect, as in this case. We do not use polynomial models in this book, and so discuss them no further.

THE THEORY OF OCCAM'S RAZOR

It is vain to do with more what can be done with less.
or
Entities are not to be multiplied beyond necessity.

—*William of Occam*

It is probably appropriate to mention Occam's Razor at this point. Those who choose to pursue scientific and technical disciplines should keep the concept of Occam's Razor firmly in mind. **Occam's Razor refers to the concept that the simplest explanation or model to describe a given situation is usually the correct one.** It is named for William of Occam, who lived in the first half of the fourteenth century and was a theologian and philosopher.

EXAMPLE 13-8

The velocity of a ball was recorded as it rolled across a floor after being released from a ramp at various heights. The velocities were then plotted versus the release heights. We want to fit a trendline to the data.

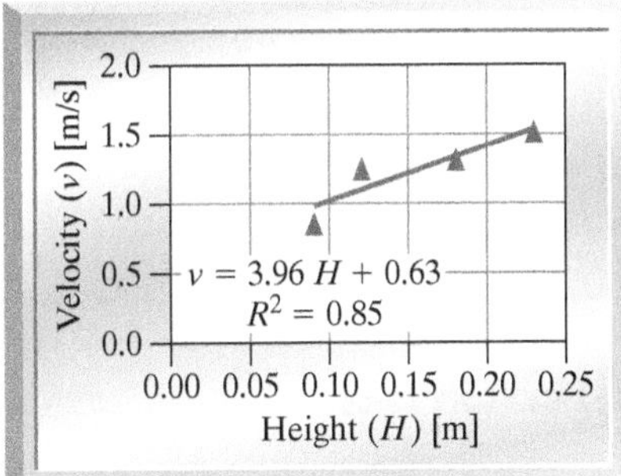

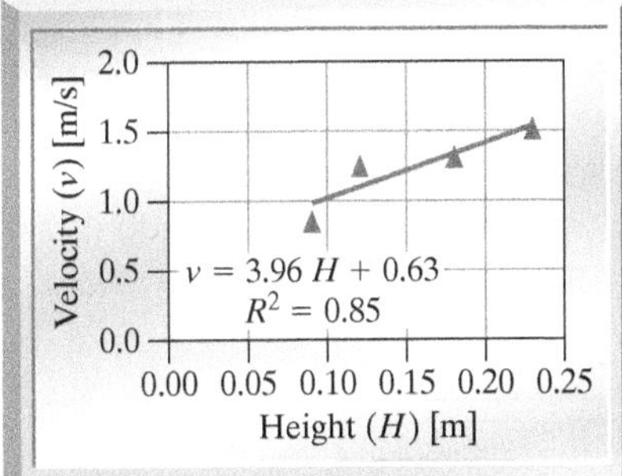

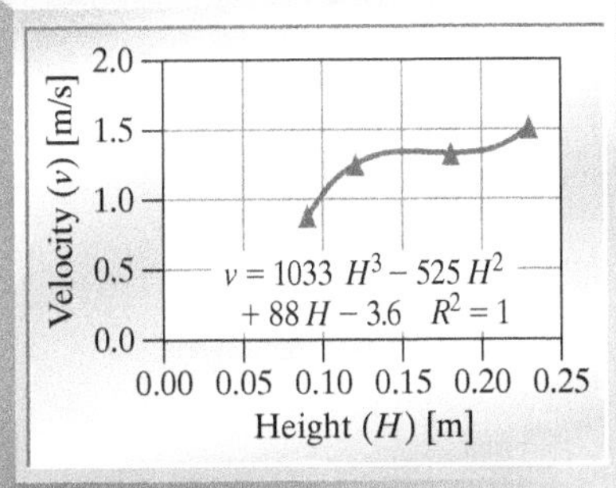

We start with the simplest form, a linear fit, shown on the left. We know that if the ramp is at a height of zero, the ball will not roll down the ramp without any external forces. The linear fit yields an intercept value of 0.6, indicating that the ball will have an initial velocity of 0.6 meter per second when the ramp is horizontal, which we know to be untrue. It seems unlikely experimental variation alone would generate an error this large, so we try another model.

We choose a power fit, shown in the center. With an R^2 value of 0.86, the equation fits the data selection well, but is there a better fit? Using the same data, we try a third-order polynomial to describe the data. The polynomial model, which gives a perfect fit, is shown on the bottom with an R^2 value of 1.

While the polynomial trendline gave the best fit, is this really the correct way to describe the data? Recall that in theory the potential energy of the ball is transformed into kinetic energy according to the conservation of energy law, written in general terms

$$PE_{\text{initial}} = KE_{\text{final}} \text{ or } mgH = \frac{1}{2}mv^2$$

Therefore, the relationship between velocity and height is a relationship of the form

$$v = (2gH)^{1/2} = (2g)^{1/2}H^{1/2}$$

The relation between velocity and height is a power relationship; velocity varies as the square root of the height. The experimental error is responsible for the inaccurate trendline fit. In most instances, the polynomial trendline will give a precise fit but an inaccurate description of the phenomenon. **It is better to have an accurate interpretation of the experimental behavior than a perfect trendline fit!**

Guideline 5: Should We Consider Model Types Not Covered Here?

Many phenomena may be accurately characterized by a linear model, power law model, or exponential model. However, there are innumerable systems for which a different model type must be chosen. Many of these are relatively simple, but some are mind-bogglingly complicated. For example, modeling electromagnetic waves (used for television, cell phones, etc.) or a mass oscillating up and down while hanging from a spring requires the use of trigonometric functions.

You should always keep in mind that the system or phenomenon you are studying may not fit the three common models we have covered in this book.

NOTE ON ADVANCED MATH

Actually, sinusoids (sine or cosine) can be represented by exponential models through a mathematical trick first concocted by Leonhard Euler, so we now refer to it as Euler's identity. The problem is that the exponents are imaginary (some number times the square root of −1).

Euler's identity comes up in the study of calculus, and frequently in the study of electrical or computer engineering, and early in the study of electric circuits. Euler's identity can be expressed in several different forms. The basic identity can be stated as the following equation, where i is the square root of −1.

$$e^{i\pi} = -1$$

Another form often used in electrical engineering is

$$\cos\theta = 0.5(e^{i\theta} + e^{-i\theta})$$

13.7 INTERPRETING LOGARITHMIC GRAPHS

A "regular" plot, shown on a graph with both axes at constant-spaced intervals, is called **rectilinear.** When a linear function is graphed on rectilinear axis, it will appear as a straight line. Often, it is convenient to use a scale on one or both axes that is not linear, where values are not equally spaced but instead "logarithmic," meaning that powers of 10 are equally spaced. Each set of 10 is called a **decade** or **cycle.** A logarithmic scale that ranges either from 10 to 1,000 would be two cycles, 10–100 and 100–1,000. Excel allows you to select a logarithmic scale for the abscissa, the ordinate, or both.

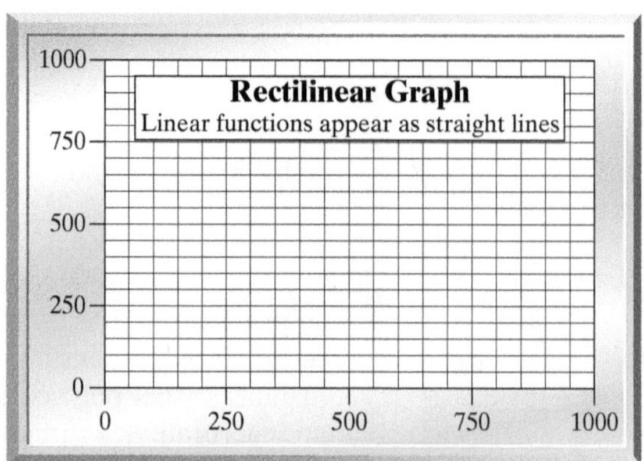

If one scale is logarithmic and the other linear, the plot is called **semilogarithmic** or **semilog.** Note in the figure that the abscissa has its values equally spaced and so is a linear scale. However, the ordinate has powers of 10 equally spaced and thus is a logarithmic scale.

If both scales are logarithmic, the plot is called **full logarithmic** or **log–log**. Note in the figure that both axes have powers of 10 equally spaced.

There are four different combinations of linear and logarithmic axes, each corresponding to one of four specific trendline types that will appear linear on that particular graph type. If the plotted data points are more or less in a straight line when plotted with a specific axis type, the corresponding trendline type is a likely candidate, as discussed earlier.

Once the data are plotted as logarithmic, how do you read data from this graph? This is perhaps best shown through examples.

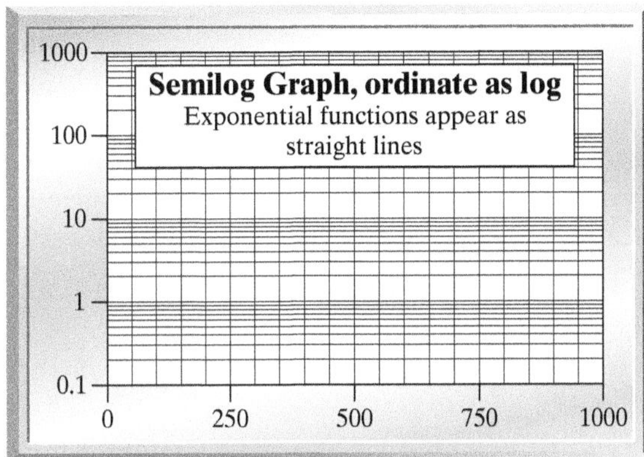

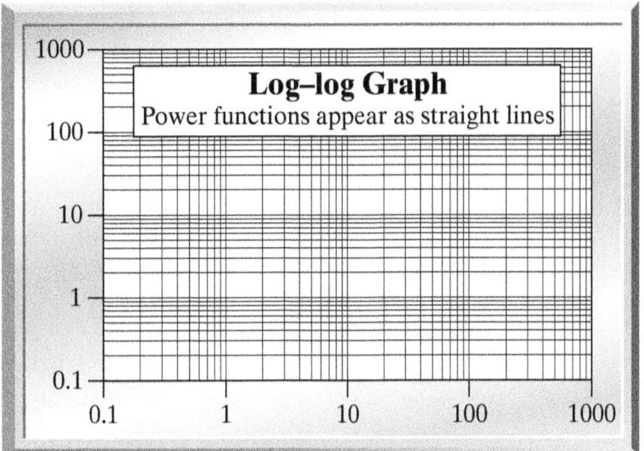

Derivation

Consider a power law model:

$$y = bx^m$$

Now take the logarithm of both sides of the equation.

$$\log y = \log (bx^m) = \log b + \log x^m = \log b + m \log x$$

Using the commutative property of addition, you can write:

$$\log y = m \log x + \log b$$

Since b is a constant, $\log b$ is also a constant. Rename $\log b$ and call it b'. Since x and y are both variables, $\log x$ and $\log y$ are also variables. Call them x' and y', respectively.

Using the new names for the transformed variables and the constant b :

$$y' = mx' + b'$$

This is a linear model! Thus, if the data set can be described by a power law model and you plot the logarithms of both variables (instead of the variables themselves), the transformed data points will lie on a straight line. The slope of this line is m, although "slope" has a somewhat different meaning than in a linear model.

EXAMPLE 13-9

An unknown amount of oxygen, kept in a piston type container at a constant temperature, was subjected to increasing pressure (P), in units of atmospheres; as the pressure (P) was increased, the resulting volume (V.) was recorded in units of liters. We have found that a log–log plot aligns the data in a straight line. Using the figure, determine the mathematical equation for volume (V.) in units of liters, and of a piston filled with an ideal gas subjected to increasing pressure (P) in units of atmospheres.

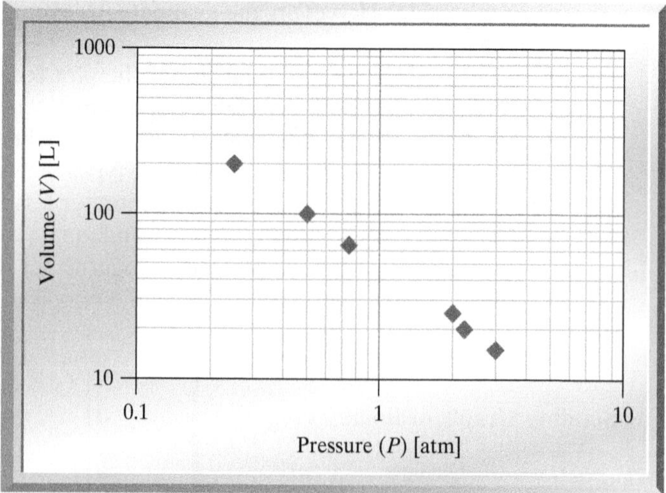

Since the graph appears linear on log–log paper, we can assume a power law relationship exists of the form:

$$V = bP^m$$

For illustration, a line has been sketched between the points for further clarification of function values.

To determine the power of the function (m), we can estimate the number of decades of "rise" (shown as a vertical arrow) divided by decades of "run" (horizontal arrow):

$$\text{Slope} = \frac{\text{Change in decades of volume}}{\text{Change in decades of pressure}}$$

$$= \frac{-1 \text{ decade}}{1 \text{ decade}} = -1$$

To establish the constant value (b), we estimate it as the ordinate value when the abscissa value is 1, shown in the shaded circle. When the pressure is 1 atmosphere, the volume is 50 liters.

The resulting function:

$$V = 50P^{-1}$$

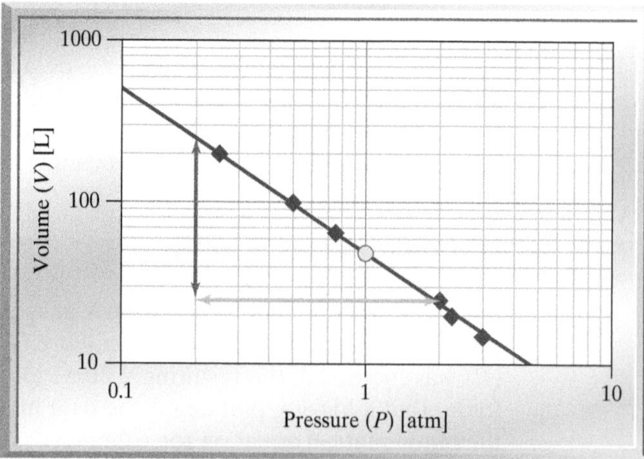

EXAMPLE 13-10

When a body falls, it undergoes a constant acceleration. Using the figure, determine the mathematical equation for distance (d), in units of meters, of a falling object as a function of time (t), in units of seconds.

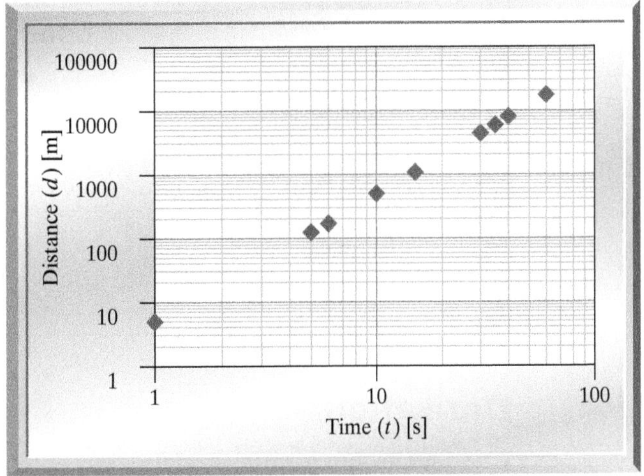

Since the graph appears linear on log–log paper, we can assume a power law relationship exists of the form:

$$d = bt^m$$

For illustration, a line has been sketched between the points for further clarification of function values.

To establish the power of the function (m), we estimate the number of decades of "rise" (shown as vertical arrows) divided by the decades of "run" (horizontal arrow):

$$\text{Slope} = \frac{\text{Change in decades of distance}}{\text{Change in decades of time}} = \frac{2 \text{ decade}}{1 \text{ decade}} = 2$$

To establish the constant value (b), we estimate it as the ordinate value when the abscissa value is 1, shown in the shaded circle. When the time is 1 second, the distance is 5 meters.

The resulting function:

$$d = 5t^2$$

This matches well with the established theory, which states

$$d = \frac{1}{2}gt^2$$

The value of $\frac{1}{2}g$ is approximately 5 m/s^2.

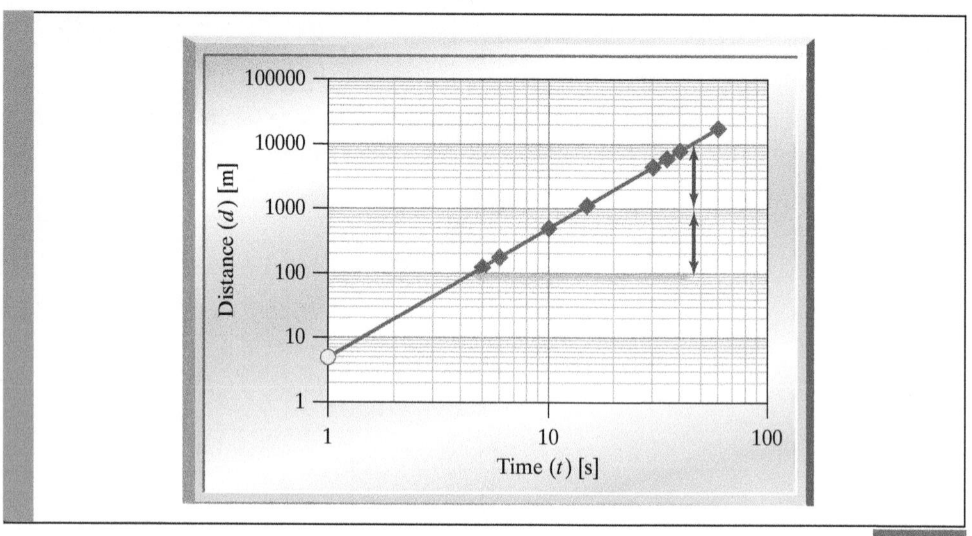

Derivation

Consider an exponential model:

$$y = be^{mx}$$

Now take the logarithm of both sides of the equation.

$$\log y = \log(be^{mx}) = \log b + \log e^{mx} = \log b + (mx)\log e$$

Using the commutative property of addition, you can write:

$$\log y = m(\log e)x + \log b$$

Since b is a constant, $\log b$ is also a constant. Rename $\log b$ and call it b'. Since y is a variable, $\log y$ is also a variable; call it y'.

Using the new names for the transformed variable y and the constant b:

$$y' = m(\log e)x + b'$$

This is a linear model! Thus, if the data set can be described by an exponential law model, and you plot the logarithm of y (instead of y itself) versus x, the transformed data points will lie on a straight line. The slope of this line is $m(\log e)$, but again, "slope" has a somewhat different interpretation. The term (log e) is a number, approximately equal to 0.4343; the slope is 0.4343 m.

EXAMPLE 13-11

A chemical reaction is being carried out in a reactor; the results are shown graphically in the figure. Determine the mathematical equation that describes the reactor concentration (C), in units of moles per liter, as a function of time spent in the reactor (t), in units of seconds.

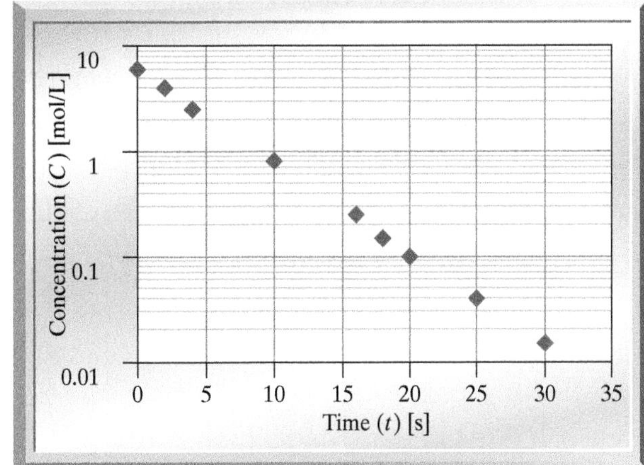

Since the graph appears linear on semilog paper where the ordinate is logarithmic, we can assume an exponential law relationship exists of the form:

$$C = be^{mt}$$

For illustration, a line has been sketched between the points for further clarification of function values.

Since this is an exponential function, to determine the value of m, we must first determine the slope:

$$\text{Slope} = \frac{\text{Change in decades of concentration}}{\text{Change in time}}$$

$$= \frac{-1 \text{ decade}}{21.5 \text{ s} - 10 \text{ s}} = -0.087 \text{ s}^{-1}$$

The value of m is then found from the relationship: slope $= m(\log e)$.

$$m = \frac{\text{slope}}{\log e} = \frac{-0.087 \text{ s}^{-1}}{0.4343} = -0.2 \text{ s}^{-1}$$

When time = 0 seconds, the constant (b) can be read directly and has a value of 6 [mol/L].

The resulting function:

$$C = 6e^{-0.2t}$$

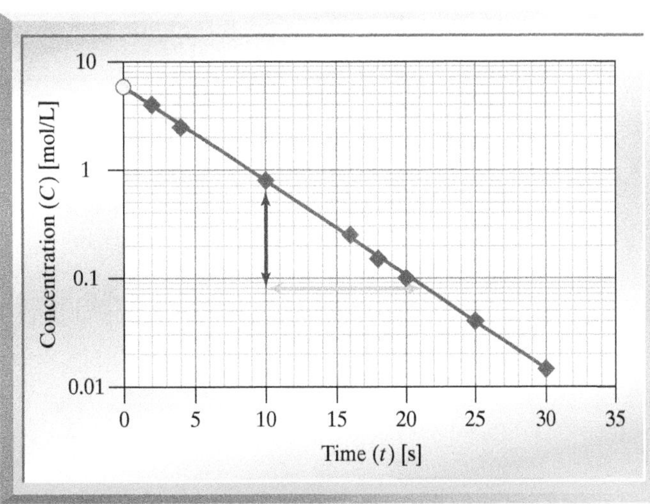

EXAMPLE 13-12

The data shown graphically in the figure describe the discharge of a capacitor through a resistor. Determine the mathematical equation that describes the voltage (V), in units of volts, as a function of time (t), in units of seconds.

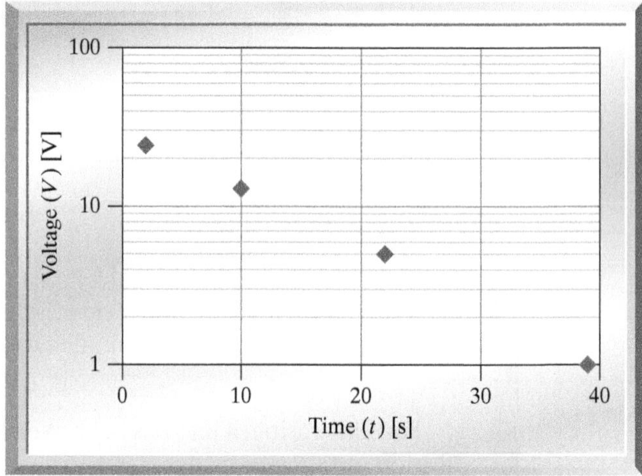

Since the graph appears linear on semilog paper where the ordinate is logarithmic, we can assume an exponential law relationship exists of the form:

$$V = be^{mt}$$

For illustration, a line has been sketched between the points for further clarification of function values.

Since this is an exponential function, to determine the value of m, we must first determine the slope:

$$\text{Slope} = \frac{\text{Change in decades of voltage}}{\text{Change in time}}$$

$$= \frac{-1 \text{ decade}}{36 \text{ s} - 10 \text{ s}} = -0.038 \text{ s}^{-1}$$

The value of m is then found from the relationship: $Slope = m(log\ e)$.

$$m = \frac{\text{slope}}{\log \text{e}} = \frac{-0.038 \text{ s}^{-1}}{0.4343} = -0.89 \text{ s}^{-1}$$

When time = 0 seconds, the constant (b) can be read directly and has a value of 30 volts.

The resulting function:

$$V = 30\text{e}^{-0.89\text{t}}$$

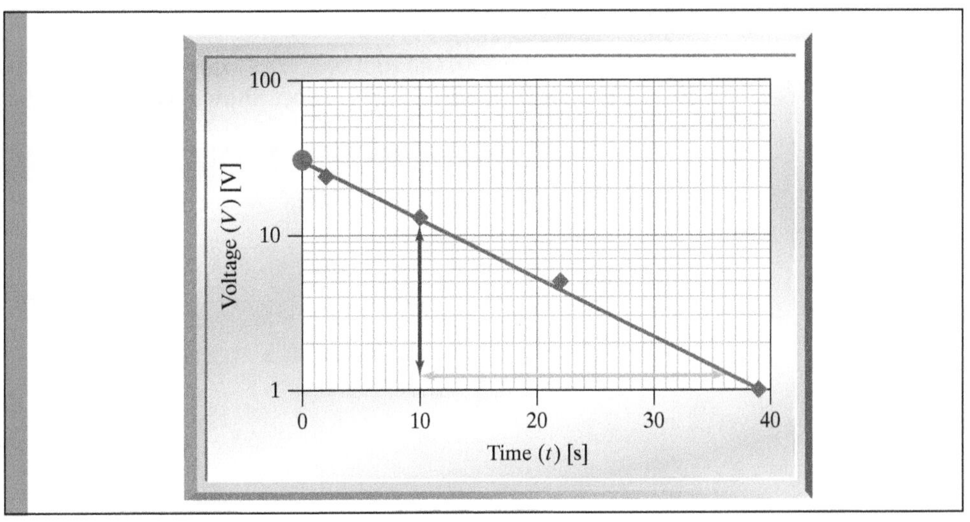

13.8 CONVERTING SCALES TO LOG IN EXCEL

To convert axis to logarithmic:

- Right-click the axis to convert to logarithmic. The **Format Axis** window will appear.
- Click **Axis Options**, then check the box for **Logarithmic scale**.

Alternatively:

- Click the chart. In the tool bar, select **Layout > Axes** and choose the axis to convert.
- In the corresponding menu, select **Show Axis with Log Scale**.

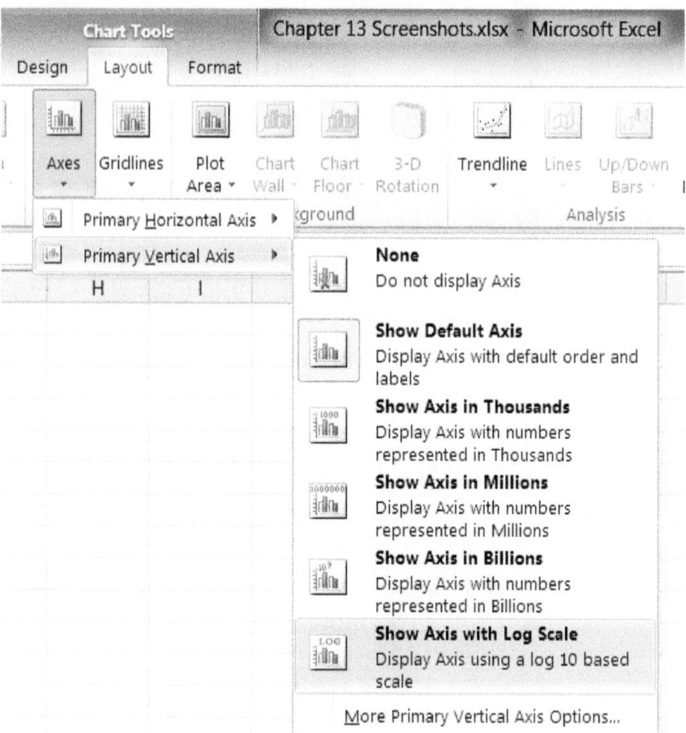

⌘ **Mac OS:** Mac OS: Double-click on the axis you want to convert to logarithmic. The Format Axis window will appear. Click **Scale** in the list on the left side of the window, and then click the checkbox near the bottom that says "Logarithmic scale."

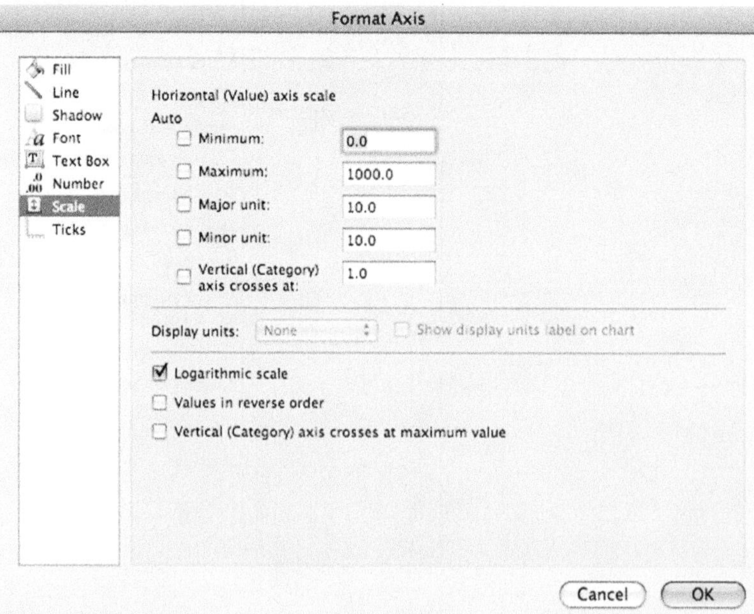

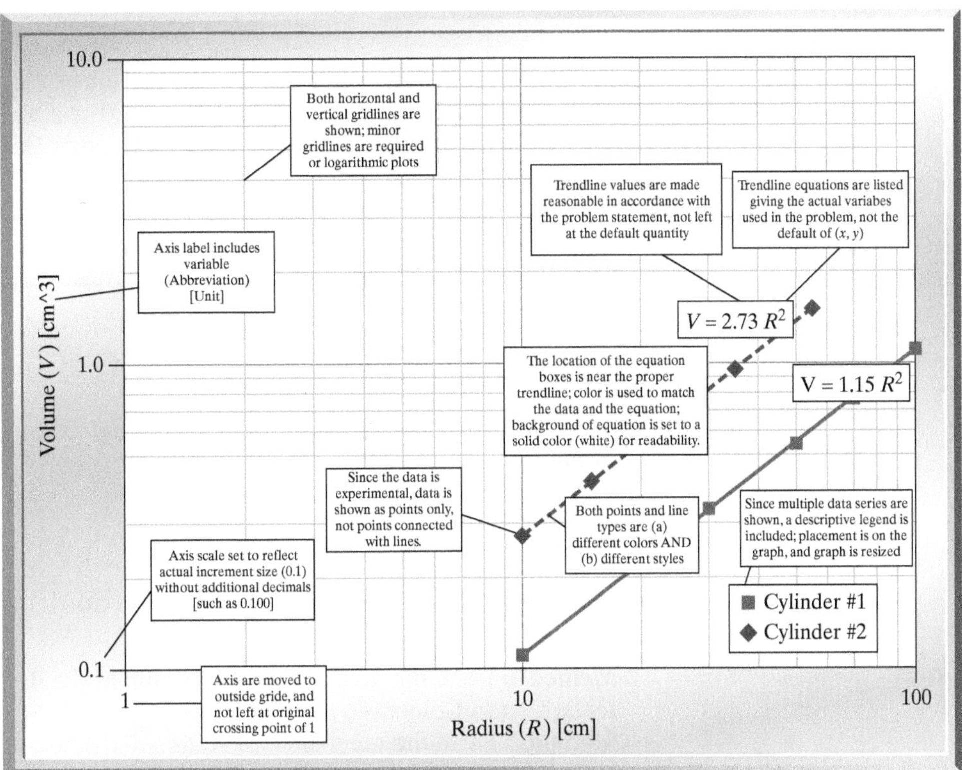

Figure 13.1 Example of a proper plot, showing multiple experimental data sets with trendlines and logarithmic axes.

Above is an example of a properly formatted graph, showing an experimental data series with power trendlines. The axes have been made logarithmic to allow the data series to appear liner.

13.9 PLOTTING AND REGRESSION WITH LINEAR SCALES

Paired Data Sets: $P_1 = (x_1, y_1), P_2 = (x_2, y_2), \ldots, P_n = (x_n, y_n)$

Data may provide information on:

- Spatial profile (e.g., distance along a piece of wire versus temperature)
- Cause-and effect relationships (e.g., launch angle versus distance)
- Temporal changes (e.g., age versus running speed)
- System output as a function of input (e.g., sucrose concentration versus microbial growth)

For each of these, think which is the dependent and which is the independent variable.

13.9.1 Using Data from the Internet

You will find yourself using data from the Internet. There is lots of information available, it can be accurate if you choose your websites carefully, and it's already in digital format, saving you from having to enter all the data manually (or pay someone else to do it).

EXAMPLE 13-13

Say we are interested in the change in annual household phone service costs over a 20-year period. We can find the data on page 3-3 (the 20th page), Table 3.1 at: http://www.fcc.gov/Bureaus/Common_Carrier/Reports/FCC-State_Link/IAD/trend801.pdf

(Data Source: Trends in Telephone Service: Industry Analysis Division Common Carrier Bureau. August 2001. Federal Communications Commission).

13.9.2 Copying the Data

Use Acrobat 'Text Select Tool' or the 'Column Select Tool' (letter "T" with a dashed line around it).

13.9.3 Pasting the Data

If you try to paste the copied data directly into Excel, the formatting will be wrong. There are two methods to format the data.

Method 1: Paste the data into Excel. Highlight the data you just pasted and use **Data, Text to Columns. . . .**

Method 2: Paste the numbers into Notepad, delete dollar signs or text you don't want, save the file as a text file, and open the file as a space-delimited file in Excel.

13.9.4 Plotting Guidelines

- Identify the independent variables vs. dependent variables
  - Which set of data belongs on the x-axis (independent variable)? Why?

    Which set of data belongs on the y-axis (dependent variable)? Why?

    Identify the plot type: XY scatter versus bar or line chart
    Want XY scatter since x-axis data is not categorical
- Create clear axis labels with units
- Create a clear plot title with unique conditions (like a newspaper headline)
- Generally, use data markers for raw data—but not if there are a large number of data points

13.10 GENERAL MODELING OF THE EQUATION OF A LINE

$y = mx + b$, where (x,y) represents the raw data points, m is the slope (change in y over change in x), and b is the y-intercept when $x = 0$.

Courtesy of Purdue University.

13.10.1 Annual Household Phone Cost Model

$C = mA + b$, where (A,C) represents the raw data points of (year, cost), m is the slope of the line in phone cost/year, and b is the intercept (the phone cost in Year 0).

We can estimate m and b using algebra skills, using just two points to simplify the math. (We're simply using the method to find the equation of a line that passes through two points, though we're choosing our points somewhat carefully so they look like they fit within the "pattern" of the data.) Choosing the first and last points, we call them point 1 (1981,360) and point 2 (1999,849).

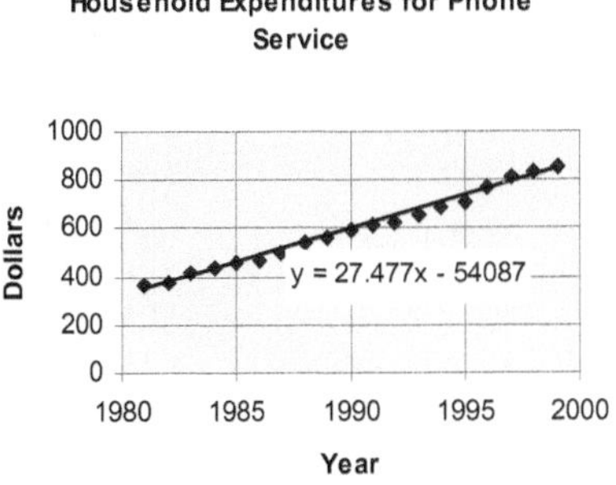

Thus, our equation for the line through the first and last points is

This is close to the actual regression line ("trendline") from Excel, shown on the graph. However, our simple equation is based on only two points, whereas the equation for the trendline found by Excel is calculated using all the data points, and is thus more accurate, and is the line that would be used to make predictions about this data. To find the exact values, we must use linear regression, which is the next topic.

13.10.2 Method of Least Squares (for Linear Regression)

Find best-fit linear equation: $f(x) = ax + b$ that best represents the relationship or trend between all data points $P_1 = (x_1, y_1)$, $P_2 = (x_2, y_2), \ldots, P_n = (x_n, y_n)$. The plot shows 10 data points, a possible best-fit line, and a vertical line representing of the error for each data point.

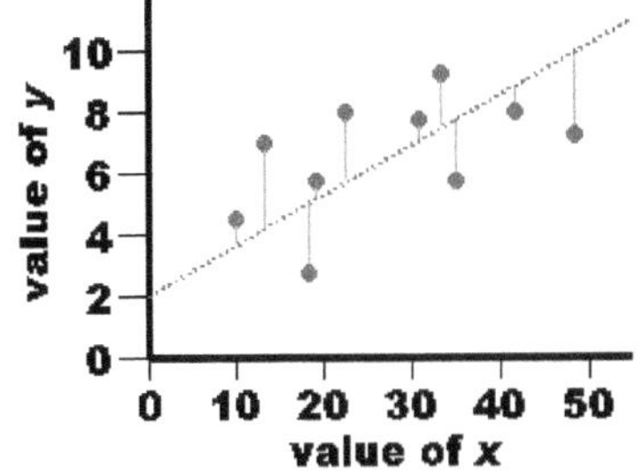

Find a linear equation for which a and b minimize the error (e_i) between the actual data point (y_i) and the fitted data point resulting from the linear equation ($f(x_i)$) for each value of the independent variable (x_i), where i ranges from 1 to n (total number of data points). $e_i = y_i - f(x_i)$, so the sum of all these errors is represented by

$$\sum_{i=1}^{n} e_i$$

The problem with trying to minimize $\sum_{i=1}^{n} e_i$**:**

e_i might be negative or positive. This creates a problem when trying to minimize the sum of the errors because the positive and negative values (whether small or large) will cancel each other. Therefore, we minimize the sum of the squares of the errors. The squares of e_i are all positive, so the positive-negative cancellation problem is eliminated.

> **Another important issue:** You may have heard of problem-solving exercises such as "You've crashed on the moon, your ship was destroyed, you were able to salvage just 15 items from the ship, and you must survive for five days until a rescue ship arrives" (http://www.kathimitchell.com/lost.htm). Items like oxygen tanks and water are absolutely necessary, whereas matches and a compass are useless. An "expert" ranks items from one to fifteen, and you compare your ranking. If you are just two rankings off on all items from the expert, you would still be likely to survive. But your friend who picked 13 items correctly, except picked water as the least important item, and matches as #2, would be toast (and dry toast at that). Being off a little bit on several points is better than being way off on even a single point; using the sum of squares of the errors "punishes" a trendline that misses even one point badly.

The alternative is to minimize $\sum_{i=1}^{n} e_i$**:**

So looking at the above graph, we are trying to find the equation for the long sloped line that will minimize the sum of the squares of the lengths of all the short vertical lines (each of which represents the difference between the actual data value for that x value, shown by the plotted points, and our best-fit estimate, which is the dashed line).

Advantages of Least Squares Regression:

- Many engineering processes are linear (or can be made linear using logs, over a short range)
- Adequate results can be obtained, even with limited datasets
- It's existed since the late 1700s/well-understood, and a "goodness of fit" can be calculated

Disadvantages of Least Squares Regression:

- Obviously not all datasets can be defined by a linear model
- It's very sensitive to outliers (data points that do not fall near the line) and skews toward them

Derivation of the Least Squares Equations for a Straight Line

- Calculating each error term: $e_i = y_i - (ax_i + b)$
- Sum of the squares of the error terms: $z = e_1^2 + e_2^2 + \ldots e_n^2$
- Sum of the error terms in terms of the data points:

$$z = [y_1 - (ax_1 + b)]^2 + [y_2 - (ax_2 + b)]^2 + [y_3 - (ax_3 + b)]^2 + \ldots + [y_n - (ax_n + b)]^2$$

$$z = \sum_{i=1}^{n} [y_i - (ax_i + b)]^2$$

We want to find the values of the coefficients a and b that will minimize z:

Partial derivative of the error with respect to a:

Want the change in the error with respect to a change in a to be small, so set equal to zero.

$$\frac{\partial z}{\partial a} = -2\sum_{i=1}^{n} x_i[y_i - (ax_i + b)] = 0 \qquad \text{[Eq. 1]}$$

Partial derivative of the error with respect to b:

Want the change in the error with respect to a change in b to be small, so set equal to zero.

$$\frac{\partial z}{\partial b} = -2\sum_{i=1}^{n} [y_i - (ax_i + b)] = 0 \qquad \text{[Eq. 2]}$$

Rearrange [Eq.1]

$$\sum_{i=1}^{n} [ax_i^2 + bx_i - x_i y_i] = 0 \qquad \text{[Eq. 3]}$$

Rearrange [Eq.2]

$$\sum_{i=1}^{n} [ax_i + b - y_i] = 0 \qquad \text{[Eq. 4]}$$

Use laws of distribution and factor out a and b in each equation:

From [Eq. 3]:

$$a\sum_{i=1}^{n} x_i^2 + b\sum_{i=1}^{n} x_i = \sum_{i=1}^{n} x_i y_i \qquad \text{[Eq. 5]}$$

From [Eq. 4]:

$$a\sum_{i=1}^{n} x_i + bn = \sum_{i=1}^{n} y_i \qquad \text{[Eq. 6]}$$

Application of the Derivation

To find a and b such that $y_i = ax_i + b$ for any data set, solve Eqs. 5 and 6 simultaneously.

Final Equation for Best-Fit Linear Regression Line

We can perform the same calculation for the telephone expenditures data (with column totals shown as the last value of the spreadsheet columns):

Solve the simultaneous equations:
75242470 a + 37810 b = 22429032
37810 a + 19 b = 11263

The roots of these are:
a = 27.47719
b = –54086.8

Thus, our equation is
y = 27.47719 x – 54086.8
which is the same equation that Excel provided on our graph (subject to rounding, of course)

This equation is based on all points, rather than our simplified method above that was based on only two. But it's good to know the method using only two points, as it provides a quick check on your regression calculation.

Year (x)	Costs (y)	x^2	x*y
1981	360	3924361	713160
1982	375	3928324	743250
1983	415	3932289	822945
1984	435	3936256	863040
1985	455	3940225	903175
1986	471	3944196	935406
1987	499	3948169	991513
1988	537	3952144	1067556
1989	567	3956121	1127763
1990	592	3960100	1178080
1991	618	3964081	1230438
1992	623	3968064	1241016
1993	658	3972049	1311394
1994	690	3976036	1375860
1995	708	3980025	1412460
1996	772	3984016	1540912
1997	809	3988009	1615573
1998	830	3992004	1658340
1999	849	3996001	1697151
37810	11263	75242470	22429032

13.10.3 Quality of the Curve Fit (R-Squared Value)

Aim: To quantitatively determine how good the fit is.

Sum of the Squares of the Errors (SSE):

$$SSE = \sum_{i=1}^{n} [y_i - f(x_i)]^2$$

difference between each y value and its predicted value, squared

Sum of the Squares of the Deviations (SST):

$$SST = \sum_{i=1}^{n} [y_i - y]^{-2}$$

difference between each y value and the mean of y, squared

R-Squared Value:

$$r^2 = 1 - \frac{SSE}{SST}$$

Varies between 0 and 1. The closer to 1, the better the fit.

EXAMPLE 13-14

Exponential Equations

$y = b10^{mx}$

$y = be^{mx}$

Sample Data		Linearized Data	
x	y		
2	0.27		
10	0.35		
20	0.50		
50	1.41		
75	3.33		
100	7.91		

Linearize the Equation

$y = b10^{mx}$

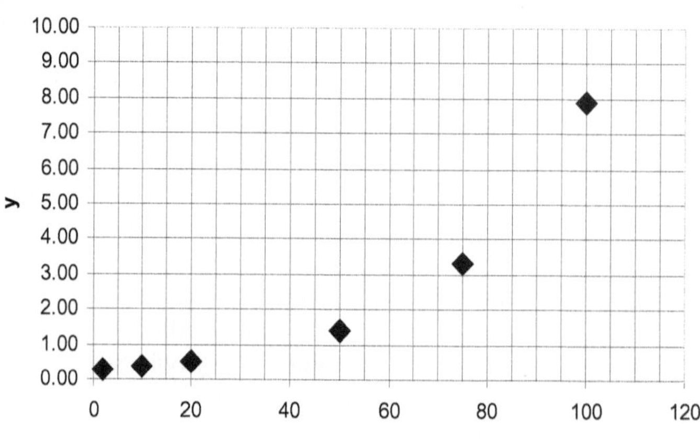

Find the Slope

Plot the Linearized Data

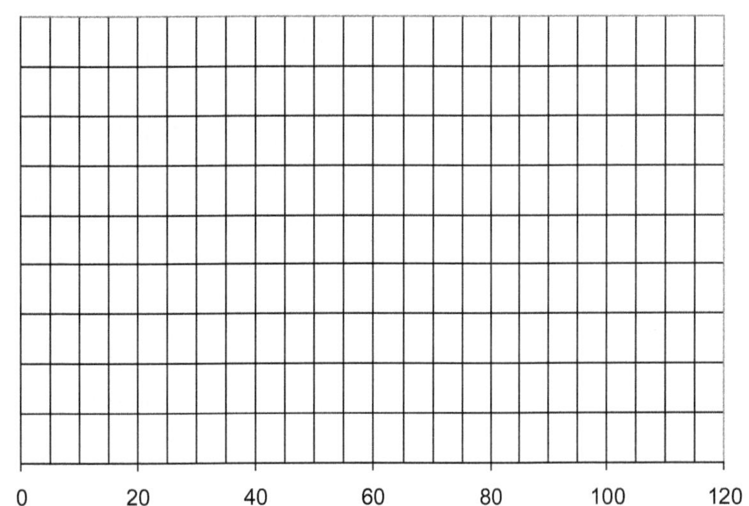

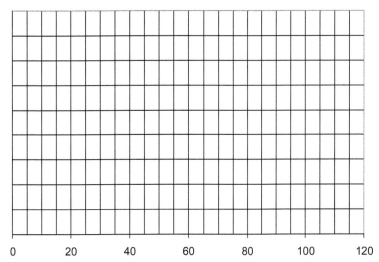

Find the Intercept

Plot the Data on a Log Scaled Plot

Write the Linearized Equation

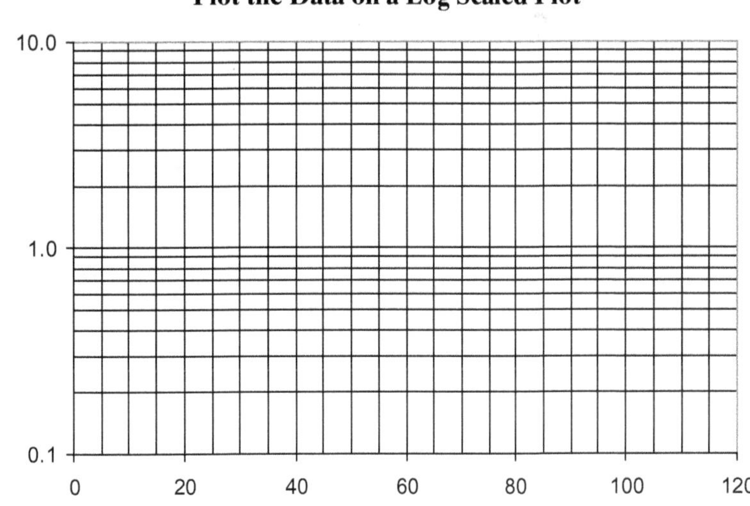

Write the Exponential Equation

Power Equations

$y = bx^m$

$x = by^m$

Sample Data		Linearized Data	
x	y		
2	3.69		
10	5.99		
20	7.37		
50	9.70		
75	10.96		
100	11.94		

Linearize the Equation

$y = bx^m$

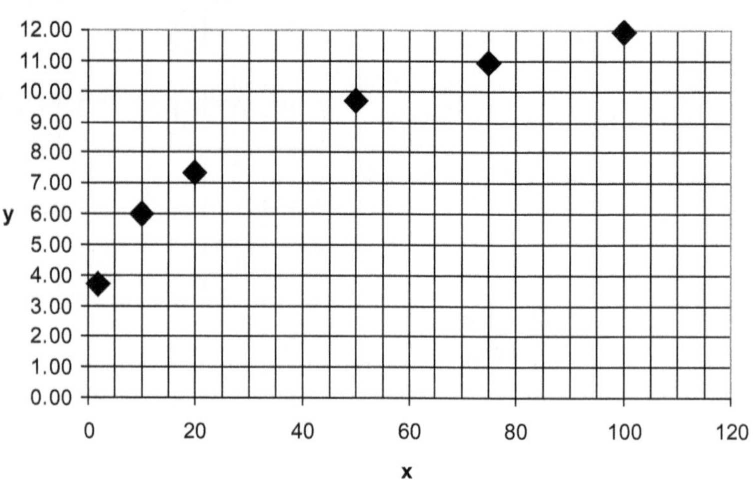

Find the Slope

Plot the Linearized Data

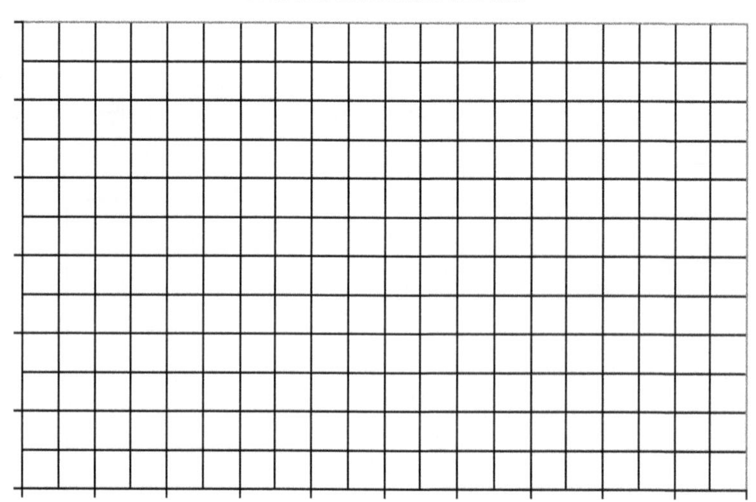

Find the Intercept

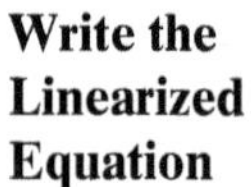

Write the Linearized Equation

Plot the Data on a Log Scaled Plot

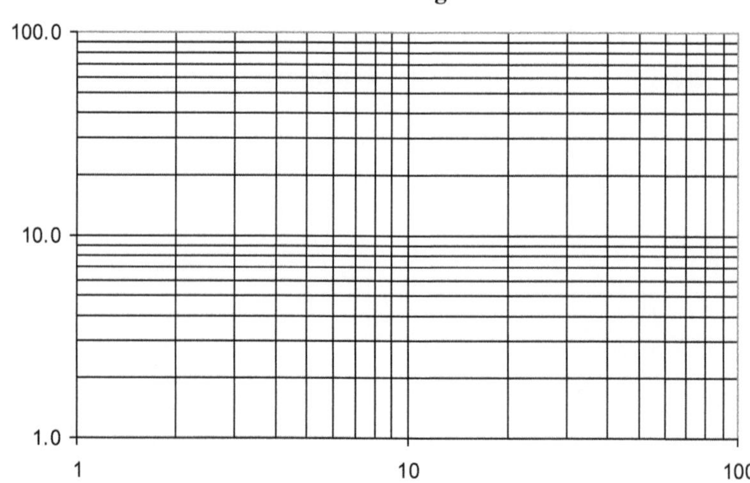

Write the Exponential Equation

Logarithmic Equations

$x = b10^{my}$

$x = be^{my}$

Sample Data		Linearized Data	
x	y		
0.44	2		
1.15	20		
5.65	50		
21.24	75		
47.00	90		
79.81	100		

Linearize the Equation

$x = b10^{my}$

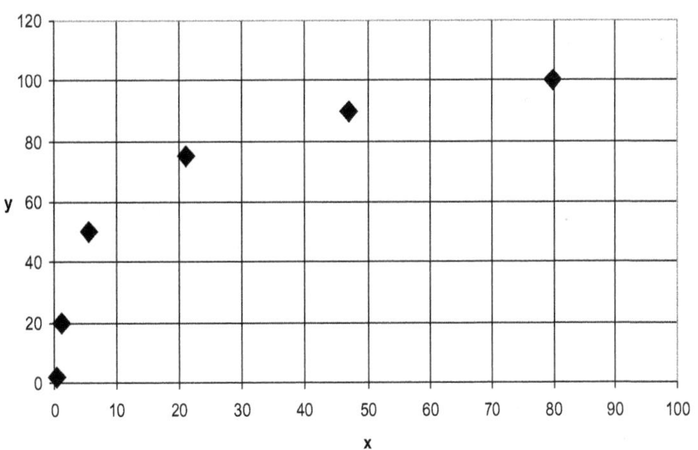

Plot the Linearized Data

Find the Slope

Find the Intercept

Plot the Data on a Log Scaled Plot

Write the Linearized Equation

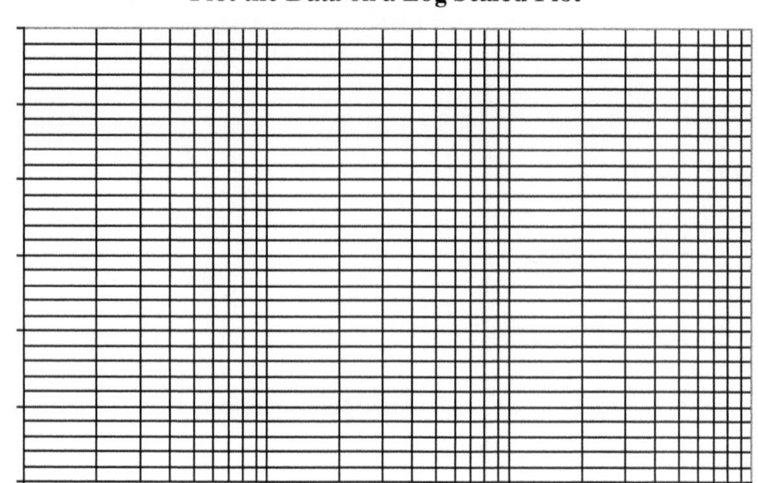

Write the Exponential Equation

	Linearized Form of the Equation	x & y linear	x linear y log	x log y linear	x &y log
		Plot	Semilog y	Semilog x	Log-Log
Linear $y = mx + b$	—	Linear	—	—	—
Exponential $y = be^{mx}$ $y = b10^{mx}$	$\ln y = my + \ln b$ $\log y = mx + \log b$	Curve	Linear	—	—
Logarithmic $x = be^{my}$ $x = b10^{my}$	$\ln x = my + \ln b$ $\log x = my + \log b$	Curve	Curve	Linear	—
Power $y = bx^{m}$ $x = by^{m}$	$\log y = m \log x + \log b$ $\log x = m \log y + \log b$	Curve	Curve	Curve	Linear

In-Class Activities

ICA 13-1

The graph shows the ideal gas law relationship ($PV = nRT$) between volume (V) and temperature (T).

(a) What are the units of the slope (0.0175)?
(b) If the tank has a pressure of 1.2 atmospheres and is filled with nitrogen (formula, N_2; molecular weight, 28 grams per mole), what is the amount of gas in the tank (n) in units of grams?
(c) If the tank is filled with 10 grams of oxygen (formula, O_2; molecular weight, 32 grams per mole), what is the pressure of the tank (P) in units of atmospheres?

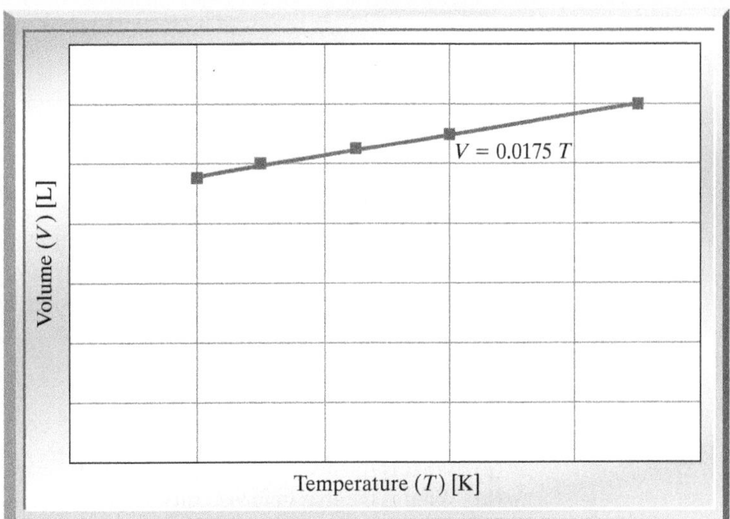

ICA 13-2

An inductor is an electrical device that can store energy in the form of a magnetic field. In the simplest form, an inductor is a cylindrical coil of wire, and its inductance (L), measured in henrys [H], can be calculated by

$$L = \frac{\mu_0 n^2 A}{\ell}$$

where

μ_0 = permeability of free space = $4\pi * 10^{-7}$ [newtons per ampere squared, N/A^2]
n = number of turns of wire [dimensionless]
A = cross-sectional area of coil [square meters, m^2]
ℓ = length of coil [meters, m]
L = inductance [henrys, H] = [J/A^2] (One henry is one joule per ampere squared.)

Several inductors were fabricated with the same number of turns of wire (n) and the same length (ℓ), but with different diameters, thus different cross-sectional areas (A). The inductances were measured and plotted as a function of cross-sectional area, and a mathematical model was developed to describe the relationship, as shown on the graph below.

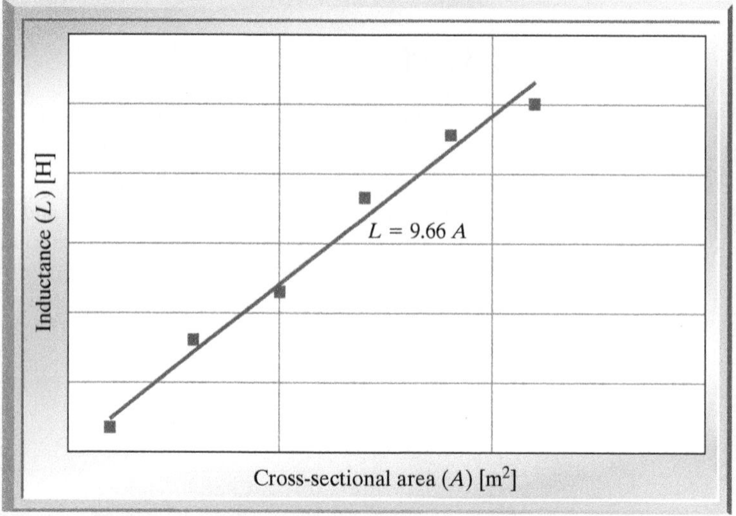

(a) What are the units of the slope (9.66)?

(b) For an inductor fabricated as described above, what is its diameter if its inductance is 0.2 henrys? Give your answer in centimeters.

(c) If the length of the coil (ℓ) equals 0.1 meter, how many turns of wire (n) are in the inductor?

ICA 13-3

Mercury has a dynamic viscosity of 1.55 centipoises and a specific gravity of 12.6.

(a) What is the density of mercury in units of kilograms per cubic meter?

(b) What is the dynamic viscosity of mercury in units of pound-mass per foot second?

(c) What is the dynamic viscosity of mercury in units of pascal seconds?

(d) What is the kinematic viscosity of mercury in units of stokes?

ICA 13-4

SAE 10W30 motor oil has a dynamic viscosity of 0.17 kilograms per meter second and a specific gravity of 0.876.

(a) What is the density of the motor oil in units of kilograms per cubic meter?

(b) What is the dynamic viscosity of the motor oil in units of pound-mass per foot second?

(c) What is the dynamic viscosity of the motor oil in units of centipoise?

(d) What is the kinematic viscosity of the motor oil in units of stokes?

ICA 13-5

You have two springs each of stiffness 1 newton per meter [N/m] and one spring of stiffness 2 newtons per meter [N/m].

(a) List all possible stiffness combinations that can be formed with these springs. Your solution should include drawings and calculations of each unique configuration.

(b) How many unique combinations can be formed?

(c) What is the stiffest configuration?

(d) What is the least stiff configuration?

ICA 13-6

You have three resistors of resistance 30 ohm [Ω].

(a) List all possible resistance combinations that can be formed with these resistors. Your solution should include drawings and calculations of each unique configuration.
(b) How many unique combinations can be formed?
(c) What is the greatest resistance configuration?
(d) What is the least resistance configuration?

ICA 13-7

Four springs were tested, with the results shown graphically below. Use the graph to answer the following questions. Be sure to justify your answers as to why you are making the choice.

(a) Which spring is the stiffest?
(b) Which spring, if placed in parallel with Spring C, would yield the stiffest combination?
(c) Which spring, if placed in series with Spring C, would yield the stiffest combination?
(d) Rank the following combinations in order of stiffness:

Spring A and Spring D are hooked in parallel

Spring B and Spring C are hooked in series, then connected with Spring D in parallel

Spring A

Spring D

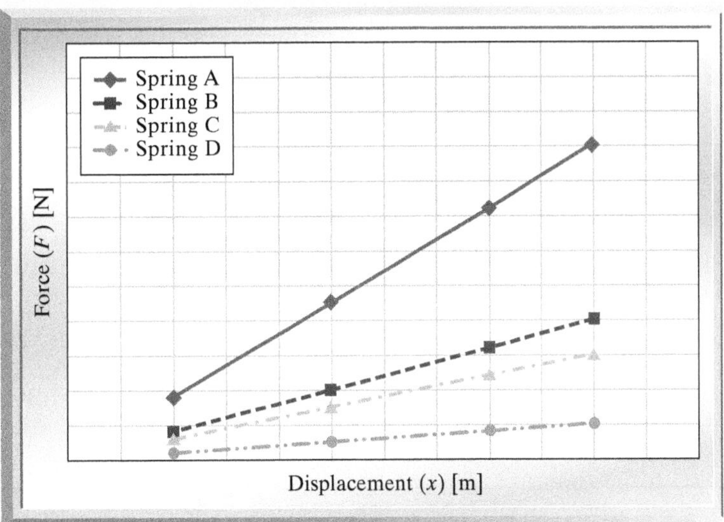

ICA 13-8

Four circuits were tested, with the results shown graphically below. Use the graph to answer the following questions. Be sure to justify your answers as to *why* you are making the choice.

(a) Which resistor gives the most resistance?
(b) What is the resistance of Resistor A?
(c) Which resistor, if placed in parallel with Resistor C, would yield the highest resistance?
(d) Which resistor, if placed in series with Resistor C, would yield the highest resistance?

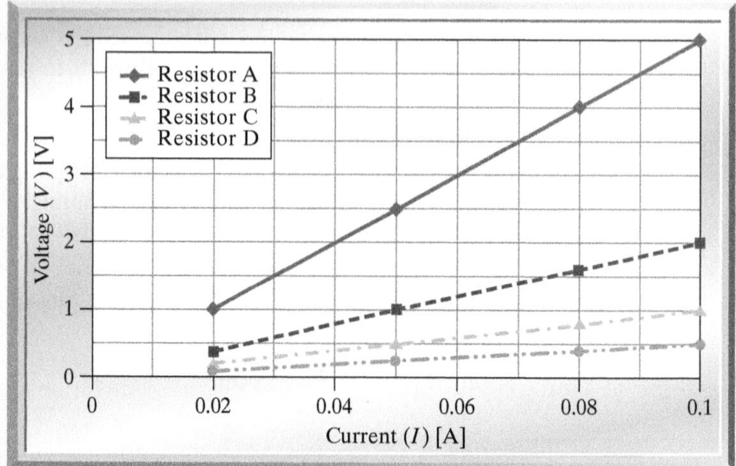

ICA 13-9

The resistance of a wire (R [ohm]) is a function of the wire dimensions (A = cross-sectional area, L = length) and material (r = resistivity) according to the relationship

$$R = \frac{\rho L}{A}$$

The resistance of three wires was tested. All wires had the same cross-sectional area.

Length (L) [m]	0.01	0.1	0.25	0.4	0.5	0.6
Wire 1	8.00E-05	8.00E-04	2.00E-03	3.50E-03	4.00E-03	4.75E-03
Wire 2	4.75E-05	4.80E-04	1.00E-03	2.00E-03	2.50E-03	3.00E-03
Wire 3	1.50E-04	1.70E-03	4.25E-03	7.00E-03	8.50E-03	1.00E-02

(a) Plot the data and fit a linear trendline model to each wire.
(b) From the following chart, match each wire (1, 2, and 3) with the correct material according to the results of the resistivity determined from the trendlines, assuming a 0.2-centimeter diameter wire was used.

Material	Resistivity (ρ) [Ωm] $\times 10^{-8}$
Aluminum	2.65
Copper	1.68
Iron	9.71
Silver	1.59
Tungsten	5.60

ICA 13-10

A piano, much like a guitar or a harp, is a stringed instrument. The primary difference is that a piano has a keyboard containing 88 keys that, when pressed, cause a small felt hammer to strike the strings (mostly 3) associated with that key. Each hammer can hit the strings harder or softer depending on the force applied to the key on the keyboard. In order to create the different pitches of sound, the strings for each key are of different lengths as well as having different mass per unit length.

The equation for the fundamental frequency of a vibrating string is given by

$$f = \frac{\sqrt{T/\mu}}{2L}$$

where

f = frequency [Hz]
T = string tension [N]
μ = mass per unit length [kg/m]
L = string length [m]

In avant-garde music, the piano is sometimes played much like a harp, where the strings are directly manipulated (e.g., plucked and strummed) without the use of the keys on the keyboard. Assume we construct a special piano for use by an avant-garde musician in which each string has the same mass per unit length and the same length on the soundboard. The only difference is the string tension on each string on the soundboard. To test our design, we collect data using a single string on the sound board and create a graph of the observed frequency at different string tensions:

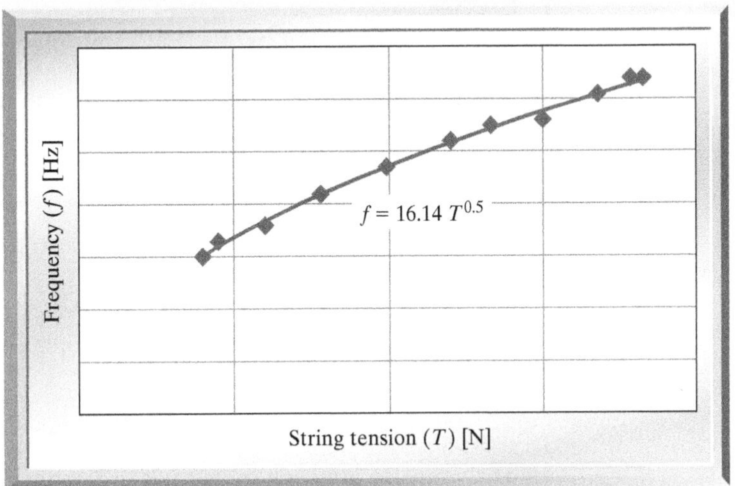

(a) What are the units of the coefficient (16.14)?
(b) If the observed frequency is 450 hertz, what is the string tension in newtons?
(c) If mass per unit length is 4.5 grams per meter, what is the length of the string in meters?
(d) If the length of the string is 0.7 meters, what is the mass per unit length in kilograms per meter?

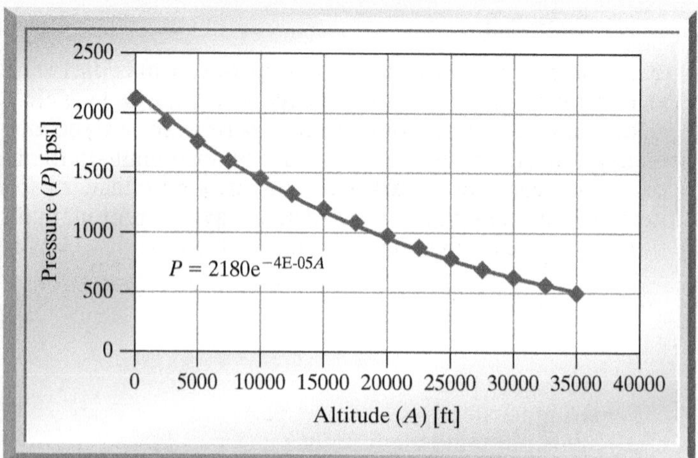

Figure 1 Earth Atmosphere Model: Troposphere

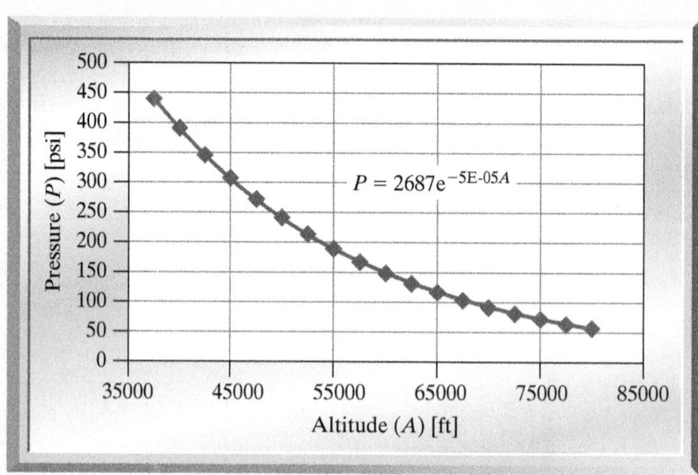

Figure 2 Earth Atmosphere Model: Lower Stratosphere

ICA 13-11

To assist airplane manufacturers, NASA and other similar agencies around the world regularly release atmosphere models of Earth that are updated based on climate change around the world. Consider the graphs (Figures 1–2) of an atmosphere model of two different atmospheric layers (troposphere and lower stratosphere) and answer the following questions. These models are based on http://www.grc.nasa.gov/WWW/K-12/airplane/atmos.html.

(a) In Figure 1, what are the units of the value "2180" given in the trendline?

(b) In Figure 2, what are the units of "–5E-05" given in the trendline?

(c) What is the pressure at an altitude of 0 feet? How does this compare to the definition of standard atmospheric pressure of 1 atmosphere?

(d) What is the altitude at an air pressure of 150 pounds-force per square foot?

ICA 13-12

Eutrophication is a process whereby lakes, estuaries, or slow-moving streams receive excess nutrients that stimulate excessive plant growth. This enhanced plant growth, often called an algal bloom, reduces dissolved oxygen in the water when dead plant material decomposes and can cause other organisms to die. Nutrients can come from many sources, such as fertilizers; deposition of nitrogen from the atmosphere; erosion of soil containing nutrients; and sewage treatment plant discharges. Water with a low concentration of dissolved oxygen is called hypoxic. A biosystems engineering models the algae growth in a lake. The concentration of algae (C), measured in grams per milliliter [g/mL], can be calculated by

$$C = C_0 e^{\left(\frac{kt}{r}\right)}$$

where

C_0 = initial concentration of algae [?]
k = multiplication rate of the algae [?]
r = estimated nutrient supply amount [mg of nutrient per mL of sample water]
t = time [days]

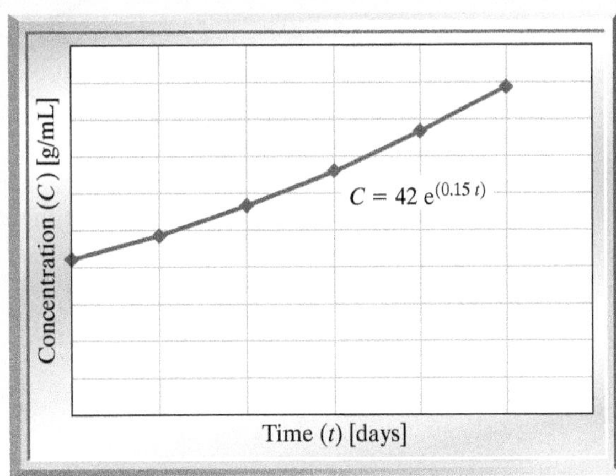

(a) For the exponential model shown, list the value and units of the parameters m and b. You do not need to simplify any units. Recall that an exponential model has the form:

Exponential $y = be^{mx}$ $\quad m$ = exponent $\quad b$ = constant

(b) What is the initial concentration of the algae (C_0)?

(c) What are the units on the multiplication rate of the algae (k)?

(d) If the algae are allowed to grow for 10 days and an estimated nutrient supply of 3 milligrams of nutrient per milliliter of water sample, what is the multiplication rate of the algae (k)?

ICA 13-13

Select the data series from the options shown on the graph below that represent each of the following model types. You may assume that power and exponential models do not have a constant offset. You may also assume that only positive values are shown on the two axes (only first quadrant shown). For each match, write "Series X," where X is the appropriate letter, A through F. If no curve matches the specified criterion, write "No Match." If more than one curve matches a given specification, list both series.

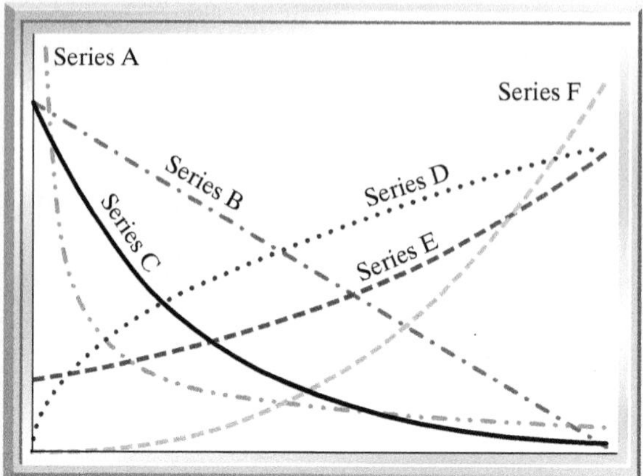

(a) Exponential, negative numeric value in exponent.
(b) Power, negative numeric value in exponent.
(c) Linear, negative slope.
(d) Exponential, positive numeric value in exponent.
(e) Power, positive numeric value in exponent.

ICA 13-14

EXAMPLE: Find best-fit straight line for this x, y data: (1,0.5), (3, 2.5), (5, 2), (7, 4), (9, 3.5)

i	x_i	y_i	x_i^2	x_iy_i
1	1	0.5		
2	3	2.5		
3	5	2		
4	7	4		
5	9	3.5		
Sums:				

SIMULTANEOUS EQUATIONS

Two unknowns, two equations.

ICA 13-15

EXAMPLE: Find the r^2 value for the equation $y = ax + b$ fit to the data.

i	x_i	y_i	$f(x_i)$	e_i	e_i^2	$[y_i - \bar{y}]^2$
1	1	0.5				
2	3	2.5				
3	5	2				
4	7	4				
5	9	3.5				
Sums:						
Mean:						

r^2 = ____, which means that our equation is a moderately good estimator.

We can also think of it this way: Our regression equation explains about _____% of the variation that exists in the data, with the other ___% due to other factors or randomness.

CHAPTER 13 REVIEW QUESTIONS

1. A capacitor is an electrical device that can store energy in the form of an electric field. A capacitor is simply two conducting plates (usually metal) separated by an insulator, with a wire connected to each of the two plates. For a simple capacitor with two flat plates, the capacitance (C) [F] can be calculated by

$$C = \frac{\varepsilon_r \varepsilon_0 A}{d}$$

where

$\varepsilon_0 = 8.854 \times 10^{-12}$ [F/m] (the permittivity of free space in farads per meter)
ε_r = relative static permittivity, a property of the insulator [dimensionless]

A = area of overlap of the plates [m^2]
d = distance between the plates [m]

Several experimental capacitors were fabricated with different plate areas (A), but with the same inter-plate distance (d = 1.2 mm) and the same insulating material, and thus the same relative static permittivity (εr). The capacitance of each device was measured and plotted versus the plate area. A mathematical model to describe the data was then obtained. The graph and equation are shown below. The numeric scales were deliberately omitted.

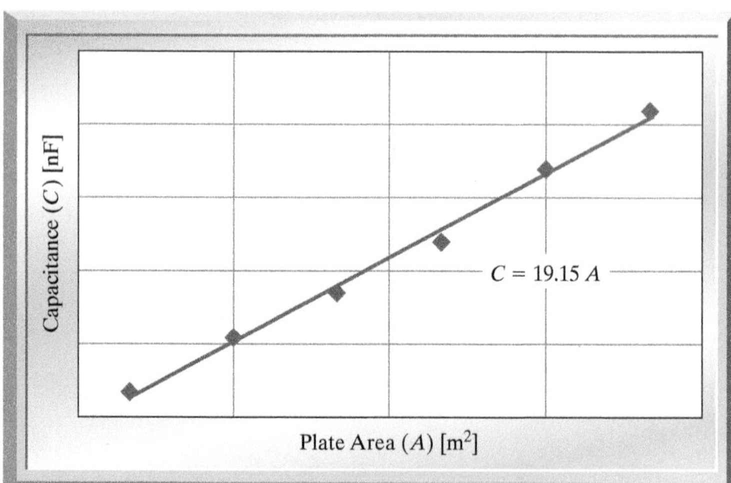

(a) What are the units of the slope (19.15)?
(b) If the capacitance is 2 nanofarads [εF], what is the area (A) of the plates?
(c) What is the relative static permittivity of the insulating layer?
(d) If the distance between the plates were doubled, how would the capacitance be affected?

2. When rain falls over an area for a sufficiently long time, it will run off and collect at the bottom of hills and eventually find its way into creeks and rivers. A simple way to estimate the maximum discharge flow rate (Q, in units of cubic feet per

second [cfs]) from a watershed of area (A, in units of acres) with a rainfall intensity (i, in units of inches per hour) is given by an expression commonly called the Rational Method, as

$$Q = CiA$$

Values of C vary between about 0 (for flat rural areas) to almost 1 (in urban areas with a large amount of paved area).

A survey of a number of rainfall events was made over a 10-year period for three different watersheds. The data that resulted is given in the table below. Watershed A is 120 acres, B is 316 acres, and C is 574 acres.

Storm event	Watershed	Rainfall Intensity (i) [in/h]	Maximum Runoff (Q) [cfs]
1	A	0.5	30
2	A	1.1	66
3	A	1.6	96
4	A	2.1	126
5	B	0.3	47
6	B	0.7	110
7	B	1.2	188
8	B	1.8	283
9	C	0.4	115
10	C	1	287
11	C	1.5	430
12	C	2.4	690

(a) Create a graph containing all three watersheds, with flowrate on the ordinate and fit trendlines to obtain a simple model for each watershed.
From the information given and the trendline model obtained, answer the following:

(b) What is the value and units of the coefficient C?

(c) What would the maximum flow rate be from a watershed of 400 acres if the rainfall intensity was 0.6 inches per hour?

(d) How long would it take at this flowrate to fill an Olympic sized swimming pool that is 50 meters long, 20 meters wide, and 2 meters deep?

3. When we wish to generate hydroelectric power, we build a dam to back up the water in a river. If the water has a height (H, in units of feet) above the downstream discharge, and we can discharge water through the turbines at a rate (Q, in units of cubic feet per second [cfs]), the maximum power (P, in units of kilowatts) we can expect to generate is:

$$P = CHQ$$

For a small "run of the river" hydroelectric facility, we have obtained the following data.

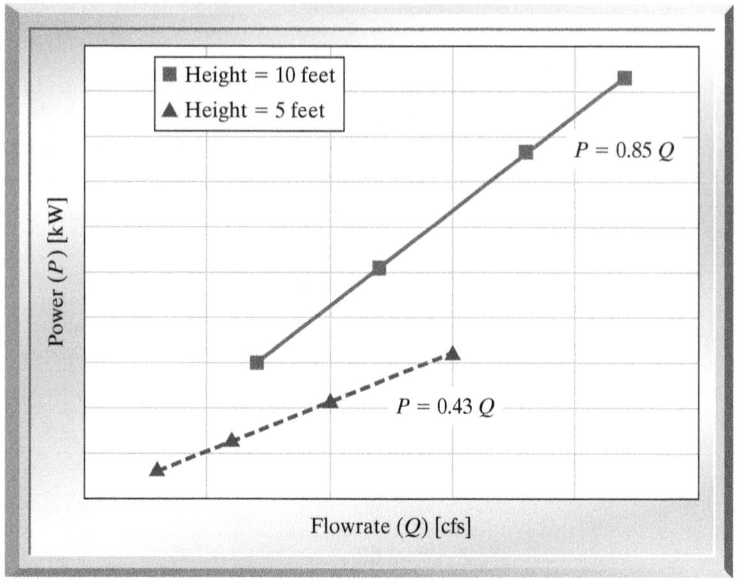

(a) Using the trendline results, and examining the general equation above, determine the value and units of the coefficient C for a height of 10 feet and a height of 5 feet.

(b) If the flowrate was 20 cubic feet per second and the height is 10 feet, what would the power output be in units of kilowatts?

(c) If the flowrate was 4,000 gallons per minute and the height 5 feet, what would the power output be in units of kilowatts?

(d) If the power output was 10 horsepower and the height was 10 feet, what would the flowrate be in cubic feet per second?

(e) If the power output was 8 horsepower and the height was 5 feet, what would the flowrate be in cubic feet per second?

(f) If the flow rate was 15 cubic feet per second and the height is 3 meters, what would the power output be in units of horsepower?

(g) If the flow rate was 10 cubic feet per second and the height is 8 meters, what would the power output be in units of horsepower?

4. You are experimenting with several liquid metal alloys to find a suitable replacement for the mercury used in thermometers. You have attached capillary tubes with a circular cross-section and an inside diameter of 0.3 millimeters to reservoirs containing 5 cubic centimeters of each alloy. You mark the position of the liquid in each capillary tube when the temperature is 20 degrees Celsius, systematically change the temperature, and measure the distance the liquid moves in the tube as it expands or contracts with changes in temperature. Note that negative values correspond to contraction of the material due to lower temperatures. The data you collected for four different alloys is shown in the table below.

Alloy G1		Alloy G2		Alloy G3		Alloy G4	
Temperature (T) [°C]	Distance (d) [cm]	Temperature (T) [°C]	Distance (d) [cm]	Temperature (T) [°C]	Distance (d) [cm]	Temperature (T) [°C]	Distance (d) [cm]
22	1.05	21	0.95	24	2.9	25	5.1
27	3.05	29	7.65	30	7.2	33	13.8
34	6.95	33	10.6	34	9.8	16	−4.3
14	−3.5	17	−2.6	19	−0.6	13	−7.05
9	−5.1	3	−14.8	12	−6.15	6	−14.65
2	−8.7	−2	−19.8	4	−11.5	−2	−22.15
−5	−11.7	−8	−25.4	−5	−18.55	−6	−26.3
−11	−15.5					−12	−32.4

(a) In Excel, create two new columns for each compound to calculate the change in temperature (ΔT) relative to 20°C (for example, 25°C gives $\Delta T = 5$°C) and the corresponding change in volume (ΔV).

(b) Plot the change in volume versus the change in temperature; fit a linear trendline to each data set.

(c) From the trendline equations, determine the coefficient of thermal expansion, β. Note that $\Delta V = \beta V \Delta T$, where V is the initial volume.

(d) There is a small constant offset (C) in each trendline equation ($\Delta V = \beta V \Delta T + C$). What is the physical origin of this constant term? Can it be safely ignored? In other words, is its effect on the determination of β negligible?

5. In order to determine the value of an unknown capacitor, it is charged with a constant current of 50 microamperes. The voltage across the capacitor was measured at several times and the results are shown below. It is known that the voltage across an initially discharged capacitor being charged by a constant current is given by $V = It/C$, where V is voltage in volts. I is the current in amperes, t is time in seconds, and C is capacitance in farads.

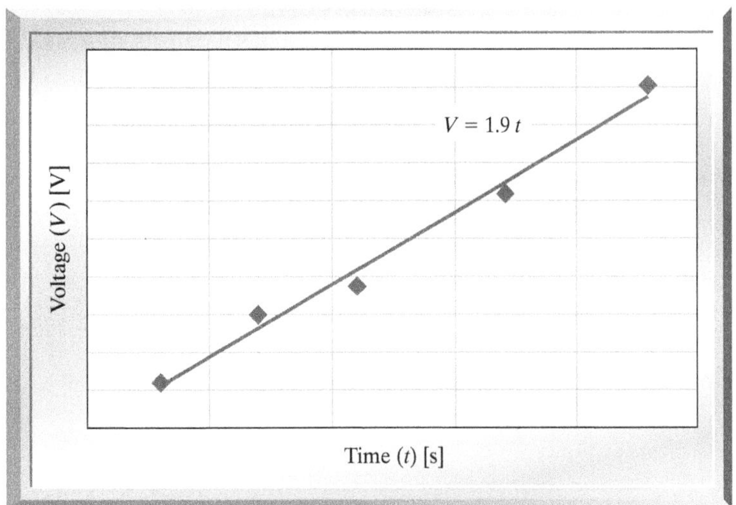

(a) What are the units on the constant (1.9)?

(b) What is the value of the capacitor?

6. Solid objects, such as your desk or a rod of aluminum, can conduct heat. The magnitude of the thermal diffusivity of the material determines how quickly the heat moves through a given amount of material. The equation for thermal diffusivity (α) is given by:

$$\alpha = \frac{k}{\rho C_p}$$

Experiments are conducted to change the thermal conductivity (k) of the material while holding the specific heat (C_p) and the density (ρ) constant. The results are shown graphically.

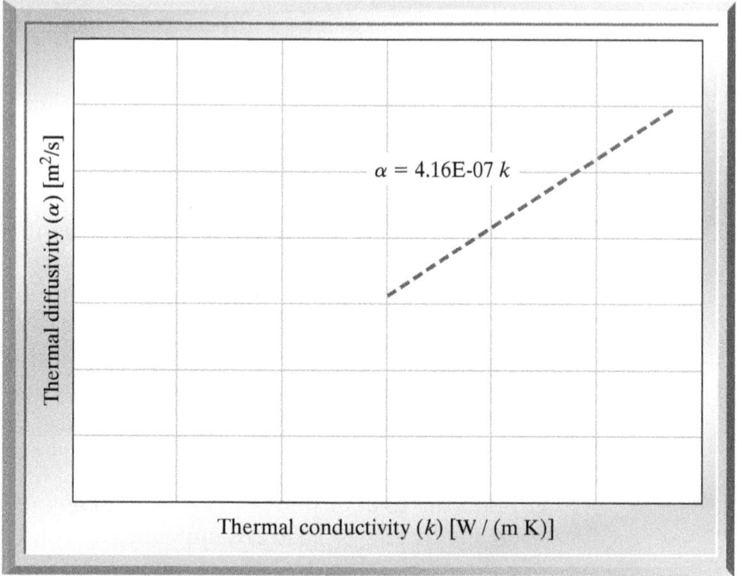

(a) What are the units of the constant 4.16×10^7? Simplify your answer.
(b) If the specific heat of the material is 890 joules per kilogram kelvin, what is the density of the material?
(c) If the material has a density of 4,500 kilograms per cubic meter, what is the specific heat of the material in units of joules per kilogram kelvin?

7. Use the figure shown to answer the following questions.

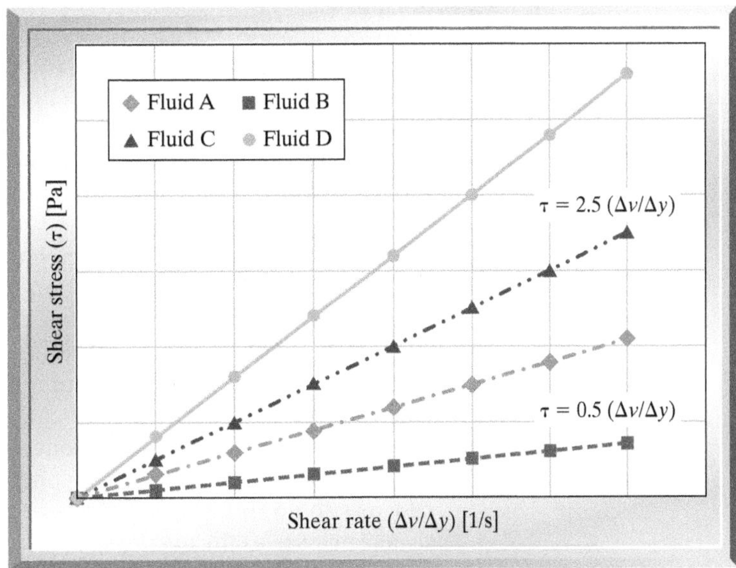

(a) Which fluid has the lowest dynamic viscosity?
(b) What is the dynamic viscosity of Fluid B?
(c) What is the dynamic viscosity of Fluid B in units of centipoise?
(d) If the specific gravity of Fluid B is 1.3, what is the kinematic viscosity of Fluid B in units of stokes?
(e) What is the dynamic viscosity of Fluid C?
(f) What is the dynamic viscosity of Fluid C in units of centipoise?
(g) If the specific gravity of Fluid C is 0.8, what is the kinematic viscosity of Fluid C in units of stokes?

8. You are given four springs, one each of 2.5, 5, 7.5, and 10 newtons per meter [N/m].

(a) What is the largest equivalent stiffness that can be made using these four springs? Draw a diagram indicating how the four springs are connected and what the value of each is.
(b) What is the smallest equivalent stiffness that can be made using these four springs? Draw a diagram indicating how the four springs are connected and what the value of each is.
(c) What is the largest equivalent stiffness that can be made using only three of these springs? Draw a diagram indicating how the three springs are connected and what the value of each is.
(d) What is the smallest equivalent stiffness that can be made using only three of these springs? Draw a diagram indicating how the three springs are connected and what the value of each is.
(e) How close an equivalent stiffness to the average of the four springs (6.25 newtons per meter) can you make using only these springs? You may use all four springs to do this, but you may use less if that will yield an equivalent stiffness closer to the average.

9. You are given four resistors, each of 7.5, 10, 15, and 20 kiloohms [kΩ].
   (a) What is the largest equivalent resistance that can be made using these four resistors? Draw a diagram indicating how the four resistors are connected and what the value of each is.
   (b) What is the smallest equivalent resistance that can be made using these four resistors? Draw a diagram indicating how the four resistors are connected and what the value of each is.
   (c) What is the largest equivalent resistance that can be made using only three of these resistors? Draw a diagram indicating how the three resistors are connected and what the value of each is.
   (d) What is the smallest equivalent resistance that can be made using only three of these resistors? Draw a diagram indicating how the three resistors are connected and what the value of each is.
   (e) How close an equivalent resistance to the average of the four resistors (13.125 kΩ) can you make using only these resistors? You may use all four resistors to do this, but you may use less if that will yield an equivalent resistance closer to the average.

10. Use the diagrams shown to answer the following questions.
   (a) Determine the equivalent stiffness of four springs connected as shown.

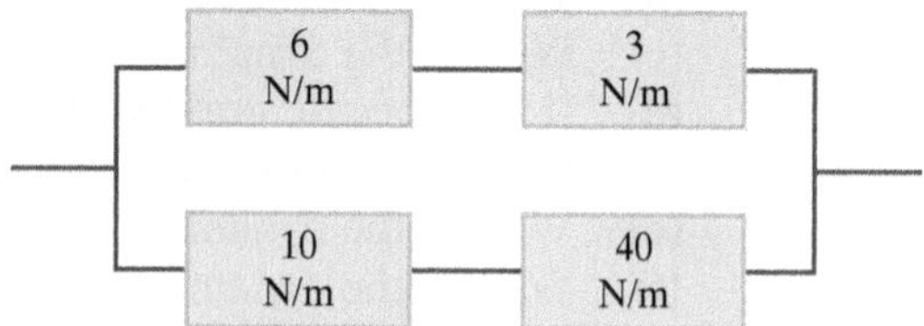

   (b) Determine the equivalent stiffness of four springs connected as shown.

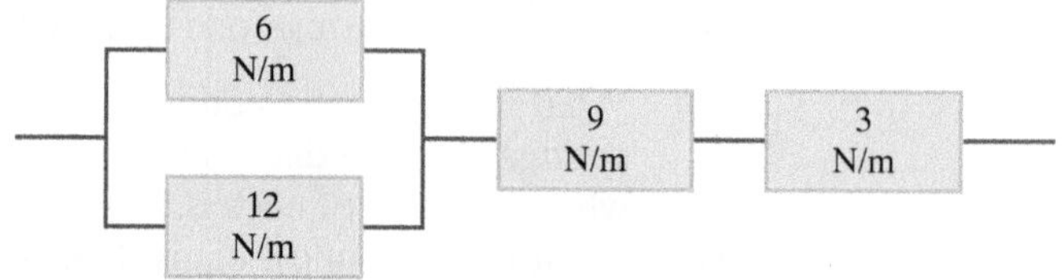

   (c) Determine the equivalent resistance of four resistors connected as shown.

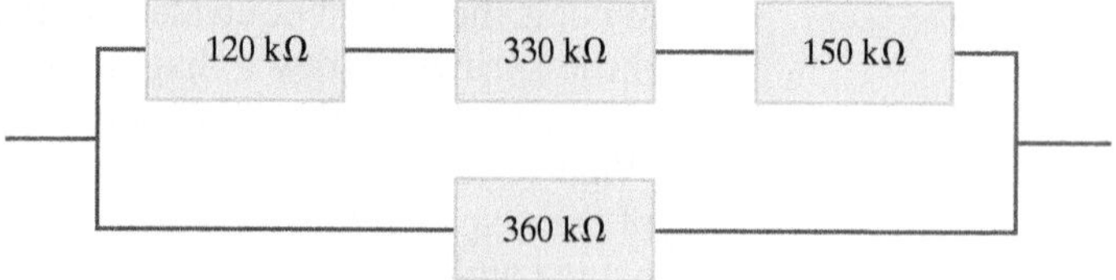

   (d) Determine the equivalent resistance of four resistors connected as shown.

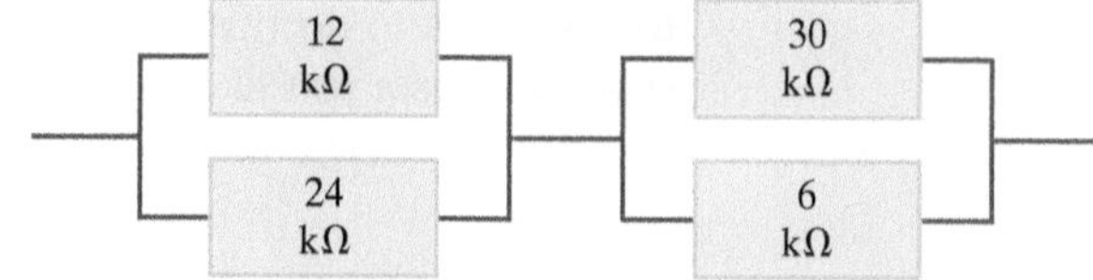

(e) Determine a SIMPLE function for the equivalent stiffness of N springs, each with a spring constant k, all connected in series. You MUST show how you derived this for credit. You may NOT use Σ or notation in your final answer.

(f) Determine a SIMPLE function for the equivalent resistance of N resistors, each with resistance R, all connected in series. You MUST show how you derived this for credit. You may NOT use Σ or Π notation in your final answer.

11. You have three springs. You conduct several tests and determine the following data.

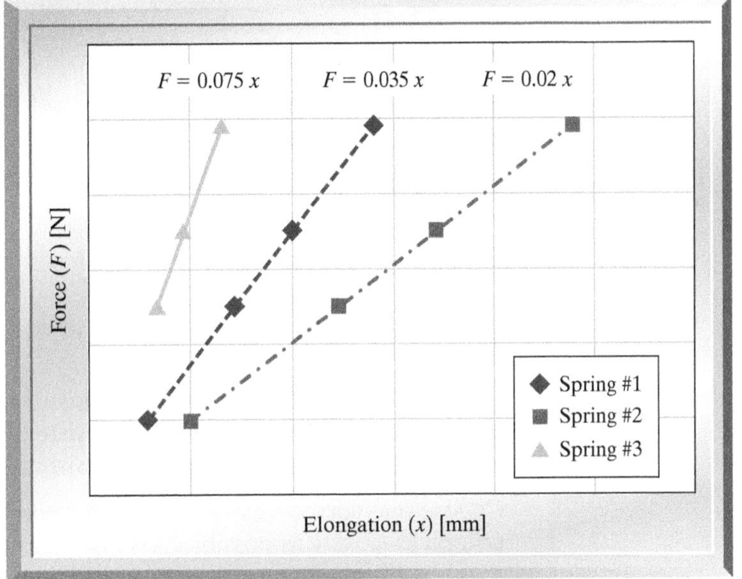

(a) Determine the stiffness of Spring 1.
(b) Determine the stiffness of Spring 2.
(c) Determine the stiffness of Spring 3.

Choose one correct spring or spring combination that will meet the following criteria as closely as possible. Assume you have one of each spring available for use. List the spring or spring combination and the resulting spring constant.

(d) You want the spring or spring system to hold 95 grams and displace approximately 1 centimeter.

(e) You want the spring or spring system to displace approximately 4 centimeter when holding 50 grams.

(f) You want the spring or spring system to displace approximately 5 millimeter when holding 75 grams.

(g) You want the spring or spring system to hold 20 grams and displace approximately 1 centimeter.

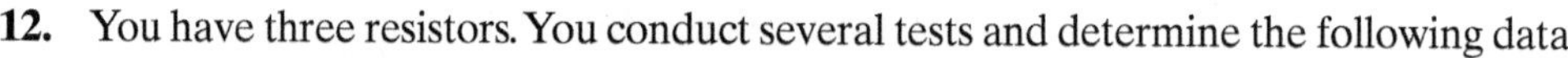

12. You have three resistors. You conduct several tests and determine the following data.

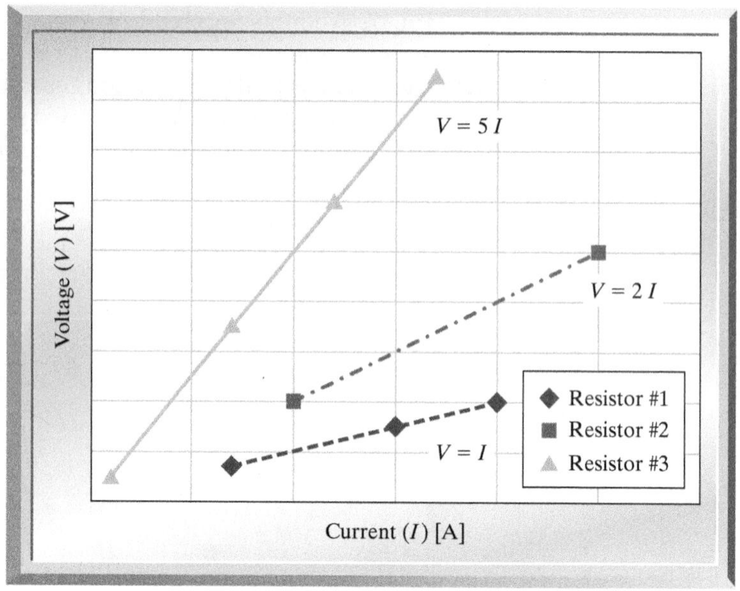

(a) Determine the resistance of Resistor 1.
(b) Determine the resistance of Resistor 2.
(c) Determine the resistance of Resistor 3.

Choose one correct resistor or resistor combination that will meet the following criteria as closely as possible. Assume you have one of each resistor available for use. List the resistor or resistor combination and the resulting resistor constant.

(d) You want the resistor or resistor system to provide approximately 20 amperes when met with 120 volts.
(e) You want the resistor or resistor system to provide approximately 46 amperes when met with 30 volts.
(f) You want the resistor or resistor system to provide approximately 15 amperes when met with 120 volts.
(g) You want the resistor or resistor system to provide approximately 33 amperes when met with 45 volts.

13. A piano, much like a guitar or a harp, is a stringed instrument. The primary difference is that a piano has a keyboard containing 88 keys that, when pressed, cause a small felt hammer to strike the strings (mostly 3) associated with that key. Each hammer can hit the strings harder or softer depending on the force applied to the key on the keyboard. In order to create the different pitches of sound, the strings for each key are of different lengths as well as having different mass per unit length.

In avant-garde music, the piano is sometimes played much like a harp, where the strings are directly manipulated (plucked, strummed, etc.) without the use of the keys on the keyboard. Assume we construct a special piano for use by an avant-garde musician in which each string has the same mass per unit length and the same tension on the soundboard. The only difference is the length of each string on the soundboard. To test our design, we collect the following data on the observed frequency at different string lengths:

Length (*L*) [M]	0.41	0.48	0.61	0.69	0.86	0.97	1.1	1.3	1.5
Frequency (*f*) [Hz]	1,500	1,300	1,000	880	740	650	600	490	400

The equation for the fundamental frequency of a vibrating string is given by

$$f = \frac{\sqrt{T/\mu}}{2L}$$

where

f = frequency [Hz]
T = string tension [N]
μ = mass per unit length [kg/m]
L = string length [m]

(a) Using the equation above, express the unit hertz [Hz] in terms of base SI units. You must prove this relationship using the equation given.

(b) Is the relationship between frequency and length linear, power, or exponential?

(c) Create a graph of the observed frequency data, including the trendline and equation generated by Excel.

(d) If the tension was reduced to half of its original value, would the frequency increase or decrease and by how much?

(e) If the tension on the strings is 200 newtons, what is the mass per unit length in grams per meter?

(f) If the mass per length of the string is 0.5 grams per meter, what is the tension in newtons?

14. Solid objects, such as your desk or a rod of aluminum, can conduct heat. The magnitude of the thermal diffusivity of the material determines how quickly the heat moves through a given amount of material. The equation for thermal diffusivity (a) is given by:

$$\alpha = \frac{k}{\rho C_p}$$

Experiments are conducted to change the specific heat (C_p) of the material while holding the thermal conductivity (k) and the density (r) constant. The results are shown graphically.

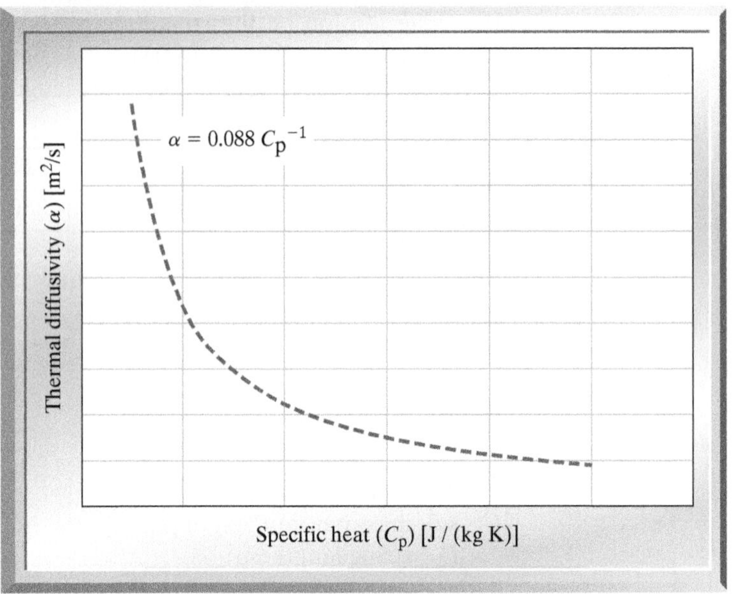

(a) What are the units of the constant 0.088? Simplify your answer.
(b) If the thermal conductivity of the material is 237 watts per meter kelvin, what is the density of the material?
(c) If the material has a density of 4,500 kilograms per cubic meter, what is the thermal conductivity of the material in units of watts per meter kelvin?

15. Your supervisor has assigned you the task of designing a set of measuring spoons with a "futuristic" shape. After considerable effort, you have come up with two geometric shapes that you believe are really interesting.

You make prototypes of five spoons for each shape with different depths and measure the volume each will hold. The table below shows the data you collected.

Depth (d) [cm]	Volume (V_A) [mL] Shape A	Volume (V_B) [mL] Shape B
0.5	1	1.2
0.9	2.5	3.3
1.3	4	6.4
1.4	5	7.7
1.7	7	11

Use Excel to plot and determine appropriate power models for this data. Use the resulting models to determine the depths of a set of measuring spoons comprising the following volumes for each of the two designs:

Volume Needed (V) [tsp or tbsp]	Depth of Design A (d_A) [cm]	Depth of Design B (d_B) [cm]
$\frac{1}{4}$ tsp		
$\frac{1}{2}$ tsp		
$\frac{3}{4}$ tsp		
1 tsp		
1 tbsp		

16. A piano, much like a guitar or a harp, is a stringed instrument. The primary difference is that a piano has a keyboard containing 88 keys that, when pressed, cause a small felt hammer to strike the strings (mostly 3) associated with that key. Each hammer can hit the strings harder or softer depending on the force applied to the key on the keyboard. In order to create the different pitches of sound, the strings for each key are of different lengths as well as having different mass per unit length.

In avant-garde music, the piano is sometimes played much like a harp, where the strings are directly manipulated (e.g. plucked and strummed) without the use of the keys on the keyboard. Assume we construct a special piano for use by an avant-garde musician in which each string has the same mass per unit length and the same tension on the soundboard. The only difference is the length of each string on the soundboard. To test our design, we collect the following data on the observed frequency at different string lengths.

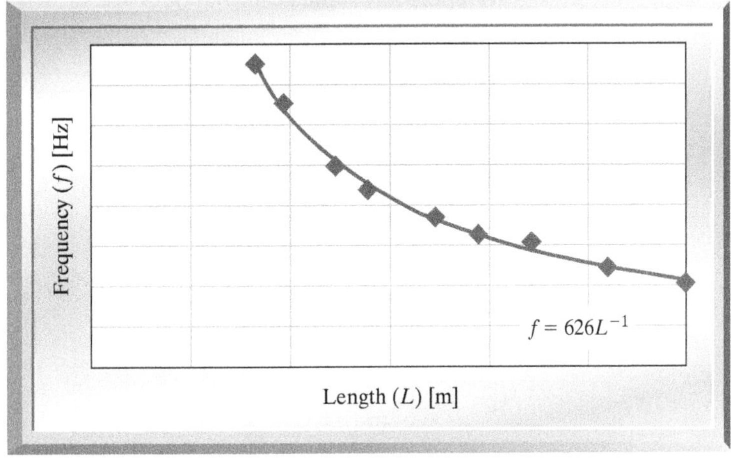

The equation for the fundamental frequency of a vibrating string is given by

$$f = \frac{\sqrt{T/\mu}}{2L}$$

where

f = frequency [Hz]
T = string tension [N]
μ = mass per unit length [kg/m]
L = string length [m]

(a) Is the relationship between frequency and length linear, power, or exponential?
(b) What are the units of the coefficient (626)?

(c) If the tension on the strings is 200 newtons, what is the mass per unit length in grams per meter?
(d) If the mass per length of the string is 0.5 grams per meter, what is the tension in newtons?

17. It is extremely difficult to bring the internet to some remote parts of the world. This can be inexpensively facilitated by installing antennas tethered to large helium balloons. To help analyze the situation, assume we have inflated a large spherical balloon. The pressure on the inside of the balloon is balanced by the elastic force exerted by the rubberized material. Since we are dealing with a gas in an enclosed space, the Ideal Gas Law will be applicable.

$$PV = nRT$$

where

P = pressure
V = volume
n = quantity of gas [moles]
R = ideal gas constant [0.08206 (atm L)/(mol K)]
T = temperature (absolute units)

If the temperature increases, the balloon will expand and/or the pressure will increase to maintain the equality. As it turns out, the increase in volume is the dominate effect, so we will treat the change in pressure as negligible.

The circumference of an inflated spherical balloon is measured at various temperatures; the resulting data are shown in the graph below.

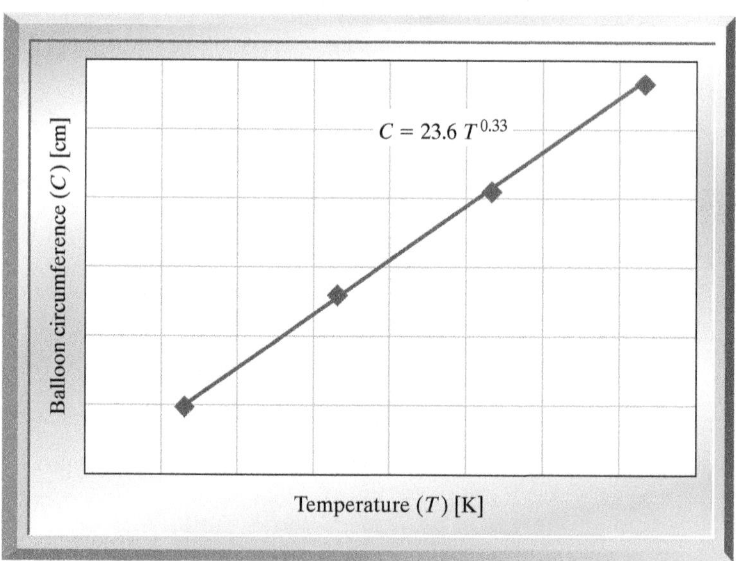

(a) What are the units of the constant 0.33?
(b) What are the units of the constant 23.6?
(c) What would the temperature of the balloon be if the circumference was 162 centimeters?
(d) If a circle with an area of 100 square centimeters is drawn on the balloon at 20 degrees Celsius, what would the area be at a temperature of 100 degrees Celsius?

(e) If the pressure inside the balloon is 1.2 atmospheres, how many moles of gas does it contain?

(f) If the balloon holds 50 grams of nitrogen, with a molecular weigth of 28 grams per mole, what is the pressure inside the ballon in units of atmospheres?

18. When a buoyant cylinder of height H, such as a fishing cork, is placed in a liquid and the top is depressed and released, it will bob up and down with a period T. We can conduct a series of tests and see that as the height of the cylinder increases, the period of oscillation also increases. A less dense cylinder will have a shorter period than a denser cylinder, assuming of course all the cylinders will float. A simple expression for the period is:

$$T = 2\pi\sqrt{\frac{\rho_{\text{cylinder}}}{\rho_{\text{liquid}}}\frac{H}{g}}$$

where g is the acceleration due to gravity [9.8 meters per second squared], ρ_{cylinder} is the density of the material, and ρ_{liquid} is the density of the fluid. By testing cylinders of differing heights, we wish to develop a model for the oscillation period, shown in the graph below.

(a) What are the units of the coefficient (0.104) shown in the model?

(b) What is the oscillation period in units of seconds of a cylinder that is 4-inches tall?

(c) If the oscillation period is 45 seconds, what is the height of the cylinder in units of inches?

(d) We will conduct a series of tests with a new plastic (polystretchypropylene) that has a specific gravity of 0.6. What is the specific gravity of the fluid?

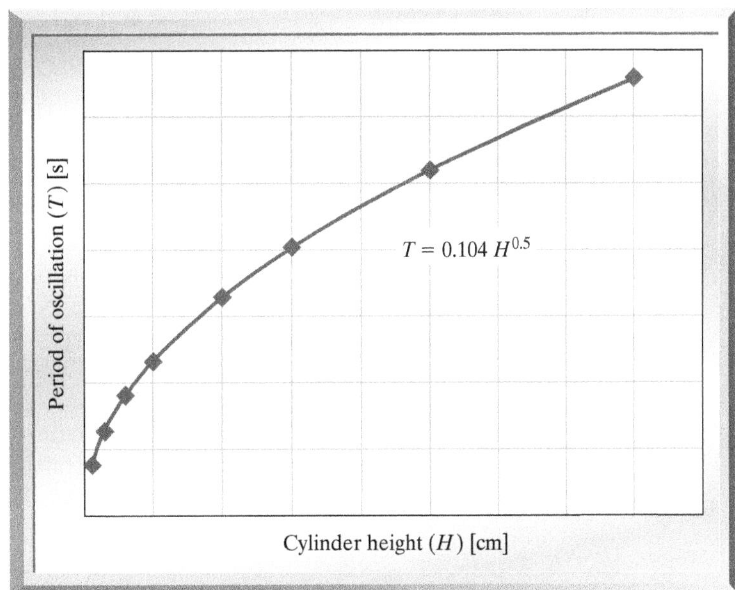

(e) We will conduct a series of tests with cylinders that have a specific gravity of 0.9. What is the density of the fluid in units of kilograms per cubic meter?

(f) Assume the tests were conducted using citric acid as the fluid, which has a specific gravity of 1.67. What is the specific gravity of the material of the cylinder?

(g) Assume the tests were conducted using acetone as the fluid, which has a specific gravity of 0.785. What is the density of the material of the cylinder in units of grams per cubic centimeter?

19. Experiments have shown that the visible flame from the back of a rocket can be estimated from the simple equation:

$$L = \sqrt{\frac{F}{f}}$$

where L is the flame length in feet, F is the thrust of the rocket in pounds-force, and f is an empirical factor found through experimentation.

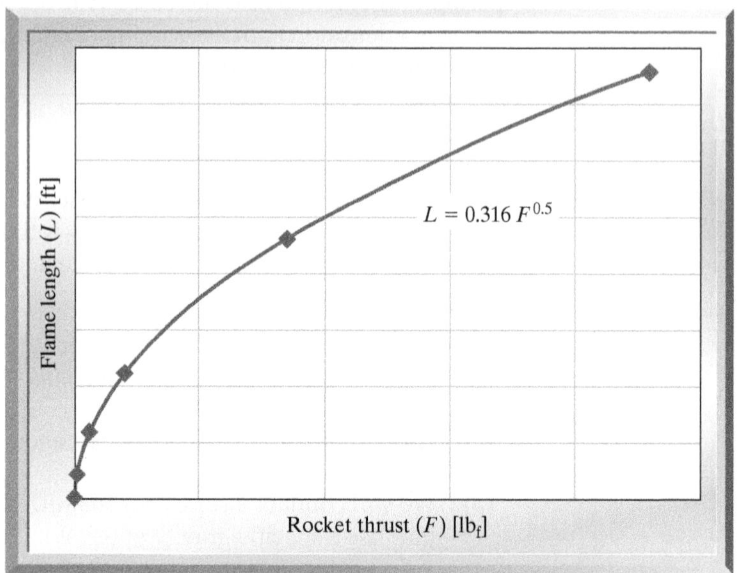

(a) What are the value and units of the factor f?
(b) If a rocket has visible flame of 30 meters, what is an estimate of the thrust in units of pounds-force?
(c) The empirical factor (f) shown is specific for the units system used in the figure. What should the value of the empirical factor (f) be if we wish to use the units of meters for length and newtons for the thrust?

20. One of the NAE Grand Challenges for Engineering is **Engineering the Tools of Scientific Discovery**. According to the NAE website: "Grand experiments and missions of exploration always need engineering expertise to design the tools, instruments, and systems that make it possible to acquire new knowledge about the physical and biological worlds."

Solar sails are a means of interplanetary propulsion using the radiation pressure of the sun to accelerate a spacecraft. The table below shows the radiation pressure at the orbits of several planets.

Planet	Distance from Sun (d) [AU]	Radiation Pressure (P) [mPa]
Mercury	0.46	43.3
Venus	0.72	17.7
Earth	1	9.15
Mars	1.5	3.96
Jupiter	5.2	0.34

NOTE

The astronomical unit (AU) is the average distance from the Earth to the Sun.

(a) Plot this data and determine the power law model for radiation pressure as a function of distance from the sun.
(b) What are the units of the exponent in the trendline?
(c) What are the units of the other constant in the trendline?
(d) What is the radiation pressure at Uranus (19.2 AU from sun)?
(e) At what distance from the sun is the radiation pressure 5 μPa?

21. The data shown graphically below was collected during testing of an electromagnetic mass driver. The energy to energize the electromagnets was obtained from a bank of capacitors. The capacitor bank was charged to various voltages, and for each voltage, the exit velocity of the projectile was measured when the mass driver was activated.

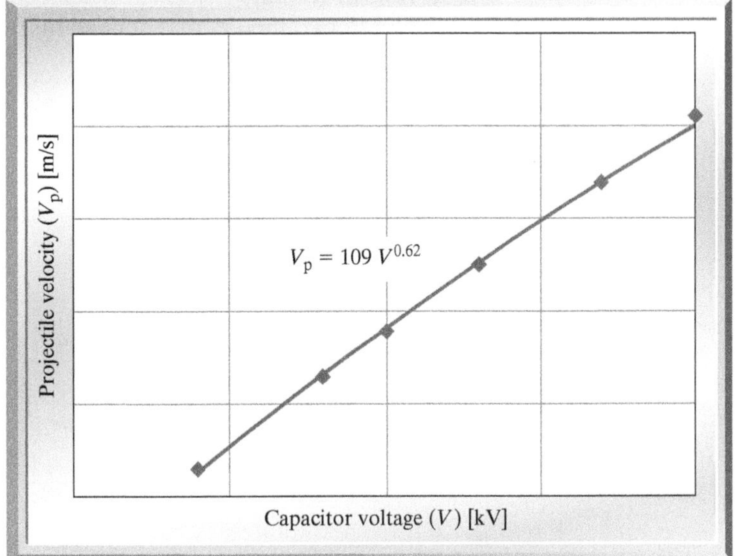

NOTE

Due to several complicated non-linear losses in the system that are far beyond the scope of this course, this is a case of a power model in which the exponent does not come out to be an integer or simple fraction, so rounding to two significant figures is appropriate. In fact, this model is only a first approximation—a really accurate model would be considerably more complicated.

(a) What would the velocity be if the capacitors were charged to 1,000 volts?
(b) What would the velocity be if the capacitors were charged to 100,000 volts?
(c) What voltage would be necessary to accelerate the projectile to 1,000 meters per second?
(d) Assume that the total capacitance is 5 farads. If the capacitors are initially charged to 10,000 volts and are discharged to 2,000 volts during the launch of a projectile, what is the mass of the projectile if the overall conversion of energy stored in the capacitors to kinetic energy in the projectile has an efficiency of 0.2? Recall that the energy stored in a capacitor is given by $E = 0.5\ CV^2$, where C is capacitance in farads and V is voltage in volts.
(e) Assuming that the capacitors are initially charged to 10,000 volts and are discharged to 2,000 volts during the launch of a projectile, what is the total capacitance in farads if the projectile has a mass of 500 grams and the overall conversion of energy stored in the capacitors to kinetic energy in the projectile has an efficiency of 0.25?
(f) Assume the capacitors are discharged to 20% of their initial voltage when a projectile is launched. Is the energy conversion efficiency a constant, or does it depend on the initial capacitor voltage? If efficiency depends on initial capacitor voltage, determine a mathematical model for efficiency (η) as a function of voltage.

22. The Ramberg–Osgood Relationship can be used to describe the relationship between stress and strain in a material near its yield strength—that is when the stress on the material is great enough to cause it to permanently deform.

This relationship is given by

$$\varepsilon = \frac{\sigma}{E} + \alpha \frac{\sigma_0}{E}\left(\frac{\sigma}{\sigma_0}\right)^n$$

where

σ is the strain [dimensionless]
ε is the stress [pascals]
σ_0 is the yield strength [pascals]
E is Young's modulus
α and n are parameters that depend on the material.

A graph of the stress/strain relationship for an aluminum bar is shown below.

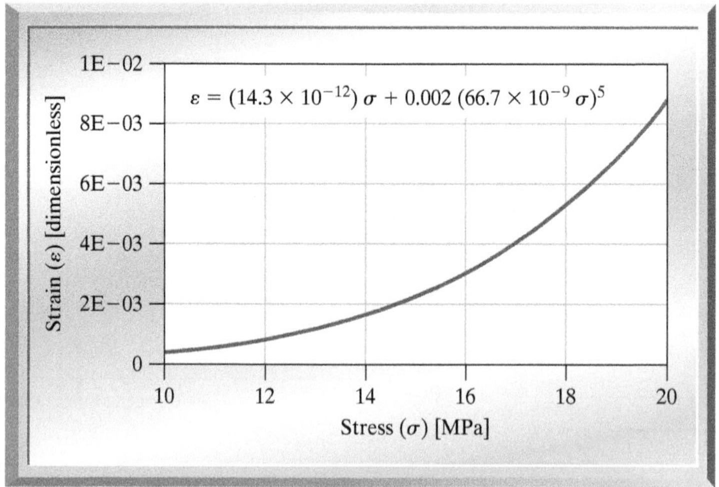

(a) What is Young's Modulus (E) for this aluminum bar? Be sure to include units with an appropriate metric prefix.
(b) What is the yield strength (σ_0) for this aluminum bar? Be sure to include units with an appropriate metric prefix.
(c) What is the value of the parameter n and its dimensions?
(d) What is the value of the parameter α and its dimensions?

If we can measure a length reliably to several millimeters, it seems reasonable that the longer a beam, the smaller would be the percentage error in length measurement. To test this hypothesis, we measure beams of differing lengths. The results are given in the figure.

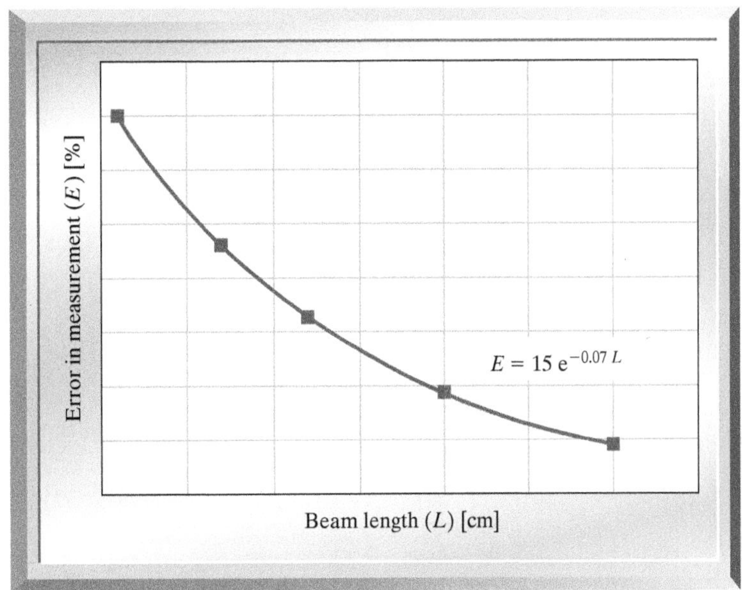

(e) What are the value and units of the coefficients in your model?

(f) How much error would you expect to have if you measured a beam that was 2 meters long?

(g) How long would a beam have to be to have a measurement error of less than 1%?

(h) Rewrite the model assuming that the measuring apparatus gives lengths in inches.

23. The total quantity (mass) of a radioactive substance decreases (decays) with time as

$$m = m_0 e^{-\frac{t}{\tau}}$$

where

t = time
τ = time constant
m_0 = initial mass (at $t = 0$)
m = mass at time t

A few milligrams each of three different isotopes of uranium were assayed for isotopic composition over a period of several days to determine the decay rate of each. The data was graphed and a mathematical model derived to describe the decay of each isotope.

(a) What are the units of τ if time is measured in days?

(b) What is the initial amount of each isotope at $t = 0$?

(c) How many days are required for only 1 milligram of the original isotope to remain in each sample?

(d) How many days are required for 99.99% of the original isotope in each sample to decay?

(e) What is the half-life, $T_{1/2}$, of each isotope? Half-life is the time required for half of the mass to decay into a different isotope.

(f) Four isotopes of uranium are shown in the table with their half-lives. Which isotope most likely matches each of the three samples?

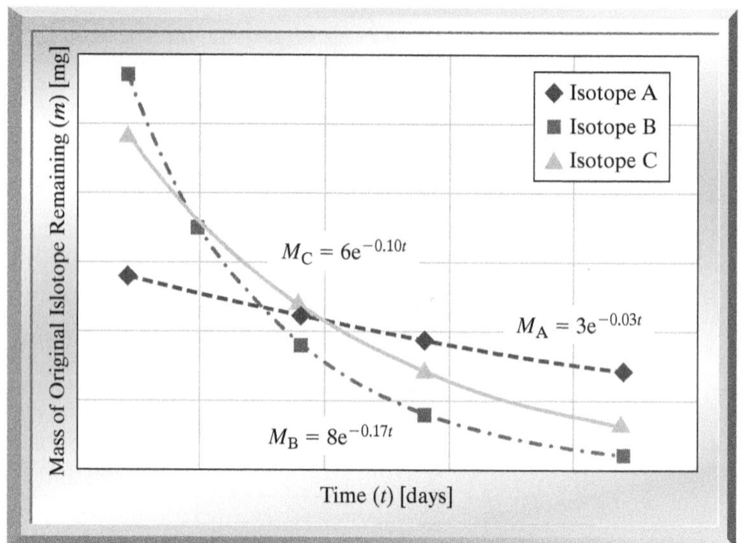

Isotope	Half-life [days]
230U	20.8
231U	4.2
237U	6.75
240U	0.59

24. When volunteers build a Habitat for Humanity house, it is found that the more houses that are completed, the faster each one can be finished since the volunteers become better trained and more efficient. A model that relates the building time and the number of homes completed can generally be given by

$$t = t_0 \, e^{-N/\nu} + t_M$$

where

t = time required to construct one house [days]

t_0 = a constant related to (but not equal) the time required to build the first house

N = the number of houses built previously [dimensionless]

ν = a constant related to the decrease in construction time as N increases

t_M = another constant related to construction time

A team of volunteers has built several houses, and their construction time was recorded for four of those houses. The construction time was then plotted as a function of number of previously built houses and a mathematical model derived as shown below. Using this information, answer the following questions:

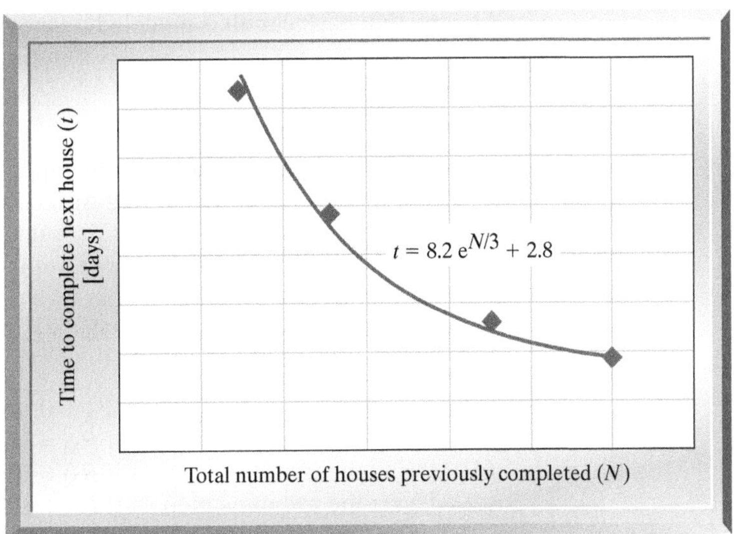

(a) What are the units of the constants 8.2, 3, and 2.8?
(b) If the same group continues building houses, what is the minimum time to construct one house that they can expect to achieve?
(c) How long did it take for them to construct the first house?
(d) How much quicker [days] was the third house built compared to the second?
(e) How many days (total) were required to build the first five houses?

25. As part of an electronic music synthesizer, you need to build a gizmo to convert a linear voltage to an exponentially related current. You build three prototype circuits, make several measurements of voltage and current in each, and graph the results as shown below.

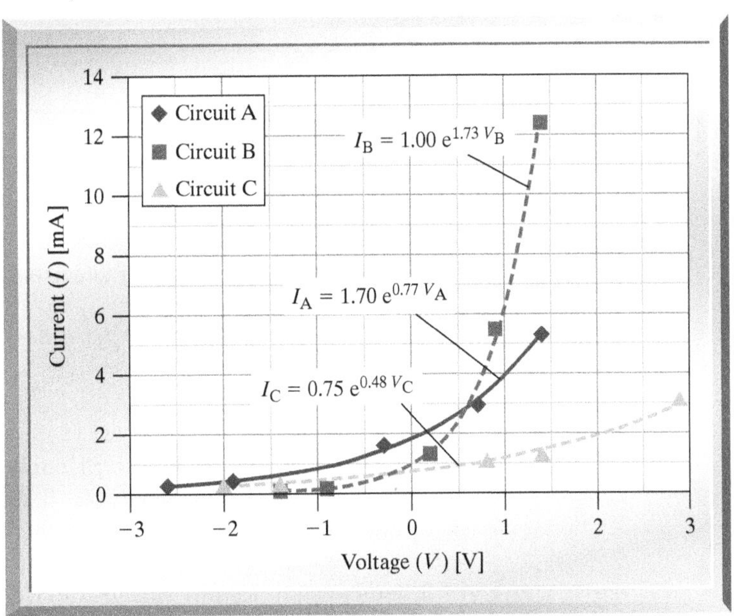

Assume that each circuit is modeled by the equation

$$I_X = A_X e^{(R_M/(R_X V_T))^{V_X}}$$

where

I_X is the current in circuit X [milliamperers, mA]
A_X is a scaling factor associated with circuit X
R_M is a master resistor, and has the same value in all circuits [ohms, Ω]
R_X is a resistor in circuit X whose value is different in each circuit [ohms, Ω]
V_T is the thermal voltage, and has a value of 25.7 volts
V_X is the voltage in circuit X [volts, V]

(a) What are the units of A_X?
(b) If you wish $I_X = 1$ mA when $V_X = 0$, what should the value of A_X be?
(c) Using the trendline models, if $R_M = 10$ kΩ, what is the value of R_A?
(d) Using the trendline models, if $R_M = 10$ kΩ, what is the value of R_B?
(e) Using the trendline models, if $R_M = 10$ kΩ, what is the value of R_C?

26. The graph below shows the relationship between current and voltage in a 1N4148 small signal diode (a semiconductor device that allows current to flow in one direction but not the other).

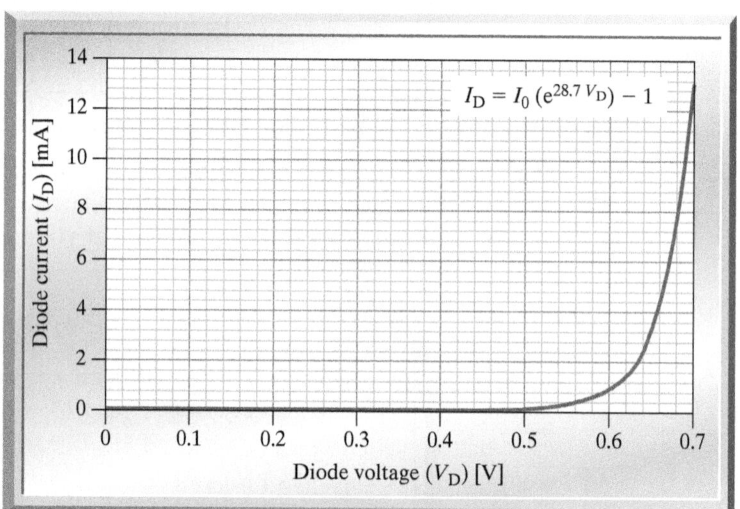

Semiconductor diodes can be characterized by the Shockley Equation:

$$I_D = I_0\left(e^{\frac{qV_D}{nkt}} - 1\right)$$

where

I_D is the diode current [amperes]
I_0 is the reverse saturation current, constant for any specific diode
q is the charge on a single electron, $\times 10^{-19}$ coulombs
V_D is the voltage across the diode [volts]
n is the emission coefficient, having a numerical value typically between 1 and 2, and constant for any specific device.
k is Boltzmann's Constant, 1.381×10^{-23} joules per kelvin
T is the temperature of the device [kelvin]

(a) What are the units of the −1 following the exponential term? Justify your answer.

(b) If the device temperature is 100 degrees Fahrenheit, what are the units of the emission coefficient, n, and what is its numerical value? (*Hint:* Electrical power [W] equals a volt times an ampere: P = VI. One ampere equals one coulomb per second.)

(c) What is the numerical value and units of the reverse saturation current, I_0? Use an appropriate metric prefix in your final answer.

27. Essentially all manufactured items are made to some "tolerance," or how close the actual product is to the nominal specifications. For example, if a company manufactures hammers, one customer might specify that the hammers should weigh 16 ounces. With rounding, this means that the actual weight of each hammer meets the specification if it weighs between 15.5 and 16.5 ounces. Such a hammer might cost 10 dollars. However, if the U.S. military, in its quest for perfection, specifies that an essentially identical hammer should have a weight of 16.000 ounces, then in order to meet specifications, the hammer must weigh between 15.9995 and 16.0005 ounces. In other words, the weight must fall within a range of one-thousandth of an ounce. Such a hammer might cost $1,000.

You have purchased a "grab bag" of 100 supposedly identical capacitors. You got a really good price, but there are no markings on the capacitors. All you know is that they are all the same nominal value. You wish to discover not only the nominal value, but the tolerance: are they within 5% of the nominal value, or within 20%? You set up a simple circuit with a known resistor and each of the unknown capacitors. You charge each capacitor to 10 volts, and then use an oscilloscope to time how long it takes for each capacitor to discharge to 2 volts. In a simple RC (resistor–capacitor) circuit, the voltage (V_C) across a capacitor (C) discharging through a resistor (R) is given by:

$$V_C = V_0 e^{-t/RC}$$

where t is time in seconds and V_0 is the initial voltage across the capacitor.

After measuring the time for each capacitor to discharge to from 10 to 2 V, you scan the list of times, and find the fastest and slowest. Since the resistor is the same in all cases, the fastest time corresponds to the smallest capacitor in the lot, and the slowest time to the largest. The fastest time was 3.3 microseconds and the slowest was 3.7 microseconds. For the two capacitors, you have the two pairs of data points.

(a) Plot these points in Excel, the pair for C1 and the pair for C2, on the same graph, using time as the independent variable. Fit exponential trendines to the data.

Time for C_1 (s)	Voltage of C_1
0	10
3.3×10^{-6}	2

Time for C_2 (s)	Voltage of C_2
0	10
3.7×10^{-6}	2

(b) Referring to the known form of the response, explain why the faster time corresponded to the smaller capacitor.

(c) The trendline for each capacitor had an R_2 value of 1, a perfect fit of trendline to data. Explain why this happened.

(d) Assuming you chose a precision resistor for these measurements that had a value of R = 1,000.0 ohms, determine the capacitance of the largest and smallest capacitors.

(e) You selected the fastest and slowest discharge times from a set of 100 samples. Since you had a fairly large sample set, it is not a bad assumption, according to the Laws of Large Numbers, that these two selected data sets represent capacitors near the lower and higher end of the range of values within the tolerance of the devices. Assuming the nominal value is the average of the minimum and maximum allowable values, what is the nominal value of the set of capacitors?

(f) What is the tolerance, in percent, of these devices? As an example, if a nominal 1 μF (microfarad) capacitor had an allowable range of $0.95\ \mu F < C < 1.05\ \mu F$, the tolerance would be 5%.

If standard tolerances of capacitors are 5%, 10%, and 20%, to which of the standard tolerances do you think these capacitors were manufactured? If you pick a smaller tolerance than you calculated, justify your selection. If you picked a higher tolerance, explain why the tolerance is so much larger than the measured value.

CHAPTER 14
ABOUT MATLAB

Objectives

By learning the material in this chapter, you should be able to

- understand what MATLAB is and why it is widely used in engineering and science
- understand the advantages and limitations of the student edition of MATLAB
- formulate problems by using a structured problem-solving approach

14.1 WHAT IS MATLAB?

MATLAB is one of a number of commercially available, sophisticated mathematical computation tools, which also include Maple, Mathematica, and MathCad. Despite what proponents may claim, no single one of these tools is "the best." Each has strengths and weaknesses. Each allows you to perform basic mathematical computations. They differ in the way they handle symbolic calculations and more complicated mathematical processes, such as matrix manipulation. For example, MATLAB (short for **Mat**rix **Lab**oratory) excels at computations involving matrices, whereas Maple excels at symbolic calculations. At a fundamental level, you can think of these programs as sophisticated computer-based calculators. They can perform the same functions as your scientific calculator—and **many more**. If you have a computer on your desk, you may find yourself using MATLAB instead of your calculator for even the simplest mathematical applications—for example, balancing your checkbook. In many engineering classes, the use of programs such as MATLAB to perform computations is replacing more traditional computer programming. Although programs such as MATLAB have become a standard tool for engineers and scientists this doesn't mean that you shouldn't learn a high-level language such as C++ or FORTRAN.

Because MATLAB is so easy to use, you can perform many programming tasks with it, but it isn't always the best tool for a programming task. It excels at numerical calculations—especially matrix calculations—and graphics, but you wouldn't want to use it to write a word-processing program. For large applications, such as operating systems or design software, C++ and FORTRAN would be the programs of choice. (In fact, MATLAB, which *is* a large application program, was originally written in FORTRAN and later rewritten in C, a precursor of C++.) Usually, high-level programs do not offer easy access to graphing—an application at which MATLAB excels. The primary area of overlap between MATLAB and high-level programs is "number crunching"—repetitive calculations or the processing of large quantities of data. Both MATLAB and high-level programs are good at processing numbers. A "number-crunching" program is generally

Taken from *MATLAB® for Engineers,* Second Edition, by Holly Moore.

Key Idea: MATLAB is optimized for matrix calculations

easier to write in MATLAB, but usually it will execute faster in C++ or FORTRAN. The one exception to this rule is calculations involving matrices. MATLAB is optimized for matrices. Thus, if a problem can be formulated with a matrix solution, MATLAB executes substantially faster than a similar program in a high-level language.

MATLAB is available in both a professional and a student version. The professional version is probably installed in your college or university computer laboratory, but you may enjoy having the student version at home. MATLAB is updated regularly; this textbook is based on MATLAB 7.5. If you are using MATLAB 6, you may notice some minor differences between it and MATLAB 7.5. There are substantial differences in versions that predate MATLAB 5.5.

The standard installation of the professional version of MATLAB is capable of solving a wide variety of technical problems. Additional capability is available in the form of function toolboxes. These toolboxes are purchased separately, and they may or may not be available to you. You can find a complete list of the MATLAB product family at The MathWorks web site, www.mathworks.com.

14.2 HOW IS MATLAB USED IN INDUSTRY?

The ability to use tools such as MATLAB is quickly becoming a requirement for many engineering positions. A recent job search on Monster.com found the following advertisement:

> *... is looking for a System Test Engineer with Avionics experience.... Responsibilities include modification of MATLAB scripts, execution of Simulink simulations, and analysis of the results data. Candidate MUST be very familiar with MATLAB, Simulink, and C++ ....*

Key Idea: MATLAB is widely used in engineering

This ad isn't unusual. The same search turned up 75 different companies that specifically required MATLAB skills for entry-level engineers. Widely used in all engineering and science fields, MATLAB is particularly popular for electrical engineering applications. The sections that follow outline a few of the many applications currently using MATLAB.

14.2.1 Electrical Engineering

MATLAB is used extensively in electrical engineering for signal-processing applications. For example, Figure 14.1 includes several images created during a research program at the University of Utah to simulate collision-detection algorithms used by the housefly (and adapted to silicon sensors in the laboratory). The research resulted in the

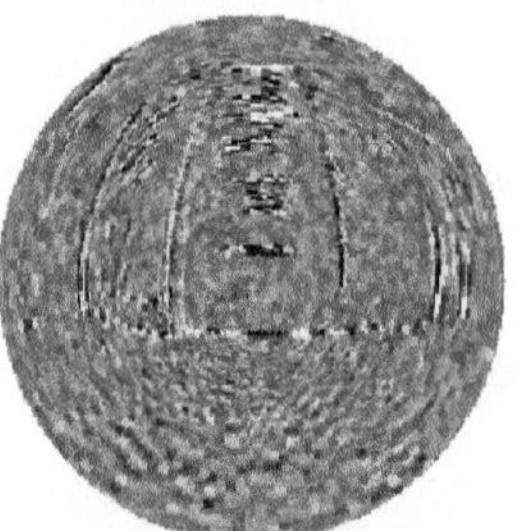
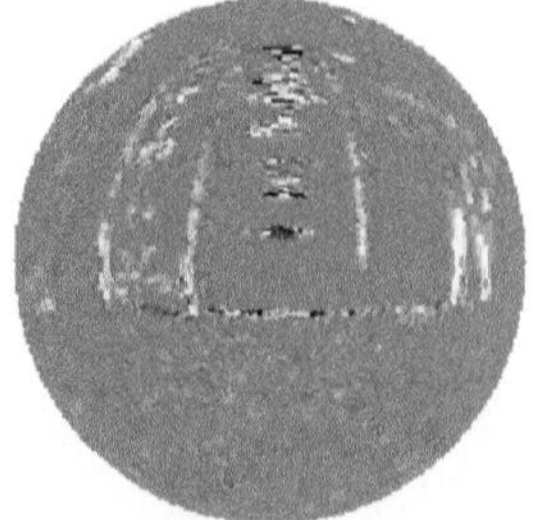

Figure 14.1 Image processing using a fisheye lens camera to simulate the visual system of a housefly's brain.

(Used by permission of Dr. Reid Harrison, University of Utah.)

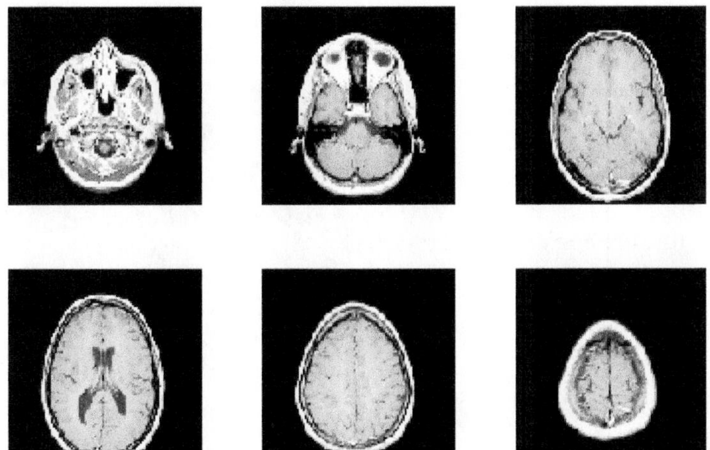

Figure 14.2 Horizontal slices through the brain, based on the sample data file included with MATLAB.

design and manufacture of a computer chip that detects imminent collisions. This has potential use in the design of autonomous robots using vision for navigation and especially in automobile safety applications.

14.2.2 Biomedical Engineering

Medical images are usually saved as dicom files (the Digital Imaging and Communications in Medicine standard). Dicom files use the file extension .dcm. The MathWorks offers an Image Processing Toolbox that can read these files, making their data available to MATLAB. (The Image Processing Toolbox is included with the student edition and is optional with the professional edition.) The Image Processing Toolbox also includes a wide range of functions, many of them especially appropriate for medical imaging. A limited MRI data set that has already been converted to a format compatible with MATLAB ships with the standard MATLAB program. This data set allows you to try out some of the imaging functions available both with the standard MATLAB installation and with the expanded imaging toolbox, if you have it installed on your computer. Figure 14.2 shows six images of horizontal slices through the brain based on the MRI data set.

The same data set can be used to construct a three-dimensional image, such as either of those shown in Figure 14.3. Detailed instructions on how to create these images are included in the MATLAB **help** tutorial.

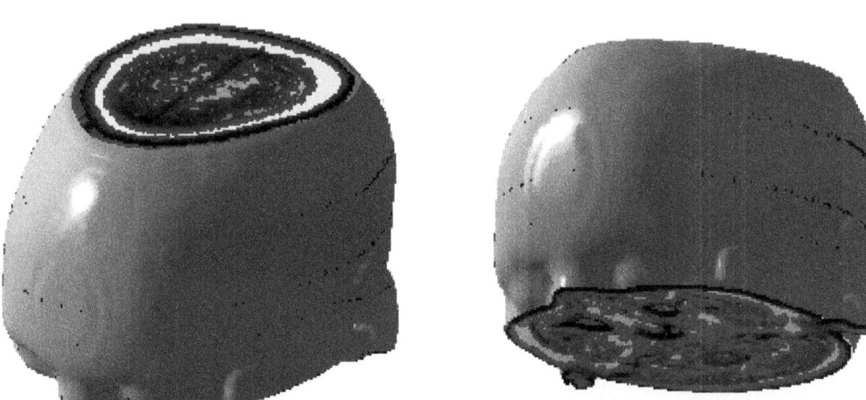

Figure 14.3 Three-dimensional visualization of MRI data, based on the sample data set included with MATLAB.

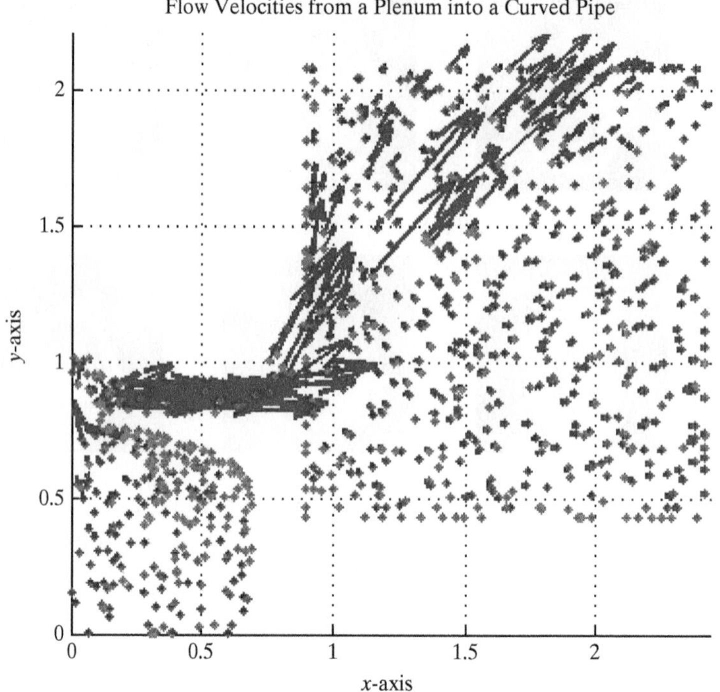

Figure 14.4 Quiver plot of gas behavior in a thrust vector control device.

14.2.3 Fluid Dynamics

Calculations describing fluid velocities (speeds and directions) are important in a number of different fields. Aerospace engineers in particular are interested in the behavior of gases, both outside an aircraft or space vehicle and inside the combustion chambers. Visualizing the three-dimensional behavior of fluids is tricky, but MATLAB offers a number of tools that make it easier. In Figure 14.4, the flow-field calculation results for a thrust-vector control device are represented as a quiver plot. Thrust-vector control is the process of changing the direction in which a nozzle points (and hence the direction a rocket travels) by pushing on an actuator (a piston-cylinder device). The model in the figure represents a high-pressure reservoir of gas (a plenum) that eventually feeds into the piston and thus controls the length of the actuator.

14.3 PROBLEM SOLVING IN ENGINEERING AND SCIENCE

Key Idea: Always use a systematic problem-solving strategy

A consistent approach to solving technical problems is important throughout engineering, science, and computer programming disciplines. The approach we outline here is useful in courses as diverse as chemistry, physics, thermodynamics, and engineering design. It also applies to the social sciences, such as economics and sociology. Different authors may formulate their problem-solving schemes differently, but they all have the same basic format:

- **State the problem.**
  - Drawing a picture is often helpful in this step.
  - If you do not have a clear understanding of the problem, you are not likely to be able to solve it.

- **Describe the input** values (knowns) **and** the required **outputs** (unknowns).
  - Be careful to include units as you describe the input and output values. Sloppy handling of units often leads to wrong answers.
  - Identify constants you may need in the calculation, such as the ideal-gas constant and the acceleration due to gravity.
  - If appropriate, label a sketch with the values you have identified, or group them into a table.
- Develop an algorithm to solve the problem. In computer applications, this can often be accomplished with a **hand example**. You'll need to
  - Identify any equations relating the knowns and unknowns.
  - Work through a simplified version of the problem by hand or with a calculator.
- **Solve** the problem. In this book, this step involves creating a **MATLAB solution**.
- **Test the solution.**
  - Do your results make sense physically?
  - Do they match your sample calculations?
  - Is your answer really what was asked for?
  - Graphs are often useful ways to check your calculations for reasonableness.

If you consistently use a structured problem-solving approach, such as the one just outlined, you'll find that "story" problems become much easier to solve. Example 14.1 illustrates this problem-solving strategy.

EXAMPLE 14.1

The Conversion of Matter to Energy

Albert Einstein (see Figure 14.5) is arguably the most famous physicist of the 20th century. Einstein was born in Germany in 1879 and attended school in both Germany and Switzerland. While working as a patent clerk in Bern, he developed his famous theory of relativity. Perhaps the best-known physics equation today is his:

$$E = mc^2$$

Figure 14.5 Albert Einstein (Courtesy of the Library of Congress, LC-USZ62-60242).

This astonishingly simple equation links the previously separate worlds of matter and energy and can be used to find the amount of energy released as matter is changed in form in both natural and human-made nuclear reactions.

The sun radiates 385×10^{24} J/s of energy, all of which is generated by nuclear reactions converting matter to energy. Use MATLAB and Einstein's equation to determine how much matter must be converted to energy to produce this much radiation in one day.

1. State the Problem
   Find the amount of matter necessary to produce the amount of energy radiated by the sun every day.
2. Describe the Input and Output

   Input

   Energy: $E = 385 \times 10^{24}$ J/s, which must be converted into the total energy radiated during one day

   Speed of light: $c = 3.0 \times 10^8$ m/s

   Output

   Mass m in kg
3. Develop a Hand Example
   The energy radiated in one day is

   $$385 \times 10^{24}\frac{\text{J}}{\text{s}} \times 3600\frac{\text{s}}{\text{hour}} \times 24\frac{\text{hours}}{\text{day}} \times 1 \text{ day} = 3.33 \times 10^{31} \text{ J}$$

   The equation $E = mc^2$ must be solved for m and the values for E and c substituted. We have

   $$m = \frac{E}{c^2}$$

   $$m = \frac{3.33 \times 10^{31} \text{ J}}{(3.0 \times 10^8 \text{ m/s})^2}$$

   $$= 3.7 \times 10^{14}\frac{\text{J}}{\text{m}^2/\text{s}^2}$$

   We can see from the output criteria that we want the mass in kg, so what went wrong? We need to do one more unit conversion:

   $$1 \text{ J} = 1 \text{ kg m}^2/\text{s}^2$$

   $$= 3.7 \times 10^{14}\frac{\text{kg m}^2/\text{s}^2}{\text{m}^2/\text{s}^2} = 3.7 \times 10^{14} \text{ kg}$$

4. Develop a MATLAB Solution
   At this point, you have not learned how to create MATLAB code. However, you should be able to see from the following sample code that MATLAB syntax is similar to that used in most algebraic scientific calculators. MATLAB commands are entered at the prompt (**>>**), and the results are reported on the next line. The code is as follows:

```
>> E=385e24
E =
  3.8500e+026
>> E=E*3600*24
E =
  3.3264e+031
>> c=3e8
```

```
c =
  300000000
>> m=E/c^2
m =
  3.6960e+014
```

From this point on, we will not show the prompt when describing interactions in the command window.

5. Test the Solution
The MATLAB solution matches the hand calculation, but do the numbers make sense? Anything times 10^{14} is a really large number. Consider, however, that the mass of the sun is 2×10^{30} kg. We can calculate how long it would take to consume the mass of the sun completely at a rate of 3.7×10^{14} kg/day. We have

$$\text{time} = (\text{mass of the sun})/(\text{rate of consumption})$$

$$\text{time} = \frac{2 \times 10^{30}\ \text{kg}}{3.7 \times 10^{14}\ \text{kg/day}} \times \frac{\text{year}}{365\ \text{days}} = 1.5 \times 10^{13}\ \text{years}$$

That's 15 trillion years! We don't need to worry about the sun running out of matter to convert to energy in our lifetimes.

CHAPTER 15
MATLAB ENVIRONMENT

Objectives

By learning the material in this chapter, you should be able to

- start the MATLAB program and solve simple problems in the command window
- understand MATLAB's use of matrices
- identify and use the various MATLAB windows
- define and use simple matrices
- name and use variables
- understand the order of operations in MATLAB
- understand the difference between scalar, array, and matrix calculations in MATLAB
- express numbers in either floating-point or scientific notation
- adjust the format used to display numbers in the command window
- save the value of variables used in a MATLAB session
- save a series of commands in an M-file

15.1 GETTING STARTED

Using MATLAB for the first time is easy; mastering it can take years. In this chapter, we'll introduce you to the MATLAB environment and show you how to perform basic mathematical computations. After reading this chapter, you should be able to start using MATLAB for homework assignments or on the job. Of course, you'll be able to do more things as you complete the rest of the chapters.

Because the procedure for installing MATLAB depends upon your operating system and your computing environment, we'll assume that you have already installed MATLAB on your computer or that you are working in a computing laboratory with MATLAB already installed. To start MATLAB in either the Windows or Apple environment, click on the icon on the desktop, or use the start menu to find the program. In the UNIX environment, type **Matlab** at the shell prompt. No matter how you start it, once MATLAB opens, you should see the MATLAB prompt (**>>** or **EDU>>**), which tells you that MATLAB is ready for you to enter a command. When you've finished your MATLAB session, you can exit MATLAB by typing **quit** or **exit** at the MATLAB prompt. MATLAB also uses the standard Windows menu bar, so you can exit the program by choosing **EXIT MATLAB** from the File menu or by selecting the close icon (**x**) at the upper right-hand corner of the screen. The default MATLAB screen, which opens each time you start the program, is shown in Figure 15.1.

Taken from *MATLAB® for Engineers*, Second Edition, by Holly Moore.

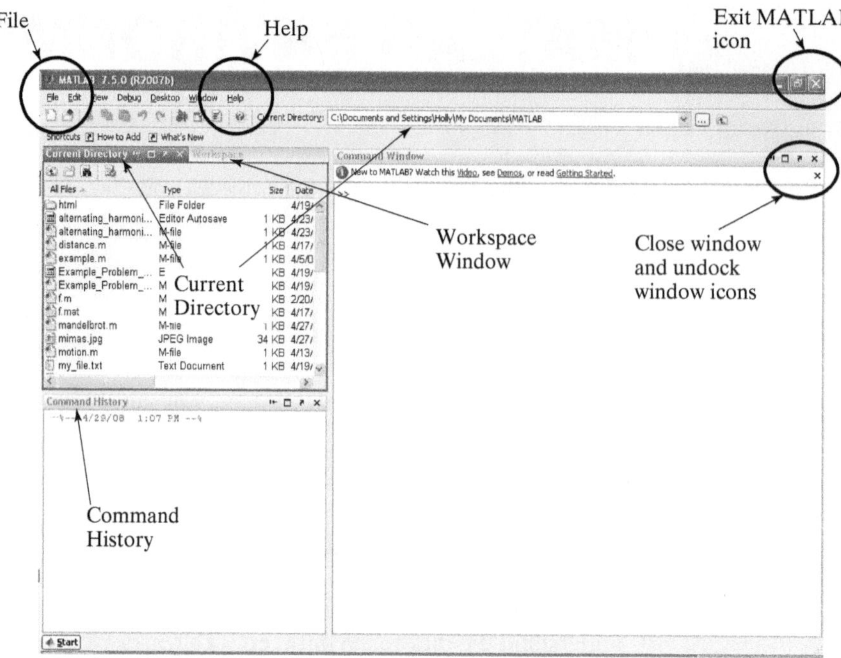

Figure 15.1 MATLAB opening window. The MATLAB environment consists of a number of windows, four of which open in the default view. Others open as needed during a MATLAB session.

To start using MATLAB, you need be concerned only with the command window (on the right of the screen). You can perform calculations in the command window in a manner similar to the way you perform calculations on a scientific calculator. Even most of the syntax is the same. For example, to compute the value of 5 squared, type the command

```
5^2
```

The following output will be displayed:

```
ans =
           25
```

Or, to find the value of type

```
cos(pi)
```

which results in the output

```
ans =
    -1
```

Key Idea: MATLAB uses the standard algebraic rules for order of operation

MATLAB uses the standard algebraic rules for order of operation, which becomes important when you chain calculations together. These rules are discussed in Section 15.3.2. Notice that the value of pi is built into MATLAB, so you don't have to enter it yourself.

HINT

You may think some of the examples are too simple to type in yourself—that just reading the material is sufficient. However, you will remember the material better if you both read it and type it!

In-Class Activity

ICA 15-1

Type the following expressions into MATLAB at the command prompt, and observe the results:

1. 5 + 2
2. 5 * 2
3. 5/2
4. 3 + 2 * (4 + 3)
5. 2.54 * 8/2.6
6. 6.3 − 2.1045
7. 3.6^2
8. 1 + 2^2
9. sqrt(5)
10. cos(pi)

HINT

You may find it frustrating to learn that when you make a mistake, you can't just overwrite your command after you have executed it. This occurs because the command window is creating a list of all the commands you've entered. You can't "un-execute" a command, or "un-create" it. What you can do is enter the command correctly and then execute your new version. **MATLAB** offers several ways to make this easier for you. One way is to use the arrow keys, usually located on the right-hand side of your keyboard. The up arrow, ↑, allows you to move through the list of commands you have executed. Once you find the appropriate command, you can edit it and then execute your new version.

15.2 MATLAB WINDOWS

MATLAB uses several display windows. The default view, shown in Figure 15.1, includes on the right a large command window and, stacked on the left, the current directory, workspace, and command history windows. Notice the tabs at the top of the windows on the left; these tabs allow you to access the hidden windows. Older versions of MATLAB also included a launch pad window, which has been replaced by the start button in the lower left-hand corner. In addition, document windows, graphics windows, and editing windows will automatically open when needed. Each is described in the sections that follow. MATLAB also includes a built-in help function that can be accessed from the menu bar, as shown in Figure 15.1. To personalize your desktop, you can resize any of these windows, close the ones you aren't using with the close icon (the **x** in the upper right-hand corner of each window), or "undock" them with the undock icon, ↰, also located in the upper right-hand corner of each window.

15.2.1 Command Window

The command window is located in the right-hand pane of the default view of the MATLAB screen, as shown in Figure 15.1. The command window offers an

Key Idea: The command window is similar to a scratch pad

environment similar to a scratch pad. Using it allows you to save the values you calculate, but not the commands used to generate those values. If you want to save the command sequence, you'll need to use the editing window to create an **M-file**. M-files are described in Section 15.4.3. Both approaches are valuable. Before we introduce M-files, we will concentrate on using the command window.

15.2.2 Command History

Key Idea: The command history records all of the commands issued in the command window

The command history window records the commands you issued in the command window. When you exit MATLAB, or when you issue the **clc** command, the command window is cleared. However, the command history window retains a list of all your commands. You may clear the command history with the edit menu. If you work on a public computer, as a security precaution, MATLAB's defaults may be set to clear the history when you exit MATLAB. If you entered the earlier sample commands, notice that they are repeated in the command history window. This window is valuable for a number of reasons, among them that it allows you to review previous MATLAB sessions and that it can be used to transfer commands to the command window. For example, first clear the contents of the command window by typing

```
clc
```

This action clears the command window but leaves the data in the command history window intact. You can transfer any command from the command history window to the command window by double-clicking (which also executes the command) or by clicking and dragging the line of code into the command window. Try double-clicking

```
cos(pi)
```

in the command history window. The command is copied into the command window and executed. It should return

```
ans =
      -1
```

Now click and drag

```
5^2
```

from the command history window into the command window. The command won't execute until you hit Enter, and then you'll get the result:

```
ans =
      25
```

You'll find the command history useful as you perform more and more complicated calculations in the command window.

15.2.3 Workspace Window

Key Idea: The workspace window lists information describing all the variables created by the program

The workspace window keeps track of the variables you have defined as you execute commands in the command window. If you've been doing the examples, the workspace window should show just one variable, **ans**, and indicate that it has a value of 25 and is a double array:

Name	Value	Class
⊞ ans	25	double

(Your view of the workspace window may be slightly different, depending on how your installation of MATLAB is configured.)

Set the workspace window to show more about the displayed variables by right-clicking on the bar with the column labels. (This feature is new to MATLAB 7 and won't work if you have an older version.) Check **size** and **bytes**, in addition to **name**, **value**, and **class**. Your workspace window should now display the following information, although you may need to resize the window to see all the columns:

Name	Value	Size	Bytes	Class
⊞ ans	25	1 × 1	8	double

The yellow gridlike symbol indicates that the variable **ans** is an array. The size, 1 × 1, tells us that it is a single value (one row by one column) and therefore a scalar. The array uses 8 bytes of memory. MATLAB was written in C, and the class designation tells us that, in the C language, **ans** is a double-precision floating-point array. For our needs, it is enough to know that the variable **ans** can store a floating-point number (a number with a decimal point). Actually, MATLAB considers every number you enter to be a floating-point number, whether you insert a decimal point or not.

Key Idea: The default data type is double-precision floating-point numbers stored in a matrix

In addition to information about the size of the arrays and type of data stored in them, you can also choose to display statistical information about the data. Once again right click the bar in the workspace window that displays the column headings. Notice that you can select from a number of different statistical measures, such as the max, min, and standard deviation.

You can define additional variables in the command window, and they will be listed in the workspace window. For example, typing

```
A = 5
```

returns

```
A =
        5
```

Notice that the variable **A** has been added to the workspace window, which lists variables in alphabetical order. Variables beginning with capital letters are listed first, followed by variables starting with lowercase letters.

Name	Value	Size	Bytes	Class
⊞ A	5	1 × 1	8	double
⊞ ans	25	1 × 1	8	double

In Section 15.3.2 we will discuss in detail how to enter matrices into MATLAB. For now, you can enter a simple one-dimensional matrix by typing

```
B = [1, 2, 3, 4]
```

This command returns

```
B =
        1       2       3       4
```

The commas are optional; you'd get the same result with

```
B = [1  2  3  4]
B =
        1        2        3        4
```

Notice that the variable **B** has been added to the workspace window and that it is a 1 × 4 array:

Name	Value	Size	Bytes	Class
A	5	1 × 1	8	double
B	[1 2 3 4]	1 × 4	32	double
ans	25	1 × 1	8	double

You can define two-dimensional matrices in a similar fashion. Semicolons are used to separate rows. For example,

```
C = [ 1 2 3 4; 10 20 30 40; 5 10 15 20]
```

returns

```
C =
        1        2        3        4
        10       20       30       40
        5        10       15       20
```

Name	Value	Size	Bytes	Class
A	5	1 × 1	8	double
B	[1 2 3 4]	1 × 4	32	double
C	<3 × 4 double>	3 × 4	96	double
ans	25	1 × 1	8	double

Notice that **C** appears in the workspace window as a 3 × 4 matrix. To conserve space, the values stored in the matrix are not listed.

You can recall the values for any variable by typing in the variable name. For example, entering

```
A
```

returns

```
A =
        5
```

Although the only variables we have introduced are matrices containing numbers, other types of variables are possible.

In describing the command window, we introduced the **clc** command. This command clears the command window, leaving a blank page for you to work on. However, it does not delete from memory the actual variables you have created. The **clear** command deletes all of the saved variables. The action of the **clear** command is reflected in the workspace window. Try it out by typing

```
clear
```

in the command window. The workspace window is now empty:

Name	Value	Size	Bytes	Class

If you suppress the workspace window (closing it either from the file menu or with the close icon in the upper right-hand corner of the window), you can still find out which variables have been defined by using the **whos** command:

whos

If executed before we entered the **clear** command, **whos** would have returned

Name	Size	Bytes	Class
A	1x1	8	double
B	1x4	32	double
C	3x4	96	double
ans	1x1	8	double

15.2.4 Current Directory Window

The current directory window lists all the files in a computer folder called the current directory. When MATLAB either accesses files or saves information, it uses the current directory unless told differently. The default for the location of the current directory varies with your version of the software and the way it was installed. However, the current directory is listed at the top of the main window. The current directory can be changed by selecting another directory from the drop-down list located next to the directory listing or by browsing through your computer files. Browsing is performed with the browse button, located next to the drop-down list. (See Figure 15.2.)

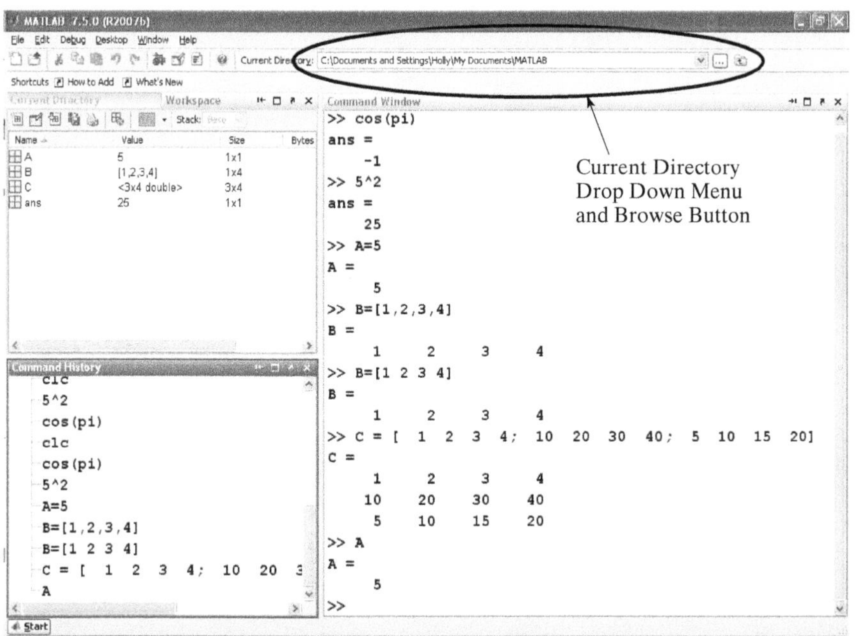

Figure 15.2 The ***Current Directory Window*** lists all the files in the current directory. You can change the current directory by using the drop-down menu or the browse button.

15.2.5 Document Window

Double-clicking on any variable listed in the workspace window automatically launches a document window, containing the **array editor**. Values stored in the variable are displayed in a spreadsheet format. You can change values in the array editor, or you can add new values. For example, if you haven't already entered the two-dimensional matrix C, enter the following command in the command window:

```
C = [ 1 2 3 4; 10 20 30 40; 5 10 15 20];
```

> ***Key Idea:***
> A semicolon suppresses the output from commands issued in the command window

Placing a semicolon at the end of the command suppresses the output, so that it is not repeated in the command window. However, **C** should now be listed in the workspace window. If you double-click on it, a document window will open above the command window, as shown in Figure 15.3. You can now add more values to the **C** matrix or change existing values.

The document window/array editor can also be used in conjunction with the workspace window to create entirely new arrays. Run your mouse slowly over the icons in the shortcut bar at the top of the workspace window. If you are patient, you should see the function of each icon appear. The new variable icon looks like a grid with a large asterisk behind it. Select the new variable icon, and a new variable called **unnamed** should appear on the variable list. You can change its name by right-clicking and selecting **rename** from the pop-up menu. To add values to this new variable, double-click on it and add your data from the array editor window. The new variable button is a new feature in MATLAB 7; if you are using an older version, you won't be able to create variables this way.

When you are finished creating new variables, close the array editor by selecting the close window icon in the upper right-hand corner of the window.

15.2.6 Graphics Window

The graphics window launches automatically when you request a graph. To demonstrate this feature, first create an array of x values:

```
x = [ 1 2 3 4 5];
```

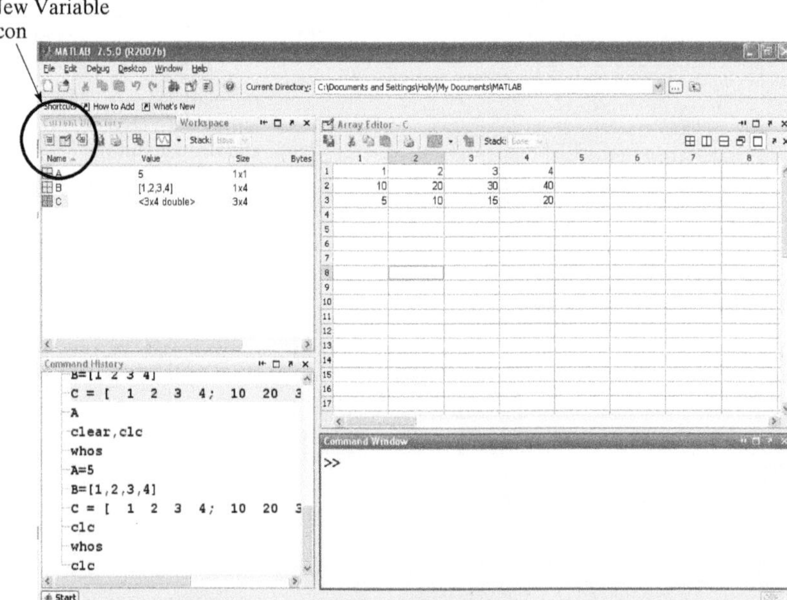

Figure 15.3 The ***Document Window*** displays the **Array Editor.**

(Remember, the semicolon suppresses the output from this command; however, a new variable, x, appears in the workspace window.)

Now create a list of y values:

```
y = [10 20 30 40 50];
```

To create a graph, use the plot command:

```
plot(x,y)
```

Key Idea: Always add a title and axis labels to graphs

The graphics window opens automatically. (See Figure 15.4.) Notice that a new window label appears on the task bar at the bottom of the windows screen. It will be titled either **<Student Version> Figure...** or simply **Figure 1**, depending on whether you are using the student or professional version, respectively, of the software. Any additional graphs you create will overwrite Figure 1, unless you specifically command MATLAB to open a new graphics window.

MATLAB makes it easy to modify graphs by adding titles, *x* and *y* labels, multiple lines, etc. Annotating graphs is covered in a separate chapter on plotting. Engineers and scientists **never** present a graph without labels!

15.2.7 Edit Window

To open the edit window, choose **File** from the menu bar, then **0**, and, finally, **M-file** (**File → New → M-file**). This window allows you to type and save a series of commands without executing them. You may also open the edit window by typing **edit** at the command prompt or by selecting the New File button on the toolbar.

15.2.8 Start Button

The start button is located in the lower left-hand corner of the MATLAB window. It offers alternative access to the various MATLAB windows, as well as to the help function, Internet products, demos and MATLAB toolboxes. Toolboxes provide additional

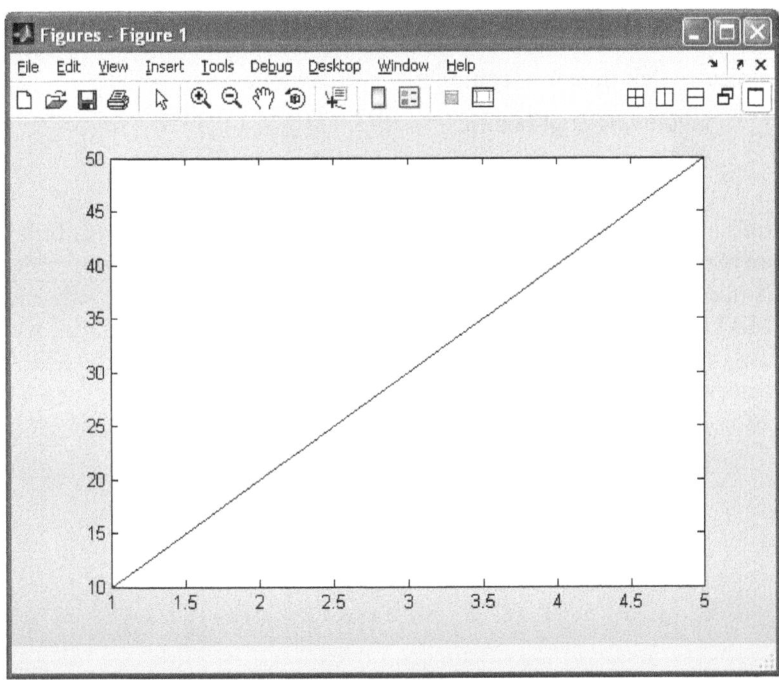

Figure 15.4 MATLAB makes it easy to create graphs.

MATLAB functionality for specific content areas. The symbolic toolbox in particular is highly useful to scientists and engineers. The start button is new to MATLAB 7 and replaces the launchpad window used in MATLAB 6.

15.3 SOLVING PROBLEMS WITH MATLAB

The command window environment is a powerful tool for solving engineering problems. To use it effectively, you'll need to understand more about how MATLAB works.

15.3.1 Using Variables

Although you can solve many problems by using MATLAB like a calculator, it is usually more convenient to give names to the values you are using. MATLAB uses the naming conventions that are common to most computer programs:

- All names must start with a letter. The names can be any length, but only the first 63 characters are used in MATLAB 7. (Use the **namelengthmax** command to confirm this.) Although MATLAB will let you create long variable names, excessive length creates a significant opportunity for error. A common guideline is to use lowercase letters and numbers in variable names and to use capital letters for the names of constants. However, if a constant is traditionally expressed as a lowercase letter, feel free to follow that convention. For example, in physics textbooks the speed of light is always lowercase *c*. Names should be short enough to remember and should be descriptive.
- The only allowable characters are letters, numbers, and the underscore. You can check to see if a variable name is allowed by using the **isvarname** command. As is standard in computer languages, the number 1 means that something is true and the number 0 means false. Hence,

```
isvarname time
ans =
        1
```

  indicates that **time** is a legitimate variable name, and

```
isvarname cool-beans
ans =
        0
```

  tells us that **cool-beans** is not a legitimate variable name. (Recall that the dash is not an allowed character.)
- Names are case sensitive. The variable **x** is different from the variable **X**.
- MATLAB reserves a list of keywords for use by the program, which you cannot assign as variable names. The **iskeyword** command causes MATLAB to list these reserved names:

```
iskeyword
ans =
  'break'
  'case'
  'catch'
  'classdef'
```

```
'continue'
'else'
'elseif'
'end'
'for'
'function'
'global'
'if'
'otherwise'
'parfor'
'persistent'
'return'
'switch'
'try'
'while'
```

- MATLAB allows you to reassign built-in function names as variable names. For example, you could create a new variable called **sin** with the command

  ```
  sin = 4
  ```

  which returns

  ```
  sin =
       4
  ```

  This is clearly a dangerous practice, since the **sin** (i.e., sine) function is no longer available. If you try to use the overwritten function, you'll get an error statement:

  ```
  sin(3)
  ??? Index exceeds matrix dimensions.
  ```

  You can check to see if a variable is a built-in MATLAB function by using the **which** command:

  ```
  which sin
  sin is a variable.
  ```

  You can reset **sin** back to a function by typing

  ```
  clear sin
  ```

  Now when you ask

  ```
  which sin
  ```

  the response is

  ```
  built-in (C:\Program
    Files\MATLAB\R2007b\toolbox\matlab\elfun\@double\sin)
  % double method
  ```

  which tells us the location of the built-in function.

In-Class Activity

ICA 15-2

Which of the following names are allowed in MATLAB? Make your predictions, then test them with the **isvarname, iskeyword,** and **which** commands.

1. test
2. Test

3. if
4. my-book
5. my_book
6. Thisisoneverylongnamebutisitstillallowed?
7. 1stgroup
8. group_one
9. zzaAbc
10. z34wAwy?12#
11. sin
12. log

15.3.2 Matrices in MATLAB

Key Idea: The matrix is the primary data type in MATLAB and can hold numeric as well as other types of information

The basic data type used in MATLAB is the *matrix*. A single value, called a *scalar*, is represented as a 1 × 1 matrix. A list of values, arranged in either a column or a row, is a one-dimensional matrix called a *vector*. A table of values is represented as a two-dimensional matrix. Although we'll limit ourselves to scalars, vectors, and two-dimensional matrices in this chapter, MATLAB can handle higher order arrays.

In mathematical nomenclature, matrices are represented as rows and columns inside square brackets:

$$A = [5] \quad B = [2 \quad 5] \quad C = \begin{bmatrix} 1 & 2 \\ 5 & 7 \end{bmatrix}$$

Vector: a matrix composed of a single row or a single column

In this example, A is a 1 × 1 matrix, B is a 1 × 2 matrix, and C is a 2 × 2 matrix. The advantage in using matrix representation is that whole groups of information can be represented with a single name. Most people feel more comfortable assigning a name to a single value, so we'll start by explaining how MATLAB handles scalars and then move on to more complicated matrices.

Scalar Operations

Scalar: a single-valued matrix

MATLAB handles arithmetic operations between two scalars much as do other computer programs and even your calculator. The syntax for addition, subtraction, multiplication, division, and exponentiation is shown in Table 15.1. The command

```
a = 1 + 2
```

should be read as "**a** is assigned a value of 1 plus 2," which is the addition of two scalar quantities. Arithmetic operations between two scalar variables use the same syntax.

Table 15.1 Arithmetic Operations between Two Scalars (Binary Operations)

Operation	Algebraic Syntax	MATLAB Syntax
Addition	$a + b$	**a + b**
Subtraction	$a - b$	**a – b**
Multiplication	$a \times b$	**a * b**
Division	$\frac{a}{b}$ or $a \div b$	**a / b**
Exponentiation	a^b	a^b

Suppose, for example that you have defined **a** in the previous statement and that **b** has a value of 5:

```
b = 5
```

Then

```
x = a + b
```

returns the following result:

```
x =
      8
```

A single equals sign (=) is called an assignment operator in MATLAB. The assignment operator causes the result of your calculations to be stored in a computer memory location. In the preceding example, **x** is assigned a value of 8. If you enter the variable name

```
x
```

into MATLAB, you get the following result:

```
x =
      8
```

Key Idea: The assignment operator is different from an equality

The assignment operator is significantly different from an equality. Consider the statement

```
x = x + 1
```

This is not a valid algebraic statement, since **x** is clearly not equal to **x + 1**. However, when interpreted as an assignment statement, it tells us to replace the current value of **x** stored in memory with a new value that is equal to the old **x** plus **1**.

Since the value stored in **x** was originally 8, the statement returns

```
x =
      9
```

indicating that the value stored in the memory location named **x** has been changed to 9. The assignment statement is similar to the familiar process of saving a file. When you first save a word-processing document, you assign it a name. Subsequently, after you've made changes, you resave your file, but still assign it the same name. The first and second versions are not equal: You've just assigned a new version of your document to an existing memory location.

Order of Operations

In all mathematical calculations, it is important to understand the order in which operations are performed. MATLAB follows the standard algebraic rules for the order of operation:

- First, perform calculations inside parentheses, working from the innermost set to the outermost.
- Next, perform exponentiation operations.
- Then perform multiplication and division operations, working from left to right.
- Finally, perform addition and subtraction operations, working from left to right.

To better understand the importance of the order of operations, consider the calculations involved in finding the surface area of a right circular cylinder.

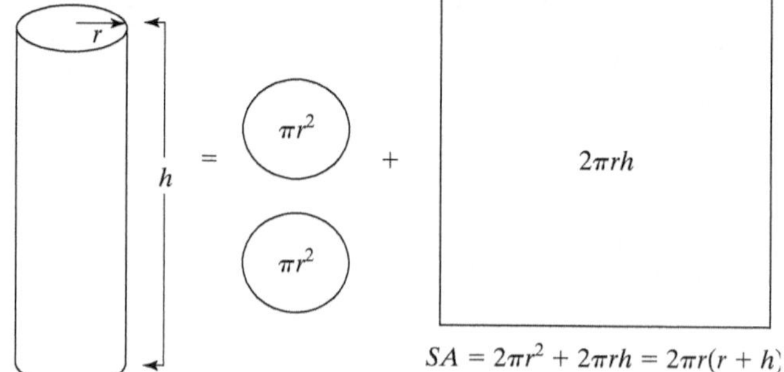

Figure 15.5 Finding the surface area of a right circular cylinder involves addition, multiplication, and exponentiation.

The surface area is the sum of the areas of the two circular bases and the area of the curved surface between them, as shown in Figure 15.5. If we let the height of the cylinder be 10 cm and the radius 5 cm, the following MATLAB code can be used to find the surface area:

```
radius = 5;
height = 10;
surface_area = 2*pi*radius^2 + 2*pi*radius*height
```

The code returns

```
surface_area =
               471.2389
```

In this case, MATLAB first performs the exponentiation, raising the radius to the second power. It then works from left to right, calculating the first product and then the second product. Finally, it adds the two products together. You could instead formulate the expression as

```
surface_area = 2*pi*radius*(radius + height)
```

which also returns

```
surface_area =
        471.2389
```

In this case, MATLAB first finds the sum of the radius and height and then performs the multiplications, working from left to right. If you forgot to include the parentheses, you would have

```
surface_area = 2*pi*radius*radius + height
```

in which case the program would have first calculated the product of **2*pi*radius*radius** and then added **height**—obviously resulting in the wrong answer. Note that it was necessary to include the multiplication operator before the parentheses, because MATLAB does not assume any operators and would misinterpret the expression

```
radius(radius + height)
```

as follows. The value of radius plus height is 15 (radius = 10 and height = 5), so MATLAB would have looked for the 15th value in an array called radius. This interpretation would have resulted in the following error statement.

```
??? Index exceeds matrix dimensions.
```

It is important to be extra careful in converting equations into MATLAB statements. There is no penalty for adding extra parentheses, and they often make the code easier to interpret, both for the programmer and for others who may use the code in the future.

Another way to make computer code more readable is to break long expressions into multiple statements. For example, consider the equation

$$f = \frac{\log(ax^2 + bx + c) - \sin(ax^2 + bx + c)}{4\pi x^2 + \cos(x - 2) * (ax^2 + bx + c)}$$

It would be very easy to make an error keying in this equation. To minimize the chance of that happening, break the equation into several pieces. For example, first assign values for **x**, **a**, **b**, and **c**:

```
x = 9;
a = 1;
b = 3;
c = 5;
```

Then define a polynomial and the denominator:

```
poly = a*x^2 + b*x + c;
denom = 4*pi*x^2 + cos(x – 2)*poly;
```

Combine these components into a final equation:

```
f = (log(poly) – sin(poly))/denom
The result is
        f =
          0.0044
```

Key Idea: Try to minimize your opportunity for error

As mentioned, this approach minimizes your opportunity for error. Instead of keying in the polynomial three times (and risking an error each time), you need key it in only once. Your MATLAB code is more likely to be accurate, and it's easier for others to understand.

HINT

MATLAB does not read "white space," so you may add spaces to your commands without changing their meaning. A long expression is easier to read if you add a space before and after plus (+) signs and minus (−) signs, but not before and after multiplication (*) and division (/) signs.

In-Class Activity

ICA 15-3

Predict the results of the following MATLAB expressions, then check your predictions by keying the expressions into the command window:

1. 6/6 + 5
2. 2 * 6^2
3. (3 + 5) * 2
4. 3 + 5 * 2
5. 4 * 3/2 * 8
6. 3 − 2/4 + 6^2

7. 2^ 3^4
8. 2^(3^4)
9. 3^5 + 2
10. 3^ (5 + 2)

Create and test MATLAB syntax to evaluate the following expressions, then check your answers with a handheld calculator.

11. $\frac{5+3}{9-1}$
12. $2^3 - \frac{4}{5+3}$
13. $\frac{5^{2+1}}{4-1}$
14. $4\frac{1}{2} * 5\frac{2}{3}$
15. $\frac{5 + 6 * \frac{7}{3} - 2^2}{\frac{2}{3} * \frac{3}{3 * 6}}$

EXAMPLE 15.1

Scalar Operations

Wind tunnels (see Figure 15.6) play an important role in our study of the behavior of high-performance aircraft. In order to interpret wind tunnel data, engineers need to understand how gases behave. The basic equation describing the properties of gases is the ideal gas law, a relationship studied in detail in first-year chemistry classes. The law states that

$$PV = nRT$$

where P = pressure in kPa,
V = volume in m^3,
n = number of kmoles of gas in the sample,

Figure 15.6 Wind tunnels are used to test aircraft designs. (Louis Bencze/Getty Images Inc.—Stone Allstock.)

R = ideal gas constant, 8.314 kPa m^3/kmol K, and
T = temperature, expressed in kelvins (K).

In addition, we know that the number of kmoles of gas is equal to the mass of the gas divided by the molar mass (also known as the molecular weight), or

$$n = m/\text{MW}$$

where

m = mass in kg and
MW = molar mass in kg/kmol.

Different units can be used in the equations if the value of R is changed accordingly.

Now suppose you know that the volume of air in the wind tunnel is $1000\ m^3$. Before the wind tunnel is turned on, the temperature of the air is 300 K, and the pressure is 100 kPa. The average molar mass (molecular weight) of air is approximately 29 kg/kmol. Find the mass of the air in the wind tunnel.

To solve this problem, use the following problem-solving methodology:

1. State the Problem
   Find the amount of matter necessary to produce the amount of energy radiated by the sun every day.
2. Describe the Input and Output

   Input

Volume	V = 1000 m^3
Temperature	T = 300 K
Pressure	P = 100 kPa
Molecular Weight	MW = 29 kg/kmol
Gas Constant	R = 8.314 kPa m^3/kmol K

   Output

Mass	m = ? kg

3. Develop a Hand Example
   Working the problem by hand (or with a calculator) allows you to outline an algorithm, which you can translate to MATLAB code later. You should choose simple data that make it easy to check your work. In this problem, we know two equations relating the data:

   $PV = nRT$ ideal gas law
   $n = m/\text{MW}$ relationship between mass and moles

   Solve the ideal gas law for n, and plug in the given values:

$$n = PV/RT$$

$$= \frac{(100 \text{ kPa} \times 1000 \text{ m}^3)}{8.314 \text{ kPa} \dfrac{\text{m}^3}{\text{kmol K}} \times 300\text{K}}$$

$$= 40.0930 \text{ kmol}$$

Convert moles to mass by solving the conversion equation for the mass m and plugging in the values:

$$m = n \times \text{MW} = 40.0930 \text{ kmol} \times 29 \text{ kg/kmol}$$

$$m = 1162.70 \text{ kg}$$

4. Develop a MATLAB Solution
   First, clear the screen and memory:

```
clear, clc
```

   Now perform the following calculations in the command window:

```
P = 100
P =

        100
T = 300
T =

        300
V = 1000
V =

        1000
MW = 29
MW =

        29
R = 8.314
R =

        8.3140
n = (P*V)/(R*T)
n =

        40.0930
m = n*MW
m =

        1.1627e+003
```

   There are several things you should notice about this MATLAB solution. First, because no semicolons were used to suppress the output, the values of the variables are repeated after each assignment statement. Notice also the use of parentheses in the calculation of n. They are necessary in the denominator, but not in the numerator. However, using parentheses in both makes the code easier to read.

5. Test the Solution
   In this case, comparing the result with that obtained by hand is sufficient. More complicated problems solved in MATLAB should use a variety of input data, to confirm that your solution works in a variety of cases. The MATLAB screen used to solve this problem is shown in Figure 15.7.

   Notice that the variables defined in the command window are listed in the workspace window. Notice also that the command history lists the commands executed in the command window. If you were to scroll up in the command history window, you would see commands from previous MATLAB sessions. All of these commands are available for you to move to the command window.

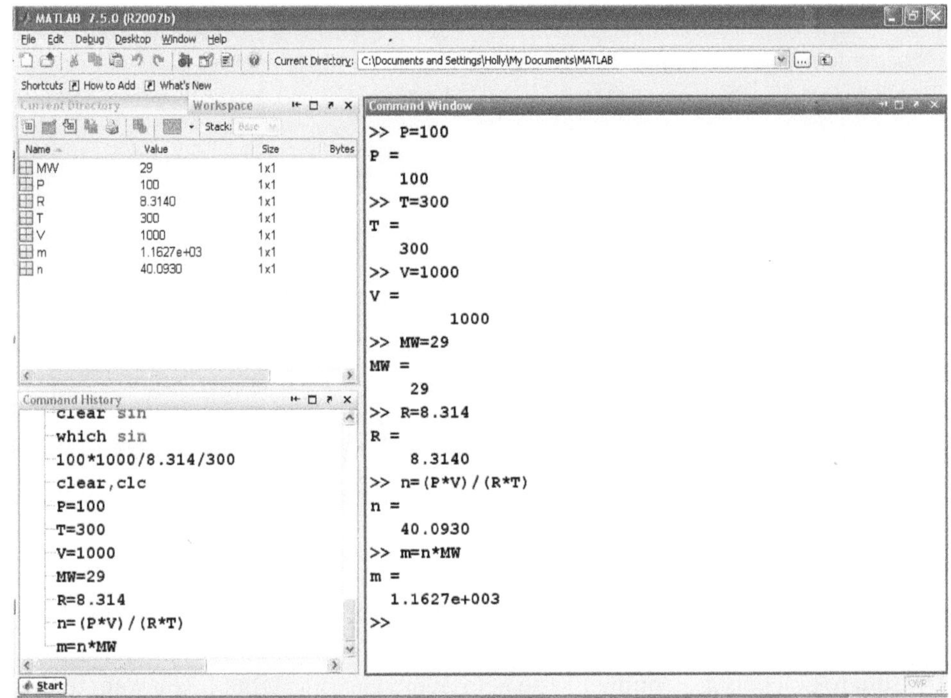

Figure 15.7 MATLAB screen used to solve the ideal gas problem.

Array Operations

Explicit List: a list identifying each member of a matrix

Using MATLAB as a glorified calculator is fine, but its real strength is in matrix manipulations. As described previously, the simplest way to define a matrix is to use a list of numbers, called an *explicit list*. The command

```
x = [1 2 3 4]
```

returns the row vector

```
x =
        1 2 3 4
```

Recall that, in defining this vector, you may list the values either with or without commas. A new row is indicated by a semicolon, so a column vector is specified as

```
y = [ 1; 2; 3; 4]
```

and a matrix that contains both rows and columns is created with the statement

```
a = [ 1 2 3 4; 2 3 4 5 ; 3 4 5 6]
```

and will return

```
a =
        1 2 3 4
        2 3 4 5
        3 4 5 6
```

HINT

It's easier to keep track of how many values you've entered into a matrix if you enter each row on a separate line:

```
a = [1 2 3 4;
2 3 4 5;
3 4 5 6]
```

While a complicated matrix might have to be entered by hand, evenly spaced matrices can be entered much more readily. The command

```
b = 1:5
```

and the command

```
b = [1:5]
```

are equivalent statements. Both return a row matrix

```
b =
    1 2 3 4 5
```

(The square brackets are optional.) The default increment is 1, but if you want to use a different increment, put it between the first and final values on the right side of the command. For example,

```
c = 1:2:5
```

indicates that the increment between values will be 2 and returns

```
c =
        1     3     5
```

If you want MATLAB to calculate the spacing between elements, you may use the **linspace** command. Specify the initial value, the final value, and how many total values you want. For example,

```
d = linspace(1,10,3)
```

returns a vector with three values, evenly spaced between 1 and 10:

```
d =
        1     5.5     10
```

You can create logarithmically spaced vectors with the **logspace** command**,** which also requires three inputs. The first two values are powers of 10 representing the initial and final values in the array. The final value is the number of elements in the array. Thus,

```
e = logspace(1,3,3)
```

returns three values:

```
e =
  10 100 1000
```

Notice that the first element in the vector is 10^1 and the last element in the array is 10^3.

HINT

New MATLAB users often err when using the **logspace** command by entering the actual first and last values requested, insteading of the corresponding power of ten. For example,

```
logspace(10,100,3)
```

is interpreted by MATLAB as: Create a vector from 10^{10} to 10^{100} with three values. The result is

```
ans =
    1.0e+100 *
    0.0000  0.0000  1.0000
```

A common multiplier (1×10^{100}) is specified for each result, but the first two values are so small in comparison to the third, that they are effectively 0.

HINT

You can include mathematical operations inside a matrix definition statement. For example, you might have **a = [0 : pi/10 : pi]**.

Matrices can be used in many calculations with scalars. If **a = [1 2 3]**, we can add 5 to each value in the matrix with the syntax

```
b = a + 5
```

which returns

```
b =
    6    7    8
```

> ***Key Idea:*** Matrix multiplication is different from element-by-element multiplication

This approach works well for addition and subtraction; however, multiplication and division are a little different. In matrix mathematics, the multiplication operator (*) has a specific meaning. Because all MATLAB operations can involve matrices, we need a different operator to indicate element-by-element multiplication. That operator is **.*** (called *dot multiplication or array multiplication*). For example,

```
a.*b
```

results in element 1 of matrix **a** being multiplied by element 1 of matrix **b**,
element 2 of matrix **a** being multiplied by element 2 of matrix **b**,
element *n* of matrix **a** being multiplied by element *n* of matrix **b**.

For the particular case of our **a** (which is **[1 2 3]**) and our **b** (which is **[6 7 8]**),

```
a.*b
```

returns

```
ans =
    6    14    24
```

(Do the math to convince yourself that these are the correct answers.)

Just using * implies a matrix multiplication, which in this case would return an error message, because **a** and **b** here do not meet the rules for multiplication in matrix algebra. The moral is, be careful to use the correct operator when you mean element-by-element multiplication.

The same syntax holds for element-by-element division (./) and exponentiation (.^) of individual elements:

```
a./b
a.^2
```

As an exercise, predict the values resulting from the preceding two expressions, and then test your predictions by executing the commands in MATLAB.

In-Class Activity

ICA 15-4

As you perform the following calculations, recall the difference between the * and .* operators, as well as the / and ./ and the ^ and .^ operators:

1. Define the matrix $a = [2.3\ 5.8\ 9]$ as a MATLAB variable.
2. Find the sine of **a.**
3. Add 3 to every element in **a.**
4. Define the matrix $b = [5.2\ 3.14\ 2]$ as a MATLAB variable.
5. Add together each element in matrix **a** and in matrix **b.**
6. Multiply each element in **a** by the corresponding element in **b.**
7. Square each element in matrix **a.**
8. Create a matrix named **c** of evenly spaced values from 0 to 10, with an increment of 1.
9. Create a matrix named **d** of evenly spaced values from 0 to 10, with an increment of 2.
10. Use the **linspace** function to create a matrix of six evenly spaced values from 10 to 20.
11. Use the **logspace** function to create a matrix of five logarithmically spaced values between 10 and 100.

Key Idea: The matrix capability of MATLAB makes it easy to do repetitive calculations

The matrix capability of MATLAB makes it easy to do repetitive calculations. For example, suppose you have a list of angles in degrees that you would like to convert to radians. First put the values into a matrix. For angles of 10, 15, 70, and 90, enter

```
degrees = [ 10 15 70 90];
```

To change the values to radians, you must multiply by $\pi/180$:

```
radians = degrees*pi/180
```

This command returns a matrix called **radians**, with the values in radians. (Try it!) In this case, you could use either the * or the **.*** operator, because the multiplication involves a single matrix (**degrees**) and two scalars (pi and 180). Thus, you could have written

```
radians = degrees.*pi/180
```

HINT

The value of π is built into MATLAB as a floating-point number called **pi**.

Because π is an irrational number, it cannot be expressed *exactly* with a floating-point representation, so the MATLAB constant **pi** is really an approximation. You can see this when you find **sin(pi).** From trigonometry, the answer should be 0. However, MATLAB returns a very small number, 1.2246e–016. In most calculations, this won't make a difference in the final result.

Another useful matrix operator is transposition. The transpose operator changes rows to columns and vice versa. For example,

```
degrees'
```

returns

```
ans =
        10
        15
        70
        90
```

This makes it easy to create tables. For example, to create a table that converts degrees to radians, enter

```
table = [degrees' , radians']
```

which tells MATLAB to create a matrix named **table**, in which column 1 is degrees and column 2 is radians:

```
table =
        10.0000   0.1745
        15.0000   0.2618
        70.0000   1.2217
        90.0000   1.5708
```

If you transpose a two-dimensional matrix, all the rows become columns and all the columns become rows. For example, the command

```
table'
```

results in

```
10.0000   15.0000   70.0000   90.0000
 0.1745    0.2618    1.2217    1.5708
```

Note that **table** is not a MATLAB command but merely a convenient variable name. We could have used any meaningful name, say, **conversions** or **degrees_to_radians.**

EXAMPLE 15.2

Matrix Calculations with Scalars

Scientific data, such as data collected from wind tunnels, is usually in SI (Système International) units. However, much of the manufacturing infrastructure in the United States has been tooled in English (sometimes called American Engineering or American Standard) units. Engineers need to be fluent in both systems and should be especially careful when sharing data with other engineers. Perhaps the most notorious example of unit confusion problems is the Mars Climate Orbiter (Figure 15.8), which was the second flight of the Mars Surveyor Program. The spacecraft burned up in the orbit of Mars in September of 1999 because of a lookup table embedded in the craft's software. The table, probably generated from wind-tunnel testing, used pounds force (lbf) when the program expected values in newtons (N).

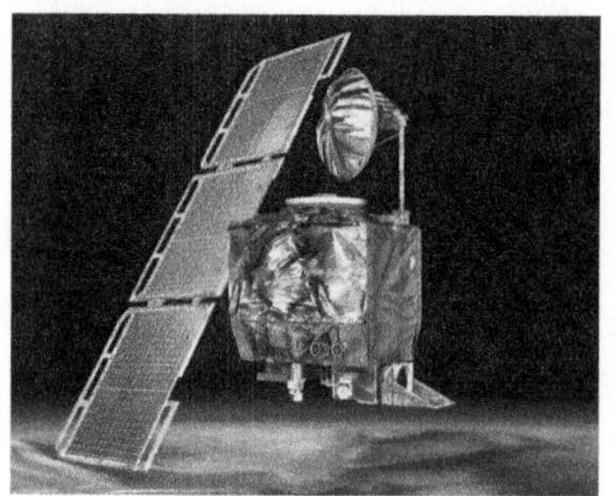

Figure 15.8 Mars Climate Orbiter. (Courtesy of NASA/Jet Propulsion Laboratory.)

In this example, we'll use MATLAB to create a conversion table of pounds force to newtons. The table will start at 0 and go to 1000 lbf, at 100-lbf intervals. The conversion factor is

$$1 \text{ lbf} = 4.4482216 \text{ N}$$

1. State the Problem
   Create a table converting pounds force (lbf) to newtons (N).
2. Describe the Input and Output

   Input

The starting value in the table is	0 lbf
The final value in the table is	1000 lbf
The increment between values is	100 lbf
The conversion from lbf to N is	1 lbf = 4.4482216 N

   Output

   Table listing pounds force (lbf) and newtons (N)
3. Develop a Hand Example
   Since we are creating a table, it makes sense to check a number of different values. Choosing numbers for which the math is easy makes the hand example simple to complete, but still valuable as a check:

   $$0 \quad * \quad 4.4482216 = 0$$
   $$100 \quad * \quad 4.4482216 = 444.82216$$
   $$1000 \quad * \quad 4.4482216 = 4448.2216$$
4. Develop a MATLAB Solution

```
clear, clc
lbf = [0:100:1000];
N = lbf * 4.44822;
[lbf',N']
ans =
  1.0e+003 *
     0         0
  0.1000    0.4448
  0.2000    0.8896
  0.3000    1.3345
  0.4000    1.7793
  0.5000    2.2241
  0.6000    2.6689
  0.7000    3.1138
  0.8000    3.5586
  0.9000    4.0034
  1.0000    4.4482
```

It is always a good idea to clear both the workspace and the command window before starting a new problem. Notice in the workspace window (Figure 15.9) that **lbf** and **N** are 1 × 11 matrices and that **ans** (which is where the table we created is stored) is an 11 × 2matrix. The output from the first two commands was suppressed by adding a semicolon at the end of each line. It would be very easy to create a table with more entries by changing the increment to 10 or even to 1. Notice also that you'll need to multiply the results shown in the table by 1000 to get the correct answers. MATLAB tells you that this is necessary directly above the table, where the common scale factor is shown.

5. Test the Solution
Comparing the results of the MATLAB solution with the hand solution shows that they are the same. Once we've verified that our solution works, it's easy to use the same algorithm to create other conversion tables. For instance, modify this example to create a table that converts newtons (N) to pounds force (lbf), with an increment of 10 N, from 0 N to 1000 N.

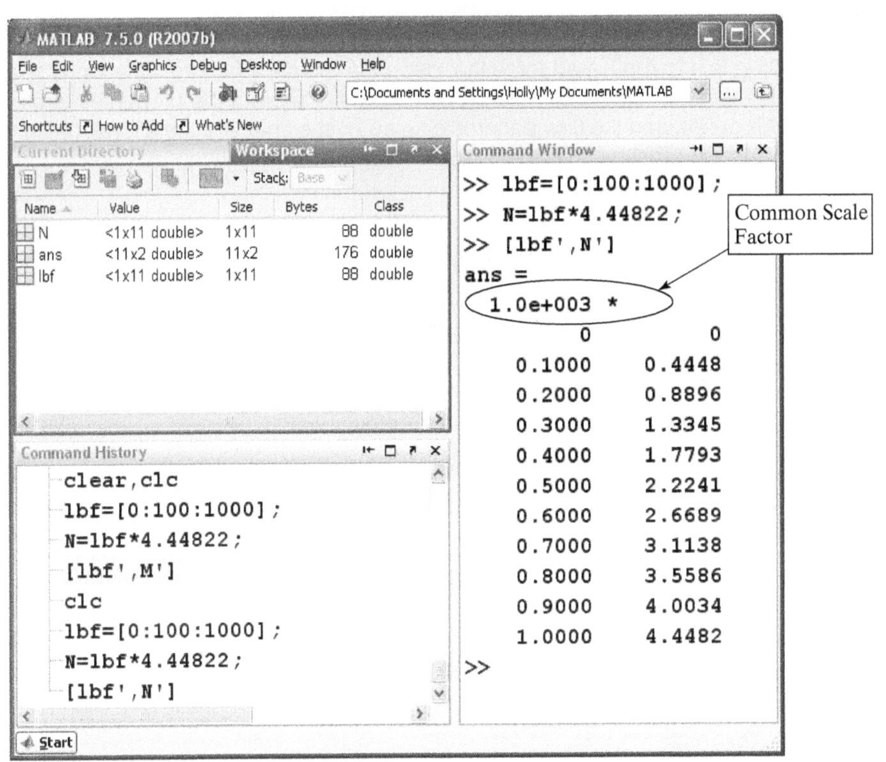

Figure 15.9 The MATLAB workspace window shows the variables as they are created.

EXAMPLE 15.3

Calculating Drag

One performance characteristic that can be determined in a wind tunnel is drag. The friction related to drag on the Mars Climate Observer (caused by the atmosphere of Mars) resulted in the spacecraft's burning up during course corrections. Drag is extremely important in the design of terrestrial aircraft as well. (See Figure 15.10.)

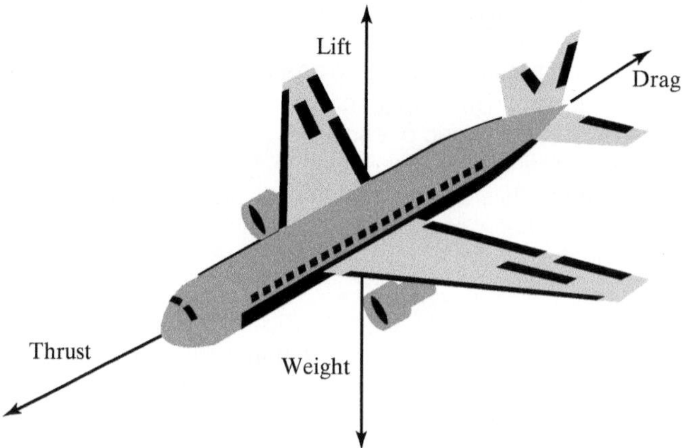

Figure 15.10 Drag is a mechanical force generated by a solid object moving through a fluid.

Drag is the force generated as an object, such as an airplane, moves through a fluid. Of course, in the case of a wind tunnel, air moves past a stationary model, but the equations are the same. Drag is a complicated force that depends on many factors. One factor is skin friction, which is a function of the surface properties of the aircraft, the properties of the moving fluid (air in this case), and the flow patterns caused by the shape of the aircraft (or, in the case of the Mars Climate Observer, by the shape of the spacecraft). Drag can be calculated with the drag equation

$$\text{drag} = C_d \frac{\rho V^2 A}{2}$$

where C_d = drag coefficient, which is determined experimentally, usually in a wind tunnel,
ρ = air density,
V = velocity of the aircraft,
A = reference area (the surface area over which the air flows).

Although the drag coefficient is not a constant, it can be taken to be constant at low speeds (less than 200 mph). Suppose the following data were measured in a wind tunnel:

drag	20,000 N
ρ	1×10^{-6} kg/m^3
V	100 mph (you'll need to convert this to meters per second)
A	1 m^2

Calculate the drag coefficient. Finally, use this experimentally determined drag coefficient to predict how much drag will be exerted on the aircraft at velocities from 0 mph to 200 mph.

1. State the Problem
   Calculate the drag coefficient on the basis of the data collected in a wind tunnel. Use the drag coefficient to determine the drag at a variety of velocities.
2. Describe the Input and Output

   Input

Drag	20,000 N
Air density ρ	1×10^{-6} kg/m^3
Velocity V	100 mph
Surface area A	1 m^2

   Output

   Drag coefficient
   Drag at velocities from 0 to 200 mph

3. Develop a Hand Example

First find the drag coefficient from the experimental data. Notice that the velocity is in miles/hr and must be changed to units consistent with the rest of the data (m/s). The importance of carrying units in engineering calculations cannot be overemphasized!

$$C_d = \text{drag} \times 2/(\rho \times V^2 \times A)$$

$$= \frac{(20{,}000\text{ N} \times 2)}{1 \times 10^{-6}\text{ kg/m}^3 \times \left(100\text{ miles/hr} \times 0.4470\dfrac{\text{m/s}}{\text{miles/hr}}\right)^2 \times 1\text{ m}^2}$$

$$= 2.0019 \times 10^7$$

Since a newton is equal to a kg m/s^2, the drag coefficient is dimensionless.

Now use the drag coefficient to find the drag at different velocities:

$$\text{drag} = C_d \times \rho \times V^2 \times A/2$$

Using a calculator, find the value of the drag with V = 200 mph:

$$\text{drag} = \frac{2.0019 \times 10^7 \times 1 \times 10^{-6}\text{ kg/m}^3 \times \left(200\text{ miles/hr} \times 0.4470\dfrac{\text{m/s}}{\text{miles/hr}}\right)^2 \times 1\text{ m}^2}{2}$$

$$\text{drag} = 80{,}000\text{ N}$$

4. Develop a MATLAB Solution

```
drag = 20000;                              % Define the variables, and change
density = 0.000001;                        % V to SI units.
velocity= 100*0.4470;
area = 1;
cd = drag*2/(density*velocity^2*area)      % Calculate the coefficient of drag.
cd =
 2.0019e+007
velocity = 0:20:200;                       % Redefine V as a matrix.
velocity = velocity*0.4470;                % Change it to SI units and
                                           % calculate the drag.
drag = cd*density*velocity.^2*area/2;
table = [velocity', drag']
table =
  1.0e+004 *
   0         0
0.0009    0.0800
0.0018    0.3200
0.0027    0.7200
0.0036    1.2800
0.0045    2.0000
0.0054    2.8800
0.0063    3.9200
0.0072    5.1200
0.0080    6.4800
0.0089    8.0000
```

Notice that the equation for drag, or

drag = cd * density * velocity.^2 * area/2;

uses the **.^** operator, because we intend that each value in the matrix **velocity** be squared, not that the entire matrix **velocity** be multiplied by itself. Using just the exponentiation operator (^) would result in an error message. Unfortunately, it is possible to compose problems in which using the wrong operator does not give us an error message but does give us a wrong answer. This makes step 5 in our problem-solving methodology especially important.

5. Test the Solution
   Comparing the hand solution with the MATLAB solution (Figure 15.11), we see that they give the same results. Once we have confirmed that our algorithm works with sample data, we can substitute new data and be confident that the results will be correct. Ideally, the results should also be compared with experimental data, to confirm that the equations we are using accurately model the real physical process.

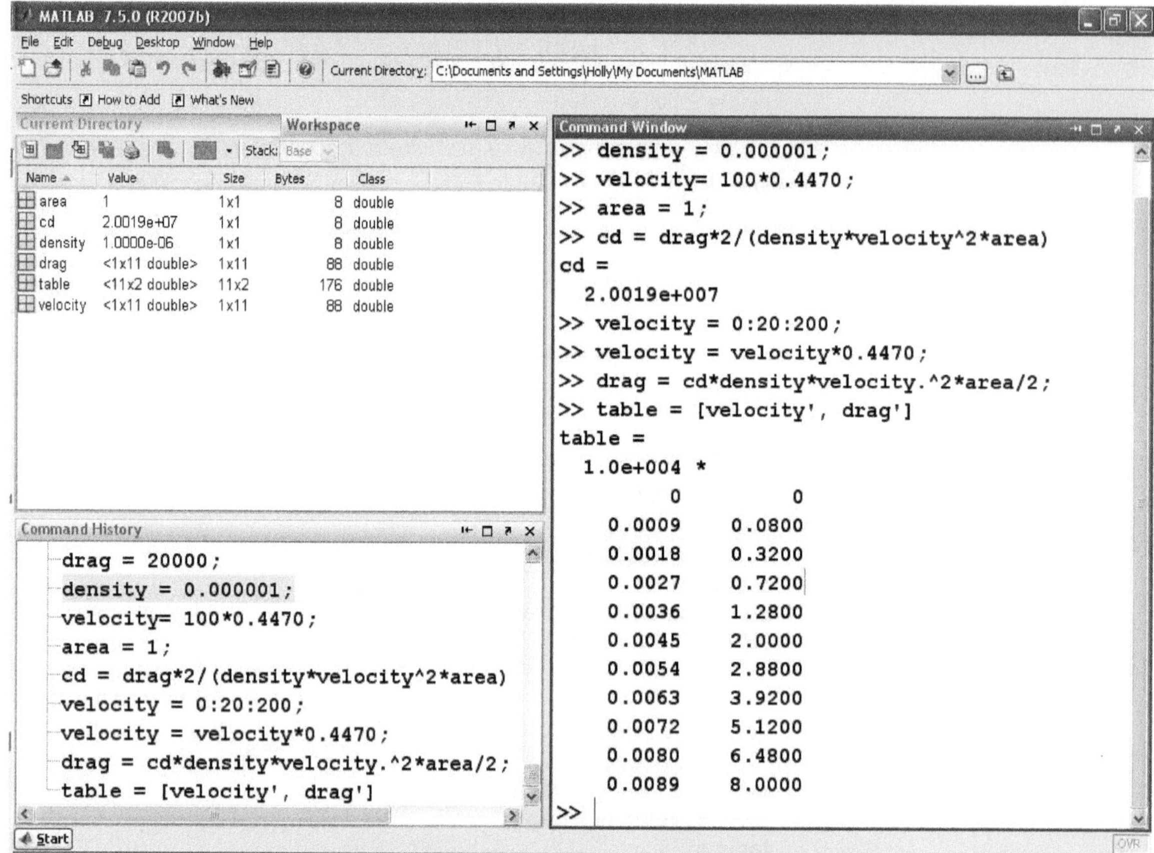

Figure 15.11 The command history window creates a record of previous commands.

15.4 SAVING YOUR WORK

Working in the command window is similar to performing calculations on your scientific calculator. When you turn off the calculator or when you exit the program, your work is gone. It *is* possible to save the *values* of the variables you defined in the command window and that are listed in the workspace window, but while doing so is useful, it is more likely that you will want to save the list of commands that generated your results. The **diary** command allows you to do just that. Also, we will show you how to save and retrieve variables (the results of the assignments you made and the calculations you performed) to MAT-files or to DAT-files. Finally, we'll introduce script M-files, which are created in the edit window. Script M-files allow you to save a list of commands and to execute them later. You will find script M-files especially useful for solving homework problems. When you create a program in MATLAB, it is stored in an M-file.

15.4.1 Diary

The diary function allows you to record a MATLAB session in a file, and retrieve it for later review. Both the MATLAB commands and the results are stored—including all your mistakes. To activate the diary function simply type

diary

or

diary on

at the command prompt. To end a recording session type **diary** again, or **diary off.** A file named diary should appear in the current directory. You can retrieve the file by double- clicking on the file name in the current directory window. An editor window will open with the recorded commands and results. You can also open the file in any text editor, such as Notepad. Subsequent sessions are added to the end of the file. If you prefer to store the diary session in a different file, specify the filename

diary <filename> or
diary('filename')

In this text we'll use angle brackets (< >) to indicate user-defined names. Thus, to save a diary session in a file named My_diary_file type

diary My_diary_file or
diary('My_diary_file')

15.4.2 Saving Variables

To preserve the variables you created in the **command window** (check the **workspace window** on the left-hand side of the MATLAB screen for the list of variables), you must save the contents of the **workspace window** to a file. The default format is a binary file called a MAT-file. To save the workspace (remember, this is just the variables, not the list of commands in the command window) to a file, type

save < file_name >

at the prompt. Recall that, although **save** is a MATLAB command, **file_name** is a user-defined file name. It can be any name you choose, as long as it conforms to the naming conventions for variables in MATLAB. Actually, you don't even need to supply a file name. If you don't, MATLAB names the file **matlab.mat**. You could also choose

File → Save Workspace As

from the menu bar, which will then prompt you to enter a file name for your data. To restore a workspace, type

load < file_name >

Again, **load** is a MATLAB command, but **file_name** is the user-defined file name. If you just type **load**, MATLAB will look for the default **matlab.mat** file.

The file you save will be stored in the current directory.

For example, type

```
clear, clc
```

This command will clear both the workspace and the command window. Verify that the workspace is empty by checking the workspace window or by typing

```
whos
```

Now define several variables—for example,

```
a = 5;
b = [1,2,3];
c = [ 1, 2; 3,4];
```

Check the workspace window once again, to confirm that the variables have been stored. Now, save the workspace to a file called my_example_file:

```
save my_example_file
```

Confirm that a new file has been stored in the current directory. If you prefer to save the file to another directory (for instance, onto a floppy drive), use the browse button (see Figure 15.2) to navigate to the directory of your choice. Remember that in a public computer lab the current directory is probably purged after each user logs off the system.

Now, clear the workspace and command window by typing

```
clear, clc
```

The workspace window should be empty. You can recover the missing variables and their values by loading the file (my_example_file.mat) back into the workspace:

```
load my_example_file
```

The file you want to load must be in the current directory, or MATLAB won't be able to find it. In the command window, type

```
a
```

which returns

```
a =
        5
```

Similarly,

```
b
```

returns

```
b =
        1 2 3
```

and typing

```
c
```

returns

```
c =
        1 2
        3 4
```

MATLAB can also store individual matrices or lists of matrices into the current directory with the command

```
save <file_name> <variable_list>
```

where **file_name** is the user-defined file name designating the location in memory at which you wish to store the information, and **variable_list** is the list of variables to be stored in the file. For example,

```
save my_new_file a b
```

would save just the variables **a** and **b** into **my_new_file.mat**.

If your saved data will be used by a program other than MATLAB (such as C or C++), the .mat format is not appropriate, because .mat files are unique to MATLAB. The ASCII format is standard between computer platforms and is more appropriate if you need to share files. MATLAB allows you to save files as ASCII files by modifying the save command to

```
save <file_name> <variable_list> -ascii
```

Ascii: binary data storage format

The command **-ascii** tells MATLAB to store the data in a standard eight-digit text format. ASCII files should be saved into a .dat file or .txt file instead of a .mat file; be sure to add .the extension to your file name:

```
save my_new_file.dat a b -ascii
```

> ***Key Idea:*** When you save the workspace, you save only the variables and their values; you do not save the commands you've executed

If you don't add .dat, MATLAB will default to .mat.

If more precision is needed, the data can be stored in a 16-digit text format:

```
save file_name variable_list -ascii -double
```

You can retrieve the data from the current directory with the load command:

```
load <file_name>
```

For example, to create the matrix **z** and save it to the file **data_2.dat** in eight-digit text format, use the following commands:

```
z = [5 3 5; 6 2 3];
save data_2.dat z –ascii
```

Together, these commands cause each row of the matrix **z** to be written to a separate line in the data file. You can view the data_2.dat file by double-clicking the file name in the current directory window. (See Figure 15.12.) Perhaps the easiest way to retrieve data from an ASCII .dat file is to enter the **load** command followed by the file name. This causes the information to be read into a matrix with the same name as the data file. However, it is also quite easy to use MATLAB's interactive Import Wizard to load the data. When you double-click a data file name in the current directory to view the contents of the file, the Import Wizard will automatically launch. Just follow the directions to load the data into the workspace, with the same name as the data file. You can use this same technique to import data from other programs, including Excel spreadsheets, or you can select **File → Import Data...** from the menu bar.

15.4.3 Script M-Files

Using the command window for calculations is an easy and powerful tool. However, once you close the MATLAB program, all of our calculations are gone. Fortunately, MATLAB contains a powerful programming language. As a programmer, you can create and

	1	2	3
1	5	3	5
2	6	2	3

Figure 15.12 Double-clicking the file name in the command directory launches the Import Wizard.

save code in files called M-files. These files can be reused anytime you wish to repeat your calculations. An M-file is an ASCII text file similar to a C or FORTRAN source-code file. It can be created and edited with the MATLAB M-file editor/debugger (the edit window discussed in Section 15.2.7), or you can use another text editor of your choice. To open the editing window, select

File → New → M-file

from the MATLAB menu bar. The MATLAB edit window is shown in Figure 15.13. Many programmers prefer to dock the editing window onto the MATLAB desktop, using the docking arrow in the upper right-hand corner of the window. This allows you to see both the contents of the M-file and the results displayed when the program is executed. The results from an M-file program are displayed in the command window.

If you choose a different text editor, make sure that the files you save are ASCII files. Notepad is an example of a text editor that defaults to an ASCII file structure. Other word processors, such as WordPerfect or Word, will require you to specify the ASCII structure when you save the file. These programs default to proprietary file structures that are not ASCII compliant and may yield some unexpected results if you try to use code written in them without specifying that the files be saved in ASCII format.

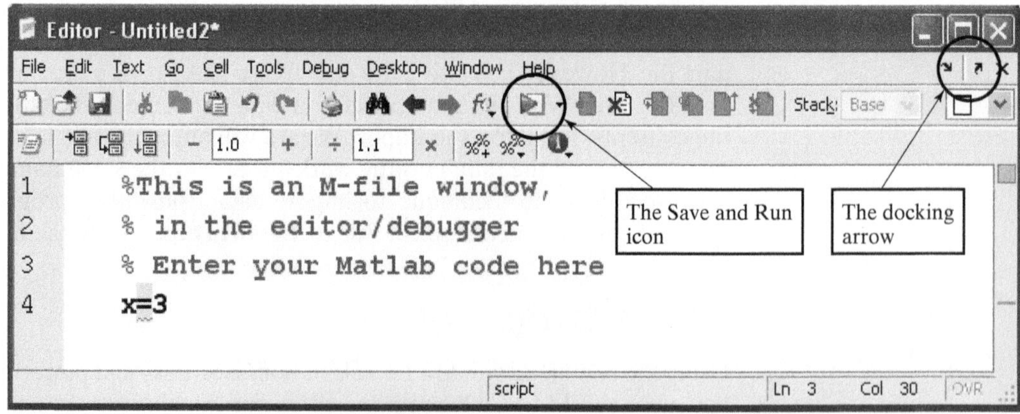

Figure 15.13 The MATLAB edit window, also called the editor/debugger.

Table 15.2 Approaches to Executing a Script M-File from the Command Window

MATLAB Command	Comments
myscript	Type the file name. The .m file extension is assumed.
run myscript	Use the run command with the file name.
run('myscript')	Use the functional form of the run command.

M-File: a list of MATLAB commands stored in a separate file

When you save an M-file, it is stored in the current directory. You'll need to name your file with a valid MATLAB variable name—that is, a name starting with a letter and containing only letters, numbers, and the underscore (_). Spaces are not allowed. (See Section 15.3.1.)

Key Idea: The two types of M-files are scripts and functions

There are two types of M-files, called scripts and functions. A script M-file is simply a list of MATLAB statements that are saved in a file with a .m file extension. The script can use any variables that have been defined in the workspace, and any variables created in the script are added to the workspace when the script finishes. You can execute a script created in the MATLAB edit window by selecting the Save and Run icon from the menu bar, as shown in Figure 15.13. (The Save and Run icon changed appearance with MATLAB 7.5. Previous versions of the program used an icon similar to an exclamation point.) You can also execute a script by typing a file name or by using the run command from the command window as shown in Table 15.2.

You can find out what M-files and MAT files are in the current directory by typing

```
what
```

into the command window. You can also browse through the current directory by looking in the current directory window.

Using script M-files allows you to work on a project and to save the list of commands for future use. Because you will be using these files in the future, it is a good idea to sprinkle them liberally with comments. The comment operator in MATLAB is the percentage sign, as in

```
% This is a comment
```

MATLAB will not execute any code on a commented line.

You can also add comments after a command, but on the same line:

```
a = 5     %The variable a is defined as 5
```

MATLAB code that could be entered into an M-file and used to solve Example 15.3 is as follows:

```
clear, clc

% A Script M-file to find Drag
% First define the variables
drag = 20000;                          %Define drag in Newtons
density= 0.000001;                     %Define air density in kg/m^3
velocity = 100*0.4470;                 %Define velocity in m/s
area = 1;                              %Define area in m^2
% Calculate coefficient of drag
cd = drag *2/(density*velocity^2*area)
% Find the drag for a variety of velocities
velocity = 0:20:200;                   %Redefine velocity
```

```
velocity = velocity*.4470              %Change velocity to m/s
drag = cd*density*velocity.^2*area/2;  %Calculate drag
table = [velocity',drag']              %Create a table of results
```

This code can be run either from the M-file or from the command window. The results will appear in the command window in either case, and the variables will be stored in the workspace. The advantage of an M-file is that you can save your program to run again later.

HINT

You can execute a portion of an M-file by highlighting a section and then right-clicking and selecting **Evaluate Section.** You can also comment or "uncomment" whole sections of code from this menu; doing so is useful when you are creating programs while you are still debugging your work.

The final example in this chapter uses a script M-file to find the velocity and acceleration that a spacecraft might reach in leaving the solar system.

EXAMPLE 15.4

Creating an M-File to Calculate the Acceleration of a Spacecraft

In the absence of drag, the propulsion power requirements for a spacecraft are determined fairly simply. Recall from basic physical science that

$$F = ma$$

In other words, force (F) is equal to mass (m) times acceleration (a). Work (W) is force times distance (d), and since power (P) is work per unit time, power becomes force times velocity (v):

$$W = Fd$$

$$P = \frac{W}{t} = F \times \frac{d}{t} = F \times v = m \times a \times v$$

This means that the power requirements for the spacecraft depend on its mass, how fast it's going, and how quickly it needs to speed up or slow down. If no power is applied, the spacecraft just keeps traveling at its current velocity. As long as we don't want to do anything quickly, course corrections can be made with very little power. Of course, most of the power requirements for spacecraft are not related to navigation. Power is required for communication, for housekeeping, and for science experiments and observations.

The *Voyager 1* and *2* spacecraft explored the outer solar system during the last quarter of the 20th century. (See Figure 15.14.) *Voyager 1* encountered both Jupiter and Saturn; *Voyager 2* not only encountered Jupiter and Saturn but continued on to Uranus and Neptune. The *Voyager* program was enormously successful, and the *Voyager* spacecraft continue to gather information as they leave the solar system. The power generators (low-level nuclear reactors) on each spacecraft are expected to function until at least 2020. The power source is a sample of plutonium-238, which, as it decays, generates heat that is used to produce electricity. At the launch of each spacecraft, its generator produced about 470 watts of power. Because the plutonium is decaying, the power production had decreased to about 335 watts in 1997, almost 20 years after launch. This power is used to operate the science package, but if it were diverted to propulsion, how much acceleration would it produce in the spacecraft? *Voyager 1* is currently

Figure 15.14 The *Voyager 1* and *Voyager 2* spacecraft were launched in 1977 and have since left the solar system. (Courtesy of NASA/Jet Propulsion Laboratory.)

traveling at a velocity of 3.50 AU/year (an AU is an astronomical unit), and *Voyager 2* is traveling at 3.15 AU/year. Each spacecraft weighs 721.9 kg.

1. State the Problem
   Find the acceleration that is possible with the power output from the spacecraft power generators.
2. Describe the Input and Output

   Input

   Mass = 721.9 kg
   Power = 335 wats = 335 J/s
   Velocity = 3.50 AU/year (*Voyager 1*)
   Velocity = 3.15 AU/year (*Voyager 2*)

   Output

   Acceleration of each spacecraft, in m/sec/sec
3. Develop a Hand Example
   We know that

$$P = m \times a \times v$$

which can be rearranged to give

$$a = P/(m \times v)$$

The hardest part of this calculation will be keeping the units straight. First let's change the velocity to m/s. For *Voyager 1*,

$$v = 3.50\frac{\text{AU}}{\text{year}} \times \frac{150 \times 10^9\ \text{m}}{\text{AU}} \times \frac{\text{year}}{365\ \text{days}} \times \frac{\text{day}}{24\ \text{hours}} \times \frac{\text{hour}}{3600\ \text{s}} = 16{,}650\frac{\text{m}}{\text{s}}$$

Then we calculate the acceleration:

$$a = \frac{335\frac{\text{J}}{\text{s}} \times 1\frac{\text{kg} \times \text{m}^2}{\text{s}^2\ \text{J}}}{721.9\ \text{kg} \times 16{,}650\frac{\text{m}}{\text{s}}} = 2.7 \times 10^{-5}\frac{\text{m}}{\text{s}^2}$$

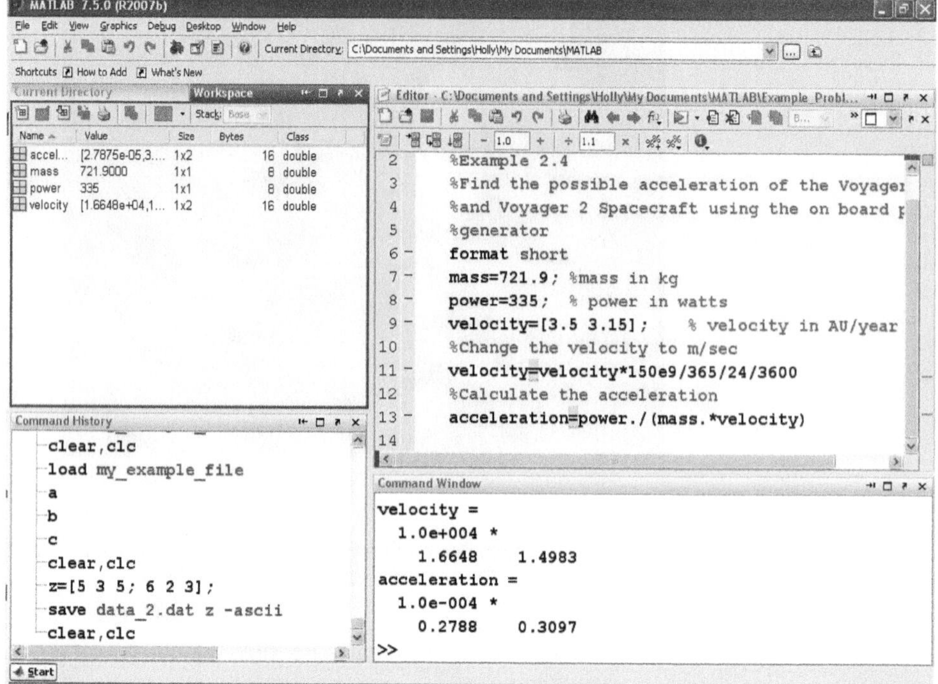

Figure 15.15 The results of an M-file execution print into the command window. The variables created are reflected in the workspace and the M-file is listed in the current directory window. The commands issued in the M-file are not mirrored in the command history.

4. Develop a MATLAB Solution

```
clear, clc
%Example 21.4
%Find the possible acceleration of the Voyager 1
%and Voyager 2 Spacecraft using the on board power
%generator
format short
mass=721.9;     %mass in kg
power=335;     % power in watts
velocity=[3.5 3.15];     % velocity in AU/year
%Change the velocity to m/sec
velocity=velocity*150e9/365/24/3600
%Calculate the acceleration
acceleration=power./(mass.*velocity)
```

The results are printed in the command window, as shown in Figure 15.15.

5. Test the Solution

Compare the MATLAB results with the hand example results. Notice that the velocity and acceleration calculated from the hand example and the MATLAB solution for *Voyager 1* match. The acceleration seems quite small, but applied over periods of weeks or months such an acceleration can achieve significant velocity changes. For example, a constant acceleration of 2.8×10^{-5} m/s^2 results in a velocity change of about 72 m/sec over the space of a month:

$$2.8 \times 10^{-5} \text{ m/s}^2 \times 3600 \text{ s/hour} \times 24 \text{ hour/day} \times 30 \text{ days/month} = 72.3 \text{ m/s}$$

Now that you have a MATLAB program that works, you can use it as the starting point for other, more complicated calculations.

SUMMARY

In this chapter, we introduced the basic MATLAB structure. The MATLAB environment includes multiple windows, four of which are open in the default view:

- Command window
- Command history window
- Workspace window
- Current directory window

In addition, the

- Document window
- Graphics window
- Edit window

open as needed during a MATLAB session.

Variables defined in MATLAB follow common computer naming conventions:

- Names must start with a letter.
- Letters, numbers, and the underscore are the only characters allowed.
- Names are case sensitive.
- Names may be any length, although only the first 63 characters are used by MATLAB.
- Some keywords are reserved by MATLAB and cannot be used as variable names.
- MATLAB allows the user to reassign function names as variable names, although doing so is not good practice.

The basic computational unit in MATLAB is the matrix. Matrices may be

- Scalars (1×1 matrix)
- Vectors ($1 \times n$ or $n \times 1$ matrix, either a row or a column)
- Two-dimensional arrays ($m \times n$ or $n \times m$)
- Multidimensional arrays

Matrices often store numeric information, although they can store other kinds of information as well. Data can be entered into a matrix manually or can be retrieved from stored data files. When entered manually, a matrix is enclosed in square brackets, elements in a row are separated by either commas or spaces, and a new row is indicated by a semicolon:

```
a = [1 2 3 4; 5 6 7 8]
```

Evenly spaced matrices can be generated with the colon operator. Thus, the command

```
b = 0:2:10
```

creates a matrix starting at 0, ending at 10, and with an increment of 2. The **linspace** and **logspace** functions can be used to generate a matrix of specified length from given starting and ending values, spaced either linearly or logarithmically. The **help** function or the MATLAB Help menu can be used to determine the appropriate syntax for these and other functions.

MATLAB follows the standard algebraic order of operations. The operators supported by MATLAB are listed in the "MATLAB Summary" section of this chapter.

MATLAB supports both standard (decimal) and scientific notation. It also supports a number of different display options, described in the "MATLAB Summary" section. No matter how values are displayed, they are stored as double-precision floating-point numbers.

Collections of MATLAB commands can be saved in script M-files. MATLAB variables can be saved or imported from either .MAT or .DAT files. The .MAT format is proprietary to MATLAB and is used because it stores data more efficiently than other file formats. The .DAT format employs the standard ASCII format and is used when data created in MATLAB will be shared with other programs.

MATLAB SUMMARY

The following MATLAB summary lists all the special characters, commands, and functions that were defined in this chapter:

Special Characters	
[ ]	forms matrices
( )	used in statements to group operations used with a matrix name to identify specific elements
,	separates subscripts or matrix elements
;	separates rows in a matrix definition suppresses output when used in commands
:	used to generate matrices indicates all rows or all columns
=	assignment operator assigns a value to a memory location; not the same as an equality
%	indicates a comment in an M-file
+	scalar and array addition
-	scalar and array subtraction
*	scalar multiplication and multiplication in matrix algebra
.*	array multiplication (dot multiply or dot star)
/	scalar division and division in matrix algebra
./	array division (dot divide or dot slash)
^	scalar exponentiation and matrix exponentiation in matrix algebra
.^	array exponentiation (dot power or dot caret)

Commands and Functions	
ans	default variable name for results of MATLAB calculations
ascii	indicates that data should be saved in standard ASCII format
clc	clears command window
clear	clears workspace
diary	creates a copy of all the commands issued in the workspace window, and most of the results
exit	terminates MATLAB
format +	sets format to plus and minus signs only
format compact	sets format to compact form
format long	sets format to 14 decimal places
format long e	sets format to scientific notation with 14 decimal places
format long eng	sets format to engineering notation with 14 decimal places
format long g	allows MATLAB to select the best format (either fixed point or floating point), using 14 decimal digits
format loose	sets format to the default, noncompact form
format short	sets format to the default, 4 decimal places
format short e	sets format to scientific notation with 4 decimal places
format short eng	sets format to engineering notation with 4 decimal places
format short g	allows MATLAB to select the best format (either fixed point or floating point), using 4 decimal digits
format rat	sets format to rational (fractional) display
help	invokes help utility
linspace	linearly spaced vector function
load	loads matrices from a file
logspace	logarithmically spaced vector function
pi	numeric approximation of the value of π
quit	terminates MATLAB
save	saves variables in a file
who	lists variables in memory
whos	lists variables and their sizes

KEY TERMS

arguments
array
array editor
ASCII
assignment
command history
command window
current directory
document window
edit window
function
graphics window
M-file
matrix
operator
prompt
scalar
scientific notation
script
start button
transpose
vector
workspace

EXERCISES AND ACTIVITIES

You can either solve these problems in the command window, using **MATLAB** as an electronic calculator, or you can create an M-file of the solutions. If you are solving these problems as a homework assignment, you will probably want to use an M-file, so that you can turn in your solutions.

Getting Started

15.1 Predict the outcome of the following MATLAB calculations:

```
1 + 3/4
5 * 6 * 4/2
5/2 * 6 * 4
5^2 * 3
5^ (2 * 3)
1 + 3 + 5/5 + 3 + 1
(1 + 3 + 5)(5 + 3 + 1)
```

Check your results by entering the calculations into the command window.

Using Variables

15.2 Identify which name in each of the following pairs is a legitimate MATLAB variable name:

fred	fred!
book_1	book-1
2ndplace	Second_Place
#1	No_1
vel_5	vel.5
tan	while

Test your answers by using **isvarname**—for example,

```
isvarname fred
```

Remember, **isvarname** returns a 1 if the name is valid and a 0 if it is not. Although it is possible to reassign a function name as a variable name, doing so is not a good idea. Use **which** to check whether the preceding names are function names—for example,

```
which sin
```

In what case would MATLAB tell you that **sin** is a variable name, not a function name?

Scalar Operations and Order of Operations

15.3 Create MATLAB code to perform the following calculations:

5^2

$\frac{5 + 3}{5 \cdot 6}$

$\sqrt{4 + 6^3}$ (*Hint*: A square root is the same thing as a $\frac{1}{2}$ power.)

$9\frac{6}{12} + 7 \cdot 5^{3+2}$

$1 + 5 \cdot 3/6^2 + 2^{2-4} \cdot 1/5.5$

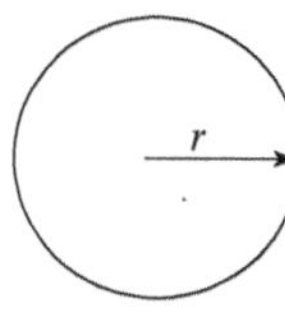

Figure P15.4(a)

Check your code by entering it into MATLAB and performing the calculations on your scientific calculator.

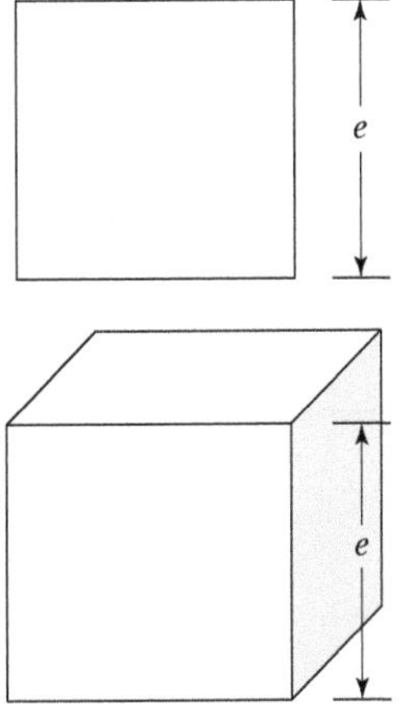

Figure P15.5(a-c)

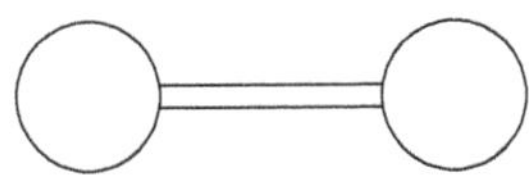

Figure P15.6 The geometry of a barbell can be modeled as two spheres and a cylindrical rod.

15.4 **(a)** The area of a circle is πr^2. Define r as 5, then find the area of a circle, using MATLAB.
(b) The surface area of a sphere is $4\pi r^2$. Find the surface area of a sphere with a radius of 10 ft.
(c) The volume of a sphere is $^4/_3\pi r^3$. Find the volume of a sphere with a radius of 2 ft.

15.5 **(a)** The area of a square is the edge length squared. (A = edge^2.) Define the edge length as 5, then find the area of a square, using MATLAB.
(b) The surface area of a cube is 6 times the edge length squared. (SA = 6 × edge^2.) Find the surface area of a cube with edge length 10.
(c) The volume of a cube is the edge length cubed. (V = edge^3.) Find the volume of a cube with edge length 12.

15.6 Consider the barbell shown in Figure P15.6.
(a) Find the volume of the figure, if the radius of each sphere is 10 cm, the length of the bar connecting them is 15 cm, and the diameter of the bar is 1 cm.
(b) Find the surface area of the figure.

15.7 The ideal gas law was introduced in Example 15.1. It describes the relationship between pressure (P), temperature (T), volume (V) and the number of moles of gas (n).

$$PV = nRT$$

The additional symbol, R, represents the ideal-gas constant. The ideal-gas law is a good approximation of the behavior of gases when the pressure is low and the temperature is high. (What constitutes low pressure and high temperature varies with different gases.) In 1873, Johannes Diderik van der Waals (Figure P15.7) proposed a modified version of the ideal gas law that

Figure P15.7 Johannes Diderik van der Waals

better models the behavior of real gases over a wider range of temperature and pressure.

$$\left(P + \frac{n^2 a}{V^2}\right)(V - nb) = nRT$$

In this equation the additional variables a and b represent values characteristic of individual gases.

Use both the ideal gas law and Van der Waals' equation to calculate the temperature of water vapor (steam), given the following data.

pressure, P	220 bar
moles, n	2 mol
volume, V	1 L
a	5.536 L^2bar/mol^2 *
b	0.03049 L/mol *
ideal gas constant, R	.08314472 L bar /K mol

*Source: Weast, R. C. (Ed.), *Handbook of Chemistry and Physics* (53rd Edn.), Cleveland: Chemical Rubber Co., 1972.

Array Operations

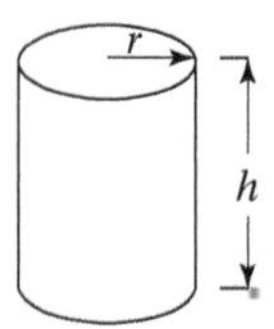

Figure P15.8(a)

15.8 **(a)** The volume of a cylinder is $\pi r^2 h$. Define r as 3 and h as the matrix

h = [1, 5, 12]

Find the volume of the cylinders. (See Figure P15.8a.)

(b) The area of a triangle is $\frac{1}{2}$ the length of the base of the triangle, times the height of the triangle. Define the base as the matrix

b = [2, 4, 6]

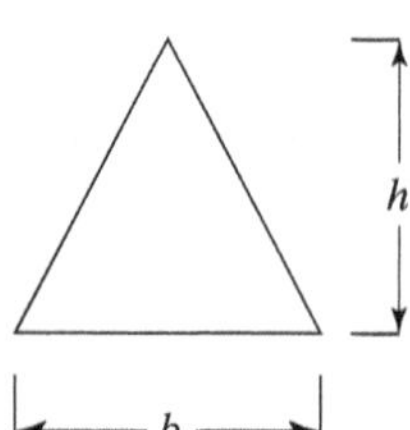

Figure P15.8(b)

and the height h as 12, and find the area of the triangles. (See Figure P15.8b.)

(c) The volume of any right prism is the area of the base of the prism, times the vertical dimension of the prism. The base of the prism can be any shape—for example, a circle, a rectangle or a triangle.

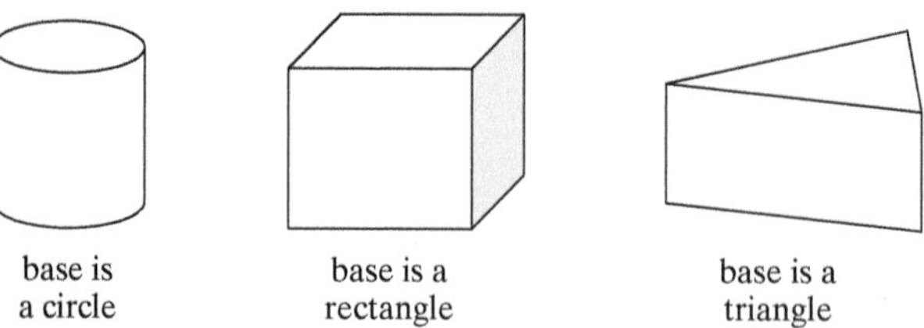

Figure P15.8(c)

Find the volume of the prisms created from the triangles of part (b). Assume that the vertical dimension of these prisms is 6. (See Figure P15.8c.)

15.9 Burning one gallon of gasoline in your car produces 19.4 pounds of CO_2. Calculate the amount of CO_2 emitted during a year for the following vehicles, assuming they all travel 12,000 miles per year. The reported fuel-efficiency numbers were extracted from the manufacturers' websites based on the EPA 2008 criteria; they are an average of the city and highway estimates.

2008	Smart Car Fortwo	37 mpg
2008	Civic Coupe	29 mpg
2008	Civic Hybrid	43 mpg
2008	Chevrolet Cobalt	30 mpg
2008	Toyota Prius (Hybrid)	46 mpg
2008	Toyota Yaris	32 mpg

15.10 **(a)** Create an evenly spaced vector of values from 1 to 20 in increments of 1.
(b) Create a vector of values from zero to 2π in increments of $\pi/10$.
(c) Create a vector containing 15 values, evenly spaced between 4 and 20. (*Hint*: Use the **linspace** command. If you can't remember the syntax, type **help linspace**.)
(d) Create a vector containing 10 values, spaced logarithmically between 10 and 1000. (*Hint*: Use the **logspace** command.)

15.11 **(a)** Create a table of conversions from feet to meters. Start the feet column at 0, increment it by 1, and end it at 10 feet. (Look up the conversion factor in a textbook or online.)
(b) Create a table of conversions from radians to degrees. Start the radians column at 0 and increment by 0.1π radian, up to π radians. (Look up the conversion factor in a textbook or online.)
(c) Create a table of conversions from mi/h to ft/s. Start the mi/h column at 0 and end it at 100 mi/h. Print 15 values in your table. (Look up the conversion factor in a textbook or online.)
(d) The acidity of solutions is generally measured in terms of pH. The pH of a solution is defined as $-\log_{10}$ of the concentration of hydronium ions. Create a table of conversions from concentration of hydronium ion to pH, spaced logarithmically from .001 to .1 mol/liter with 10 values. Assuming that you have named the concentration of hydronium ions **H_conc**, the syntax for calculating the logarithm of the concentration is

```
log10(H_conc)
```

15.12 The general equation for the distance that a freely falling body has traveled (neglecting air friction) is

$$d = \frac{1}{2}gt^2$$

Assume that $g = 9.8\ \text{m/s}^2$. Generate a table of time versus distance traveled for values of time from 0 to 100 seconds. Choose a suitable increment for your time vector. (*Hint*: Be careful to use the correct operators; t^2 is an array operation!)

15.13 Newton's law of universal gravitation tells us that the force exerted by one particle on another is

$$F = G\frac{m_1 m_2}{r^2}$$

where the universal gravitational constant G is found experimentally to be

$$G = 6.673 \times 10^{-11}\ \text{N m}^2/\text{kg}^2$$

The mass of each particle is m_1 and m_2, respectively, and r is the distance between the two particles. Use Newton's law of universal gravitation to find the force exerted by the earth on the moon, assuming that

the mass of the earth is approximately 6×10^{24} kg,
the mass of the moon is approximately 7.4×10^{22} kg, and
the earth and the moon are an average of 3.9×10^{8} m apart.

15.14 We know that the earth and the moon are not always the same distance apart. Find the force the moon exerts on the earth for 10 distances between 3.8×10^{8} m and 4.0×10^{8} m.

15.15 Recall from problem 15.7 that the ideal gas law is:

$$PV = nRT$$

and that the Van der Waals modification of the ideal gas law is

$$\left(P + \frac{n^2 a}{V^2}\right)(V - nb) = nRT$$

Using the data from Problem 15.7, find the value of temperature (T), for

(a) 10 values of pressure from 0 bar to 400 bar for volume of 1 L
(b) 10 values of volume from 0.1 L to 10 L for a pressure of 220 bar

Number Display

15.16 Create a matrix **a** equal to $[-1/3, 0, 1/3, 2/3]$, and use each of the built-in format options to display the results:

format short (which is the default)
format long
format bank
format short e
format long e
format short eng
format long eng
format short g
format long g
format +
format rat

Saving Your Work in Files

15.17
- Create a matrix called D_to_R composed of two columns, one representing degrees and the other representing the corresponding value in radians. Any value set will do for this exercise.
- Save the matrix to a file called degrees.dat.
- Once the file is saved, clear your workspace and then load the data from the file back into MATLAB.

15.18 Create a script M-file and use it to do the homework problems you've been assigned from this chapter. Your file should include appropriate comments to identify each problem and to describe your calculation process. Don't forget to include your name, the date, and any other information your instructor requests.

CHAPTER 16
BUILT-IN MATLAB FUNCTIONS

Objectives

By learning the material in this chapter, you should be able to

- use a variety of common mathematical functions
- understand and use trigonometric functions in MATLAB
- compute and use statistical and data analysis functions
- generate uniform and Gaussian random-number matrices
- understand the computational limits of MATLAB
- recognize and be able to use the special values and functions built into MATLAB

Introduction

The vast majority of engineering computations require quite complicated mathematical functions, including logarithms, trigonometric functions, and statistical analysis functions. MATLAB has an extensive **library** of built-in functions to allow you to perform these calculations.

16.1 USING BUILT-IN FUNCTIONS

Many of the names for MATLAB's built-in functions are the same as those defined not only in the C programming language, but in Fortran and Java as well. For example, to take the square root of the variable **x**, we type

```
b = sqrt(x)
```

A big advantage of MATLAB is that function arguments can generally be either scalars or matrices. In our example, if **x** is a scalar, a scalar result is returned. Thus, the statement

```
x = 9;
b = sqrt(x)
```

returns a scalar:

```
b =
   3
```

Taken from *MATLAB® for Engineers,* Second Edition, by Holly Moore.

However, the square-root function, **sqrt**, can also accept matrices as input. In this case, the square root of each element is calculated, so

```
x = [4, 9, 16];
b = sqrt(x)
```

returns

```
b =
    2  3  4
```

Key Idea: Most of the MATLAB function names are the same as those used in other computer programs

All functions can be thought of as having three components: a name, input, and output. In the preceding example, the name of the function is **sqrt**, the required input (also called the *argument*) goes inside the parentheses and can be a scalar or a matrix, and the output is a calculated value or values. In this example, the output was assigned the variable name **b**.

Some functions require multiple inputs. For example, the remainder function, **rem**, requires two inputs: a dividend and a divisor. We represent this as **rem(x,y)**, so

```
rem(10,3)
```

Argument: input to a function

calculates the remainder of 10 divided by 3:

```
ans =
      1
```

The **size** function is an example of a function that returns two outputs, which are stored in a single array. It determines the number of rows and columns in a matrix. Thus,

```
d = [1, 2, 3; 4, 5, 6];
f = size(d)
```

returns the 1×2 result matrix

```
f =
    2  3
```

You can also assign variable names to each of the answers by representing the left-hand side of the assignment statement as a matrix. For example,

```
[rows,cols] = size(d)
```

gives

```
rows =
       2
cols =
       3
```

Nesting: using one function as the input to another

You can create more complicated expressions by nesting functions. For instance,

```
g = sqrt(sin(x))
```

finds the square root of the sine of whatever values are stored in the matrix named **x**. If **x** is assigned a value of 2,

```
x = 2;
```

the result is

```
g =
    0.9536
```

Nesting functions can result in some complicated MATLAB code. Be sure to include the arguments for each function inside their own set of parentheses. Often, your code will be easier to read if you break nested expressions into two separate statements. Thus,

```
a = sin(x);
g = sqrt(a)
```

gives the same result as **g = sqrt(sin(x))** and is easier to follow.

HINT

You can probably *guess* the name and syntax for many MATLAB functions. However, check to make sure that the function of interest is working the way you assume it is, before you do any important calculations.

16.2 USING THE HELP FEATURE

MATLAB includes extensive help tools, which are especially useful in understanding how to use functions. There are two ways to get help from within MATLAB: a command-line help function (**help**) and an HTML-based set of documentation available by selecting **Help** from the menu bar or by using the *F1* function key, usually located at the top of your keyboard (or found by typing **helpwin** in the command window). There is also an online help set of documentation, available through the Start button or the Help icon on the menu bar. However, the online help usually just reflects the HTML-based documentation. You should use both help options, since they provide different information and insights into how to use a specific function.

To use the command-line help function, type **help** in the command window:

```
help
```

A list of help topics will appear:

> ***Key Idea:*** Use the help function to help you use MATLAB's built-in functions

```
HELP topics:
MATLAB\general      — General-purpose commands
MATLAB\ops          — Operators and special characters
MATLAB\lang         — Programming language constructs
MATLAB\elmat        — Elementary matrices and matrix
                      manipulation
MATLAB\elfun        — Elementary math functions
MATLAB\specfun      — Specialized math functions

and so on
```

To get help on a particular topic, type **help <topic>**. (Recall that the angle brackets, < and >, identify where you should type your input; they are not included in your actual MATLAB statement.)

For example, to get help on the **tangent** function, type

```
help tan
```

The following should be displayed:

```
TAN    Tangent of argument in radians.
 TAN(X) is the tangent of the elements of X.
See also atan, tand, atan2.
```

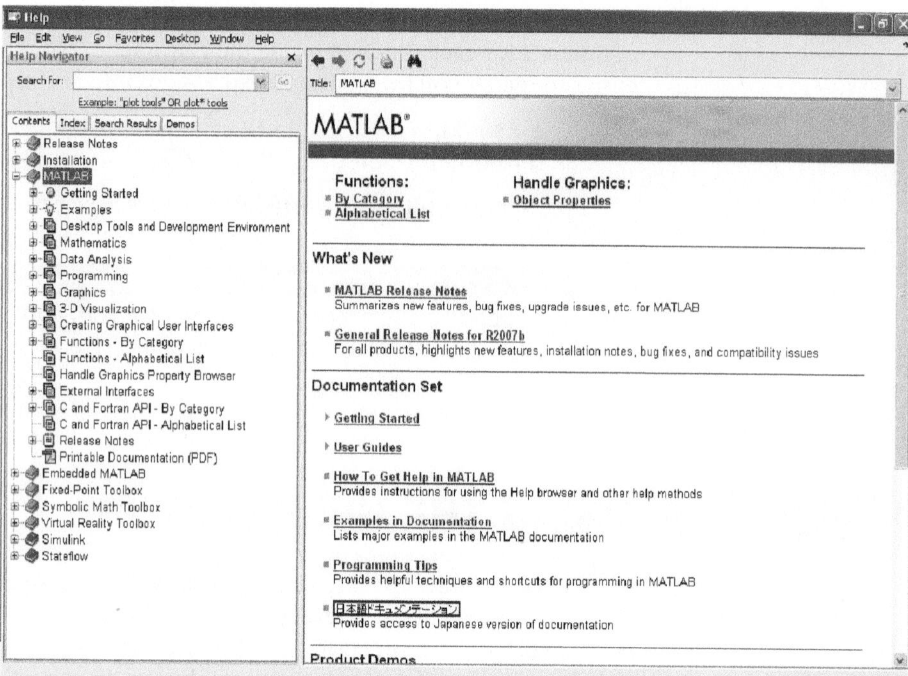

Figure 16.1 The MATLAB help environment.

To use the windowed help screen, select **Help → MATLAB Help** from the menu bar. A windowed version of the help list will appear. (See Figure 16.1.) You can then navigate to the appropriate topic. To access this version of the help utility directly from the command window, type **doc <topic>.** Thus, to access the windowed help for tangent, type

```
doc tan
```

The contents of the two methods for getting help on a function are different. If your question isn't immediately answered by whichever method you try first, it's often useful to try the other technique. The windowed help utility includes a MATLAB tutorial that you will find extremely useful. The list in the left-hand window is a table of contents. Notice that it includes a link to a list of functions, organized both by category and alphabetically by name. You can use this link to find out what MATLAB functions are available to solve many problems. For example, you might want to round a number you've calculated. Use the MATLAB help window to determine whether an appropriate MATLAB function is available.

Select the **MATLAB Functions-By Category** link (see Figure 16.1) and then the **Mathematics** link (see Figure 16.2).

Near the middle of the page is the category Elementary Math, (Figure 16.3) which lists rounding as a topic. Follow the links and you will find a whole category devoted to rounding functions. For example, **round** rounds to the nearest integer.

You could have also found the syntax for the round function by selecting **Functions—Alphabetical List.**

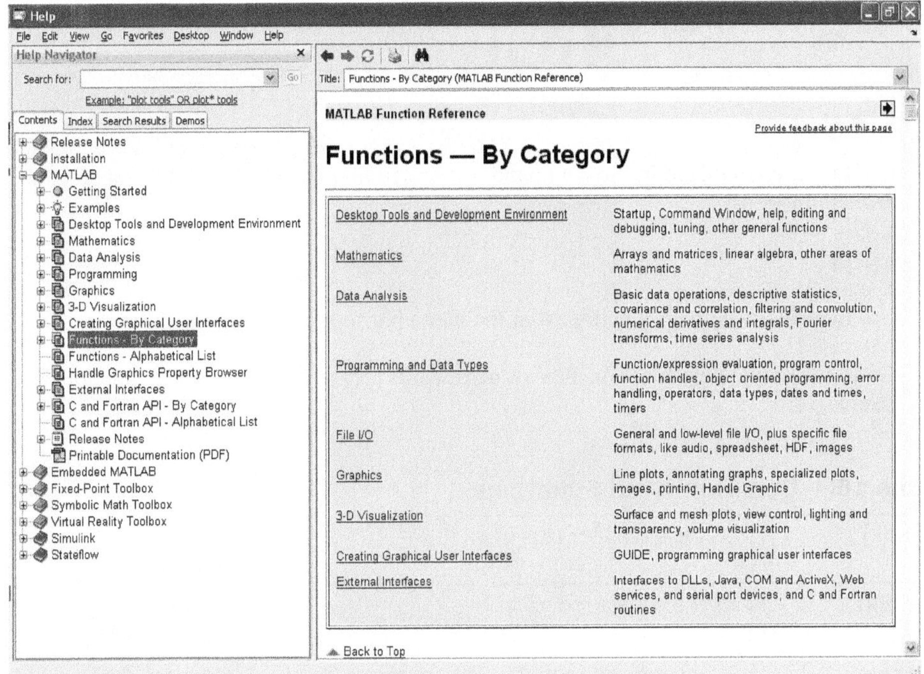

Figure 16.2 Functions-By Category help window. Notice the link to Mathematics functions in the righthand pane.

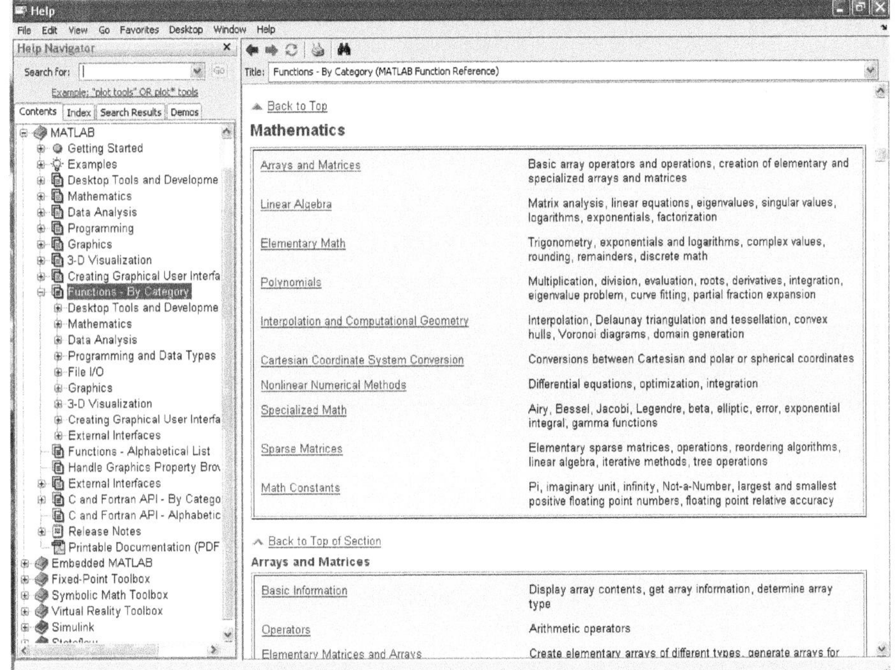

Figure 16.3 Mathematics Help Window.

In-Class Activity

ICA 16-1

1. Use the help command in the command window to find the appropriate syntax for the following functions:
   a. cos
   b. sqrt
   c. exp
2. Use the windowed help function from the menu bar to learn about the functions in Exercise 1.
3. Go to the online help function at www.mathworks.com to learn about the functions in Exercise 1.

Table 16.1 Common Math Functions

abs(x)	Finds the absolute value of **x.**	**abs(–3)** **ans = 3**
sqrt(x)	Finds the square root of **x.**	**sqrt(85)** **ans = 9.2195**
nthroot(x,n)	Finds the real *n*th root of **x.** This function will not return complex results. Thus, **(–2)^(1/3)** does not return the same result, yet both answers are legitimate third roots of –2.	**nthroot(–2,3)** **ans =** **–1.2599** **(–2)^(1/3)** **ans =** **0.6300 + 1.0911i**
sign(x)	Returns a value of –1 if **x** is less than zero, a value of 0 if **x** equals zero, and a value of +1 if **x** is greater than zero.	**sign(–8)** **ans = –1**
rem(x,y)	Computes the remainder of **x/y.**	**rem(25,4)** **ans = 1**
exp(x)	Computes the value of e^x, where *e* is the base for natural logarithms, or approximately 2.7183.	**exp(10)** **ans = 2.2026e+004**
log(x)	Computes ln(**x**), the natural logarithm of **x** (to the base *e*).	**log(10)** **ans = 2.3026**
log10(x)	Computes $\log_{10}$(**x**), the common logarithm of **x** (to the base 10).	**log10(10)** **ans = 1**

Table 16.2 Rounding Functions

round(x)	Rounds **x** to the nearest integer.	**round(8.6)** **ans = 9**
fix(x)	Rounds (or truncates) **x** to the nearest integer toward zero. Notice that 8.6 truncates to 8, not 9, with this function.	**fix(8.6)** **ans = 8** **fix(–8.6)** **ans = –8**
floor(x)	Rounds **x** to the nearest integer toward negative infinity.	**floor(–8.6)** **ans = –9**
ceil(x)	Rounds **x** to the nearest integer toward positive infinity.	**ceil(–8.6)** **ans = –8**

16.3 TRIGONOMETRIC FUNCTIONS

MATLAB includes a complete set of the standard trigonometric functions and the hyperbolic trigonometric functions. Most of these functions assume that angles are expressed in radians. To convert radians to degrees or degrees to radians, we need to take advantage of the fact that π radians equals 180 degrees:

$$\text{degrees} = \text{radians}\left(\frac{180}{\pi}\right) \quad \text{and} \quad \text{radians} = \text{degrees}\left(\frac{\pi}{180}\right)$$

> ***Key Idea:*** Most trig functions require input in radians

The MATLAB code to perform these conversions is

```
degrees = radians * 180/pi;
radians = degrees * pi/180;
```

To carry out these calculations, we need the value of π, so a constant, **pi**, is built into MATLAB. However, since π cannot be expressed as a floating-point number, the constant **pi** in MATLAB is only an approximation of the mathematical quantity π. Usually this is not important; however, you may notice some surprising results. For example, for

```
sin(pi)
ans =
        1.2246e-016
```

when you expect an answer of zero.

You may access the help function from the menu bar for a complete list of trigonometric functions available in MATLAB. Table 16.3 shows some of the more common ones.

HINT

Math texts often use the notation $\sin^{-1}(x)$ to indicate an inverse sine function, also called an arcsine. Students are often confused by this notation and try to create parallel MATLAB code. Note, however, that

```
a = sin^ - 1(x)
```

is *not* a valid MATLAB statement, but instead should be

```
a = asin(x)
```

In-Class Activity

ICA 16-2

Calculate the following (remember that mathematical notation is not necessarily the same as MATLAB notation):

1. $\sin(2\theta)$ for $\theta = 3\pi$.
2. $\cos(\theta)$ for $0 \le \theta \le 2\pi$; let θ change in steps of 0.2π
3. $\sin^{-1}(1)$
4. $\cos^{-1}(x)$ for $-1 \le x \le 1$; let x change in steps of 0.2.
5. Find the cosine of 45°.
   a. Convert the angle from degrees to radians, and then use the **cos** function.
   b. Use the **cosd** function.
6. Find the angle whose sine is 0.5. Is your answer in degrees or radians?
7. Find the cosecant of 60 degrees. You may have to use the help function to find the appropriate syntax.

Table 16.3 Trigonometric Functions

sin(x)	Finds the sine of **x** when **x** is expressed in radians.	**sin(0)** **ans = 0**
cos(x)	Finds the cosine of **x** when **x** is expressed in radians.	**cos(pi)** **ans = −1**
tan(x)	Finds the tangent of **x** when **x** is expressed in radians.	**tan(pi)** **ans =** **−1.2246** **e-016**
asin(x)	Finds the arcsine, or inverse sine, of **x**, where **x** must be between −1 and 1. The function returns an angle in radians between π/2 and −π/2.	**asin(−1)** **ans =** **−1.5708**
sinh(x)	Finds the hyperbolic sine of **x** when **x** is expressed in radians.	**sinh(pi)** **ans =** **11.5487**
asinh(x)	Finds the inverse hyperbolic sine of **x**.	**asinh(1)** **ans =** **0.8814**
sind(x)	Finds the sin of **x** when **x** is expressed in degrees.	**sind(90)** **ans = 1**
asind(x)	Finds the inverse sine of **x** and reports the result in degrees.	**asind(90)** **ans = 1**

EXAMPLE 16.1

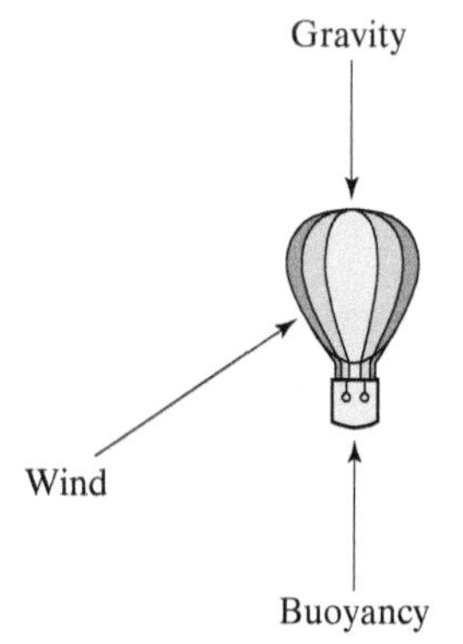

Figure 16.4 Force balance on a balloon.

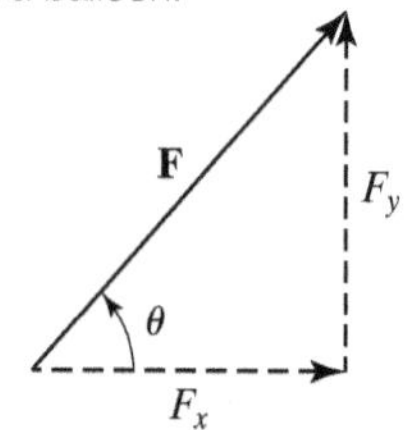

Using Trigonometric Functions

A basic calculation in engineering is finding the resulting force on an object that is being pushed or pulled in multiple directions. Adding up forces is the primary calculation performed in both statics and dynamics classes. Consider a balloon that is acted upon by the forces shown in Figure 16.4.

To find the net force acting on the balloon, we need to add up the force due to gravity, the force due to buoyancy, and the force due to the wind. One approach is to find the force in the *x* direction and the force in the *y* direction for each individual force and then to recombine them into a final result.

The forces in the *x* and *y* directions can be found by trigonometry:

F = total force
F_x = force in the *x* direction
F_y = force in the *y* direction

We know from trigonometry that the sine is the opposite side over the hypotenuse, so

$$\sin(\theta) = F_y/F$$

and therefore,

$$F_y = F\sin(\theta)$$

Similarly, since the cosine is the adjacent side over the hypotenuse,

$$F_x = F\cos(\theta)$$

We can add up all the forces in the x direction and all the forces in the y direction and use these totals to find the resulting force:

$$F_{x\,\text{total}} = \Sigma F_{xi} \qquad F_{y\,\text{total}} = \Sigma F_{yi}$$

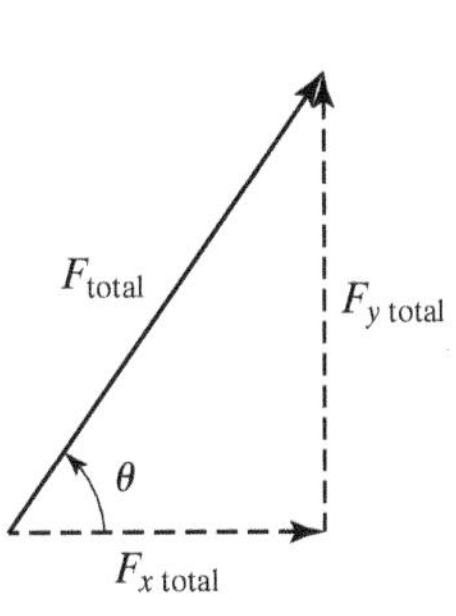

To find the magnitude and angle for F_{total}, we use trigonometry again. The tangent is the opposite side over the adjacent side. Therefore,

$$\tan(\theta) = \frac{F_{y\,\text{total}}}{F_{x\,\text{total}}}$$

We use an inverse tangent to write

$$\theta = \tan^{-1}\left(\frac{F_{y\,\text{total}}}{F_{x\,\text{total}}}\right)$$

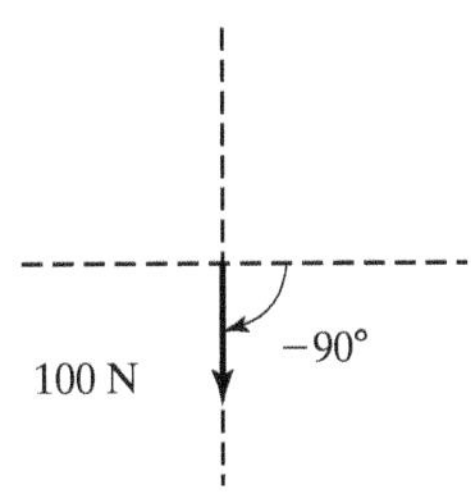

(The inverse tangent is also called the *arctangent*; you'll see it on your scientific calculator as atan.)

Once we know θ, we can find F_{total}, using either the sine or the cosine. We have

$$F_{x\,\text{total}} = F_{\text{total}} \cos(\theta)$$

and rearranging terms gives

$$F_{\text{total}} = \frac{F_{x\,\text{total}}}{\cos(\theta)}$$

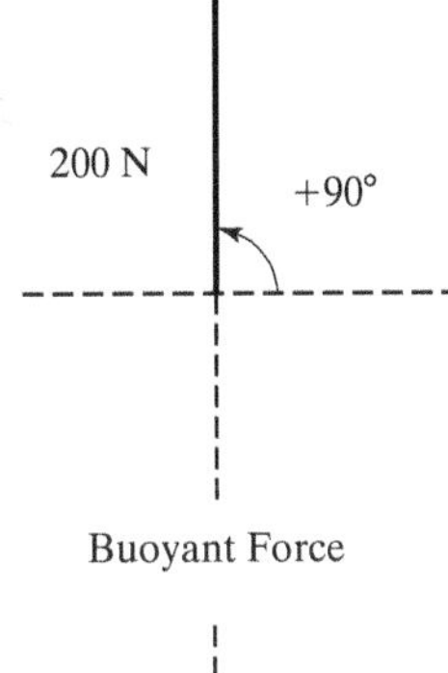

Now consider a balloon. Assume that the force due to gravity on this particular balloon is 100 N, pointed downward. Assume further that the buoyant force is 200 N, pointed upward. Finally, assume that the wind is pushing on the balloon with a force of 50 N, at an angle of 30 degrees from horizontal.

Find the resulting force on the balloon.

1. State the Problem
   Find the resulting force on a balloon. Consider the forces due to gravity, buoyancy, and the wind.
2. Describe the Input and Output

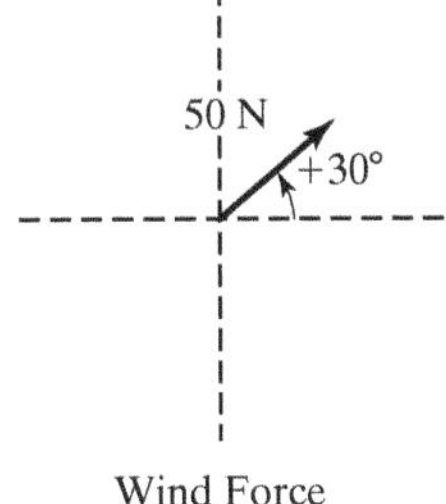

Input

Force	Magnitude	Direction
Gravity	100 N	–90 degrees
Buoyancy	200 N	+90 degrees
Wind	50 N	+30 degrees

Output

We'll need to find both the magnitude and the direction of the resulting force.

3. Develop a Hand Example
   First find the x and y components of each force and sum the components:

Force	Horizontal Component	Vertical Component
Gravity	$F_x = F\cos(\theta)$ $F_x = 100\cos(-90°) = 0$ N	$F_y = F\sin(\theta)$ $F_y = 100\sin(-90°) = -100$ N
Buoyancy	$F_x = F\cos(\theta)$ $F_x = 200\cos(+90°) = 0$ N	$F_y = F\sin(\theta)$ $F_y = 200\sin(+90°) = +200$ N
Wind	$F_x = F\cos(\theta)$ $F_x = 50\cos(+30°) = 43.301$ N	$F_y = F\sin(\theta)$ $F_y = 50\sin(+30°) = +25$ N
Sum	$F_{x\,total} = 0 + 0 + 43.301$ $= 43.301$ N	$F_{y\,total} = -100 + 200 + 25$ $= 125$ N

Find the resulting angle:

$$\theta = \tan^{-1}\left(\frac{F_{y\ total}}{F_{x\ total}}\right)$$

$$\theta = \tan^{-1}\frac{125}{43.301} = 70.89°$$

Find the magnitude of the total force:

$$F_{total} = \frac{F_{x\ total}}{\cos(\theta)}$$

$$F_{total} = \frac{43.301}{\cos(70.89°)} = 132.29\text{ N}$$

4. Develop a MATLAB Solution
   One solution is

```
%Example 22.1
clear, clc
%Define the input
Force =[100, 200, 50];
theta = [-90, +90, +30];
%convert angles to radians
theta = theta*pi/180;
%Find the x components
ForceX = Force.*cos(theta);
%Sum the x components
ForceX_total = sum(ForceX);
%Find and sum the y components in the same step
ForceY_total = sum(Force.*sin(theta));
%Find the resulting angle in radians
result_angle = atan(ForceY_total/ForceX_total);
%Find the resulting angle in degrees
result_degrees = result_angle*180/pi
%Find the magnitude of the resulting force
Force_total = ForceX_total/cos(result_angle)
```

which returns

result_degrees =
70.8934

Force_total =
132.2876

Notice that the values for the force and the angle were entered into an array. This makes the solution more general. Notice also that the angles were converted to radians. In the program listing, the output from all but the final calculations was suppressed. However, while developing the program, we left off the semicolons so that we could observe the intermediate results.

5. Test the Solution
   Compare the MATLAB solution with the hand solution. Now that you know it works, you can use the program to find the resultant of multiple forces. Just add the additional information to the definitions of the force vector **Force** and the angle vector **theta.** Note that we assumed a two-dimensional world in this example, but it would be easy to extend our solution to forces in all three dimensions.

16.4 DATA ANALYSIS FUNCTIONS

Analyzing data statistically in MATLAB is particularly easy, partly because whole data sets can be represented by a single matrix and partly because of the large number of built-in data analysis functions.

16.4.1 Maximum and Minimum

Table 16.4 lists functions that find the minimum and maximum in a data set and the element at which those values occur.

HINT

All of the functions in this section work on the *columns* in two-dimensional matrices. If your data analysis requires you to evaluate data in rows, the data must be transposed. (In other words, the rows must become columns and the columns must become rows.) The transpose operator is a single quote ('). For example, if you want to find the maximum value in each *row* of the matrix

$$x = \begin{bmatrix} 1 & 5 & 3 \\ 2 & 4 & 6 \end{bmatrix}$$

use the command

max(x')

which returns

ans =
5 6

Table 16.4 Maxima and Minima

Function	Description	Example
max(x)	Finds the largest value in a **vector x**. For example, if $x = [1 \quad 5 \quad 3]$, the maximum value is 5.	**x=[1, 5, 3];** **max(x)** **ans = 5**
	Creates a row vector containing the maximum element from each column of a **matrix x**. For example, if $x = \begin{bmatrix} 1 & 5 & 3 \\ 2 & 4 & 6 \end{bmatrix}$, then the maximum value in column 1 is 2, the maximum value in column 2 is 5, and the maximum value in column 3 is 6.	**x=[1, 5, 3; 2, 4, 6];** **max(x)** **ans = 2 5 6**
[a,b]=max(x)	Finds both the largest value in a **vector x** and its location in vector **x**. For $x = [1 \quad 5 \quad 3]$ the maximum value is named **a** and is found to be 5. The location of the maximum value is element 2 and is named **b**.	**x=[1, 5, 3];** **[a,b]=max(x)** **a = 5** **b = 2**
	Creates a row vector containing the maximum element from each column of a matrix **x** and returns a row vector with the location of the maximum in each column of matrix **x**. For example, if $x = \begin{bmatrix} 1 & 5 & 3 \\ 2 & 4 & 6 \end{bmatrix}$, then the maximum value in column 1 is 2, the maximum value in column 2 is 5, and the maximum value in column 3 is 6. These maxima occur in row 2, row 1, and row 2, respectively.	**x=[1, 5, 3; 2, 4, 6];** **[a,b]=max(x)** **a = 2 5 6** **b = 2 1 2**
max(x,y)	Creates a matrix the same size as **x** and **y**. (Both **x** and **y** must have the same number of rows and columns.) Each element in the resulting matrix contains the maximum value from the corresponding positions in **x** and **y**. For example, if $x = \begin{bmatrix} 1 & 5 & 5 \\ 2 & 4 & 6 \end{bmatrix}$ and $y = \begin{bmatrix} 10 & 2 & 4 \\ 1 & 8 & 7 \end{bmatrix}$ then the resulting matrix will be $x = \begin{bmatrix} 10 & 5 & 4 \\ 2 & 8 & 7 \end{bmatrix}$	**x=[1, 5, 3; 2, 4, 6];** **y=[10,2,4; 1, 8, 7];** **ans =** **10 5 4** **2 8 7**
min(x)	Finds the smallest value in a **vector x**. For example, if x = [1 5 3] the minimum value is 1.	**x=[1, 5, 3];** **min(x)** **ans = 1**
	Creates a row vector containing the minimum element from each column of a **matrix x**. For example, if $x = \begin{bmatrix} 1 & 5 & 3 \\ 2 & 4 & 6 \end{bmatrix}$, then the minimum value in column 1 is 1, the minimum value in column 2 is 4, and the minimum value in column 3 is 3.	**x=[1, 5, 3; 2, 4, 6];** **min(x)** **ans = 1 4 3**

[a,b]=min(x)	Finds both the smallest value in a **vector x** and its location in vector **x**. For $x = [1 \quad 5 \quad 3]$, the minimum value is named **a** and is found to be 1. The location of the minimum value is element 1 and is named **b**.	**x=[1, 5, 3];** **[a,b]=min(x)** **a = 1** **b = 1**
	Creates a row vector containing the minimum element from each column of a matrix **x** and returns a row vector with the location of the minimum in each column of matrix **x**. For example, if $x = \begin{bmatrix} 1 & 5 & 3 \\ 2 & 4 & 6 \end{bmatrix}$, then the minimum value in column 1 is 1, the minimum value in column 2 is 4, and the minimum value in column 3 is 3. These minima occur in row 1, row 2, and row 1, respectively.	**x=[1, 5, 3; 2, 4, 6];** **[a,b]=min(x)** **a = 1 4 3** **b = 1 2 1**
min(x,y)	Creates a matrix the same size as **x** and **y**. (Both **x** and **y** must have the same number of rows and columns.) Each element in the resulting matrix contains the minimum value from the corresponding positions in **x** and **y**. For example, if $x = \begin{bmatrix} 1 & 5 & 3 \\ 2 & 4 & 6 \end{bmatrix}$ and $y = \begin{bmatrix} 10 & 2 & 4 \\ 1 & 8 & 7 \end{bmatrix}$, then the resulting matrix will be $= \begin{bmatrix} 1 & 2 & 3 \\ 1 & 4 & 6 \end{bmatrix}$	**x=[1, 5, 3; 2, 4, 6];** **y=[10,2,4; 1, 8, 7];** **min(x,y)** **ans =** **1 2 3** **1 4 6**

In-Class Activity

ICA 16-3

Consider the following matrix:

$$x = \begin{bmatrix} 4 & 90 & 85 & 75 \\ 2 & 55 & 65 & 75 \\ 3 & 78 & 82 & 79 \\ 1 & 84 & 92 & 93 \end{bmatrix}$$

1. What is the maximum value in each column?
2. In which row does that maximum occur?
3. What is the maximum value in each row? (You'll have to transpose the matrix to answer this question.)
4. In which column does the maximum occur?
5. What is the maximum value in the entire table?

16.4.2 Mean and Median

Mean: the average of all the values in the data set

Median: the middle value in a data set

There are several ways to find the "average" value in a data set. In statistics, the **mean** of a group of values is probably what most of us would call the average. The mean is the sum of all the values, divided by the total number of values. Another kind of average is the **median**, or the middle value. There are an equal number of values both larger and smaller than the median. The **mode** is the value that appears most often in a data set. MATLAB provides functions for finding the mean, median and the mode, as shown in Table 16.5.

16.4.3 Sums and Products

Often it is useful to add up (sum) all of the elements in a matrix or to multiply all of the elements together. MATLAB provides a number of functions to calculate both sums and products, as shown in Table 16.6.

Table 16.5 Averages

mean(x)	Computes the mean value (or average value) of a **vector x**. For example if $x = [1 \quad 5 \quad 3]$, the mean value is 3.	**x=[1, 5, 3];** **mean(x)** **ans = 3.0000**
	Returns a row vector containing the mean value from each column of a **matrix x**. For example, if $x = \begin{bmatrix} 1 & 5 & 3 \\ 2 & 4 & 6 \end{bmatrix}$ then the mean value of column 1 is 1.5, the mean value of column 2 is 4.5, and the mean value of column 3 is 4.5.	**x=[1, 5, 3; 2, 4, 6];** **mean(x)** **ans = 1.5 4.5 4.5**
median(x)	Finds the median of the elements of a **vector x**. For example, if $x = [1 \quad 5 \quad 3]$, the median value is 3.	**x=[1, 5, 3];** **median(x)** **ans = 3**
	Returns a row vector containing the median value from each column of a **matrix x**. For example, if $x = \begin{bmatrix} 1 & 5 & 3 \\ 2 & 4 & 6 \\ 3 & 8 & 4 \end{bmatrix}$, then the median value from column 1 is 2, the median value from column 2 is 5, and the median value from column 3 is 4.	**x=[1, 5, 3;** **2, 4, 6;** **3, 8, 4];** **median(x)** **ans = 2 5 4**
mode(x)	Finds the value that occurs most often in an array. Thus, for the array $\underline{x} = [1, 2, 3, 3]$ the mode is 3.	**x=[1,2,3,3]** **mode(x)** **ans = 3**

In-Class Activity

ICA 16-4

Consider the following matrix:

$$x = \begin{bmatrix} 4 & 90 & 85 & 75 \\ 2 & 55 & 65 & 75 \\ 3 & 78 & 82 & 79 \\ 1 & 84 & 92 & 93 \end{bmatrix}$$

1. What is the mean value in each column?
2. What is the median for each column?
3. What is the mean value in each row?
4. What is the median for each row?
5. What is returned when you request the mode?
6. What is the mean for the entire matrix?

In addition to simply adding up all the elements, which returns a single value for each column in the array, the **cumsum** function (cumulative sum) adds all of the previous elements in an array and creates a new array of these intermediate totals. This

Table 16.6 Sums and Products

sum(x)	Sums the elements in **vector x**. For example, if $x = [1 \quad 5 \quad 3]$, the sum is 9.	**x=[1, 5, 3];** **sum(x)** **ans = 9**
	Computes a row vector containing the sum of the elements in each column of a **matrix x**. For example, if $x = \begin{bmatrix} 1 & 5 & 3 \\ 2 & 4 & 6 \end{bmatrix}$ then the sum of column 1 is 3, the sum of column 2 is 9, and the sum of column 3 is 9.	**x=[1, 5, 3; 2, 4, 6];** **sum(x)** **ans = 3 9 9**
prod(x)	Computes the product of the elements of a **vector x**. For example, if $x = [1 \quad 5 \quad 3]$, the product is 15.	**x=[1, 5, 3];** **prod(x)** **ans = 15**
	Computes a row vector containing the product of the elements in each column of a **matrix x**. For example, if $x = \begin{bmatrix} 1 & 5 & 3 \\ 2 & 4 & 6 \end{bmatrix}$, then the product of column 1 is 2, the product of column 2 is 20, and the product of column 3 is 18.	**x=[1, 5, 3; 2, 4, 6];** **prod(x)** **ans = 2 20 18**
cumsum(x)	Computes a vector of the same size as, and containing cumulative sums of the elements of, a **vector x**. For example, if $x = [1 \quad 5 \quad 3]$, the resulting vector is $x = [1 \quad 6 \quad 9]$.	**x=[1, 5, 3];** **cumsum(x)** **ans = 1 6 9**
	Computes a matrix containing the cumulative sum of the elements in each column of a **matrix x**. For example, if $x = \begin{bmatrix} 1 & 5 & 3 \\ 2 & 4 & 6 \end{bmatrix}$, the resulting matrix is $x = \begin{bmatrix} 1 & 5 & 3 \\ 3 & 9 & 9 \end{bmatrix}$.	**x=[1, 5, 3; 2, 4, 6];** **cumsum(x)** **ans =** **1 5 3** **3 9 9**
cumprod(x)	Computes a vector of the same size as, and containing cumulative products of the elements of, a **vector x**. For example, if $x = [1 \quad 5 \quad 3]$, the resulting vector is $x = [1 \quad 5 \quad 15]$.	**x=[1, 5, 3];** **cumprod(x)** **ans = 1 5 15**
	Computes a matrix containing the cumulative product of the elements in each column of a **matrix x.** For example, if $x = \begin{bmatrix} 1 & 5 & 3 \\ 2 & 4 & 6 \end{bmatrix}$, the resulting matrix is $x = \begin{bmatrix} 1 & 5 & 3 \\ 2 & 20 & 18 \end{bmatrix}$.	**x=[1, 5, 3; 2, 4, 6];** **cumprod(x)** **ans =** **1 5 3** **2 20 18**

is useful when dealing with the sequences of numbers in a series. Consider the harmonic series

$$\sum_{k=1}^{n} \frac{1}{k}$$

which is equivalent to

$$\frac{1}{1} + \frac{1}{2} + \frac{1}{3} + \frac{1}{4} + \ldots + \frac{1}{n}$$

We could use MATLAB to create a sequence representing the first five values in the sequence as follows

```
k = 1:5;
sequence = 1./5
```

which gives us

```
sequence =
 1.0000   0.5000   0.3333   0.2500   0.2000
```

We could view the series as a sequence of fractions by changing the format to rational with the following code

```
format rat
sequence =
     1    1/2    1/3    1/4    1/5
```

Now we could use the **cumsum** function to find the value of the entire series for values of n from 1 to 5

```
format short
series = cumsum(sequence)
series =
 1.0000  1.5000  1.8333  2.0833  2.2833
```

Similarly the **cumprod** function finds the cumulative product of a sequence of numbers stored in an array.

16.4.4 Sorting Values

Table 16.7 lists several commands to sort data in a matrix into ascending or descending order. For example, if we define an array **x**

```
x = [ 1 6 3 9 4]
```

we can use the **sort** function to rearrange the values.

```
sort(x)
ans =
        1   3   4   6   9
```

The default is ascending order, but adding the string 'descend' to the second field will force the function to list the values in descending order.

```
sort(x, 'descend')
ans =
        9  6  4  3  1
```

Table 16.7 Sorting Functions

sort(x)	Sorts the elements of a vector **x** into ascending order. For example, if $x = [1 \quad 5 \quad 3]$, the resulting vector is $x = [1 \quad 3 \quad 5]$.	**x=[1, 5, 3];** **sort(x)** **ans = 1 3 5**
	Sorts the elements in each column of a matrix **x** into ascending order. For example, if $x = \begin{bmatrix} 1 & 5 & 3 \\ 2 & 4 & 6 \end{bmatrix}$, the resulting matrix is $x = \begin{bmatrix} 1 & 4 & 3 \\ 2 & 5 & 6 \end{bmatrix}$.	**x=[1, 5, 3; 2, 4, 6];** **sort(x)** **ans =** **1 4 3** **2 5 6**
sort(x,'descend')	Sorts the elements in each column in descending order.	**x=[1, 5, 3; 2, 4, 6];** **sort(x,'descend')** **ans =** **2 5 6** **1 4 3**
sortrows(x)	Sorts the rows in a matrix in ascending order on the basis of the values in the first column, and keeps each row intact. For example, if $x = \begin{bmatrix} 3 & 1 & 2 \\ 1 & 9 & 3 \\ 4 & 3 & 6 \end{bmatrix}$, then using the **sortrows** command will move the middle row into the top position. The first column defaults to the basis for sorting.	**x=[3, 1, 3; 1, 9, 3;** **4, 3, 6]** **sortrows(x)** **ans =** **1 9 3** **3 1 2** **4 3 6**
sortrows(x,n)	Sorts the rows in a matrix on the basis of the values in column *n*. If *n* is negative, the values are sorted in descending order. If *n* is not specified, the default column used as the basis for sorting is column 1.	**sortrows(x,2)** **ans =** **3 1 2** **4 3 6** **1 9 3**

You can also use the sort command to rearrange entire matrices. This function is consistent with other MATLAB functions, and sorts based on columns. Each column will be sorted independently. Thus

```
x = [ 1 3; 10 2; 3 1; 82 4; 5 5]
```

gives

```
x =
    1   3
    10  2
    3   1
    82  4
    5   5
```

When we sort the array

```
sort(x)
```

each column is sorted in ascending order.

```
ans =
        1  1
        3  2
        5  3
        10  4
        82  5
```

The **sortrows** allows you to sort entire rows, based on the value in a specified column. Thus

```
sortrows(x,1)
```

sorts based on the first column, but maintains the relationship between values in columns one and two.

```
ans =
        1 3
        3 1
        5 5
        10 2
        82 4
```

Similarly you can sort based on values in the second column.

```
sortrows(x,2)
ans =
        3 1
        10 2
        1 3
        2 4
        5 5
```

These functions are particularly useful in analyzing data. Consider the results of the Men's 2006 Olympic 500-meter speed skating event shown in Table 16.8.

The skaters were given a random number for this illustration, but once the race is over we'd like to sort the table in ascending order, based on the times in the second column.

```
skating_results = [1.0000 42.0930
                   2.0000 42.0890
                   3.0000 41.9350
                   4.0000 42.4970
                   5.0000 42.0020]
sortrows(skating_results,2)
ans =
        3.0000  41.9350
        5.0000  42.0020
        2.0000  42.0890
        1.0000  42.0930
        4.0000  42.4970
```

As you may remember, the winning time was posted by Apolo Anton Ohno, who in our example, is skater number 3.

Table 16.8 2006 Olympic Speed Skating Times

Skater Number	Time (min)
1	42.093
2	42.089
3	41.935
4	42.497
5	42.002

The **sortrows** function can also sort in descending order but uses a different syntax from the **sort** function. To sort in descending order, place a minus sign in front of the column number used for sorting. Thus

```
sortrows(skating_results, -2)
```

sorts the array in descending order, based on the second column. The result of this command is

```
ans =
      4.0000  42.4970
      1.0000  42.0930
      2.0000  42.0890
      5.0000  42.0020
      3.0000  41.9350
```

16.4.5 Determining Matrix Size

MATLAB offers two functions (Table 16.9) that allow us to determine how big a matrix is: **size** and **length**. The **size** function returns the number of rows and columns in a matrix. The **length** function returns the larger of the matrix dimensions. For example, if

```
x = [1 2 3; 4 5 6];
size(x);
```

Table 16.9 Size Functions

size(x)	Determines the number of rows and columns in matrix **x**. (If **x** is a multidimensional array, **size** determines how many dimensions exist and how big they are.)	**x=[1, 5, 3; 2, 4, 6];** **size(x)** **ans = 2 3**
[a,b] = size(x)	Determines the number of rows and columns in matrix **x** and assigns the number of rows to **a** and the number of columns to **b**.	**[a,b]=size(x)** **a = 2** **b = 3**
length(x)	Determines the largest dimension of a matrix **x**.	**x=[1, 5, 3; 2, 4, 6];** **length(x)** **ans = 3**

MATLAB returns the following result

```
ans =
      2   3
```

This tells us that the **x** array has two rows and three columns. However, if we use the **length** function

```
length(x)
```

the result is

```
ans =
      3
```

because the largest of the array dimensions is 3. The **length** function is particularly useful when used with a loop structure, since it can easily determine how many times to execute the loop—based on the dimensions of an array.

EXAMPLE 16.2

Weather Data

Figure 16.5 Satellite photo of a hurricane. (Courtesy of NASA/Jet Propulsion Laboratory).

The National Weather Service collects massive amounts of weather data every day (Figure 16.5). Those data are available to all of us on the agency's online service at http://cdo.ncdc.noaa.gov/CDO/cdo. Analyzing large amounts of data can be confusing, so it's a good idea to start with a small data set, develop an approach that works, and then apply it to the larger data set that we are interested in.

We have extracted precipitation information from the National Weather Service for one location for all of 1999 and stored it in a file called Weather_Data.xls. (The .xls indicates that the data are in an Excel spreadsheet.) Each row represents a month, so there are 12 rows, and each column represents the day of the month (1 to 31), so there are 31 rows. Since not every month has the same number of days, data are missing for some locations in the last several columns. We place the number –99999 in those locations. The precipitation information is presented in hundredths of an inch. For example, on February 1 there was 0.61 inch of precipitation, and on April 1, 2.60 inches. A sample of the data is displayed in Table 16.10, with labels added for clarity; however, **the data in the file contain only numbers.**

Use the data in the file to find the following:

a. the total precipitation in each month.
b. the total precipitation for the year.
c. the month and day on which the maximum precipitation during the year was recorded.

1. State the Problem
   Using the data in the file Weather_Data.xls, find the total monthly precipitation, the total precipitation for the year, and the day on which it rained the most.
2. Describe the Input and Output

   Input The input for this example is included in a data file called Weather_Data. xls and consists of a two-dimensional matrix. Each row represents a month, and each column represents a day.

   Output The output should be the total precipitation for each month, the total precipitation for the year, and the day on which the precipitation was a maximum. We have decided to present precipitation in inches, since no other units were specified in the statement of the problem.

Table 16.10 Precipitation Data from Asheville, North Carolina

1999	Day1	Day2	Day3	Day4		Day28	Day29	Day30	Day31
January	0	0	272	0	etc. . . .	0	0	33	33
February	61	103	0	2		62	–99999	–99999	–99999
March	2	0	17	27		0	5	8	0
April	260	1	0	0		13	86	0	–99999
May	47	0	0	0		0	0	0	0
June	0	0	30	42		14	14	8	–99999
July	0	0	0	0		5	0	0	0
August	0	45	0	0		0	0	0	0
September	0	0	0	0		138	58	10	–99999
October	0	0	0	14		0	0	0	1
November	1	163	5	0		0	0	0	–99999
December	0	0	0	0		0	0	0	0

3. Develop a Hand Example

For the hand example, deal only with a small subset of the data. The information included in Table 16.10 is enough. The total for January, days 1 to 4, is

$$\text{total\_1} = (0 + 0 + 272 + 0)/100 = 2.72 \text{ inches}$$

The total for February, days 1 to 4, is

$$\text{total\_2} = (61 + 103 + 0 + 2)/100 = 1.66 \text{ inches}$$

Now add the months together to get the combined total. If our sample "year" is just January and February, then

$$\text{total} = \text{total\_1} + \text{total\_2} = 2.72 + 1.66 = 4.38 \text{ inches}$$

To find the day on which the maximum precipitation occurred, first find the maximum in the table, and then determine which row and which column it is in.

Working through a hand example allows you to formulate the steps required to solve the problem in MATLAB.

4. Develop a MATLAB Solution

First we'll need to save the data file into MATLAB as a matrix. Because the file is an Excel spreadsheet, the easiest approach is to use the Import Wizard. Double-click on the file in the current directory window to launch the Import Wizard.

Once the Import Wizard has completed execution, the variable name **Sheet1** will appear in the workspace window. (See Figure 16.6; your version may name the variable **Weather_data.**)

Because not every month has 31 days, there are a number of entries for nonexistent days. The value –99999 was inserted into those fields. You can double-click the variable name, **Sheet1,** in the workspace window, to edit this matrix and change the "phantom" values to 0. (See Figure 16.7.)

Now write the script M-file to solve the problem:

```
clc
%Example 22.2 - Weather Data
%In this example we will find the total precipitation
%for each month, and for the entire year, using a data file
%We will also find the month and day on which the
%precipitation was the maximum
weather_data=Sheet1;
%Use the transpose operator to change rows to columns
weather_data = weather_data';
%Find the sum of each column, which is the sum for each %month
monthly_total=sum(weather_data)/100
%Find the annual total
yearly_total = sum(monthly_total)
%Find the annual maximum and the day on which it occurs
[maximum_precip,month]=max(max(weather_data))
%Find the annual maximum and the month in which it occurs
[maximum_precip,day]=max(max(weather_data'))
```

Notice that the code did not start with our usual **clear, clc** commands, because that would clear the workspace, effectively deleting the **Sheet1** variable. Next we rename **Sheet1** to weather_data.

Next, the matrix **weather_data** is transposed, so that the data for each month are in a column instead of a row. That allows us to use the **sum** command to add up all the precipitation values for the month.

Now we can add up all the monthly totals to get the total for the year. An alternative syntax is

```
yearly_total = sum(sum(weather_data))
```

Finding the maximum daily precipitation is easy; what makes this example hard is determining the day and month on which the maximum occurred. The command

```
[maximum_precip,month] = max(max(weather_data))
```

is easier to understand if we break it up into two commands. First,

```
[a,b] = max(weather_data)
```

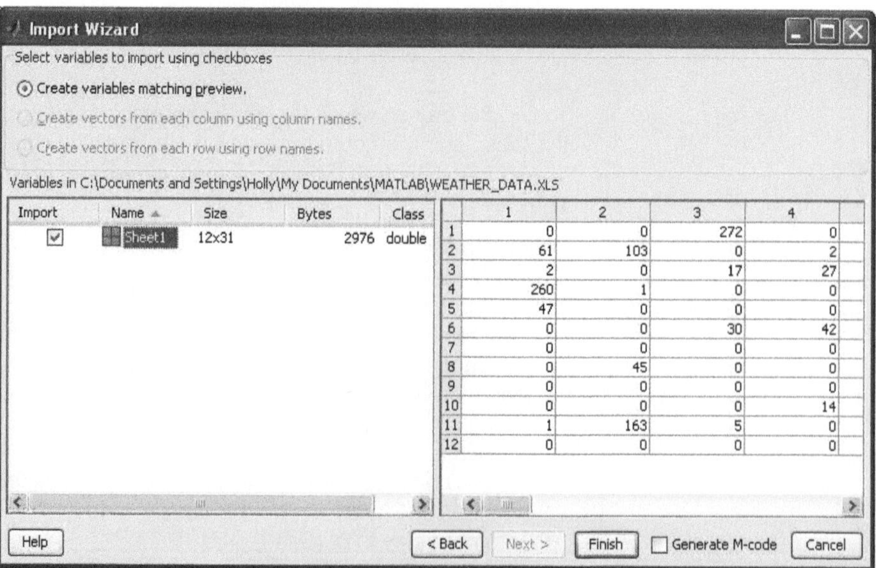

Figure 16.6 MATLAB Import Wizard.

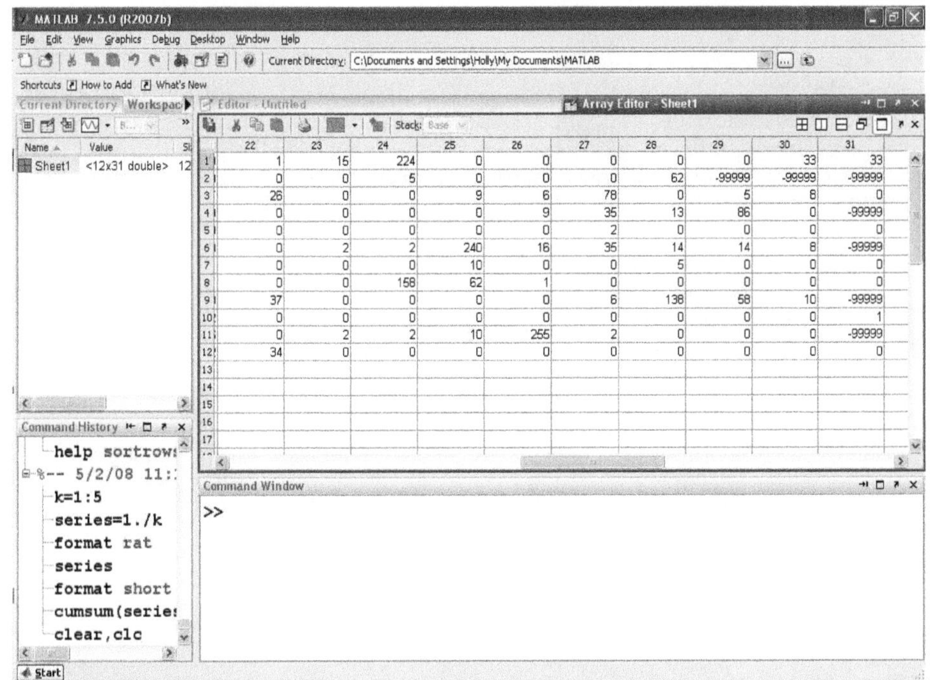

	22	23	24	25	26	27	28	29	30	31
1	1	15	224	0	0	0	0	0	33	33
2	0	0	5	0	0	0	62	-99999	-99999	-99999
3	26	0	0	9	6	78	0	5	8	0
4	0	0	0	0	9	35	13	86	0	-99999
5	0	0	0	0	0	2	0	0	0	0
6	0	2	2	240	16	35	14	14	8	-99999
7	0	0	0	10	0	0	5	0	0	0
8	0	0	158	62	1	0	0	0	0	0
9	37	0	0	0	0	6	138	58	10	-99999
10	0	0	0	0	0	0	0	0	0	1
11	0	2	2	10	255	2	0	0	0	-99999
12	34	0	0	0	0	0	0	0	0	0

Figure 16.7 MATLAB array editor. You can edit the array in this window and change all of the "phantom values" from −99999 to 0.

returns a matrix of maxima for each column, which in this case is the maximum for each month. This value is assigned to the variable name **a**. The variable **b** becomes a matrix of index numbers that represent the row in each column at which the maximum occurred. The result, then, is

```
a =
   Columns 1 through 9
    272  135  78  260  115  240  157  158  138
   Columns 10 through 12
    156   255  97
b =
   Columns 1 through 9
     3   18   27   1    6   25  12   24   28
   Columns 10 through 12
   5   26         14
```

Now when we execute the **max** command the second time, we determine the maximum precipitation for the entire data set, which is the maximum value in matrix **a**. Also, from matrix **a**, we find the index number for that maximum:

```
[c,d]=max(a)
c =
     272
d =
    1
```

These results tell us that the maximum precipitation occurred in column 1 of the **a** matrix, which means that it occurred in the first month.

Similarly, transposing the **weather_data** matrix (i.e., obtaining **weather_data'**) and finding the maximum twice allows us to find the day of the month on which the maximum occurred.

There are several things you should notice about the MATLAB screen shown in Figure 16.8. In the **workspace window**, both **Sheet1** and **weather_data** are listed. **Sheet1** is a

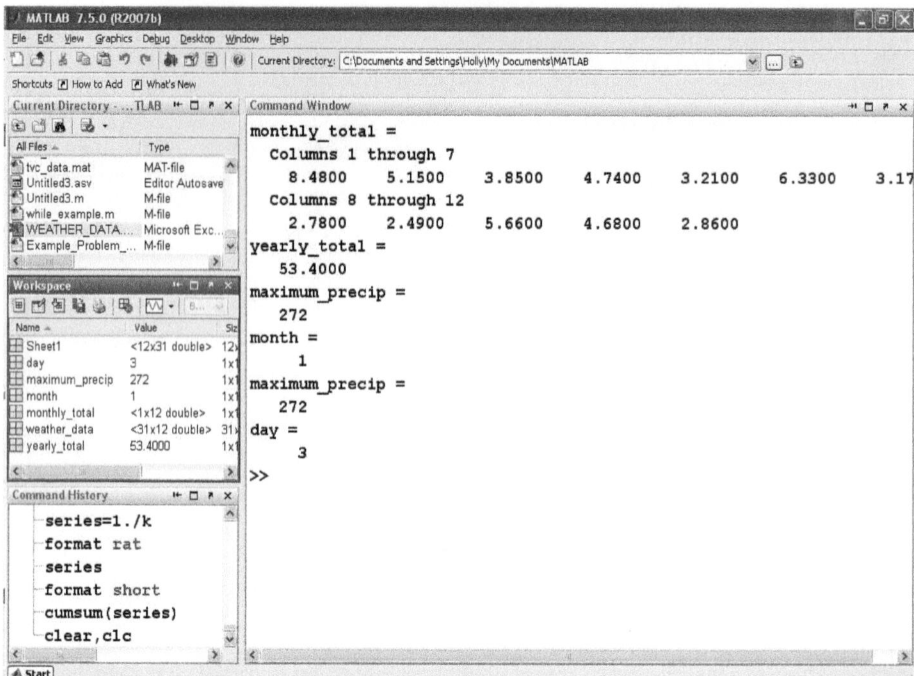

Figure 16.8 Results from precipitation calculations.

12 × 31 matrix, whereas **weather_data** is a 31 × 12 matrix. All of the variables created when the M-file was executed are now available to the command window. This makes it easy to perform additional calculations in the command window after the M-file has completed running. For example, notice that we forgot to change the **maximum_precip** value to inches from hundredths of an inch. Adding the command

maximum_precip = maximum_precip/100

would correct that oversight. Notice also that the Weather_Data.xls file is still in the current directory. Finally, notice that the **command history window** reflects only commands issued from the **command window**; it does not show commands executed from an M-file.

5. Test the Solution
   Open the Weather_Data.xls file, and confirm that the maximum precipitation occurred on January 3. Once you've confirmed that your M-file program works, you can use it to analyze other data. The National Weather Service maintains similar records for all of its recording stations.

16.4.6 Variance and Standard Deviation

Standard Deviation: a measure of the spread of values in a data set

The standard deviation and variance are measures of how much elements in a data set vary with respect to each other. Every student knows that the average score on a test is important, but you also need to know the high and low scores to get an idea of how well you did. Test scores, like many kinds of data that are important in engineering, are often distributed in a "bell"-shaped curve. In a normal (Gaussian) distribution of a large amount of data, approximately 68% of the data falls within one standard deviation (sigma) of the mean (± two sigma). If you extend the range to a two-sigma variation (± two sigma), approximately 95% of the data should fall inside these bounds, and if you

In-Class Activity

ICA 16-5

Consider the following matrix:

$$X = \begin{bmatrix} 4 & 90 & 85 & 75 \\ 2 & 55 & 65 & 75 \\ 3 & 78 & 82 & 79 \\ 1 & 84 & 92 & 93 \end{bmatrix}$$

1. Use the **size** function to determine the number of rows and columns in this matrix.
2. Use the **sort** function to sort each column in ascending order.
3. Use the **sort** function to sort each column in descending order.
4. Use the **sortrows** function to sort the matrix so that the first column is in ascending order, but each row still retains its original data. Your matrix should look like this:

$$X = \begin{bmatrix} 1 & 84 & 92 & 93 \\ 2 & 55 & 65 & 75 \\ 3 & 78 & 82 & 79 \\ 4 & 90 & 85 & 75 \end{bmatrix}$$

5. Use the **sortrows** function to sort the matrix from Exercise 4 in descending order, based on the third column.

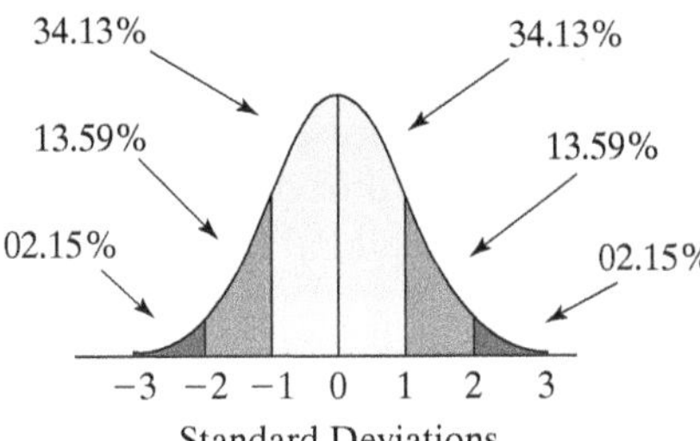

Figure 16.9 Normal distribution.

go out to three sigma, over 99% of the data should fall in this range (Figure 16.9). Usually, measures such as the standard deviation and variance are meaningful only with large data sets.

Variance: the standard deviation squared

Consider the data graphed in Figure 16.10. Both sets of data have the same average (mean) value of 50. However, it is easy to see that the first data set has more variation than the second.

The mathematical definition of variance is

$$\text{variance} = \sigma^2 = \frac{\sum_{k=1}^{N}(x_k - \mu)^2}{N-1}$$

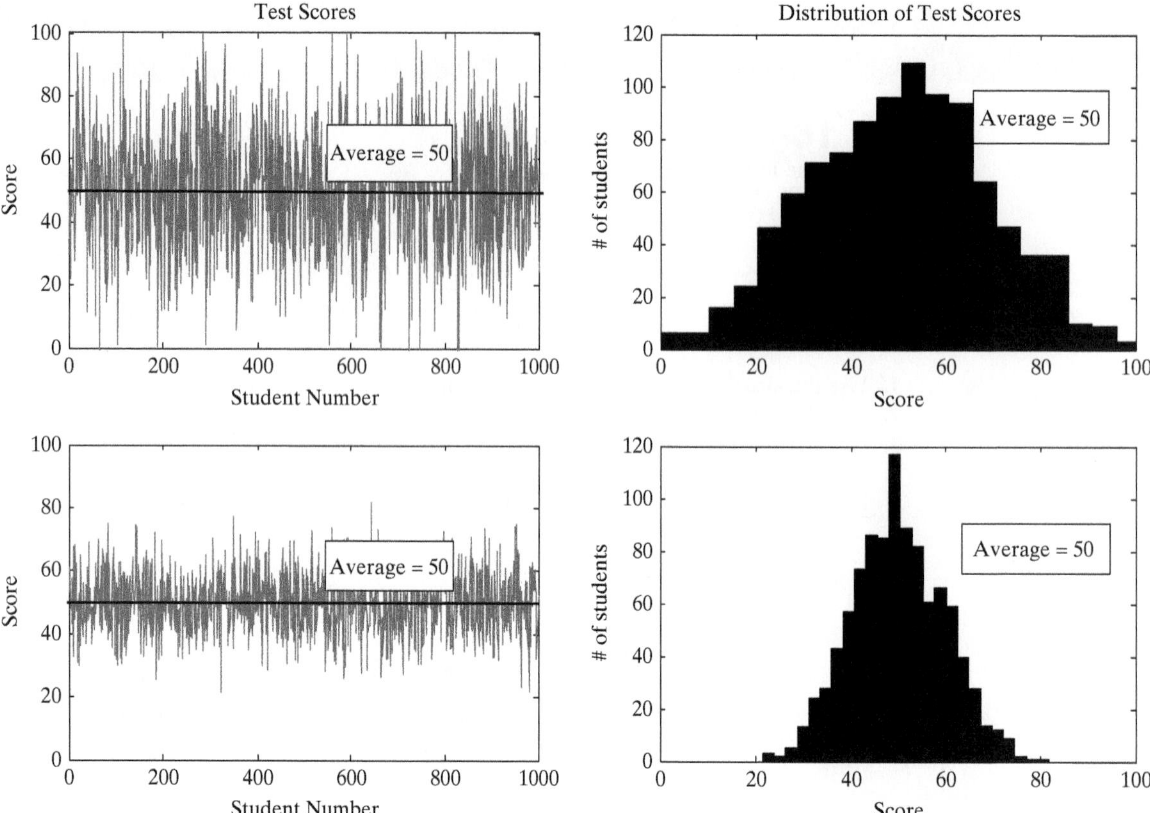

Figure 16.10 Test scores from two different tests.

In this equation, the symbol μ represents the mean of the values x_k in the data set. Thus, the term $x_k - \mu$ is simply the difference between the actual value and the average value. The terms are squared and added together:

$$\sum_{k=1}^{N}(x_k - \mu)^2$$

Finally, we divide the summation term by the number of values in the data set (N), minus 1.

The standard deviation (σ) which is used more often than the variance, is the square root of the variance.

The MATLAB function used to find the standard deviation is **std**. When we applied this function on the large data set shown in Figure 16.10, we obtained the following output:

```
std(scores1)
ans =
   20.3653
std(scores2)
ans =
   9.8753
```

In other words, approximately 68% of the data in the first data set fall between the average, 50, and ±20.3653. Similarly 68% of the data in the second data set fall between the same average, 50, and ±9.8753.

The variance is found in a similar manner with the **var** function:

```
var(scores1)
ans =
  414.7454
var(scores2)
ans =
 97.5209
```

The syntax for calculating both standard deviation and variance is shown in Table 16.11.

Table 16.11 Statistical Functions

std(x)	Computes the standard deviation of the values in a vector **x**. For example, if $x = [1\ \ 5\ \ 3]$, the standard deviation is 2. However, standard deviations are not usually calculated for small samples of data.	**x=[1, 5, 3];** **std(x)** **ans = 2**
	Returns a row vector containing the standard deviation calculated for each column of a matrix **x**. For example, if $x = \begin{bmatrix} 1 & 5 & 3 \\ 2 & 4 & 6 \end{bmatrix}$ the standard deviation in column 1 is 0.7071, the standard deviation in column 2 is 0.7071, and standard deviation in column 3 is 2.1213. Again, standard deviations are not usually calculated for small samples of data.	**x=[1, 5, 3; 2, 4, 6];** **std(x)** **ans =** **0.7071 0.7071** **2.1213**
var(x)	Calculates the variance of the data in **x**. For example, if $x = [1\ \ 5\ \ 3]$, the variance is 4. However, variance is not usually calculated for small samples of data. Notice that the standard deviation in this example is the square root of the variance.	**var(x)** **ans = 4**

In-Class Activity

ICA 16-6

Consider the following matrix:

$$x = \begin{bmatrix} 4 & 90 & 85 & 75 \\ 2 & 55 & 65 & 75 \\ 3 & 78 & 82 & 79 \\ 1 & 84 & 92 & 93 \end{bmatrix}$$

1. Find the standard deviation for each column.
2. Find the variance for each column.
3. Calculate the square root of the variance you found for each column.
4. How do the results from Exercise 3 compare against the standard deviation you found in Exercise 1?

EXAMPLE 16.3

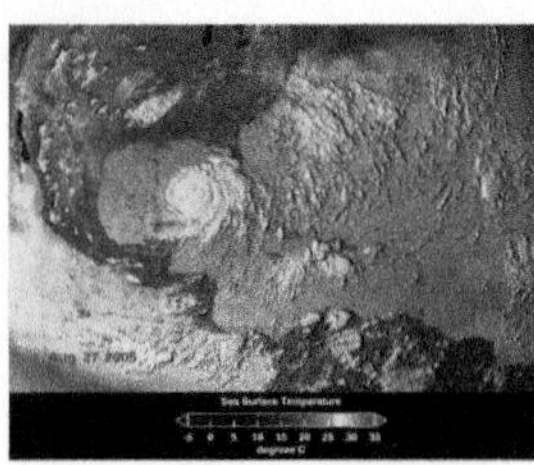

Figure 16.11 A hurricane over Florida. (Courtesy of NASA/Jet Propulsion Laboratory.)

Climatologic Data

Climatologists examine weather data over long periods of time, trying to find a pattern. Weather data have been kept reliably in the United States since the 1850s; however, most reporting stations have been in place only since the 1930s and 1940s (Figure 16.11). Climatologists perform statistical calculations on the data they collect. Although the data in Weather_Data.xls represent just one location for one year, we can use them to practice statistical calculations. Find the mean daily precipitation for each month and the mean daily precipitation for the year, and then find the standard deviation for each month and for the year.

1. State the Problem
   Find the mean daily precipitation for each month and for the year, on the basis of the data in Weather_Data.xls. Also, find the standard deviation of the data during each month and during the entire year.

2. Describe the Input and Output

   Input Use the Weather_Data.xls file as input to the problem.

   Output Find

   The mean daily precipitation for each month.
   The mean daily precipitation for the year.
   The standard deviation of the daily precipitation data for each month.
   The standard deviation of the daily precipitation data for the year.

3. Develop a Hand Example
   Use just the data for the first four days of the month:
   January average = (0 + 0 + 272 + 0)/4 = 68 hundredths of an inch of precipitation, or 0.68 inch.
   The standard deviation is found from the following equation:

$$\sigma = \sqrt{\frac{\sum_{k=1}^{N}(x_k - \mu)^2}{N-1}}$$

   Using just the first four days of January, first calculate the sum of the squares of the difference between the mean and the actual value:

$$(0 - 68)^2 + (0 - 68)^2 + (272 - 68)^2 + (0 - 68)^2 = 55{,}488$$

   Divide by the number of data points minus 1:

$$55{,}488/(4 - 1) = 18{,}496$$

   Finally, take the square root, to give 136 hundredths of an inch of precipitation, or 1.36 inches.

4. Develop a MATLAB Solution
   First we need to load the Weather_Data.xls file and edit out the –99999 entries. Although we could do that as described in Example 16.2, there is an easier way: The data from Example 16.2 could be saved to a file, so that they are available to use later. If we want to save the entire workspace, just type

   save <filename>

   where **filename** is a user-defined file name. If you just want to save one variable, type

   save <filename> <variable_name>

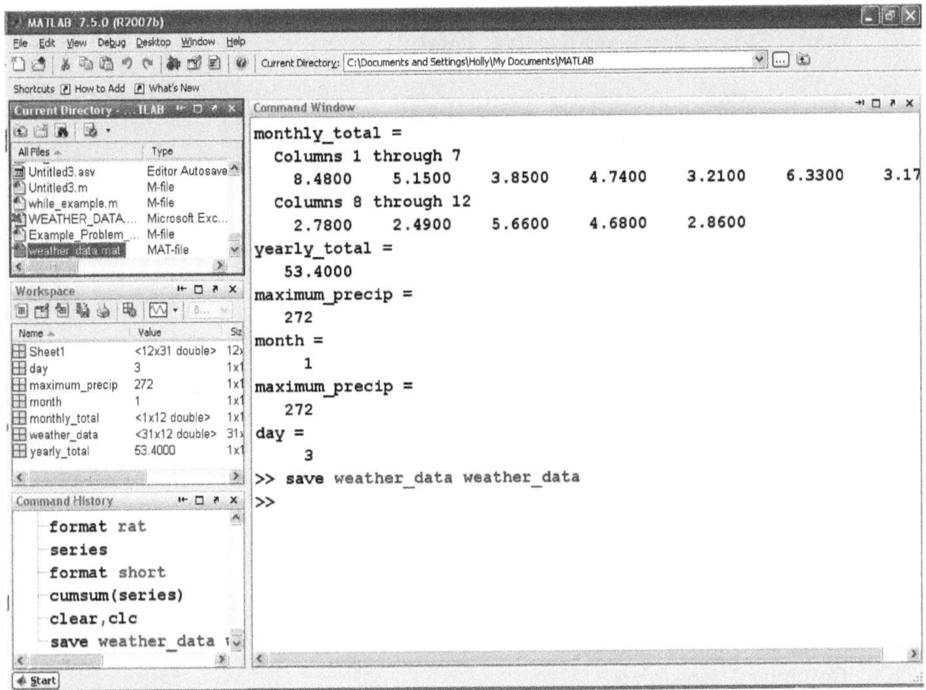

Figure 16.12 The current directory records the name of the saved file.

which saves a single variable or a list of variables to a file. All we need to save is the variable **weather_data**, so the following command is sufficient:

```
save weather_data weather_data
```

This command saves the matrix **weather_data** into the **weather_data.mat** file. Check the current directory window to make sure that **weather_data.mat** has been stored (Figure 16.12).

Now the M-file we create to solve this example can load the data automatically:

```
clear, clc
% Example 22.3 Climatological Data
% In this example, we find the mean daily
% precipitation for each month
% and the mean daily precipitation for the year
% We also find the standard deviation of the data
%
% Changing the format to bank often makes the output
% easier to read
format bank
% By saving the variable weather_data from the last example, it is
% available to use in this problem
load weather_data
Average_daily_precip_monthly = mean(weather_data)
Average_daily_precip_yearly = mean(weather_data(:))
% Another way to find the average yearly precipitation
Average_daily_precip_yearly = mean(mean(weather_data))
% Now calculate the standard deviation
```

```
Monthly_Stdeviation = std(weather_data)
Yearly_Stdeviation = std(weather_data(:))
```

The results, shown in the command window, are

```
Average_daily_precip_monthly =
 Columns 1 through 3
   27.35 16.61 12.42
 Columns 4 through 6
   15.29 10.35 20.42
 Columns 7 through 9
   10.23 8.97   8.03
 Columns 10 through 12
   18.26 15.10  9.23
Average_daily_precip_yearly =
   14.35
Average_daily_precip_yearly =
   14.35
Monthly_Stdeviation =
 Columns 1 through 3
   63.78    35.06    20.40
 Columns 4 through 6
   48.98    26.65   50.46
 Columns 7 through 9
   30.63    30.77    27.03
 Columns 10 through 12
   42.08    53.34    21.01
Yearly_Stdeviation =
   39.62
```

The mean daily precipitation for the year was calculated in two equivalent ways. The mean of each month was found, and then the mean (average) of the monthly values was found. This works out to be the same as taking the mean of all the data at once. Some new syntax was introduced in this example. The command

```
weather_data(:)
```

converts the two-dimensional matrix **weather_data** into a one-dimensional matrix, thus making it possible to find the mean in one step.

The situation is different for the standard deviation of daily precipitation for the year. Here, we need to perform just one calculation:

```
std(weather_data(:))
```

Otherwise you would find the standard deviation of the standard deviation—not what you want at all.

5. Test the Solution
First, check the results to make sure they make sense. For example, the first time we executed the M-file, the **weather_data** matrix still contained –99999 values. That resulted in mean values less than 1. Since it isn't possible to have negative rainfall, checking the data for reasonability alerted us to the problem. Finally, although calculating the mean daily rainfall for one month by hand would serve as an excellent check, it would be tedious. You can use MATLAB to help you by calculating the mean without

using a predefined function. The command window is a convenient place to perform these calculations:

```
load weather_data
sum(weather_data(:,1))  %Find the sum of all the rows in
                        %column one of matrix weather_data
ans =
   848.00
ans/31
ans =
   27.35
```

Compare these results with those for January (month 1).

HINT

Use the colon operator to change a two-dimensional matrix into a single column:

```
A = X(:)
```

16.5 RANDOM NUMBERS

Random numbers are often used in engineering calculations to simulate measured data. Measured data rarely behave exactly as predicted by mathematical models, so we can add small values of random numbers to our predictions to make a model behave more like a real system. Random numbers are also used to model games of chance. Two different types of random numbers can be generated in MATLAB: uniform random numbers and Gaussian random numbers (often called a normal distribution).

16.5.1 Uniform Random Numbers

Uniform random numbers are generated with the **rand** function. These numbers are evenly distributed between 0 and 1. (Consult the help function for more details.) Table 16.12 lists several MATLAB commands for generating random numbers.

We can create a set of random numbers over other ranges by modifying the numbers created by the **rand** function. For example, to create a set of 100 evenly distributed numbers between 0 and 5, first create a set over the default range with the command

```
r = rand(100,1);
```

This results in a 100×1 matrix of values. Now we just need to multiply by 5 to expand the range to 0 to 5:

```
r = r * 5;
```

If we want to change the range to 5 to 10, we can add 5 to every value in the array:

```
r = r + 5;
```

Table 16.12 Random-Number Generators

rand(n)	Returns an $n \times n$ matrix. Each value in the matrix is a random number between 0 and 1.	**rand(2)** **ans =** **0.9501 0.6068** **0.2311 0.4860**
rand(m,n)	Returns an $m \times n$ matrix. Each value in the matrix is a random number between 0 and 1.	**rand(3,2)** **ans =** **0.8913 0.0185** **0.7621 0.8214** **0.4565 0.4447**
randn(n)	Returns an $n \times n$ matrix. Each value in the matrix is a Gaussian (or normal) random number with a mean of 0 and a variance of 1.	**randn(2)** **ans =** **–0.4326 0.1253** **–1.6656 0.2877**
randn(m,n)	Returns an $m \times n$ matrix. Each value in the matrix is a Gaussian (or normal) random number with a mean of 0 and a variance of 1.	**randn(3,2)** **ans =** **–1.1465 –0.0376** **1.1909 0.3273** **1.1892 0.1746**

The result will be random numbers varying from 5 to 10. We can generalize these results with the equation

$$x = (\text{max} - \text{min}) \cdot \text{random\_number\_set} + \text{mean}$$

16.5.2 Gaussian Random Numbers

Gaussian random numbers have the normal distribution shown in Figure 16.9. There is no absolute upper or lower bound to a data set of this type; we are just less and less likely to find data, the farther away from the mean we get. Gaussian random-number sets are described by specifying their average and the standard deviation of the data set.

MATLAB generates Gaussian values with a mean of 0 and a variance of 1.0, using the **randn** function. For example,

```
randn(3)
```

returns a 3 × 3 matrix

```
ans =
  -0.4326   0.2877   1.1892
  -1.6656  -1.1465  -0.0376
   0.1253   1.1909   0.3273
```

If we need a data set with a different average or a different standard deviation, we start with the default set of random numbers and then modify it. Since the default standard deviation is 1, we must *multiply* by the required standard deviation for the new data set. Since the default mean is 0, we'll need to *add* the new mean:

$$x = \text{standard\_deviation} \cdot \text{random\_data\_set} + \text{mean}$$

For example, to create a sequence of 500 Gaussian random variables with a standard deviation of 2.5 and a mean of 3, type

```
x = randn(1,500)*2.5 + 3;
```

Notice that both **rand** and **randn** can accept either one or two input values. If only one is specified the result is a square matrix. If two values are specified they represent the number of rows and the number of columns in the resulting matrix.

In-Class Activity

ICA 16-7

1. Create a 3 × 3 matrix of evenly distributed random numbers.
2. Create a 3 × 3 matrix of normally distributed random numbers.
3. Create a 100 × 5 matrix of evenly distributed random numbers. Be sure to suppress the output.
4. Find the maximum, the standard deviation, the variance, and the mean for each column in the matrix that you created in Exercise 3.
5. Create a 100 × 5 matrix of normally distributed random numbers. Be sure to suppress the output.
6. Find the maximum, the standard deviation, the variance, and the mean for each column in the matrix you created in Exercise 5.
7. Explain why your results for Exercises 4 and 6 are different.

EXAMPLE 16.4

Noise

Random numbers can be used to simulate the noise we hear as static on the radio. By adding this noise to data files that store music, we can study the effect of static on recordings.

MATLAB has the ability to play music files by means of the **sound** function. To demonstrate this function, it also has a built-in music file with a short segment of Handel's *Messiah*. In this example, we will use the **randn** function to create noise, and then we'll add the noise to the music clip.

Music is stored in MATLAB as an array with values from –1 to 1. To convert this array into music, the **sound** function requires a sample frequency. The **handel.mat** file contains both an array representing the music and the value of the sample frequency. To hear the *Messiah*, you must first load the file, using the command

```
load handel
```

Notice that two new variables—**y** and **Fs**—were added to the workspace window when the **handel** file was loaded. To play the clip, type

```
sound(y, Fs)
```

Experiment with different values of **Fs** to hear the effect of different sample frequencies on the music. (Clearly, the sound must be engaged on your computer, or you won't be able to hear the playback.)

Figure 16.13 Utah Symphony Orchestra.

1. State the Problem
   Add a noise component to the recording of Handel's *Messiah* included with MATLAB.

2. Describe the Input and Output

   Input MATLAB data file of Handel's *Messiah*, stored as the built-in file **handel**

   Output An array representing the *Messiah*, with static added
   A graph of the first 200 elements of the data file

3. Develop a Hand Example
   Since the data in the music file vary between –1 and +1, we should add noise values of a smaller order of magnitude. First we'll try values centered on 0 and with a standard deviation of 0.1.

4. Develop a MATLAB Solution

```
%Example 22.4
%Noise
load handel   %Load the music data file
sound(y,Fs)   %Play the music data file
pause         %Pause to listen to the music
% Be sure to hit enter to continue after playing the music
% Add random noise
noise=randn(length(y),1)*0.10;
sound(y+noise,Fs)
```

This program allows you to play the recording of the *Messiah*, both with and without the added noise. You can adjust the multiplier on the noise line to observe the effect of changing the magnitude of the added static. For example:

```
noise=randn(length(y),1)*0.20
```

5. Test the Solution
In addition to playing back the music both with and without the added noise, we could plot the results. Because the file is quite large (73,113 elements), we'll just plot the first 200 points:

```
%  Plot the first 200 data points in each file
t=1:length(y);
noisy = y + noise;
plot(t(1,1:200),y(1:200,1),t(1,1:200),noisy(1:200,1),':')
title('Handel''s Messiah')
xlabel('Element Number in Music Array')
ylabel('Frequency')
```

These commands tell MATLAB to plot the index number of the data on the *x*-axis and the value stored in the music arrays on the *y*-axis.

In Figure 16.14, the solid line represents the original data and the dotted line the data to which we've added noise. As expected, the noisy data has a bigger range and doesn't always follow the same pattern as the original.

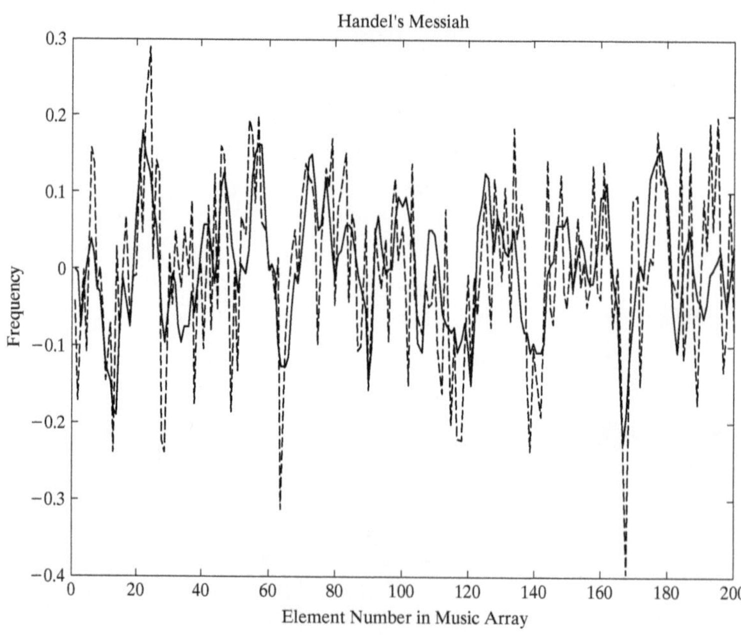

Figure 16.14 Handel's *Messiah*. The solid line represents the original data, and the dotted line is the data to which we've added noise.

Table 16.13 Computational Limits

realmax	Returns the largest possible floating-point number used in MATLAB.	**realmax** **ans = 1.7977e+308**
realmin	Returns the smallest possible floating-point number used in MATLAB.	**realmin** **ans = 2.2251e-308**
intmax	Returns the largest possible integer number used in MATLAB.	**intmax** **ans = 2147483647**
intmin	Returns the smallest possible integer number used in MATLAB.	**intmin** **ans = –2147483648**

The value of **realmax** corresponds roughly to 2^{1024}, since computers actually perform their calculations in binary (base-2) arithmetic. Of course, it is possible to formulate a problem in which the result of an expression is larger or smaller than the permitted maximum. For example, suppose that we execute the following commands:

```
x = 2.5e200;
y = 1.0e200;
z = x*y
```

MATLAB responds with

```
z =
   Inf
```

Overflow: a calculational result that is too large for the computer program to handle

Underflow: a calculational result that is too small for the computer program to distinguish from zero

because the answer (2.5**e**400) is outside the allowable range. This error is called *exponent overflow*, because the exponent of the result of an arithmetic operation is too large to store in the computer's memory.

Exponent underflow is a similar error, caused by the exponent of the result of an arithmetic operation being too *small* to store in the computer's memory. Using the same allowable range, we obtain an exponent underflow with the following commands:

```
x = 2.5e-200;
y = 1.0e200
z = x/y
```

Together, these commands return

```
z = 0
```

The result of an exponent underflow is zero.

Key Idea: Careful planning can help you avoid calculational overflow or underflow

We also know that division by zero is an invalid operation. If an expression results in a division by zero, the result of the division is infinity:

```
z = y/0
z =
   Inf
```

MATLAB may print a warning telling you that division by zero is not possible.

16.6 SPECIAL VALUES AND MISCELLANEOUS FUNCTIONS

Most, but not all, functions require an input argument. Although used as if they were scalar constants, the functions listed in Table 16.14 do *not* require any input.

MATLAB allows you to redefine these special values as variable names; however, doing so can have unexpected consequences. For example, the following MATLAB code is allowed, even though it is not wise:

```
pi = 12.8;
```

From this point on, whenever the variable **pi** is called, the new value will be used. Similarly, you can redefine **any** function as a variable name, such as

```
sin = 10;
```

To restore **sin** to its job as a trigonometric function (or to restore the default value of **pi**), you must clear the workspace with

```
clear
```

Now check to see the result by issuing the command for π.

```
pi
```

This command returns

```
pi =
    3.1416
```

HINT

The function *i* is the most common of these functions to be unintentionally renamed by MATLAB users.

In-Class Activity

ICA 16-8

1. Use the **clock** function to add the time and date to your work sheet.
2. Use the **date** function to add the date to your work sheet.
3. Convert the following calculations to MATLAB code and explain your results:
   - **a.** 322! (Remember that, to a mathematician, the symbol ! means factorial.)
   - **b.** 5×10^{500}
   - **c.** $1/5 \times 10^{500}$
   - **d.** 0/0

Table 16.14 Special Functions

pi	Mathematical constant π.	**pi** **ans = 3.1416**
i	Imaginary number.	**i** **ans = 0 + 1.0000i**
j	Imaginary number.	**j** **ans = 0 + 1.0000i**
Inf	Infinity, which often occurs during a calculational overflow or when a number is divided by zero.	**5/0** **Warning: Divide by zero.** **ans = Inf**
NaN	Not a number. Occurs when a calculation is undefined.	**0/0** **Warning: Divide by zero.** **ans = NaN** **inf/inf** **ans = NaN**
clock	Current time. Returns a six-member array [year month day hour minute second]. When the **clock** function was called on July 19, 2008, at 5:19 P.M. and 30.0 seconds, MATLAB returned the output shown at the right.	**clock** **ans = 1.0e+003 *** **2.0080 0.0070 0.0190** **0.0170 0.0190 0.0300**
	The **fix** and **clock** functions together result in a format that is easier to read.	**fix(clock)**
	The **fix** function rounds toward zero. A similar result could be obtained by setting **format bank**.	**ans =** **2008 7 19** **17 19 30**
date	Current date.	**date**
	Similar to the **clock** function. However, it returns the date in a "string format."	**ans = 19-Jul-2008**
eps	The distance between 1 and the next-larger double-precision floating-point number.	**eps** **ans = 2.2204e-016**

SUMMARY

In this chapter, we explored a number of predefined MATLAB functions, including the following:

- general mathematical functions, such as
  - exponential functions
  - logarithmic functions
  - roots
- rounding functions
- functions used in discrete mathematics, such as
  - factoring functions
  - prime-number functions
- trigonometric functions, including
  - standard trigonometric functions
  - inverse trigonometric functions
  - hyperbolic trigonometric functions
  - trigonometric functions that use degrees instead of radians

- data analysis functions, such as
  - maxima and minima
  - averages (mean and median)
  - sums and products
  - sorting
  - standard deviation and variance
- random-number generation for both
  - uniform distributions
  - Gaussian (normal) distributions
- functions used with complex numbers

We explored the computational limits inherent in MATLAB and introduced special values, such as **pi**, that are built into the program.

MATLAB SUMMARY

The following MATLAB summary lists and briefly describes all of the special characters, commands, and functions that were defined in this chapter:

Special Characters and Functions	
eps	smallest difference recognized
i	imaginary number
clock	returns the time
date	returns the date
Inf	infinity
intmax	returns the largest possible integer number used in MATLAB
intmin	returns the smallest possible integer number used in MATLAB
j	imaginary number
NaN	not a number
pi	mathematical constant π
realmax	returns the largest possible floating-point number used in MATLAB
realmin	returns the smallest possible floating-point number used in MATLAB

Commands and Functions	
abs	computes the absolute value of a real number or the magnitude of a complex number
angle	computes the angle when complex numbers are represented in polar coordinates
asin	computes the inverse sine (arcsine)
asind	computes the inverse sine and reports the result in degrees
ceil	rounds to the nearest integer toward positive infinity
complex	creates a complex number
conj	creates the complex conjugate of a complex number

Commands and Functions	
cos	computes the cosine
cumprod	computes a cumulative product of the values in an array
cumsum	computes a cumulative sum of the values in an array
erf	calculates the error function
exp	computes the value of e^x
factor	finds the prime factors
factorial	calculates the factorial
fix	rounds to the nearest integer toward zero
floor	rounds to the nearest integer toward minus infinity
gcd	finds the greatest common denominator
help	opens the help function
helpwin	opens the windowed help function
imag	extracts the imaginary component of a complex number
isprime	determines whether a value is prime
isreal	determines whether a value is real or complex
lcn	finds the least common denominator
length	determines the largest dimension of an array
log	computes the natural logarithm, or the logarithm to the base *e* ($\log_e$)
log10	computes the common logarithm, or the logarithm to the base 10 ($\log_{10}$)
log2	computes the logarithm to the base 2 ($\log_2$)
max	finds the maximum value in an array and determines which element stores the maximum value
mean	computes the average of the elements in an array
median	finds the median of the elements in an array
min	finds the minimum value in an array and determines which element stores the minimum value
mode	finds the most common number in an array
nchoosek	finds the number of possible combinations when a subgroup of *k* values is chosen from a group of *n* values.
nthroot	find the real *n*th root of the input matrix
primes	finds the prime numbers less than the input value
prod	multiplies the values in an array
rand	calculates evenly distributed random numbers
randn	calculates normally distributed (Gaussian) random numbers
rats	converts the input to a rational representation (i.e., a fraction)
	(Continued)

Commands and Functions (*Continued*)	
real	extracts the real component of a complex number
rem	calculates the remainder in a division problem
round	rounds to the nearest integer
sign	determines the sign (positive or negative)
sin	computes the sine, using radians as input
sind	computes the sine, using angles in degrees as input
sinh	computes the hyperbolic sine
size	determines the number of rows and columns in an array
sort	sorts the elements of a vector
sortrows	sorts the rows of a vector on the basis of the values in the first column
sound	plays back music files
sqrt	calculates the square root of a number
std	determines the standard deviation
sum	sums the values in an array
tan	computes the tangent, using radians as input
var	computes the variance

KEY TERMS

argument
average
complex numbers
discrete mathematics
function
function input
Gaussian random variation
mean
median
nesting
normal random variation
overflow
rational numbers
real numbers
seed
standard deviation
underflow
uniform random number
variance

EXERCISES AND ACTIVITIES

Elementary Math Functions

16.1 Find the cube root of -5 both by using the **nthroot** function and by raising -5 to the 1/3 power. Explain the difference in your answers. Prove that both results are indeed correct answers by cubing them and showing that they equal -5.

16.2 MATLAB contains functions to calculate the natural logarithm (**log**), the logarithm to the base 10 (**log10**), and the logarithm to the base 2 (**log2**). However, if you want to find a logarithm to another base—for example, base *b*—you'll have to do the math yourself with the formula

$$\log_b(x) = \frac{\log_e(x)}{\log_e(b)}$$

What is the $\log_b$ of 10 when b is defined from 1 to 10 in increments of 1?

16.3 Populations tend to expand exponentially. That is,

$$P = P_0 e^{rt}$$

where

P = current population,
P_0 = original population,
r = continuous growth rate, expressed as a fraction, and
t = time.

If you originally have 100 rabbits that breed at a continuous growth rate of 90% ($r = 0.9$) per year, find how many rabbits you will have at the end of 10 years.

16.4 Chemical reaction rates are proportional to a rate constant k that changes with temperature according to the Arrhenius equation

$$k = k_0 e^{-Q/RT}$$

For a certain reaction,

$$Q = 8000 \text{ cal/mol}$$
$$R = 1.987 \text{ cal/mol K}$$
$$k_0 = 1200 \text{ min}^{-1}$$

Find the values of k for temperatures from 100 K to 500 K, in 50-degree increments. Create a table of your results.

16.5 Consider the air-conditioning requirements of the large home shown in Figure P16.5. The interior of the house is warmed by waste heat from lighting and electrical appliances, by heat leaking in from the outdoors, and by heat generated by the people in the home. An air conditioner must be able to remove all this thermal energy in order to keep the inside temperature from rising. Suppose there are 20 light bulbs emitting 100 J/s of energy each and four appliances emitting 500 J/s each. Suppose also that heat leaks in from the outside at a rate of 3000 J/s.

(a) How much heat must the air conditioner be able to remove from the home per second?

(b) One particular air-conditioning unit can handle 2000 J/s. How many of these units are needed to keep the home at a constant temperature?

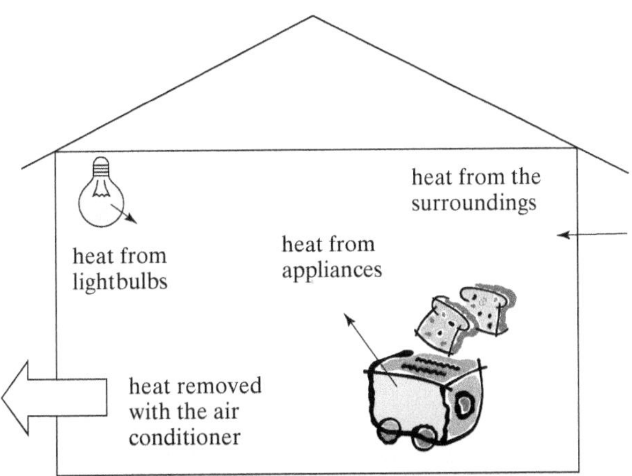

Figure P16.5 Air conditioning must remove heat from a number of sources.

16.6 **(a)** If you have four people, how many different ways can you arrange them in a line?
(b) If you have 10 different tiles, how many different ways can you arrange them?

16.7 **(a)** If you have 12 people, how many different committees of two people each can you create? Remember that a committee of Bob and Alice is the same as a committee of Alice and Bob.
(b) How many different soccer teams of 11 players can you form from a class of 30 students? (Combinations—order does not matter)
(c) Since each player on a soccer team is assigned a particular role, order *does* matter. Recalculate the possible number of different soccer teams that can be formed when order is taken into account.

16.8 There are 52 *different* cards in a deck. How many different hands of 5 cards each are possible? Remember, every hand can be arranged 120 (5!) different ways.

16.9 Very large prime numbers are used in cryptography. How many prime numbers are there between 10,000 and 20,000? (These aren't big enough primes to be useful in ciphers.) (*Hint*: Use the **primes** function and the **length** command.)

Trigonometric Functions

16.10 Sometimes it is convenient to have a table of sine, cosine, and tangent values instead of using a calculator. Create a table of all three of these trigonometric functions for angles from 0 to 2π, with a spacing of 0.1 radian. Your table should contain a column for the angle and then for the sine, cosine, and tangent.

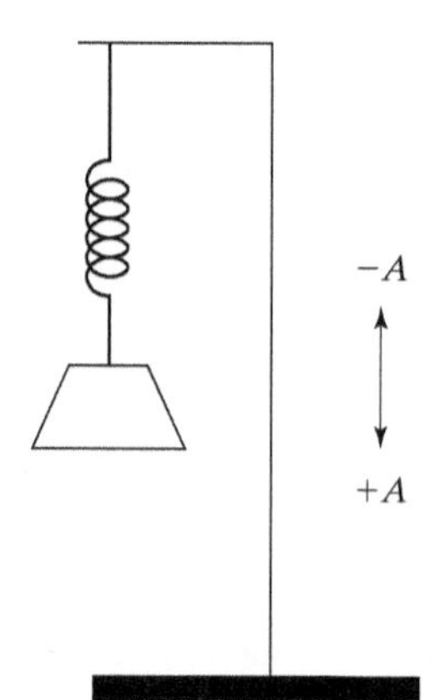

Figure P16.11 An oscillating spring.

16.11 The displacement of the oscillating spring shown in Figure P16.11 can be described by

$$x = A\cos(\omega t)$$

where

x = displacement at time t,
A = maximum displacement,
ω = angular frequency, which depends on the spring constant and the mass attached to the spring, and
t = time.

Find the displacement x for times from 0 to 10 seconds when the maximum displacement A is 4 cm and the angular frequency is 0.6 radian/sec. Present your results in a table of displacement and time values.

16.12 The acceleration of the spring described in the preceding exercise is

$$a = -A\omega^2\cos(\omega t)$$

Find the acceleration for times from 0 to 10 seconds, using the constant values from the preceding problem. Create a table that includes the time, the displacement from corresponding values in the previous exercise, and the acceleration.

16.13 You can use trigonometry to find the height of a building as shown in Figure P16.13. Suppose you measure the angle between the line of sight and the horizontal line connecting the measuring point and the building. You can calculate the height of the building with the following formulas:

$$\tan(\theta) = h/d$$
$$h = d\tan(\theta)$$

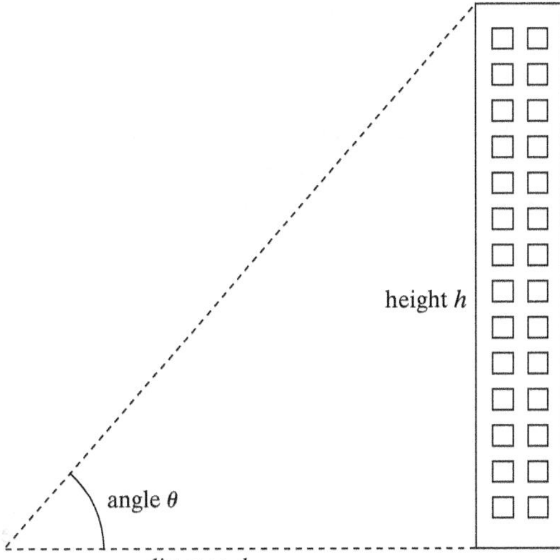

Figure P16.13 You can determine the height of a building with trigonometry.

Assume that the distance to the building along the ground is 120 meters and the angle measured along the line of sight is $30° \pm 3°$. Find the maximum and minimum heights the building can be.

16.14 Consider the building from the previous exercise.

(a) If it is 200 feet tall and you are 20 feet away, at what angle from the ground will you have to tilt your head to see the top of the building? (Assume that your head is even with the ground.)

(b) How far is it from your head to the top of the building?

Data Analysis Functions

16.15 Consider the following table of data representing temperature readings in a reactor:

Thermocouple 1	Thermocouple 2	Thermocouple 3
84.3	90.0	86.7
86.4	89.5	87.6
85.2	88.6	88.3
87.1	88.9	85.3
83.5	88.9	80.3
84.8	90.4	82.4
85.0	89.3	83.4
85.3	89.5	85.4
85.3	88.9	86.3
85.2	89.1	85.3
82.3	89.5	89.0
84.7	89.4	87.3
83.6	89.8	87.2

Your instructor may provide you with a file named **thermocouple.dat**, or you may need to enter the data yourself.

Use MATLAB to find

(a) the maximum temperature measured by each thermocouple.
(b) the minimum temperature measured by each thermocouple.

16.16 The range of an object shot at an angle θ with respect to the x-axis and an initial velocity v_0 (Figure P16.16) is given by

$$\text{Range} = \frac{v_0^2}{g}\sin(2\theta)$$

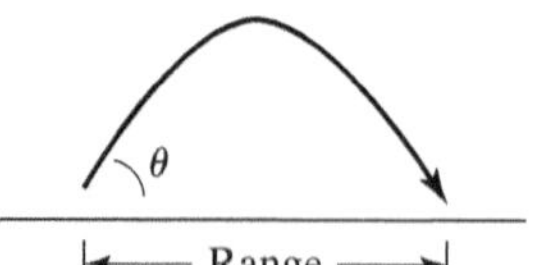

Figure P16.11 The range depends on the launch angle and the launch velocity.

for $0 \le \theta \le \pi/2$ and neglecting air resistance. Use $g = 9.81$ m/s^2 and an initial velocity v_0 of 100 m/s. Show that the maximum range is obtained at approximately $\theta = \pi/4$ by computing the range in increments of $\pi/100$ between $0 \le \theta \le \pi/2$. You won't be able to find the exact angle that results in the maximum range, because your calculations are at evenly spaced angles of $\pi/100$ radian.

16.17 The vector

$$G = [68, 83, 61 ,70, 75, 82, 57, 5, 76, 85, 62, 71, 96, 78, 76, 68, 72, 75, 83, 93]$$

represents the distribution of final grades in a dynamics course. Compute the mean, median, mode, and standard deviation of **G**. Which better represents the "most typical grade," the mean, median or mode? Why? Use MATLAB to determine the number of grades in the array (don't just count them) and to sort them into ascending order.

16.18 Generate 10,000 Gaussian random numbers with a mean of 80 and standard deviation of 23.5. (You'll want to suppress the output so that you don't overwhelm the command window with data.) Use the **mean** function to confirm that your array actually has a mean of 80. Use the **std** function to confirm that your standard deviation is actually 23.5.

16.19 Use the **date** function to add the current date to your homework.

Random Numbers

16.20 Many games require the player to roll two dice. The number on each die can vary from 1 to 6.

(a) Use the **rand** function in combination with a rounding function to create a simulation of one roll of one die.
(b) Use your results from part (a) to create a simulation of the value rolled with a second die.
(c) Add your two results to create a value representing the total rolled during each turn.
(d) Use your program to determine the values rolled in a favorite board game, or use the game shown in Figure P16.20.

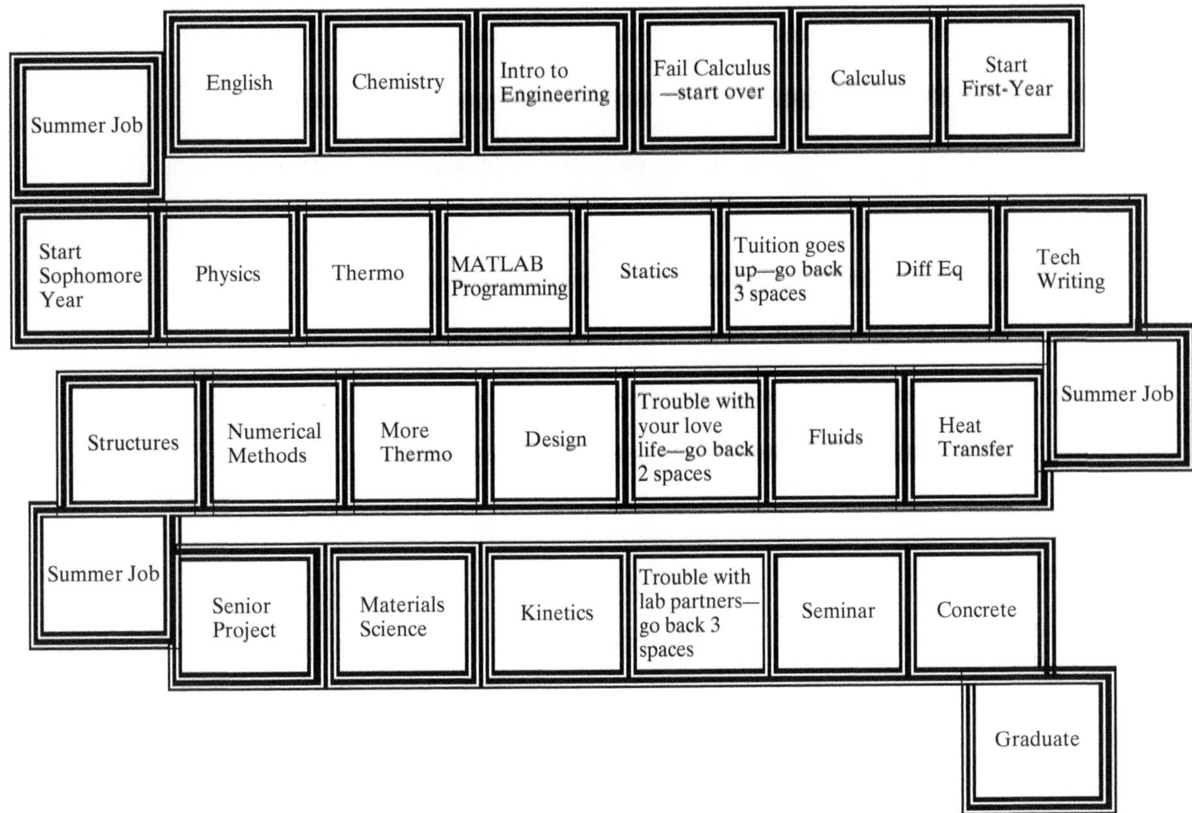

Figure P16.20 The college game.

16.21 Suppose you are designing a container to ship sensitive medical materials between hospitals. The container needs to keep the contents within a specified temperature range. You have created a model predicting how the container responds to the exterior temperature, and you now need to run a simulation.

(a) Create a normal distribution (Gaussian distribution) of temperatures with a mean of 70°F and a standard deviation of 2°, corresponding to two hours' duration. You'll need a temperature for each time value from 0 to 120 minutes. (That's 122 values.)

(b) Plot the data on an *x*–*y* plot. Don't worry about labels. Recall that the MATLAB function for plotting is **plot(x,y)**.

(c) Find the maximum temperature, the minimum temperature, and the times at which they occur.

CHAPTER 17

MANIPULATING MATLAB MATRICES

Objectives

By learning the material in this chapter, you should be able to

- manipulate matrices
- extract data from matrices
- solve problems with two matrix variables of different size
- create and use special matrices

17.1 MANIPULATING MATRICES

As you solve more and more complicated problems with MATLAB, you'll find that you will need to combine small matrices into larger matrices, extract information from large matrices, create very large matrices, and use matrices with special properties.

17.1.1 Defining Matrices

In MATLAB, you can define a matrix by typing in a list of numbers enclosed in square brackets. You can separate the numbers by spaces or by commas, at your discretion. (You can even combine the two techniques in the same matrix definition.) To indicate a new row, you can use a semicolon. For example,

```
A = [3.5];
B = [1.5, 3.1]; or B = [1.5   3.1];
C = [-1, 0, 0; 1, 1, 0; 0, 0, 2];
```

You can also define a matrix by listing each row on a separate line, as in the following set of MATLAB commands:

```
C =    [-1,  0, 0;
         1,  1, 0;
         1, -1, 0;
         0,  0, 2]
```

Taken from *MATLAB® for Engineers*, Second Edition, by Holly Moore.

You don't even need to enter the semicolon to indicate a new row. MATLAB interprets

```
C =     [-1, 0, 0
          1, 1, 0
          1,-1, 0
          0, 0, 2]
```

as a 4 × 3 matrix. You could also enter a column matrix in this manner:

```
A =
    1
    2
    3
```

Ellipsis: a set of three periods used to indicate that a row is continued on the next line

If there are too many numbers in a row to fit on one line, you can continue the statement on the next line, but a comma and an ellipsis (. . .) are required at the end of the line, indicating that the row is to be continued. You can also use the ellipsis to continue other long assignment statements in MATLAB.

If we want to define **F** with 10 values, we can use either of the following statements:

```
F = [1, 52, 64, 197, 42, -42, 55, 82, 22, 109]; or
F = [1, 52, 64, 197, 42, -42, ...
    55, 82, 22, 109];
```

MATLAB also allows you to define a matrix in terms of another matrix that has already been defined. For example, the statements

```
B = [1.5, 3.1];
S = [3.0, B]
```

return

```
S =
    3.0   1.5   3.1
```

Similarly,

```
T = [1, 2, 3; S]
```

returns

```
T =
    1   2   3
    3   1.5 3.1
```

Index: a number used to identify elements in an array

We can change values in a matrix, or include additional values, by using an index number to specify a particular element. This process is called *indexing into an array*. Thus, the command

```
S(2) = -1.0;
```

changes the second value in the matrix **S** from 1.5 to −1. If we type the matrix name

```
S
```

into the command window, then MATLAB returns

```
S =
    3.0   -1.0   3.1
```

We can also extend a matrix by defining new elements. If we execute the command

```
S(4) = 5.5;
```

we extend the matrix **S** to four elements instead of three. If we define element

```
S(8) = 9.5;
```

matrix **S** will have eight values, and the values of **S(5)**, **S(6)**, and **S(7)** will be set to 0. Thus,

```
S
```

returns

```
S =
    3.0  −1.0  3.1  5.5  0  0  0  9.5
```

17.1.2 Using the Colon Operator

The colon operator is very powerful for defining new matrices and modifying existing ones. First, we can use it to define an evenly spaced matrix. For example,

```
H = 1:8
```

returns

```
H =
    1  2  3  4  5  6  7  8
```

The default spacing is 1. However, when colons are used to separate three numbers, the middle value becomes the spacing. Thus,

```
time = 0.0 : 0.5 : 2.0
```

returns

```
time =
    0  0.5000  1.0000  1.5000  2.0000
```

The colon operator can also be used to extract data from matrices, a feature that is very useful in data analysis. When a colon is used in a matrix reference in place of a specific index number, the colon represents the entire row or column.

Suppose we define **M** as

```
M = [1 2 3 4 5;
     2 3 4 5 6;
     3 4 5 6 7];
```

We can extract column 1 from matrix **M** with the command

```
x = M(:, 1)
```

which returns

```
x =
     1
     2
     3
```

We read this syntax as "all the rows in column 1." We can extract any of the columns in a similar manner. For instance,

```
y = M(:, 4)
```

returns

```
y =
     4
     5
     6
```

and can be interpreted as "all the rows in column 4." Similarly, to extract a row,

```
z = M(1,:)
```

returns

```
z =
     1   2   3   4   5
```

and is read as "row 1, all the columns."

We don't have to extract an entire row or an entire column. The colon operator can also be used to mean "from row _ to row _" or "from column _ to column _." To extract the two bottom rows of the matrix **M**, type

```
w = M(2:3,:)
```

which returns

```
w =
     2   3   4   5   6
     3   4   5   6   7
```

and reads "rows 2 to 3, all the columns." Similarly, to extract just the four numbers in the lower right-hand corner of matrix **M**,

```
w = M(2:3, 4:5)
```

returns

```
w =
     5   6
     6   7
```

and reads "rows 2 to 3 in columns 4 to 5."

In MATLAB, it is valid to have a matrix that is empty. For example, each of the following statements will generate an empty matrix:

```
a = [ ];
b = 4:-1:5;
```

Finally, using the matrix name with a single colon, such as

```
M(:)
```

transforms the matrix into one long column.

> ***Key Idea:*** You can identify an element using either a single number, or indices representing the row and column

```
M =
 1
 2
 3
 2
 3
 4
 3
 4
 5
 4
 5
 6
 5
 6
 7
```

The matrix was formed by first listing column 1, then adding column 2 onto the end, tacking on column 3, and so on. Actually, the computer does not store two-dimensional arrays in a two-dimensional pattern. Rather, it "thinks" of a matrix as one long list, just like the matrix **M** at the left. There are two ways you can extract a single value from an array: by using a single index number or by using the row, column notation. To find the value in row 2, column 3, use the following commands:

```
M
M =
     1   2   3   4   5
     2   3  (4)  5   6
     3   4   5   6   7
M(2, 3)
ans =
      4
```

Alternatively, you can use a single index number. The value in row 2, column 3 of matrix **M** is element number 8. (Count down column 1, then down column 2, and finally down column 3 to the correct element.) The associated MATLAB command is

```
M(8)
      ans = 4
```

HINT

You can use the word "end" to identify the final row or column in a matrix, even if you don't know how big it is. For example,

```
M(1,end)
```

returns

```
M(1,end)
ans =
     5
```

and

```
M(end, end)
```

returns

```
ans =
     7
```

as does

```
M(end)
ans =
     7
```

In-Class Activity

ICA 17-1

Create MATLAB variables to represent the following matrices, and use them in the exercises that follow:

$$a = [12\ 17\ 3\ 6] \qquad b = \begin{bmatrix} 5 & 8 & 3 \\ 1 & 2 & 3 \\ 2 & 4 & 6 \end{bmatrix} \qquad c = \begin{bmatrix} 22 \\ 17 \\ 4 \end{bmatrix}$$

1. Assign to the variable **x1** the value in the second column of matrix a. This is sometimes represented in mathematics textbooks as element $a_{1,2}$ and could be expressed as **x1** = $a_{1,2}$.
2. Assign to the variable **x2** the third column of matrix *b*.
3. Assign to the variable **x3** the third row of matrix *b*.
4. Assign to the variable **x4** the values in matrix *b* along the diagonal (i.e., elements $b_{1,1}$, $b_{2,2}$, and $b_{3,3}$).
5. Assign to the variable **x5** the first three values in matrix *a* as the first row and all the values in matrix *b* as the second through the fourth row.
6. Assign to the variable **x6** the values in matrix *c* as the first column, the values in matrix *b* as columns 2, 3, and 4, and the values in matrix *a* as the last row.
7. Assign to the variable **x7** the value of element 8 in matrix *b*, using the single-index-number identification scheme.
8. Convert matrix *b* to a column vector named **x8.**

EXAMPLE 17.1

Using Temperature Data

The data collected by the National Weather Service are extensive but are not always organized in exactly the way we would like (Figure 17.1). Take, for example, the summary of the 1999 Asheville, North Carolina, Climatological Data. We'll use these data to practice manipulating matrices—both extracting elements and recombining elements to form new matrices.

The numeric information has been extracted from the table and is in an Excel file called **Asheville_1999.xls**. Use MATLAB to confirm that the reported values on the annual row are correct for the mean maximum temperature and the mean minimum temperature, as well as for the annual high temperature and the annual low temperature. Combine these four columns of data into a new matrix called **temp_data**.

1. State the Problem
   Calculate the annual mean maximum temperature, the annual mean minimum temperature, the highest temperature reached during the year, and the lowest temperature reached during the year for 1999 in Asheville, North Carolina.
2. Describe the Input and Output

   Input

   Import a matrix from the Excel file **Asheville_1999.xls.**

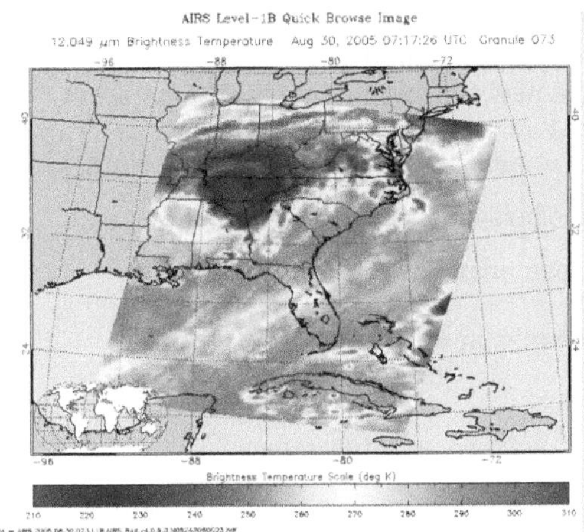

Figure 17.1 Temperature data collected from a weather satellite were used to create this composite false-color image. (Courtesy of NASA/Jet Propulsion Laboratory.)

Output

Find the following four values: annual mean maximum temperature
annual mean minimum temperature
highest temperature
lowest temperature

Create a matrix composed of the mean maximum temperature values, the mean minimum temperature values, the highest monthly temperatures, and the lowest monthly temperatures. Do not include the annual data.

3. Develop a Hand Example
   Using a calculator, add the values in column 2 of the table and divide by 12.
4. Develop a MATLAB Solution
   First import the data from Excel, then save them in the current directory as **Asheville_1999**. Save the variable **Asheville_1999** as the file **Asheville_1999.mat**. This makes it available to be loaded into the workspace from our M-file program:

```
% Example 16.1
% In this example, we extract data from a large matrix and
% use the data analysis functions to find the mean high
% and mean low temperatures for the year and to find the
% high temperature and the low temperature for the year
%
clear, clc
% load the data matrix from a file
load asheville_1999
% extract the mean high temperatures from the large matrix
mean_max = asheville_1999(1:12,2);
% extract the mean low temperatures from the large matrix
mean_min = asheville_1999(1:12,3);
% Calculate the annual means
annual_mean_max = mean(mean_max)
annual_mean_min = mean(mean_min)
% extract the high and low temperatures from the large
% matrix
high_temp = asheville_1999(1:12,8);
low_temp = asheville_1999(1:12,10);
% Find the max and min temperature for the year
```

```
max_high = max(high_temp)
min_low = min(low_temp)
% Create a new matrix with just the temperature
% information
new_table =[mean_max, mean_min, high_temp, low_temp]
```

The results are displayed in the command window:

```
annual_mean_max =
  68.0500
annual_mean_min =
  46.3250
max_high =
  96
min_low =
  9
new_table =
  51.4000   31.5000   78.0000    9.0000
  52.6000   32.1000   66.0000   16.0000
  52.7000   32.5000   76.0000   22.0000
  70.1000   48.2000   83.0000   34.0000
  75.0000   51.5000   83.0000   40.0000
  80.2000   60.9000   90.0000   50.0000
  85.7000   64.9000   96.0000   56.0000
  86.4000   63.0000   94.0000   54.0000
  79.1000   54.6000   91.0000   39.0000
  67.6000   45.5000   78.0000   28.0000
  62.2000   40.7000   76.0000   26.0000
  53.6000   30.5000   69.0000   15.0000
```

5. Test the Solution
   Compare the results against the bottom line of the table from the Asheville, North Carolina, Climatological Survey. It is important to confirm that the results are accurate before you start to use any computer program to process data.

17.2 PROBLEMS WITH TWO VARIABLES

All of the calculations we have done thus far have used only one variable. Of course, most physical phenomena can vary with many different factors. In this section, we consider how to perform the same calculations when the variables are represented by vectors.

Consider the following MATLAB statements:

```
x = 3;
y = 5;
A = x * y
```

Since **x** and **y** are scalars, it's an easy calculation: $\mathbf{x} \cdot \mathbf{y} = 15$, or

```
A =
    15
```

Now let's see what happens if **x** is a matrix and **y** is still a scalar:

```
x = 1:5;
```

returns five values of **x**. Because **y** is still a scalar with only one value (5),

```
A = x * y
```

returns

```
A =
    5   10   15   20   25
```

This is still all review. But what happens if **y** is now a vector? Then

```
y = 1:3;
A = x * y
```

returns an error statement:

```
??? Error using ==> *
Inner matrix dimensions must agree.
```

> ***Key Idea:*** When formulating problems with two variables, the matrix dimensions must agree

This error statement reminds us that the asterisk is the operator for matrix multiplication—which is not what we want. We want the dot-asterisk operator (.*), which will perform an element-by-element multiplication. However, the two vectors, **x** and **y**, will need to be the same length for this to work. Thus,

```
y = linspace(1,3,5)
```

creates a new vector **y** with five evenly spaced elements:

```
y =
    1.0000   1.5000   2.0000   2.5000   3.0000
A = x .* y
A =
    1   3   6   10   15
```

EXERCISES AND ACTIVITIES

Manipulating Matrices

17.1 Create the following matrices, and use them in the exercises that follow:

$$a = \begin{bmatrix} 15 & 3 & 22 \\ 3 & 8 & 5 \\ 14 & 3 & 82 \end{bmatrix} \quad b = \begin{bmatrix} 1 \\ 5 \\ 6 \end{bmatrix} \quad c = \begin{bmatrix} 12 & 18 & 5 & 2 \end{bmatrix}$$

(a) Create a matrix called **d** from the third column of matrix **a**.
(b) Combine matrix **b** and matrix **d** to create matrix **e**, a two-dimensional matrix with three rows and two columns.
(c) Combine matrix **b** and matrix **d** to create matrix **f**, a one-dimensional matrix with six rows and one column.
(d) Create a matrix **g** from matrix **a** and the first three elements of matrix **c**, with four rows and three columns.
(e) Create a matrix **h** with the first element equal to $a_{1,3}$, the second element equal to $c_{1,2}$, and the third element equal to $b_{2,1}$.

17.2 Load the file **thermo_scores.dat** provided by your instructor.

(a) Extract the scores and student number for student 5 into a row vector named **student_5**.

(b) Extract the scores for Test 1 into a column vector named **test_1**.

(c) Find the standard deviation and variance for each test.

(d) Assuming that each test was worth 100 points, find each student's final total score and final percentage. (Be careful not to add in the student number.)

(e) Create a table that includes the final percentages and the scores from the original table.

Student No.	Test 1	Test 2	Test 3
1	68	45	92
2	83	54	93
3	61	67	91
4	70	66	92
5	75	68	96
6	82	67	90
7	57	65	89
8	5	69	89
9	76	62	97
10	85	52	94
11	62	34	87
12	71	45	85
13	96	56	45
14	78	65	87
15	76	43	97
16	68	76	95
17	72	65	89
18	75	67	88
19	83	68	91
20	93	90	92

(f) Sort the matrix on the basis of the final percentage, from high to low (in descending order), keeping the data in each row together. (You may need to consult the **help** function to determine the proper syntax.)

17.3 Consider the following table:

Time (hr)	Thermocouple 1 °F	Thermocouple 2 °F	Thermocouple 3 °F
0	84.3	90.0	86.7
2	86.4	89.5	87.6
4	85.2	88.6	88.3
6	87.1	88.9	85.3
8	83.5	88.9	80.3
10	84.8	90.4	82.4
12	85.0	89.3	83.4
14	85.3	89.5	85.4
16	85.3	88.9	86.3
18	85.2	89.1	85.3
20	82.3	89.5	89.0
22	84.7	89.4	87.3
24	83.6	89.8	87.2

(a) Create a column vector named **times** going from 0 to 24 in 2-hour increments.

(b) Your instructor may provide you with the thermocouple temperatures in a file called **thermocouple.dat**, or you may need to create a matrix named **thermocouple** yourself by typing in the data.

(c) Combine the **times** vector you created in part (a) with the data from **thermocouple** to create a matrix corresponding to the table in this problem.

(d) Recall that both the **max** and **min** functions can return not only the maximum values in a column, but also the element number where those values occur. Use this capability to determine the values of **times** at which the maxima and minima occur in each column.

17.4 Suppose that a file named **sensor.dat** contains information collected from a set of sensors. Your instructor may provide you with this file, or you may need to enter it by hand from the following data:

Time (s)	Sensor 1	Sensor 2	Sensor 3	Sensor 4	Sensor 5
0.0000	70.6432	68.3470	72.3469	67.6751	73.1764
1.0000	73.2823	65.7819	65.4822	71.8548	66.9929
2.0000	64.1609	72.4888	70.1794	73.6414	72.7559
3.0000	67.6970	77.4425	66.8623	80.5608	64.5008
4.0000	68.6878	67.2676	72.6770	63.2135	70.4300
5.0000	63.9342	65.7662	2.7644	64.8869	59.9772
6.0000	63.4028	68.7683	68.9815	75.1892	67.5346
7.0000	74.6561	73.3151	59.7284	68.0510	72.3102
8.0000	70.0562	65.7290	70.6628	63.0937	68.3950
9.0000	66.7743	63.9934	77.9647	71.5777	76.1828
10.0000	74.0286	69.4007	75.0921	77.7662	66.8436
11.0000	71.1581	69.6735	62.0980	73.5395	58.3739
12.0000	65.0512	72.4265	69.6067	79.7869	63.8418
13.0000	76.6979	67.0225	66.5917	72.5227	75.2782
14.0000	71.4475	69.2517	64.8772	79.3226	69.4339
15.0000	77.3946	67.8262	63.8282	68.3009	71.8961
16.0000	75.6901	69.6033	71.4440	64.3011	74.7210
17.0000	66.5793	77.6758	67.8535	68.9444	59.3979
18.0000	63.5403	66.9676	70.2790	75.9512	66.7766
19.0000	69.6354	63.2632	68.1606	64.4190	66.4785

Each row contains a set of sensor readings, with the first row containing values collected at 0 seconds, the second row containing values collected at 1.0 seconds, and so on.

(a) Read the data file and print the number of sensors and the number of seconds of data contained in the file. (*Hint*: Use the **size** function—don't just count the two numbers.)

(b) Find both the maximum value and the minimum value recorded on each sensor. Use MATLAB to determine at what times they occurred.

(c) Find the mean and standard deviation for each sensor and for all the data values collected. Remember, column 1 does not contain sensor data; it contains time data.

CHAPTER 18

PLOTTING

Objectives

By learning the material in this chapter, you should be able to

- create and label two-dimensional plots
- adjust the appearance of your plots
- divide the plotting window into subplots
- create three-dimensional plots
- use the interactive MATLAB plotting tools

Introduction

Large tables of data are difficult to interpret. Engineers use graphing techniques to make the information easier to understand. With a graph, it is easy to identify trends, pick out highs and lows, and isolate data points that may be measurement or calculation errors. Graphs can also be used as a quick check to determine whether a computer solution is yielding expected results.

18.1 TWO-DIMENSIONAL PLOTS

The most useful plot for engineers is the *x–y plot.* A set of ordered pairs is used to identify points on a two-dimensional graph; the points are then connected by straight lines. The values of x and y may be measured or calculated. Generally, the independent variable is given the name x and is plotted on the x-axis, and the dependent variable is given the name y and is plotted on the y-axis.

18.1.1 Basic Plotting

Simple x–y Plots

Once vectors of x-values and y-values have been defined, MATLAB makes it easy to create plots. Suppose a set of time-versus-distance data were obtained through measurement.

We can store the time values in a vector called **x** (the user can define any convenient name) and the distance values in a vector called **y**:

```
x = [0:2:18];
y = [0, 0.33, 4.13, 6.29, 6.85, 11.19, 13.19, 13.96, 16.33, 18.17];
```

To plot these points, use the **plot** command, with **x** and **y** as arguments:

```
plot(x,y)
```

Taken from *MATLAB® for Engineers,* Second Edition, by Holly Moore.

Time, sec	Distance, ft
0	0
2	0.33
4	4.13
6	6.29
8	6.85
10	11.19
12	13.19
14	13.96
16	16.33
18	18.17

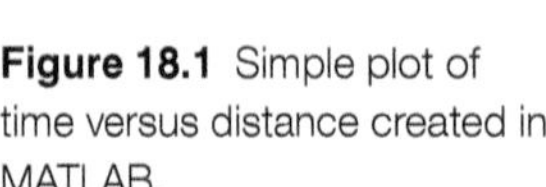

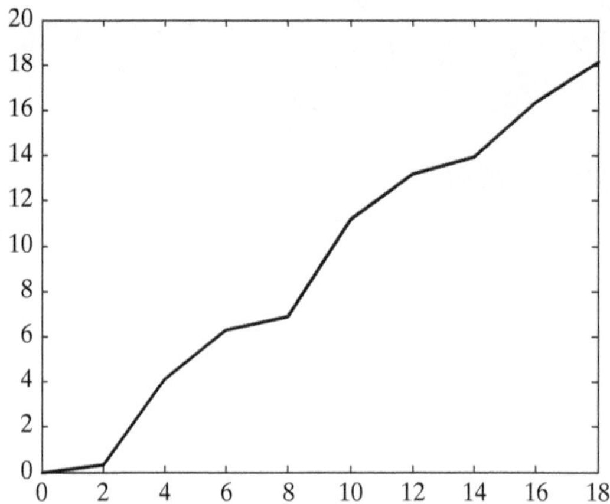

Figure 18.1 Simple plot of time versus distance created in MATLAB.

A graphics window automatically opens, which MATLAB calls Figure 18.1. The resulting plot is shown in Figure 18.1. (Slight variations in scaling of the plot may occur, depending on the size of the graphics window.)

Titles, Labels, and Grids

Good engineering practice requires that we include units and a title in our plot. The following commands add a title, *x*- and *y*-axis labels, and a background grid:

Key Idea: Always include units on axis labels

```
plot(x,y)
xlabel('Time, sec' )
ylabel('Distance, ft')
grid on
```

These commands generate the plot in Figure 18.2. They could also be combined onto one or two lines, separated by commas:

```
plot(x,y) , title('Laboratory Experiment 1')
xlabel('Time, sec' ), ylabel('Distance, ft'), grid
```

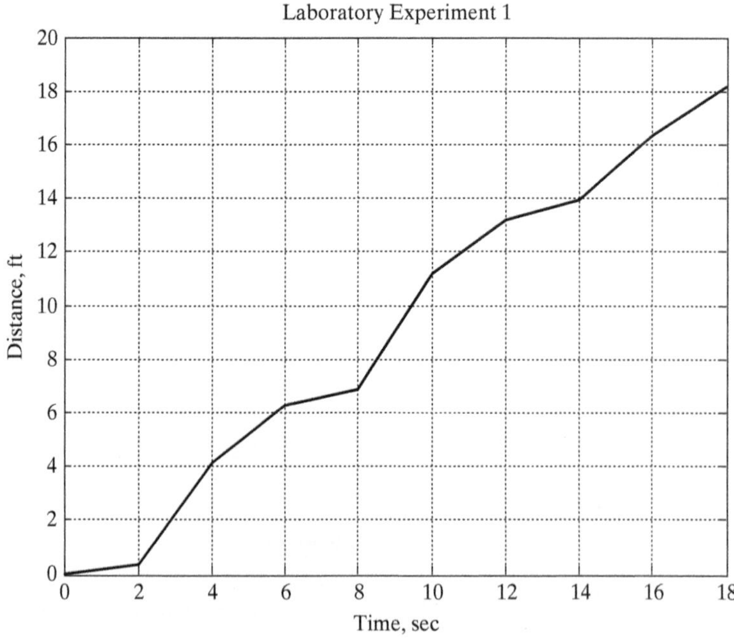

Figure 18.2 Adding a grid, a title, and labels makes a plot easier to interpret.

String: a list of characters enclosed by single quotes

As you type the preceding commands into MATLAB, notice that the text color changes to red when you enter a single quote ('). This alerts you that you are starting a string. The color changes to purple when you type the final single quote ('), indicating that you have completed the string. Paying attention to these visual aids will help you avoid coding mistakes. MATLAB 6 used different color cues, but the idea is the same.

If you are working in the command window, the graphics window will open on top of the other windows. (See Figure 18.3.) To continue working, either click in the command window or minimize the graphics window. You can also resize the graphics window to whatever size is convenient for you or add it to the MATLAB desktop by selecting the docking arrow underneath the exit icon in the upper right-hand corner of the figure window.

HINT

Once you click in the command window, the figure window is hidden behind the current window. To see the changes to your figure, you will need to select the figure from the Windows task bar at the bottom of the screen.

HINT

You must create a graph *before* you add the title and labels. If you specify the title and labels first, they are erased when the plot command executes.

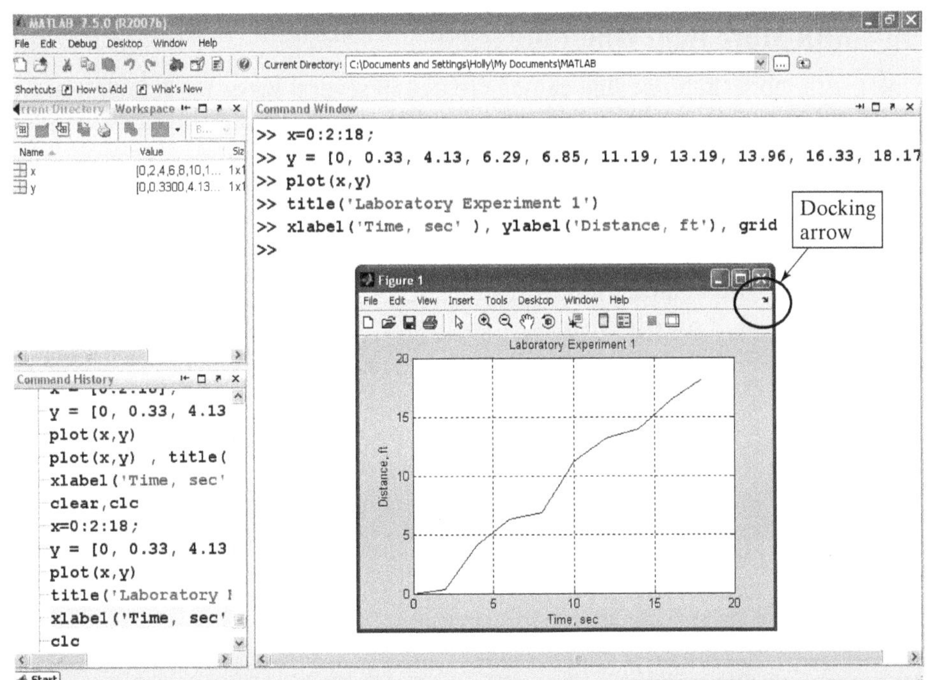

Figure 18.3 The graphics window opens on top of the command window. You can resize it to a convenient shape, or dock it with the MATLAB desktop.

HINT

Because a single quote is used to end the string used in **xlabel, ylabel,** and **title** commands, MATLAB interprets an apostrophe (as in the word *it's*) as the end of the string. Entering the single quote twice, as in **xlabel('Holly''s Data'),** will allow you to use apostrophes in your text. (Don't use a double quote, which is a different character)

Creating Multiple Plots

If you are working in an M-file when you request a plot, and then you continue with more computations, MATLAB will generate and display the graphics window and then return immediately to execute the rest of the commands in the program. If you request a second plot, the graph you created will be overwritten. There are two possible solutions to this problem: Use the **pause** command to temporarily halt the execution of your M-file program, or create a second figure, using the **figure** function.

The **pause** command stops the program execution until any key is pressed. If you want to pause for a specified number of seconds, use the **pause(n)** command, which will cause execution to pause for **n** seconds before continuing.

The **figure** command allows you to open a new figure window. The next time you request a plot, it will be displayed in this new window. For example,

```
figure(2)
```

opens a window named Figure 2, which then becomes the window used for subsequent plotting. Executing **figure** without an input parameter causes a new window to open, numbered consecutively one up from the current window. For example, if the current figure window is named "Figure 2," executing **figure** will cause "Figure 3" to open. The commands used to create a simple plot are summarized in Table 18.1.

Plots with More than One Line

A plot with more than one line can be created in several ways. By default, the execution of a second **plot** statement will erase the first plot. However, you can layer plots on

Table 18.1 Basic Plotting Functions

plot	Creates an *x–y* plot	**plot(x,y)**
title	Adds a title to a plot	**title('My Graph')**
xlabel	Adds a label to the *x*-axis	**xlabel('Independent Variable')**
ylabel	Adds a label to the *y*-axis	**ylabel('Dependent Variable')**
grid	Adds a grid to the graph	**grid** **grid on** **grid off**
pause	Pauses the execution of the program, allowing the user to view the graph	**pause**
figure	Determines which figure will be used for the current plot	**figure** **figure(2)**
hold	Freezes the current plot, so that an additional plot can be overlaid	**hold on** **hold off**

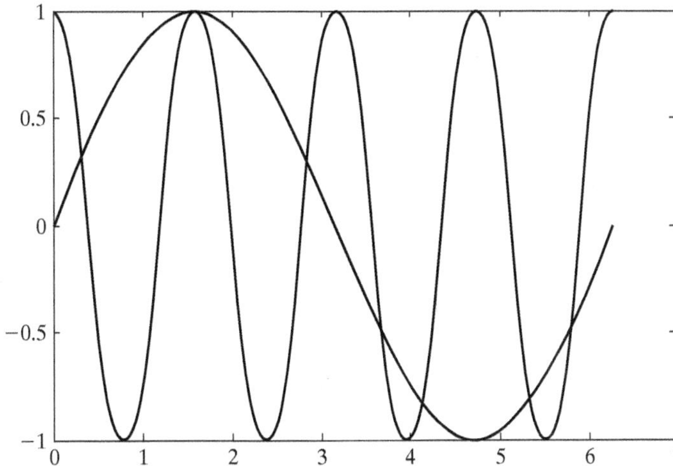

Figure 18.4 The **hold on** command can be used to layer plots onto the same figure.

top of one another by using the **hold on** command. Execute the following statements to create a plot with both functions plotted on the same graph, as shown in Figure 18.4:

```
x = 0:pi/100:2*pi;
y1 = cos(x*4);
plot(x,y1)
y2 = sin(x);
hold on;
plot(x, y2)
```

Semicolons are optional on both the **plot** statement and the **hold on** statement. MATLAB will continue to layer the plots until the **hold off** command is executed:

```
hold off
```

Another way to create a graph with multiple lines is to request both lines in a single **plot** command. MATLAB interprets the input to **plot** as alternating x and y vectors, as in

```
plot(X1, Y1, X2,Y2)
```

where the variables **X1**, **Y1** form an ordered set of values to be plotted and **X2**, **Y2** form a second ordered set of values. Using the data from the previous example,

```
plot(x,y1, x, y2)
```

produces the same graph as Figure 18.4, with one exception: The two lines are different colors. MATLAB uses a default plotting color (blue) for the first line drawn in a **plot** command. In the **hold on** approach, each line is drawn in a separate plot command and thus is the same color. By requesting two lines in a single command, such as **plot(x,y1, x, y2),** the second line defaults to green, allowing the user to distinguish between the two plots.

If the **plot** function is called with a single matrix argument, MATLAB draws a separate line for each column of the matrix. The x-axis is labeled with the row index vector, 1:k, where k is the number of rows in the matrix. This produces an evenly spaced plot, sometimes called a line plot. If **plot** is called with two arguments, one a vector and the other a matrix, MATLAB successively plots a line for each row in the matrix. For example, we can combine **y1** and **y2** into a single matrix and plot against **x**:

```
Y = [y1; y2];
plot(x,Y)
```

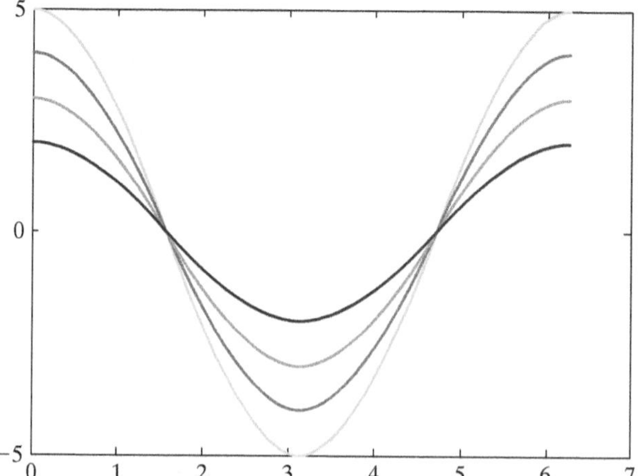

Figure 18.5 Multiple plots on the same graph.

This creates the same plot as Figure 18.4, with each line a different color.

Here's another more complicated example:

```
X = 0:pi/100:2*pi;
Y1 = cos(X)*2;
Y2 = cos(X)*3;
Y3 = cos(X)*4;
Y4 = cos(X)*5;
Z = [Y1; Y2; Y3; Y4];
plot(X, Y1, X, Y2, X, Y3, X, Y4)
```

This code produces the same result (Figure 18.5) as

```
plot(X, Z)
```

A function of two variables, the **peaks** function produces sample data that are useful for demonstrating certain graphing functions. (The data are created by scaling and translating Gaussian distributions.) Calling **peaks** with a single argument **n** will create an $n \times n$ matrix. We can use **peaks** to demonstrate the power of using a matrix argument in the **plot** function. The command

```
plot(peaks(100))
```

results in the impressive graph in Figure 18.6. The input to the plot function created by peaks is a 100×100 matrix. Notice that the x-axis goes from 1 to 100, the index

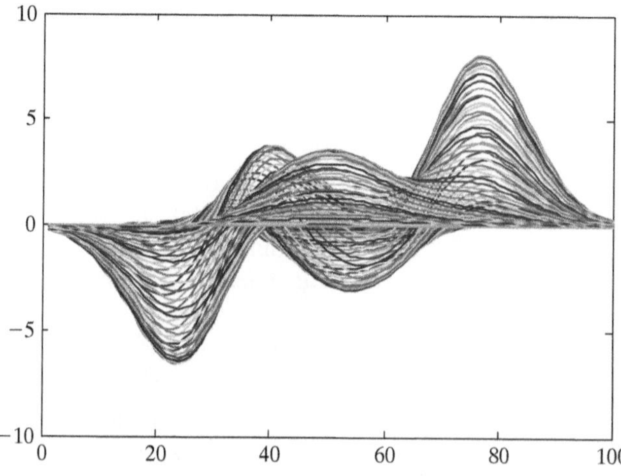

Figure 18.6 The **peaks** function, plotted with a single argument in the **plot** command.

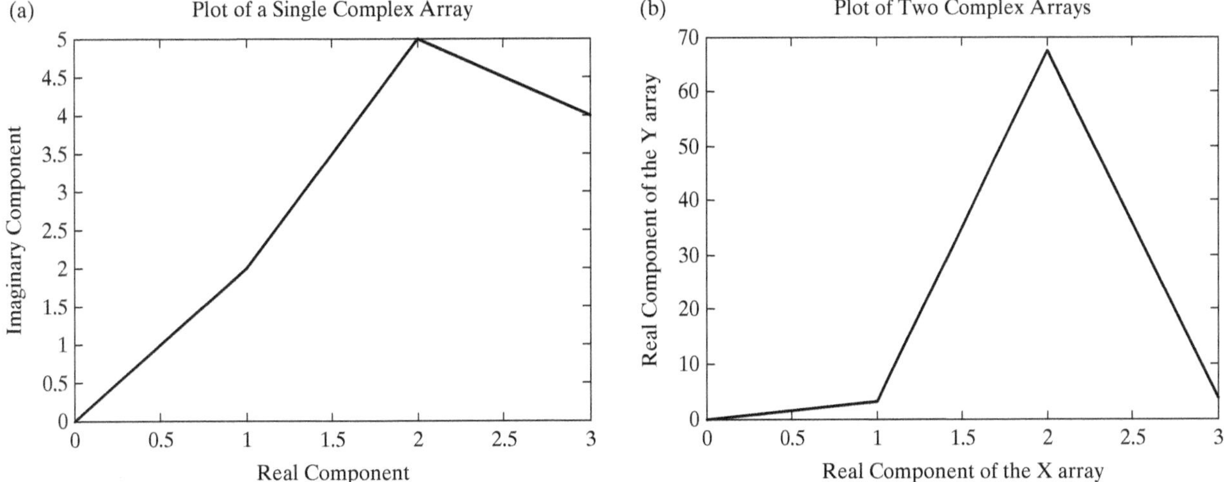

Figure 18.7 (a) Complex numbers are plotted with the real component on the *x*-axis and the imaginary component on the *y*-axis when a single array is used as input. (b) When two complex arrays are used in the **plot** function, the imaginary components are ignored.

numbers of the data. You undoubtedly can't tell, but there are 100 lines drawn to create this graph—one for each column.

Plots of Complex Arrays

If the input to the **plot** command is a single array of complex numbers, MATLAB plots the real component on the *x*-axis and the imaginary component on the *y*-axis. For example, if

```
A = [0+0i,1+2i, 2+5i, 3+4i]
```

then

```
plot(A)
title('Plot of a Single Complex Array')
xlabel('Real Component')
ylabel('Imaginary Component')
```

returns the graph shown in Figure 18.7a.

If we attempt to use two arrays of complex numbers in the **plot** function, the imaginary components are ignored. The real portion of the first array is used for the *x*-values, and the real portion of the second array is used for the *y*-values. To illustrate, first create another array called **B** by taking the sine of the complex array **A**:

```
B = sin(A)
```

returns

```
B =
   0 3.1658 + 1.9596i 67.4789 -30.8794i 3.8537 -27.0168i
```

and

```
plot(A,B)
title('Plot of Two Complex Arrays')
xlabel('Real Component of the X array')
ylabel('Real Component of the Y array')
```

gives us an error statement.

Warning: Imaginary parts of complex X and/or Y arguments ignored.

The data are still plotted, as shown in Figure 18.7b.

18.1.2 Line, Color, and Mark Style

You can change the appearance of your plots by selecting user-defined line styles and line colors and by choosing to show the data points on the graph with user-specified mark styles. The command

```
help plot
```

returns a list of the available options. You can select solid (the default), dashed, dotted, and dash-dot line styles, and you can choose to show the points. The choices among marks include plus signs, stars, circles, and x-marks, among others. There are seven different color choices. (See Table 18.2 for a complete list.)

The following commands illustrate the use of line, color, and mark styles:

```
x = [1:10];
y = [ 58.5, 63.8, 64.2, 67.3, 71.5, 88.3, 90.1, 90.6, 89.5,90.4];
plot(x,y, ':ok')
```

The resulting plot (Figure 18.8a) consists of a dashed line, together with data points marked with circles. The line, the points, and the circles are drawn in black. The indicators were listed inside a string, denoted with single quotes. The order in which they are entered is arbitrary and does not affect the output.

To specify line, mark, and color styles for multiple lines, add a string containing the choices after each pair of data points. If the string is not included, the defaults are used. For example,

```
plot(x,y, ':ok',x,y*2, '—xr',x,y/2, '–b')
```

results in the graph shown in Figure 18.8b.

The **plot** command offers additional options to control the way the plot appears. For example, the line width can be controlled. Plots intended for overhead presentations may

Table 18.2 Line, Mark, and Color Options

Line Type	Indicator	Point Type	Indicator	Color	Indicator
solid	-	point	.	blue	b
dotted	:	circle	o	green	g
dash-dot	-.	x-mark	x	red	r
dashed	—	plus	+	cyan	c
		star	*	magenta	m
		square	s	yellow	y
		diamond	d	black	k
		triangle down	v	white	w
		triangle up	^		
		triangle left	<		
		triangle right	>		
		pentagram	p		
		hexagram	h		

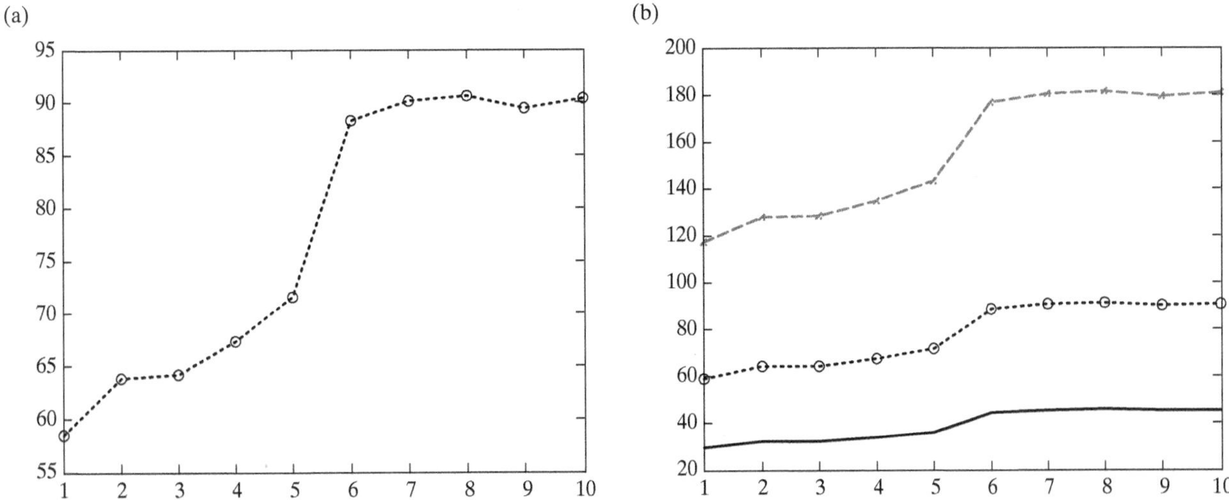

Figure 18.8 (a) Adjusting the line, mark, and color style. (b) Multiple plots with varying line styles, colors, and point styles.

look better with thicker lines. Use the **help** function to learn more about controlling the appearance of the plot.

18.1.3 Axis Scaling and Annotating Plots

MATLAB automatically selects appropriate *x*-axis and *y*-axis scaling. Sometimes it is useful for the user to be able to control the scaling. Control is accomplished with the **axis** function, shown in Table 18.3. Executing the **axis** function without any input

```
axis
```

freezes the scaling of the plot. If you use the **hold on** command to add a second line to your graph, the scaling cannot change. To return control of the scaling to MATLAB, simply re-execute the **axis** function.

The **axis** function also accepts input defining the *x*-axis and *y*-axis scaling. The argument is a single matrix, with four values representing

- the minimum *x* value shown on the *x*-axis
- the maximum *x* value shown on the *x*-axis
- the minimum *y* value shown on the *y*-axis
- the maximum *y* value shown on the *y*-axis

Thus the command

```
axis([-2, 3, 0, 10])
```

fixes the plot axes to *x* from −2 to +3 and *y* from 0 to 10.

MATLAB offers several additional functions, also listed in Table 18.3, that allow you to annotate your plots. The **legend** function requires the user to specify a legend in the form of a string for each line plotted, and displays it in the upper right-hand corner of the plot. The **text** function allows you to add a text box to your plot, which is useful for describing features on the graph. It requires the user to specify the location of the lower left-hand corner of the box in the plot window as the first two input fields, with a string specifying the contents of the text box in the third input field. The use of both

Table 18.3 Axis Scaling and Annotating Plots

axis	When the **axis** function is used without inputs, it freezes the axis at the current configuration. Executing the function a second time returns axis control to MATLAB.
axis(v)	The input to the **axis** command must be a four-element vector that specifies the minimum and maximum values for both the *x*- and *y*-axes—for example, **[xmin, xmax,ymin,ymax]**
legend('string1', 'string 2', etc)	Allows you to add a legend to your graph. The legend shows a sample of the line and lists the string you have specified.
text(x_coordinate,y_coordinate, 'string')	Allows you to add a text box to the graph. The box is placed at the specified *x*- and *y*-coordinates and contains the string value specified.
gtext('string')	Similar to text. The box is placed at a location determined interactively by the user by clicking in the figure window.

legend and **text** is demonstrated in the following code, which modifies the graph from Figure 18.8b.

```
legend('line 1', 'line 2', 'line3')
text(1,100, 'Label plots with the text command')
```

We added a title, *x* and *y* labels, and adjusted the axis with the following commands:

```
xlabel('My x label'), ylabel('My y label')
title('Sample graph for Chapter 17')
axis([0,11,0,200])
```

The results are shown in Figure 18.9.

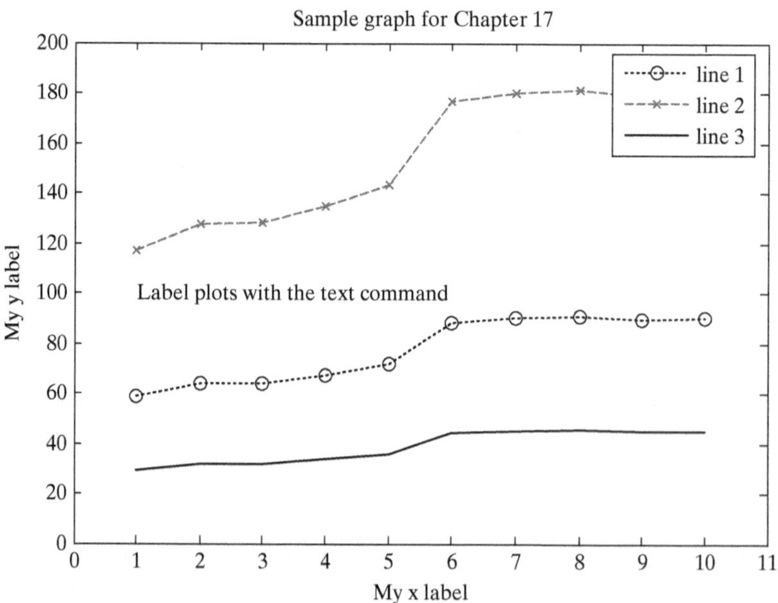

Figure 18.9 Final version of the sample graph, annotated with a legend, a text box, a title, *x* and *y* labels, and a modified axis.

HINT

You can use Greek letters in your titles and labels by putting a backslash (\) before the name of the letter. For example,

title('\alpha \beta \gamma')

creates the plot title

$\alpha\beta\gamma$

To create a superscript, use a caret. Thus,

title('x^2')

gives

x^2

To create a subscript, use an underscore.

title('x_5')

gives

x_5

If your expression requires a group of characters as either a subscript or superscript, enclose them in curly braces. For example,

title('k^{-1}')

which returns

k^{-1}

MATLAB has the ability to create more complicated mathematical expressions for use as titles, axis labels, and other text strings, using the TEX markup language. To learn more, consult the **help** feature. (Search on "text properties.")

In-Class Activity

ICA 18-1

1. Plot x versus y for y = sin(x). Let x vary from 0 to 2π in increments of 0.1π.
2. Add a title and labels to your plot.
3. Plot x versus y_1 and y_2 for y_1 = sin(x) and y_2 = cos(x). Let x vary from 0 to 2π in increments of 0.1π Add a title and labels to your plot.
4. Re-create the plot from Exercise 3, but make the sin(x) line dashed and red. Make the cos(x) line green and dotted.
5. Add a legend to the graph in Exercise 4.
6. Adjust the axes so that the x-axis goes from -1 to $2\pi + 1$ and the y-axis from -1.5 to $+1.5$.
7. Create a new vector, **a** = cos(**x**). Let **x** vary from 0 to 2π in increments of 0.1π Plot just **a** (**plot(a)**) and observe the result. Compare this result with the graph produced by plotting **x** versus **a** (**plot(x,a)**).

EXAMPLE 18.1

Using the Clausius–Clapeyron Equation

The Clausius–Clapeyron equation can be used to find the saturation vapor pressure of water in the atmosphere, for different temperatures. The saturation water vapor pressure is useful to meteorologists because it can be used to calculate relative humidity, an important component of weather prediction, when the actual partial pressure of water in the air is known.

The following table presents the results of calculating the saturation vapor pressure of water in the atmosphere for various air temperatures with the use of the Clausius–Clapeyron equation:

Air Temperature, °F	Saturation Vapor Pressure, mbar
−60.0000	0.0698
−50.0000	0.1252
−40.0000	0.2184
−30.0000	0.3714
−20.0000	0.6163
−10.0000	1.0000
0	1.5888
10.0000	2.4749
20.0000	3.7847
30.0000	5.6880
40.0000	8.4102
50.0000	12.2458
60.0000	17.5747
70.0000	24.8807
80.0000	34.7729
90.0000	48.0098
100.0000	65.5257
110.0000	88.4608
120.0000	118.1931

Let us present these results graphically as well.

The Clausius–Clapeyron equation is

$$\ln\,(P^0/6.11) = \left(\frac{\Delta H_v}{R_{\text{air}}}\right) * \left(\frac{1}{273} - \frac{1}{T}\right)$$

where

P^0 = saturation vapor pressure for water, in mbar, at temperature T,
ΔH_v = latent heat of vaporization for water, 2.453 × 106 J/kg.
R_v = gas constant for moist air, 461 J/kg, and
T = temperature in kelvins

1. State the Problem
   Find the saturation vapor pressure at temperatures from −60°F to 120°F, using the Clausius–Clapeyron equation.
2. Describe the Input and Output

   Input

$$\Delta H_v = 2.453 \times 10^6 \text{ J/kg}$$
$$R_{air} = 461 \text{ J/kg}$$
$$T = -60°\text{F to } 120°\text{F}$$

Since the number of temperature values was not specified, we'll choose to recalculate every 10°F.

Output

Table of temperature versus saturation vapor pressures
Graph of temperature versus saturation vapor pressures

3. Develop a Hand Example
Change the temperatures from Fahrenheit to Kelvin:

$$T_k = \frac{(T_f + 459.6)}{1.8}$$

Solve the Clausius–Clapeyron equation for the saturation vapor pressure (P^0):

$$\ln\left(\frac{P^0}{6.11}\right) = \left(\frac{\Delta H_v}{R_{air}}\right) \times \left(\frac{1}{273} - \frac{1}{T}\right)$$

$$P^0 = 6.11 * \exp\left(\left(\frac{\Delta H_v}{R_{air}}\right) \times \left(\frac{1}{273} - \frac{1}{T}\right)\right)$$

Notice that the expression for the saturation vapor pressure, P^0 is an exponential equation. We would thus expect the graph to have the following shape:

Pressure

Temperature

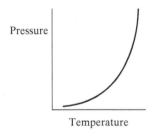

4. Develop a MATLAB Solution

```
%Example 17.1
%Using the Clausius–Clapeyron equation, find the
%saturation vapor pressure for water at different
%temperatures
%
 TF=[-60:10:120];           %Define temp matrix in F
 TK=(TF + 459.6)/1.8;       %Convert temp to K
 Delta_H=2.45e6;            %Define latent heat of
                            %vaporization
 R_air = 461;               %Define ideal gas constant
                            %for air
%
%Calculate the vapor pressures
 Vapor_Pressure=6.11*exp((Delta_H/R_air)*(1/273 – 1./TK));
 %Display the results in a table
  my_results = [TF',Vapor_Pressure']
%
%Create an x-y plot
  plot(TF,Vapor_Pressure)
  title('Clausius–Clapeyron Behavior')
  xlabel('Temperature, F')
  ylabel('Saturation Vapor Pressure, mbar')
```

The resulting table is

```
my_results =
         –60.0000        0.0698
         –50.0000        0.1252
         –40.0000        0.2184
         –30.0000        0.3714
         –20.0000        0.6163
         –10.0000        1.0000
                0        1.5888
          10.0000        2.4749
          20.0000        3.7847
```

30.0000	5.6880
40.0000	8.4102
50.0000	12.2458
60.0000	17.5747
70.0000	24.8807
80.0000	34.7729
90.0000	48.0098
100.0000	65.5257
110.0000	88.4608
120.0000	118.1931

A figure window opens to display the graphical results, shown in Figure 18.10.

5. Test the Solution
   The plot follows the expected trend. It is almost always easier to determine whether computational results make sense if a graph is produced. Tabular data are extremely difficult to interpret.

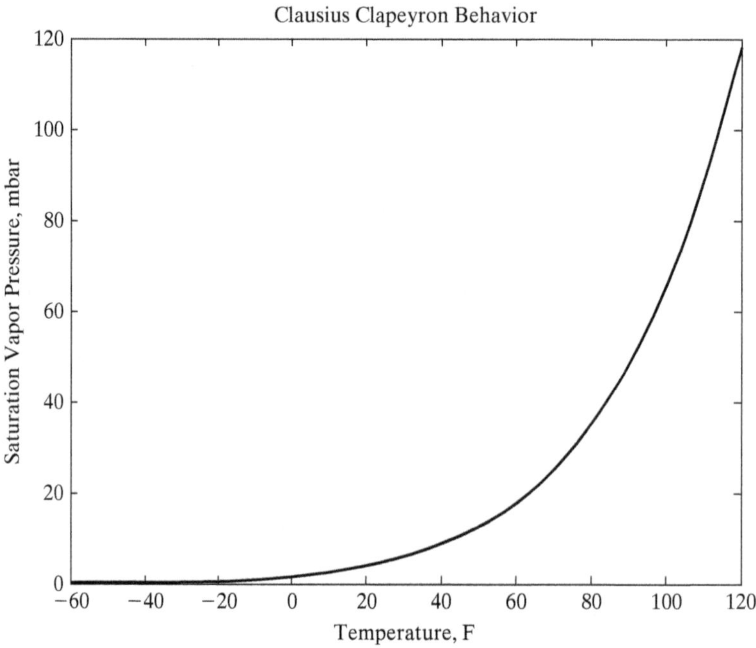

Figure 18.10 A plot of the Clausius–Clapeyron equation.

EXAMPLE 18.2

Ballistics

The range of an object (see Figure 18.11) shot at an angle θ with respect to the x-axis and an initial velocity v_0 is given by

$$R(\theta) = \frac{v^2}{g}\sin(2\theta) \text{ for } 0 \le \theta \le \frac{\pi}{2} \text{ (neglecting air resistance)}$$

Use $g = 9.9$ m/s^2 and an initial velocity of 100 m/s. Show that the maximum range is obtained at $\theta = \pi/4$ by computing and plotting the range for values of theta from

$$0 \le \theta \le \frac{\pi}{2}$$

in increments of 0.05.

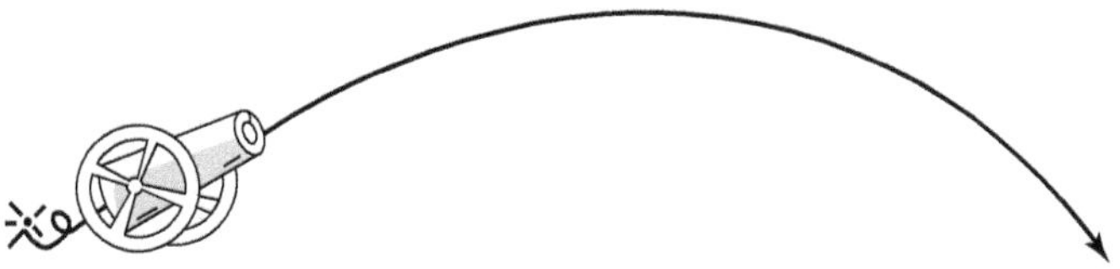

Figure 18.11 Ballistic motion.

Repeat your calculations with an initial velocity of 50 m/s, and plot both sets of results on a single graph.

1. State the Problem
   Calculate the range as a function of the launch angle.
2. Describe the Input and Output

   Input

   $g = 9.9 \text{ m/s}^2$
   $\theta = 0 \text{ to } \pi/2$, incremented by 0.05
   $v_0 = 50$ m/s and 100 m/s

   Output
   Range R
   Present the results as a plot.
3. Develop a Hand Example
   If the cannon is pointed straight up, we know that the range is zero, and if the cannon is horizontal, the range is also zero. (See Figure 18.12.)
   This means that the range must increase with the cannon angle up to some maximum and then decrease. A sample calculation at 45 degrees ($\pi/4$ radians) shows that

$$R(\theta) = \frac{v^2}{g}\sin(2\theta)$$

$$R\left(\frac{\pi}{4}\right) = \frac{100^2}{9.9}\sin\left(\frac{2\cdot\pi}{4}\right) = 1010 \text{ meters when the initial velocity is 100 m/s}$$

4. Develop a MATLAB Solution

```
%Example 17.2
%The program calculates the range of a ballistic projectile
%
% Define the constants
   g = 9.9;
   v1 = 50;
   v2 = 100;
```

Figure 18.12 The range is zero if the cannon is perfectly vertical, or perfectly horizontal.

```
% Define the angle vector
   angle = 0:0.05:pi/2;
% Calculate the range
   R1 = v1^2/g*sin(2*angle);
   R2 = v2^2/g*sin(2*angle);
%Plot the results
   plot(angle,R1,angle,R2, ':')
   title('Cannon Range')
   xlabel('Cannon Angle')
   ylabel('Range, meters')
   legend('Initial  Velocity=50 m/s',  'Initial  Velocity=100  m/s')
```

Notice that in the **plot** command we requested MATLAB to print the second set of data as a dashed line. A title, labels, and a legend were also added. The results are plotted in Figure 18.13.

5. Test the Solution
   Compare the MATLAB results with those from the hand example. Both graphs start and end at zero. The maximum range for an initial velocity of 100 m/s is approximately 1000 m, which corresponds well to the calculated value of 1010 m. Notice that both solutions peak at the same angle, approximately 0.8 radian. The numerical value for $\pi/4$ is 0.785 radian, confirming the hypothesis presented in the problem statement that the maximum range is achieved by pointing the cannon at an angle of $\pi/4$ radians (45 degrees).

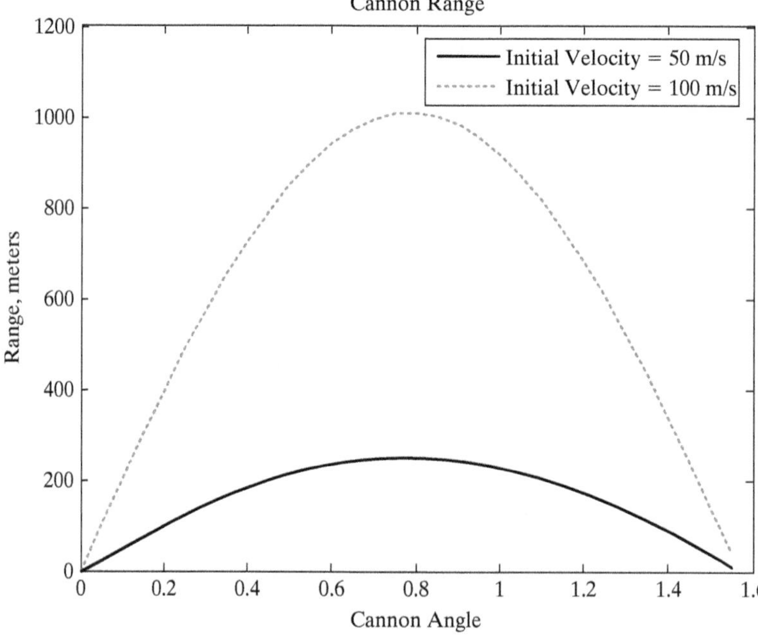

Figure 18.13 The predicted range of a projectile.

HINT

To clear a figure, use the **clf** command. To close a figure window, use the **close** command.

A function similar to **text** is **gtext**, which allows the user to interactively place a text box in an existing plot. The **gtext** function requires a single input, the string to be displayed.

```
gtext('This string will display on the graph')
```

Once executed, a crosshair appears on the graph. The user positions the crosshair to the appropriate position. The text is added to the graph when any key on the keyboard is depressed, or a mouse button is selected.

18.2 SUBPLOTS

The **subplot** command allows you to subdivide the graphing window into a grid of m rows and n columns. The function

```
subplot(m,n,p)
```

splits the figure into an $m \times n$ matrix. The variable **p** identifies the portion of the window where the next plot will be drawn. For example, if the command

```
subplot(2,2,1)
```

is used, the window is divided into two rows and two columns, and the plot is drawn in the upper left-hand window (Figure 18.14).

$p = 1$	$p = 2$
$p = 3$	$p = 4$

Figure 18.14 Subplots are used to subdivide the figure window into an $m \times n$ matrix.

The windows are numbered from left to right, top to bottom. Similarly, the following commands split the graph window into a top plot and a bottom plot:

```
x = 0:pi/20:2*pi;
subplot(2,1,1)
plot(x,sin(x))
subplot(2,1,2)
plot(x,sin(2*x))
```

The first graph is drawn in the top window, since **p** = 1. Then the **subplot** command is used again to draw the next graph in the bottom window. Figure 18.15 shows both graphs.

Titles are added above each subwindow as the graphs are drawn, as are x- and y-axis labels and any annotation desired. The use of the **subplot** command is illustrated in several of the sections that follow.

In-Class Activity

ICA 18-2

1. Subdivide a figure window into two rows and one column.
2. In the top window, plot $y = \tan(x)$ for $-1.5 \leq x \leq 1.5$. Use an increment of 0.1.
3. Add a title and axis labels to your graph.
4. In the bottom window, plot $y = \sinh(x)$ for the same range.
5. Add a title and labels to your graph.
6. Try the preceding exercises again, but divide the figure window vertically instead of horizontally.

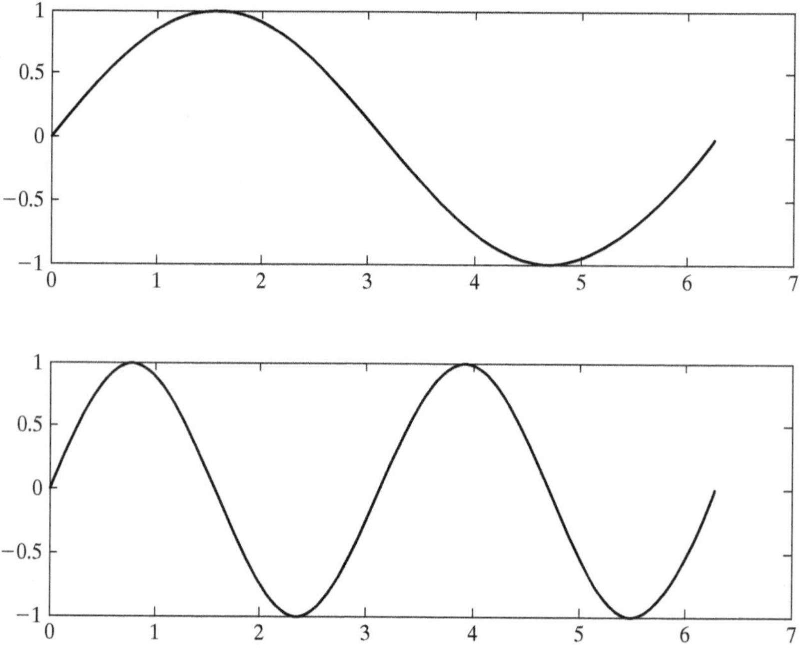

Figure 18.15 The **subplot** command allows the user to create multiple graphs in the same figure window.

18.3 OTHER TYPES OF TWO-DIMENSIONAL PLOTS

Although simple *x–y* plots are the most common type of engineering plot, there are many other ways to represent data. Depending on the situation, these techniques may be more appropriate than an *x–y* plot.

18.3.1 Logarithmic Plots

> ***Key Idea:***
> Logarithmic plots are especially useful if the data vary exponentially

For most plots that we generate, the *x*- and *y*-axes are divided into equally spaced intervals; these plots are called *linear* or *rectangular* plots. Occasionally, however, we may want to use a logarithmic scale on one or both of the axes. A logarithmic scale (to the base 10) is convenient when a variable ranges over many orders of magnitude, because the wide range of values can be graphed without compressing the smaller values. Logarithmic plots are also useful for representing data that vary exponentially.

The MATLAB commands for generating linear and logarithmic plots of the vectors **x** and **y** are listed in Table 18.4.

Table 18.4 Rectangular and Logarithmic Plots

plot(x,y)	Generates a linear plot of the vectors **x** and **y**
semilogx(x,y)	Generates a plot of the values of **x** and **y**, using a logarithmic scale for **x** and a linear scale for **y**
semilogy(x,y)	Generates a plot of the values of **x** and **y**, using a linear scale for **x** and a logarithmic scale for **y**
loglog(x,y)	Generates a plot of the vectors **x** and **y**, using a logarithmic scale for both **x** and **y**

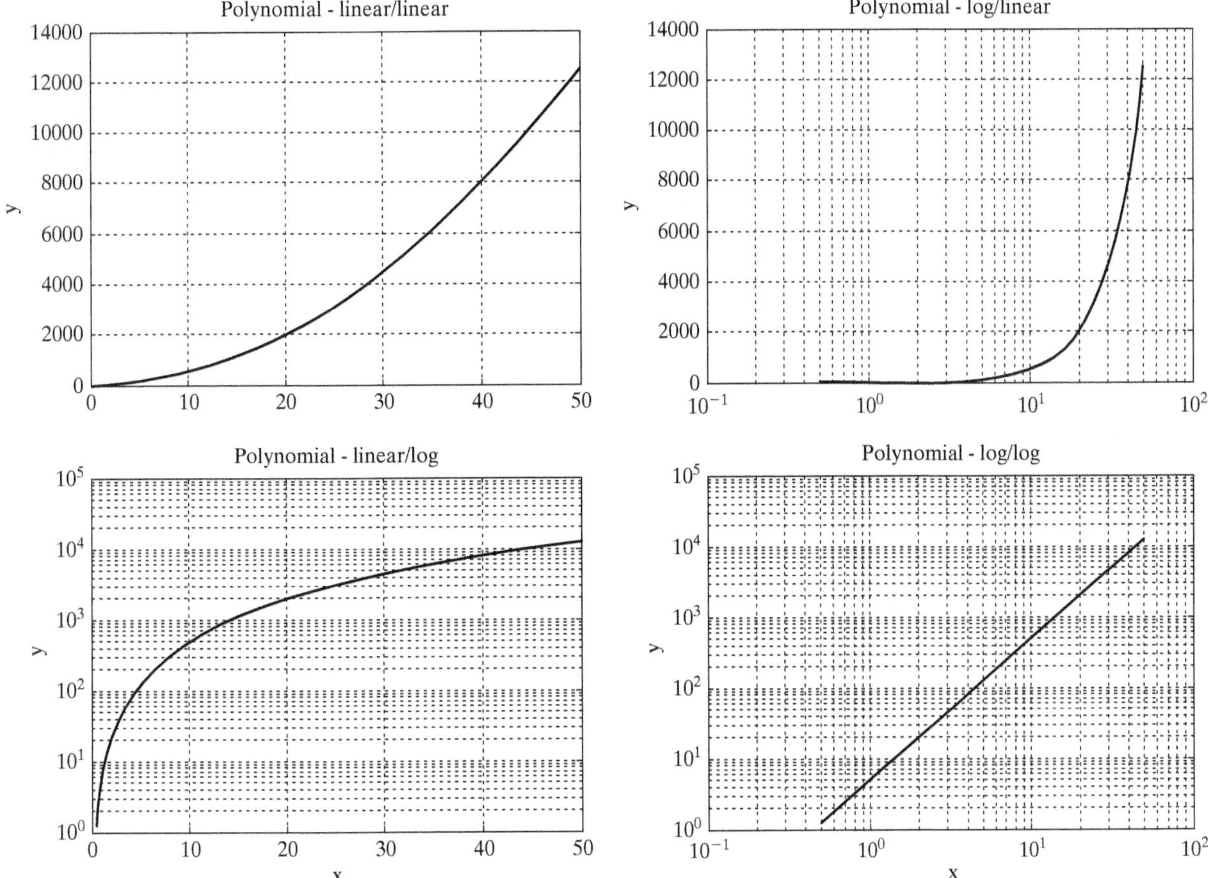

Figure 18.16 Linear and logarithmic plots, displayed using the subplot function.

Remember that the logarithm of a negative number or of zero does not exist. If your data include these values, MATLAB will issue a warning message and will not plot the points in question. However, it will generate a plot based on the remaining points.

Each command for logarithmic plotting can be executed with one argument, as we saw in **plot(y)** for a linear plot. In these cases, the plots are generated with the values of the indices of the vector **y** used as **x** values.

As an example, plots of $y = 5x^2$ were created using all four scaling approaches, as shown in Figure 18.16. The linear (rectangular) plot, semilog plot along the x-axis, semilog plot along the y-axis, and log–log plot are all shown on one figure, plotted with the **subplot** function in the following code:

```
x = 0:0.5:50;
y = 5*x.^2;
subplot(2,2,1)
plot(x,y)
    title('Polynomial - linear/linear')
    ylabel('y'), grid
subplot(2,2,2)
semilogx(x,y)
    title('Polynomial - log/linear')
    ylabel('y'), grid
```

```
subplot(2,2,3)
semilogy(x,y)
    title('Polynomial - linear/log')
    xlabel('x'), ylabel('y'), grid
subplot(2,2,4)
loglog(x,y)
    title('Polynomial - log/log')
    xlabel('x'), ylabel('y'), grid
```

Key Idea: Since MATLAB ignores white space, use it to make your code more readable

The indenting is intended to make the code easier to read—MATLAB ignores white space. As a matter of style, notice that only the bottom two subplots have x-axis labels.

EXAMPLE 18.3

Rates of Diffusion

Metals are often treated to make them stronger and therefore wear longer. One problem with making a strong piece of metal is that it becomes difficult to form it into a desired shape. A strategy that gets around this problem is to form a soft metal into the shape you desire and then harden the surface. This makes the metal wear well without making it brittle.

A common hardening process is called *carburizing*. The metal part is exposed to carbon, which diffuses into the part, making it harder. This is a very slow process if performed at low temperatures, but it can be accelerated by heating the part. The diffusivity is a measure of how fast diffusion occurs and can be modeled as

$$D = D_0 \, exp\left(\frac{-Q}{RT}\right)$$

where

D = diffusivity, cm^2/s,
D_0 = diffusion coefficient, cm^2/s,
Q = activation energy, J/mol, 8.314 J/mol K,
R = ideal gas constant, J/mol K, and
T = temperature, K.

As iron is heated, it changes structure and its diffusion characteristics change. The values of D_0 and Q are shown in the following table for carbon diffusing through each of iron's structures:

Type of Metal	D_0 (cm^2/s)	Q (J/mol K)
alpha Fe (BCC)	.0062	80,000
gamma Fe (FCC)	0.23	148,000

Create a plot of diffusivity versus inverse temperature ($1/T$), using the data provided. Try the rectangular, semilog and log–log plots to see which you think might represent the results best. Let the temperature vary from room temperature (25°C) to 1200°C.

1. State the Problem
   Calculate the diffusivity of carbon in iron.
2. Describe the Input and Output

   Input

   For C in alpha iron, D_0 = 0.0062 cm^2/s and Q = 80,000 J/mol K
   For C in gamma iron, D_0 = 0.23 cm^2/s and Q = 148,000 J/mol K
   R = 8.314 J/mol K
   T varies from 25°C to 1200°C

Output

Calculate the diffusivity and plot it.

3. Develop a Hand Example
   The diffusivity is given by

$$D = D_0 \exp\left(\frac{-Q}{RT}\right)$$

At room temperature, the diffusivity for carbon in alpha iron is

$$D = .0062 \exp\left(\frac{-80{,}000}{8.314 \cdot (25 + 273)}\right)$$
$$D = 5.9 \times 10^{-17}$$

(Notice that the temperature had to be changed from Celsius to Kelvin.)

4. Develop a MATLAB Solution

```
% Example 17.3
% Calculate the diffusivity of carbon in iron
  clear, clc
% Define the constants
  D0alpha = .0062;
  D0gamma = 0.23;
  Qalpha = 80000;
  Qgamma = 148000;
  R = 8.314;
  T = 25:5:1200;
% Change T from C to K
  T = T+273;
% Calculate the diffusivity
  Dalpha = D0alpha*exp(-Qalpha./(R*T));
  Dgamma = D0gamma*exp(-Qgamma./(R*T));
% Plot the results
  subplot(2,2,1)
  plot(1./T,Dalpha, 1./T,Dgamma)
  title('Diffusivity of C in Fe')
  xlabel('Inverse Temperature, K^{-1}'),
  ylabel('Diffusivity, cm^2/s')
  grid on

  subplot(2,2,2)
  semilogx(1./T,Dalpha, 1./T,Dgamma)
  title('Diffusivity of C in Fe')
  xlabel('Inverse Temperature, K^{-1}'),
  ylabel('Diffusivity, cm^2/s')
  grid on

  subplot(2,2,3)
  semilogy(1./T,Dalpha, 1./T,Dgamma)
  title('Diffusivity of C in Fe')
  xlabel('Inverse Temperature, K^{-1}'),
  ylabel('Diffusivity, cm^2/s')
  grid on

  subplot(2,2,4)
  loglog(1./T,Dalpha, 1./T,Dgamma)
  title('Diffusivity of C in Fe')
  xlabel('Inverse Temperature, K^{-1}'),
  ylabel('Diffusivity, cm^2/s')
  grid on
```

Subplots were used in Figure 18.17, so that all four variations of the plot are in the same figure. Notice that x-labels were added only to the bottom two graphs, to reduce clutter, and that a legend was added only to the first plot. The **semilogy** plot resulted in straight lines and allows a user to read values off the graph easily over a wide range of both temperatures and diffusivities. This is the plotting scheme usually used in textbooks and handbooks to present diffusivity values.

5. Test the Solution
   Compare the MATLAB results with those from the hand example.
   We calculated the diffusivity to be

$$5.9 \times 10^{-17}\ \text{cm}^2/\text{s at } 25°\text{C}$$

for carbon in alpha iron. To check our answer, we'll need to change 25°C to kelvins and take the inverse:

$$\frac{1}{(25 + 273)} = 3.36 \times 10^{-3}$$

From the **semilogy** graph (lower left-hand corner), we can see that the diffusivity for alpha iron is approximately 10^{-17}.

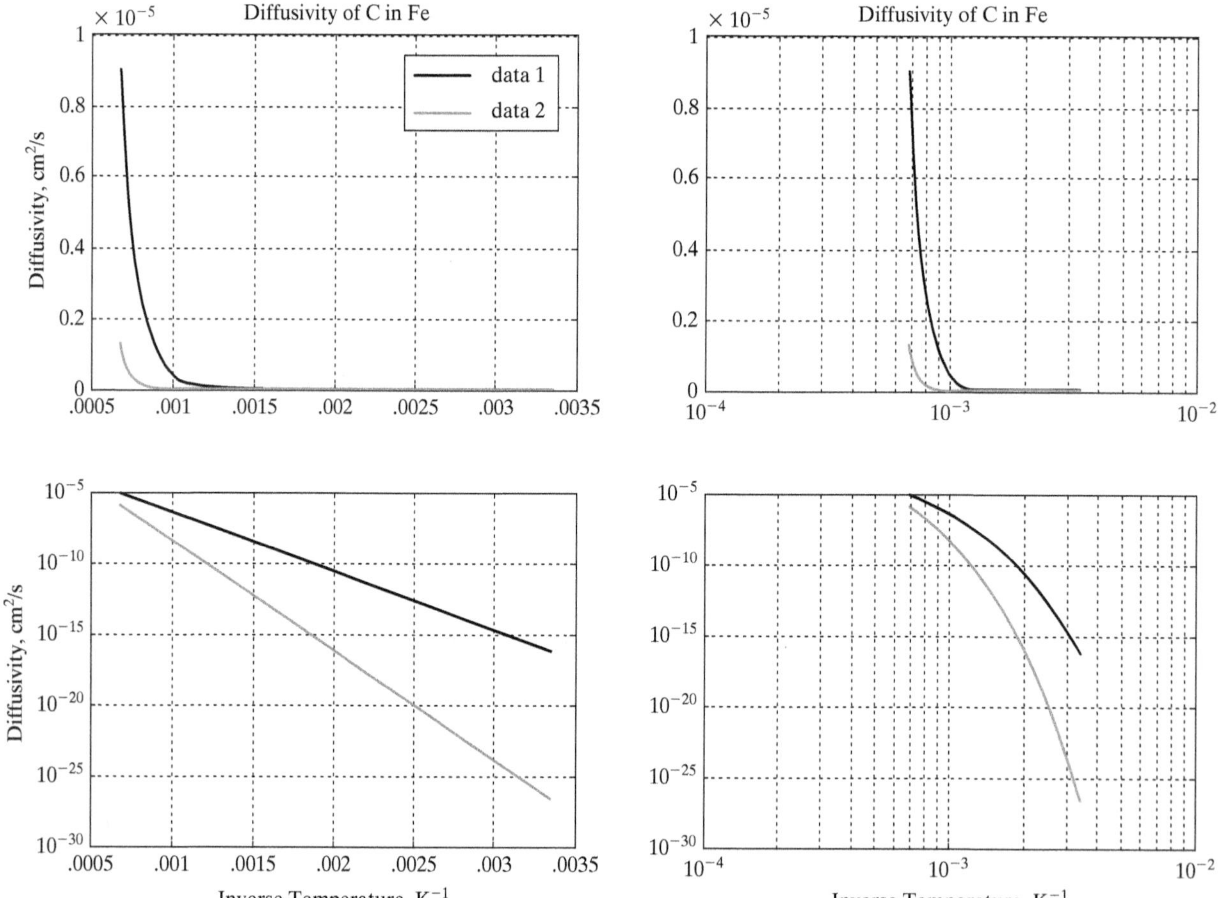

Figure 18.17 Diffusivity data plotted on different scales. The data follows a straight line when the $\log_{10}$ of the diffusivity is plotted on the y-axis vs. the inverse temperature on the x-axis.

In-Class Activity

ICA 18-3

Create appropriate **x** and **y** arrays to use in plotting each of the expressions that follow. Use the **subplot** command to divide your figures into four sections, and create each of these four graphs for each expression:

- rectangular
- semilogx
- semilogy
- loglog

1. $y = 5x + 3$
2. $y = 3x^2$
3. $y = 12e^{(x+2)}$
4. $y = 1/x$

Physical data usually are plotted so that they fall on a straight line. Which of the preceding types of plot results in a straight line for each problem?

18.3.2 Bar Graphs and Pie Charts

Bar graphs, histograms, and pie charts are popular forms for reporting data. Some of the commonly used MATLAB functions for creating bar graphs and pie charts are listed in Table 18.5.

Examples of some of these graphs are shown in Figure 18.18. The graphs make use of the **subplot** function to allow four plots in the same figure window:

```
clear, clc
x = [1,2,5,4,8];
y = [x;1:5];
subplot(2,2,1)
   bar(x),title('A bar graph of vector x')
subplot(2,2,2)
   bar(y),title('A bar graph of matrix y')
subplot(2,2,3)
   bar3(y),title('A three-dimensional bar graph')
subplot(2,2,4)
   pie(x),title('A pie chart of x')
```

Table 18.5 Bar Graphs and Pie Charts

bar(x)	When **x** is a vector, **bar** generates a vertical bar graph. When **x** is a two-dimensional matrix, **bar** groups the data by row.
barh(x)	When **x** is a vector, **barh** generates a horizontal bar graph. When **x** is a two-dimensional matrix, **barh** groups the data by row.
bar3(x)	Generates a three-dimensional bar chart
bar3h(x)	Generates a three-dimensional horizontal bar chart
pie(x)	Generates a pie chart. Each element in the matrix is represented as a slice of the pie.
pie3(x)	Generates a three-dimensional pie chart. Each element in the matrix is represented as a slice of the pie.
hist(x)	Generates a histogram

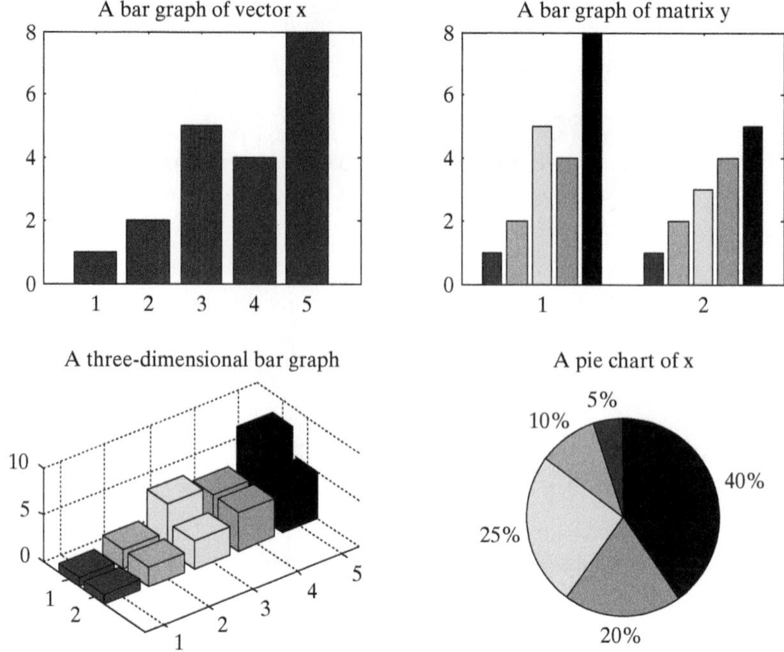

Figure 18.18 Sample bar graphs and pie charts. The **subplot** function was used to divide the window into quadrants.

18.3.3 Histograms

> ***Key Idea:*** Histograms are useful in statistical analysis

A histogram is a special type of graph that is particularly useful for the statistical analysis of data. It is a plot showing the distribution of a set of values. In MATLAB, the histogram computes the number of values falling into 10 bins (categories) that are equally spaced between the minimum and maximum values. For example, if we define a matrix **x** as the set of grades from the Introduction to Engineering final, the scores could be represented in a histogram, shown in Figure 18.19 and generated with the following code:

```
x = [100,95,74,87,22,78,34,35,93,88,86,42,55,48];
hist(x)
```

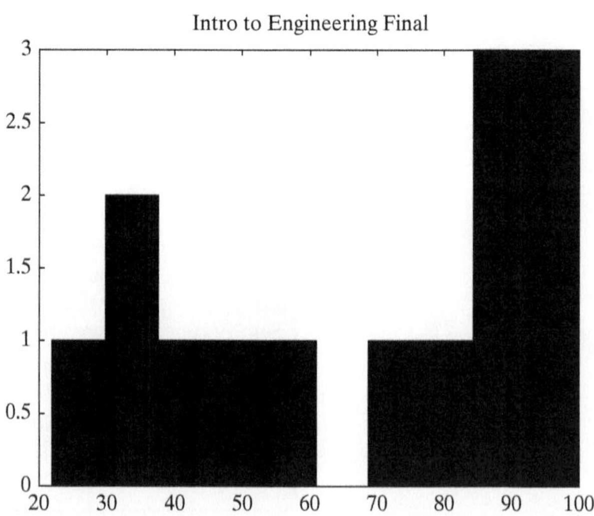

Figure 18.19 A histogram of grade data.

The default number of bins is 10, but if we have a large data set, we may want to divide the data up into more bins. For example, to create a histogram with 25 bins, the command would be

```
hist(x, 25)
```

If you set the **hist** function equal to a variable, as in

```
A = hist(x)
```

the data used in the plot are stored in **A**:

```
A =
  1  2  1  1  1  0  1  1  3  3
```

EXAMPLE 18.4

Weight Distributions

The average 18-year-old American male weighs 152 pounds. A group of 100 young men were weighed and the data stored in a file called **weight.dat**. Create a graph to represent the data.

1. State the Problem
   Use the data file to create a line graph and a histogram. Which is a better representation of the data?
2. Describe the Input and Output

   Input weight.dat, an ASCII data file that contains weight data

   Output A line plot of the data
   A histogram of the data
3. Develop a Hand Example
   Since this is a sample of actual weights, we would expect the data to approximate a normal random distribution (a Gaussian distribution). The histogram should be bell shaped.
4. Develop a MATLAB Solution
   The following code generates the plots shown in Figure 18.20:

```
% Example 17.4
% Using Weight Data
%
load weight.dat
% Create the line plot of weight data
subplot(1,2,1)
plot(weight)
title('Weight of First-Year Class Men')
xlabel('Student Number')
ylabel('Weight, lb')
grid on
% Create the histogram of the data
subplot(1,2,2)
hist(weight)
xlabel('Weight, lb')
ylabel('Number of students')
title('Weight of First-Year Class Men')
```

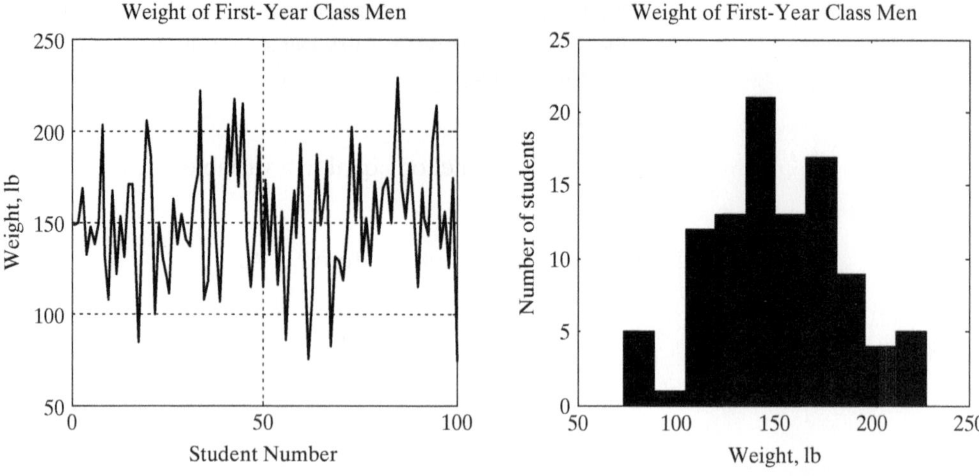

Figure 18.20 Histograms and line plots are two different ways to visualize numeric information.

5. Test the Solution
   The graphs match our expectations. The weight appears to average about 150 lb and varies in what looks like a normal distribution. We can use MATLAB to find the average and the standard deviation of the data, as well as the maximum and minimum weights in the data set. The MATLAB code

```
average_weight = mean(weight)
standard_deviation = std(weight)
maximum_weight = max(weight)
minimum_weight = min(weight)
```

   returns

```
average_weight =
  151.1500
standard_deviation =
  32.9411
maximum_weight =
  228
minimum_weight =
  74
```

EXERCISE 18.5

Histograms in MATLAB

It is well accepted that the normal body temperature is 98.6 F. However, Mackowiak, Wasserman, and Levine (1992) proposed that the mean normal body temperature is lower.

We will look at two questions:

- Is the true population mean really 98.6 degrees F?
- Is the distribution of temperatures normal?

Sources:

Shoemaker, A. (1996), "What's Normal?—Temperature, Gender, and Heart Rate," *Journal of Statistics Education*, 4(2), http://www.amstat.org/publications/jse/v4n2/datasets.shoemaker.html. accessed: August 10, 2007.

Mackowiak, P. A., Wasserman, S. S., and Levine, M. M. (1992), "A Critical Appraisal of 98.6 Degrees F, the Upper Limit of the Normal Body Temperature, and Other Legacies of Carl Reinhold August Wunderlich," *Journal of the American Medical Association*, 268, 1578–1580.

A histogram shows how data is distributed over the data range. Typically, divide the data into about ten bins or sub-ranges (but having no bins with more than eight entries probably means you have too many bins) and count the frequency of the data in each bin.

The man_temp data looks somewhat like a normal curve. Each tick mark on the Frequency axis represents two occurrences, so there is one bin with a single occurrence.

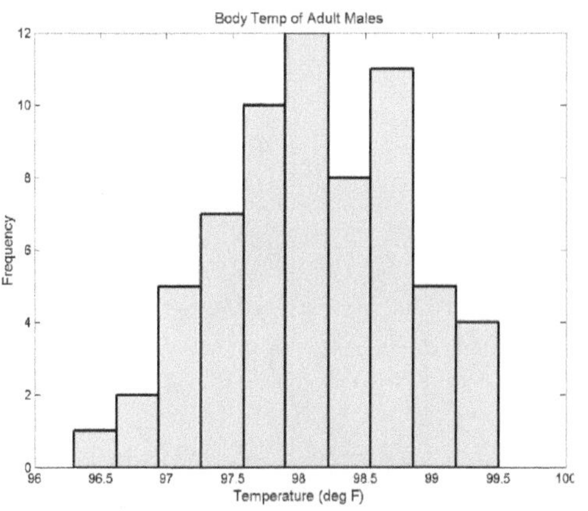

To generate a histogram with ten equally-spaced bins default (ten bins is the default):

```
hist(temp)
xlabel('Temperature (deg F)')
ylabel('Frequency')
title('Body Temp of Adults')
```

MATLAB finds the range, divides that by the number of bins, and finds the appropriate centers for these bins. Here, the bin range is (99.5-96.3)/10 = 3.2/10 = 0.320. Thus, the first center is 96.3+(0.5*0.320) = 96.4600, and the first bin ranges from 96.30...01 to 96.620...00.

The number of bins can be adjusted:

```
hist(temp,7)
```

Generates histogram with seven bins.

Bin range is 3.2/7 = 0.4571 and the first center is 96.3+(0.5*0.4571) = 96.5286.

Notice that the x-axis labels do not change. You have to be very careful with the x-axis labels.

The number of data points in each bin can be assigned to an output variable:

freq10 = hist(temp)	In this case, it's the default 10-bin histogram.
freq7 = hist(temp,7)	In this case, it's the user-chosen 7-bin histogram.

The center value of each bin can be found also, but only in conjunction with the previous info

```
[freq7,cent7] = hist(temp,7)
```

Essentially, if you give MATLAB one output variable name, the variable is assigned the number of data points in each bin. If you provide two output variable names in an array, MATLAB gives you the number of data points in each bin and the center value for each bin. Centers of the bins can be set manually (so that bin 1 ranges from 96.0...01 to 96.5...00). Then, **hist** can be used to create a histogram using specified bin centers

```
cent_temp = 96.25:0.5:99.75
hist(temp,cent_temp)
```

Note that this histogram has eight bins, though there is no data in the eighth. You can verify the center values of this histogram.

[freq8centered cent8centered] = hist(temp,cent_temp)--

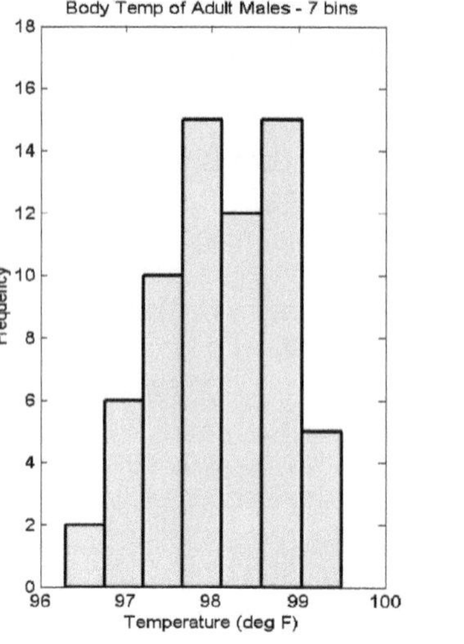

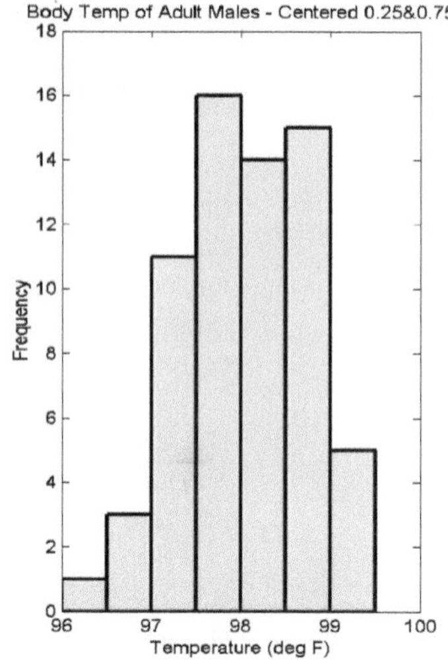

18.3.4 Function Plots

The **fplot** function allows you to plot a function without defining arrays of corresponding x- and y-values. For example,

fplot('sin(x)',[-2*pi,2*pi])

creates a plot (Figure 18.21) of x versus $\sin(x)$ for x-values from -2π to 2π. MATLAB automatically calculates the spacing of x-values to create a smooth curve. Notice that the first argument in the **fplot** function is a string containing the function and the second argument is an array. For more complicated functions that may be inconvenient to enter as a string, you may define an anonymous function and enter the function handle.

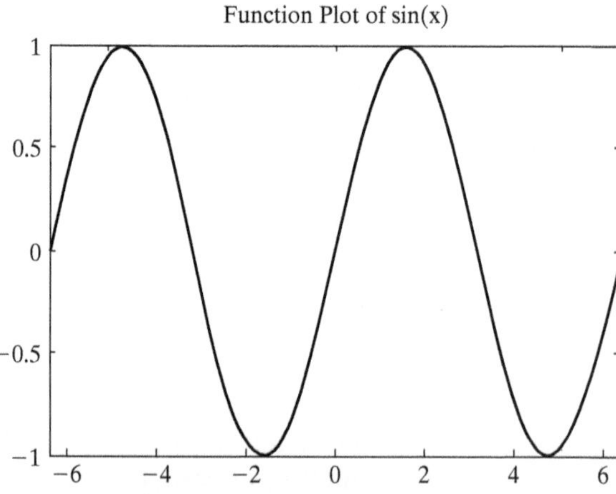

Figure 18.21 Function plots do not require the user to define arrays of ordered pairs.

In-Class Activity

ICA 18-4

Create a plot of the functions that follow, using **fplot**. You'll need to select an appropriate range for each plot. Don't forget to title and label your graphs.

1. $f(t) = 5t^2$
2. $f(t) = 5\sin^2(t) + t\cos^2(t)$
3. $f(t) = te^t$
4. $f(t) = \ln(t) + \sin(t)$

HINT

The correct MATLAB syntax for the mathematical expression $\sin^2(t)$ is **sin(t).^2**.

18.4 THREE-DIMENSIONAL PLOTTING

MATLAB offers a variety of three-dimensional plotting commands, several of which are listed in Table 18.6.

18.4.1 Three-Dimensional Line Plot

The **plot3** function is similar to the **plot** function, except that it accepts data in three dimensions. Instead of just providing **x** and **y** vectors, the user must also provide a **z** vector. These ordered triples are then plotted in three-space and connected with straight lines. For example

```
clear, clc
x = linspace(0,10*pi,1000);
y = cos(x);
z = sin(x);
plot3(x,y,z)
grid
xlabel('angle'), ylabel('cos(x)') zlabel('sin(x)') title('A Spring')
```

Table 18.6 Three-Dimensional Plots

plot3(x,y,z)	Creates a three-dimensional line plot
comet3(x,y,z)	Generates an animated version of **plot3**
mesh(z) or mesh(x,y,z)	Creates a meshed surface plot
surf(z) or surf(x,y,z)	Creates a surface plot; similar to the mesh function
shading interp	Interpolates between the colors used to illustrate surface plots
shading flat	Colors each grid section with a solid color
colormap(map_name)	Allows the user to select the color pattern used on surface plots
contour(z) or contour(x,y,z)	Generates a contour plot
surfc(z) or surfc(x,y,z)	Creates a combined surface plot and contour plot
pcolor(z) or pcolor(x,y,z)	Creates a pseudo color plot

The title, labels, and grid are added to the graph in Figure 18.22 in the usual way, with the addition of **zlabel** for the *z*-axis.

The coordinate system used with **plot3** is oriented using the right-handed coordinate system familiar to engineers.

Key Idea: The axes used for three-dimensional plotting correspond to the right-hand rule

HINT

Just for fun, re-create the plot shown in Figure 18.22, but this time with the **comet3** function:

```
comet3(x,y,z)
```

This plotting function "draws" the graph in an animation sequence. If your animation runs too quickly, add more data points. For two-dimensional line graphs, use the **comet** function.

18.4.2 Surface Plots

Surface plots allow us to represent data as a surface. We will be experimenting with two types of surface plots: **mesh** plots and **surf** plots.

Mesh Plots

There are several ways to use **mesh** plots. They can be used to good effect with a single two-dimensional $m \times n$ matrix. In this application, the value in the matrix represents the **z**-value in the plot. The **x**- and **y**-values are based on the matrix dimensions. Take, for example, the following very simple matrix:

```
z = [1, 2, 3, 4, 5, 6, 7, 8, 9, 10;
     2, 4, 6, 8, 10, 12, 14, 16, 18, 20;
     3, 4, 5, 6, 7, 8, 9, 10, 11, 12];
```

The code

```
mesh(z)
xlabel('x-axis')
ylabel('y-axis')
zlabel('z-axis')
```

generates the graph in Figure 18.23.

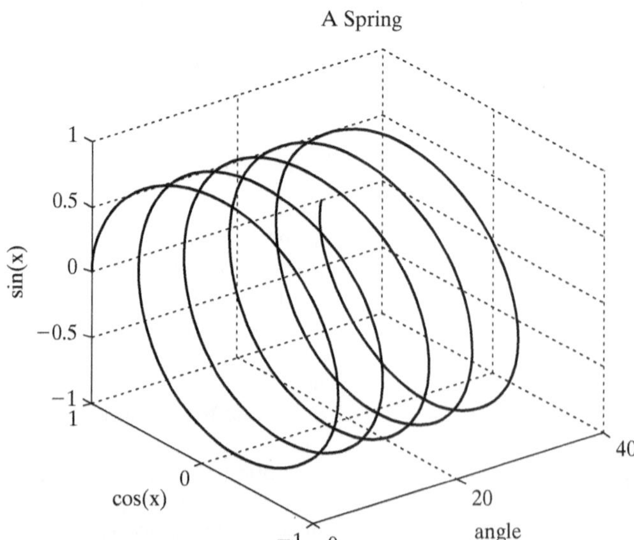

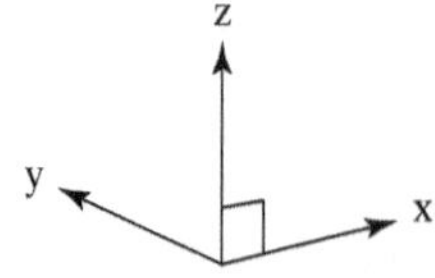

Figure 18.22 A three-dimensional plot of a spring. MATLAB uses a coordinate system consistent with the right-hand rule.

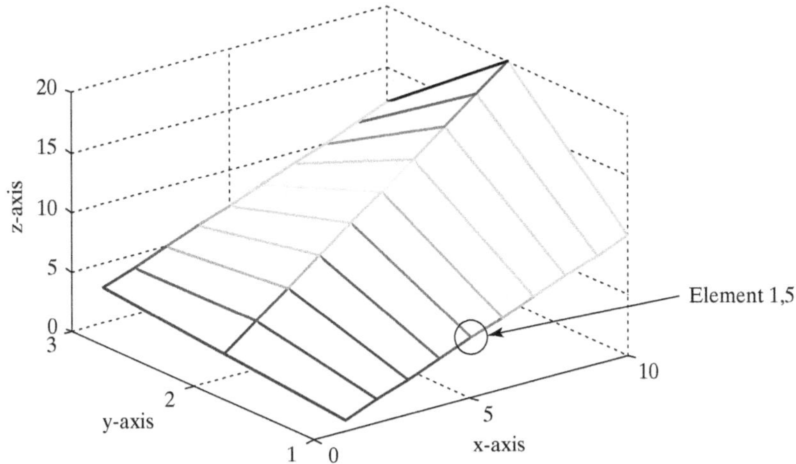

Figure 18.23 Simple mesh created with a single two-dimensional matrix.

The graph is a "mesh" created by connecting the points defined in **z** into a rectilinear grid. Notice that the *x*-axis goes from 0 to 10 and *y* goes from 0 to 3. The matrix index numbers were used for the axis values. For example, note that $z_{1,5}$—the value of *z* in row 1, column 5—is equal to 5. This element is circled in Figure 18.23.

The **mesh** function can also be used with three arguments: **mesh(x,y,z).** In this case, **x** is a list of *x*-coordinates, **y** is a list of *y*-coordinates, and **z** is a list of *z*-coordinates.

```
x = linspace(1,50,10)
y = linspace(500,1000,3)
z = [1,  2,  3,  4,  5,  6,  7,  8,  9,  10;
     2,  4,  6,  8,  10, 12, 14, 16, 18, 20;
     3,  4,  5,  6,  7,  8,  9,  10, 11, 12]
```

The **x** vector must have the same number of elements as the number of columns in the **z** vector; the **y** vector must have the same number of elements as the number of rows in the **z** vector. The command

```
mesh(x,y,z)
```

creates the plot in Figure 18.24a. Notice that the *x*-axis varies from 0 to 60, with data plotted from 1 to 50. Compare this scaling with that in Figure 18.23, which used the **z** matrix index numbers for the *x*- and *y*-axes.

Surf Plots

Surf plots are similar to **mesh** plots, but **surf** creates a three-dimensional colored surface instead of a mesh. The colors vary with the value of **z**.

The **surf** command takes the same input as **mesh**: either a single input—for example, **surf(z)**, in which case it uses the row and column indices as *x*- and *y*-coordinates—or three matrices. Figure 18.24b was generated with the same commands as those used to generate Figure 18.24a, except that **surf** replaced **mesh**.

The shading scheme for surface plots is controlled with the shading command. The default, shown in Figure 18.24b, is "faceted flat." Interpolated shading can create interesting effects. The plot shown in Figure 18.24c was created by adding

```
shading interp
```

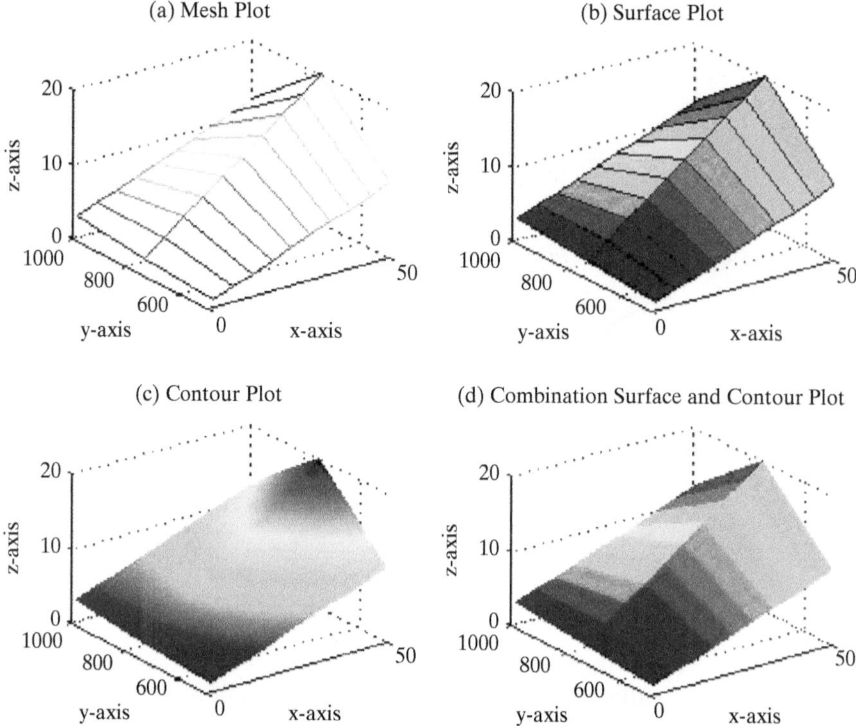

Figure 18.24 Mesh and surf plots created with three input arguments.

> ***Key Idea:*** The colormap function controls the colors used on surface plots

to the previous list of commands. Flat shading without the grid is generated when

```
shading flat
```

is used, as shown in Figure 18.24d.

The color scheme used in surface plots can be controlled with the **colormap** function. For example,

```
colormap(gray)
```

forces a grayscale representation for surface plots. This may be appropriate if you'll be making black-and-white copies of your plots. Other available **colormaps** are

autumn	**bone**	**hot**
spring	**colorcube**	**hsv**
summer	**cool**	**pink**
winter	**copper**	**prism**
jet (default)	**flag**	**white**

Use the **help** command to see a description of the various options:

```
help colormap
```

Another Example

A more complicated surface can be created by calculating the values of **Z**:

```
x= [–2:0.2:2];
y= [–2:0.2:2];
 [X,Y] = meshgrid(x,y);
Z = X.*exp(–X.^2 - Y.^2);
```

In the preceding code, the **meshgrid** function is used to create the two-dimensional matrices **X** and **Y** from the one-dimensional vectors **x** and **y**. The values in **Z** are then calculated. The following code plots the calculated values:

```
subplot(2,2,1)
mesh(X,Y,Z)
title('Mesh Plot'), xlabel('x-axis'), ylabel('y-axis'), zlabel('z-axis')

subplot(2,2,2)
surf(X,Y,Z)
title('Surface Plot'), xlabel('x-axis'), ylabel('y-axis'), zlabel('z-axis')
```

Either the **x**, **y** vectors or the **X**, **Y** matrices can be used to define the x- and y-axes. Figure 18.25a is a **mesh** plot of the given function, and Figure 18.25b is a **surf** plot of the same function.

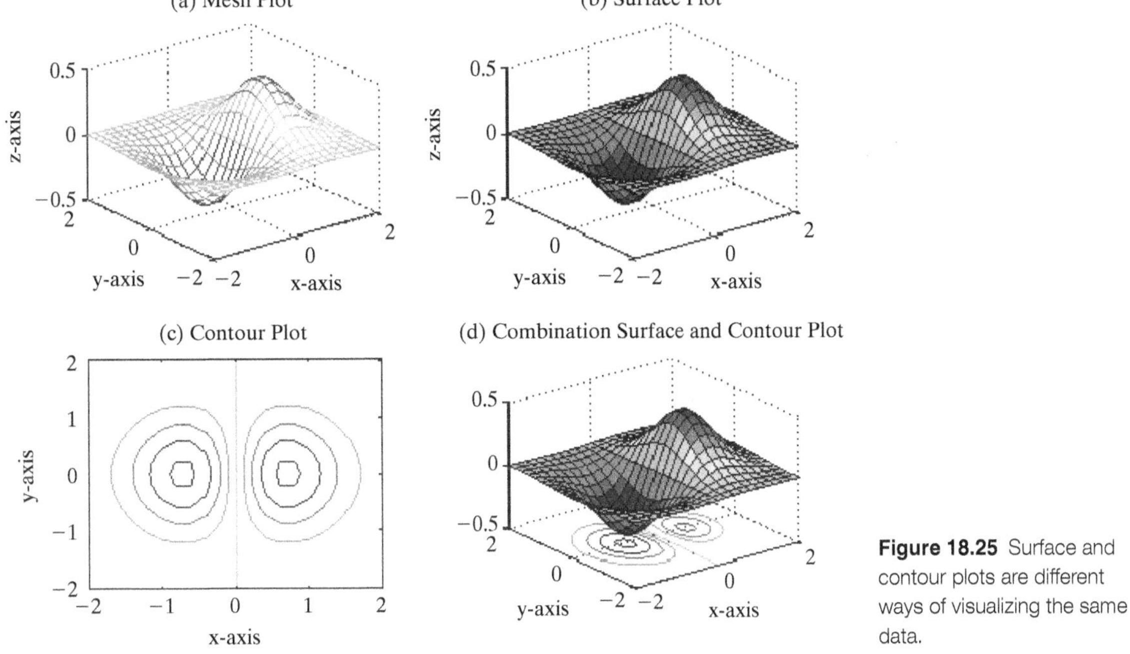

Figure 18.25 Surface and contour plots are different ways of visualizing the same data.

HINT

If a single vector is used in the **meshgrid** function, the program interprets it as

```
[X,Y] = meshgrid(x,x)
```

You could also use the vector definition as input to **meshgrid**:

```
[X,Y] = meshgrid(-2:0.2:2)
```

Both of these lines of code would produce the same result as the commands listed in the example.

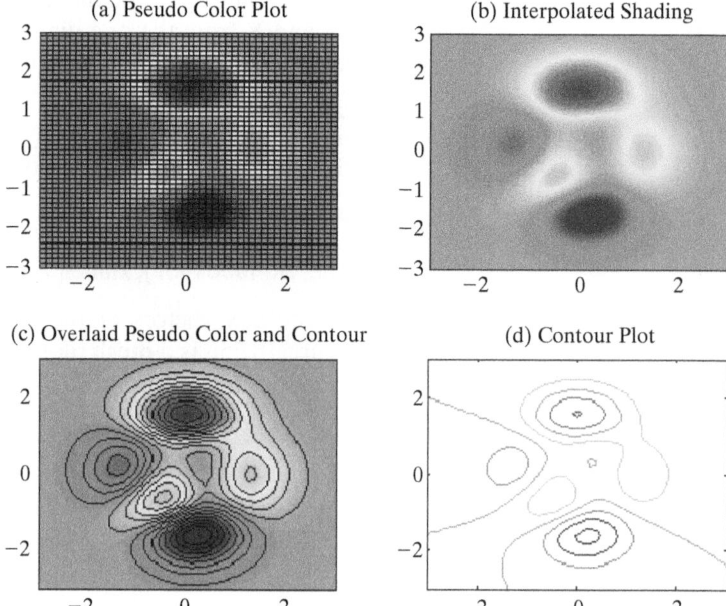

Figure 18.26 A variety of contour plots is available in MATLAB.

Contour Plots

Contour plots are two-dimensional representations of three-dimensional surfaces. The **contour** command was used to create Figure 18.25c, and the **surfc** command was used to create Figure 18.25d:

```
subplot(2,2,3)
contour(X,Y,Z)
xlabel('x-axis'), ylabel('y-axis'), title('Contour Plot')
subplot(2,2,4)
surfc(X,Y,Z)
xlabel('x-axis'), ylabel('y-axis')
title('Combination Surface and Contour Plot')
```

Pseudo Color Plots

Pseudo color plots are similar to contour plots, except that instead of lines outlining a specific contour, a two-dimensional shaded map is generated over a grid. MATLAB includes a sample function called **peaks** that generates the **x**, **y**, and **z** matrices of an interesting surface that looks like a mountain range:

```
[x,y,z] = peaks;
```

With the following code, we can use this surface to demonstrate the use of pseudo color plots, shown in Figure 18.26:

```
subplot(2,2,1)
pcolor(x,y,z)
```

The grid is deleted when interpolated shading is used:

```
subplot(2,2,2)
pcolor(x,y,z)
shading interp
```

You can add contours to the image by overlaying a contour plot:

```
subplot(2,2,3)
pcolor(x,y,z)
shading interp
hold on
contour(x,y,z,20,'k')
```

The number **20** specifies that 20 contour lines are drawn, and the **'k'** indicates that the lines should be black. If we hadn't specified black lines, they would have been the same color as the pseudo color plot and would have disappeared into the image. Finally, a simple contour plot was added to the figure for comparison:

```
subplot(2,2,4)
contour(x,y,z)
```

Additional options for using all the three-dimensional plotting functions are included in the help window.

18.5 SAVING YOUR PLOTS

There are several ways to save plots created in MATLAB:

- If you created the plot with programming code stored in an M-file, simply rerunning the code will re-create the figure.
- You can also save the figure from the file menu, using the **Save As . . .** option. You'll be presented with several choices:

  1. You may save the figure as a **.fig** file, which is a MATLAB-specific file format. To retrieve the figure, just double-click on the file name in the current directory.
  2. You may save the figure in a number of different standard graphics formats, such as jpeg (**.jpg**) and enhanced metafile (**.emf**). These versions of the figure can be inserted into other documents, such as a Word document.
  3. You can select Edit from the menu bar, then select **copy figure**, and paste the figure into another document.
  4. You can use the file menu to create an M-file that will re-create the figure.

In-Class Activity

ICA 18-5

Create a plot of $y = \cos(x)$. Practice saving the file and inserting it into a Word document.

SUMMARY

The most commonly used graph in engineering is the x–y plot. This two-dimensional plot can be used to graph data or to visualize mathematical functions. No matter what a graph represents, it should always include a title and x- and y-axis labels. Axis labels should be descriptive and should include units, such as ft/s or kJ/kg.

MATLAB includes extensive options for controlling the appearance of your plots. The user can specify the color, line style, and marker style for each line on a graph. A grid can be added to the graph, and the axis range can be adjusted. Text boxes and a legend can be employed to describe the graph. The subplot function is used to divide the plot window into an $m \times n$ grid. Inside each of these subwindows, any of the MATLAB plots can be created and modified.

In addition to *x–y* plots, MATLAB offers a variety of plotting options, including polar plots, pie charts, bar graphs, histograms, and *x–y* graphs with two *y*-axes. The scaling on *x–y* plots can be modified to produce logarithmic plots on either or both *x*- and *y*-axes. Engineers often use logarithmic scaling to represent data as a straight line.

The function **fplot** allows the user to plot a function without defining a vector of *x*- and *y*-values. MATLAB automatically chooses the appropriate number of points and spacing to produce a smooth graph. Additional function-plotting capability is available in the symbolic toolbox.

The three-dimensional plotting options in MATLAB include a line plot, a number of surface plots, and contour plots. Most of the options available in two-dimensional plotting also apply to these three-dimensional plots. The **meshgrid** function is especially useful in creating three-dimensional surface plots.

Interactive tools allow the user to modify existing plots. These tools are available from the figure menu bar. Plots can also be created with the interactive plotting option from the workspace window. The interactive environment is a rich resource. You'll get the most out of it by exploring and experimenting.

Figures created in MATLAB can be saved in a variety of ways, either to be edited later or to be inserted into other documents. MATLAB offers both proprietary file formats that minimize the storage space required to store figures and standard file formats suitable to import into other applications.

MATLAB SUMMARY

The following MATLAB summary lists all the special characters, commands, and functions that were defined in this chapter:

Special Characters

Line Type	Indicator	Point Type	Indicator	Color	Indicator
solid	-	point	.	blue	**b**
dotted	:	circle	**o**	green	**g**
dash-dot	-.	x-mark	**x**	red	**r**
dashed	--	plus	+	cyan	**c**
		star	*	magenta	**m**
		square	**s**	yellow	**y**
		diamond	**d**	black	**k**
		triangle down	**v**	white	**w**
		triangle up	^		
		triangle left	<		
		triangle right	>		
		pentagram	**p**		
		hexagram	**h**		

Commands and Functions

autumn	optional colormap used in surface plots
axis	freezes the current axis scaling for subsequent plots or specifies the axis dimensions
axis equal	forces the same scale spacing for each axis

Commands and Functions (Continued)	
bar	generates a bar graph
bar3	generates a three-dimensional bar graph
barh	generates a horizontal bar graph
bar3h	generates a horizontal three-dimensional bar graph
bone	optional colormap used in surface plots
colorcube	optional colormap used in surface plots
colormap	color scheme used in surface plots
comet	draws an *x–y* plot in a pseudo animation sequence
comet3	draws a three-dimensional line plot in a pseudo animation sequence
contour	generates a contour map of a three-dimensional surface
cool	optional colormap used in surface plots
copper	optional colormap used in surface plots
figure	opens a new figure window
flag	optional colormap used in surface plots
fplot	creates an *x–y* plot based on a function
gtext	similar to text; the box is placed at a location determined interactively by the user by clicking in the figure window
grid	adds a grid to the current plot only
grid off	turns the grid off
grid on	adds a grid to the current and all subsequent graphs in the current figure
hist	generates a histogram
hold off	instructs MATLAB **to** erase figure contents before adding new information
hold on	instructs MATLAB **not to** erase figure contents before adding new information
hot	optional colormap used in surface plots
hsv	optional colormap used in surface plots
jet	default colormap used in surface plots
legend	adds a legend to a graph
linspace	creates a linearly spaced vector
loglog	generates an *x–y* plot with both axes scaled logarithmically
mesh	generates a mesh plot of a surface
meshgrid	places each of two vectors into separate two-dimensional matrices, the size of which is determined by the source vectors
pause	pauses the execution of a program until any key is hit
pcolor	creates a pseudo color plot similar to a contour map
peaks	creates a sample matrix used to demonstrate graphing functions
pie	generates a pie chart
pie3	generates a three-dimensional pie chart
pink	optional colormap used in surface plots
plot	creates an *x–y* plot
plot3	generates a three-dimensional line plot
plotyy	creates a plot with two *y*-axes
polar	creates a polar plot
prism	optional colormap used in surface plots
semilogx	generates an *x–y* plot with the *x*-axis scaled logarithmically
semilogy	generates an *x–y* plot with the *y*-axis scaled logarithmically
shading flat	shades a surface plot with one color per grid section
shading interp	shades a surface plot by interpolation
sphere	sample function used to demonstrate graphing
spring	optional colormap used in surface plots
subplot	divides the graphics window into sections available for plotting
summer	optional colormap used in surface plots

Commands and Functions (Continued)	
surf	generates a surface plot
surfc	generates a combination surface and contour plot
text	adds a text box to a graph
title	adds a title to a plot
white	optional colormap used in surface plots
winter	optional colormap used in surface plots
xlabel	adds a label to the *x*-axis
ylabel	adds a label to the *y*-axis
zlabel	adds a label to the *z*-axis

EXERCISES AND ACTIVITIES

Two-Dimensional (*x–y*) Plots

18.1 Create plots of the following functions from $x = 0$ to 10.

(a) $y = e^x$
(b) $y = \sin(x)$
(c) $y = ax^2 + bx + c$, where $a = 5, b = 2$, and $c = 4$
(d) $y = \sqrt{x}$

Each of your plots should include a title, an *x*-axis label, a *y*-axis label, and a grid.

18.2 Plot the following set of data:

$$y = [12, 14, 12, 22, 8, 9]$$

Allow MATLAB to use the matrix index number as the parameter for the *x*-axis.

18.3 Plot the following functions on the same graph for *x* values from $-\pi$ to π, selecting spacing to create a smooth plot:

$$y_1 = \sin(x)$$
$$y_2 = \sin(2x)$$
$$y_3 = \sin(3x)$$

(*Hint*: Recall that the appropriate MATLAB syntax for $2x$ is **2 * x**.)

18.4 Adjust the plot created in Problem 18.3 so that

- line 1 is red and dashed.
- line 2 is blue and solid.
- line 3 is green and dotted.

Do not include markers on any of the graphs. In general, markers are included only on plots of measured data, not for calculated values.

18.5 Adjust the plot created in Problem 18.4 so that the *x*-axis goes from −6 to +6.

- Add a legend.
- Add a text box describing the plots.

x–y Plotting with Projectiles

Use the following information in Problems 18.6 through 18.10:

The distance a projectile travels when fired at an angle θ is a function of time and can be divided into horizontal and vertical distances according to the formulas

$$\text{horizontal}(t) = tV_0 \cos(\theta)$$

and

$$\text{vertical}(t) = tV_0 \sin(\theta) - \tfrac{1}{2}gt^2$$

where

horizontal	= distance traveled in the x direction,
vertical	= distance traveled in the y direction,
V_0	= initial velocity,
g	= acceleration due to gravity, 9.8 m/s^2,
t	= time, s.

18.6 Suppose the projectile just described is fired at an initial velocity of 100 m/s and a launch angle of $\pi/4$ (45°). Find the distance traveled both horizontally and vertically (in the x and y directions) for times from 0 to 20 s with a spacing of .01 seconds.

(a) Graph horizontal distance versus time.

(b) In a new figure window, plot vertical distance versus time (with time on the x-axis).

Don't forget a title and labels.

18.7 In a new figure window, plot horizontal distance on the x-axis and vertical distance on the y-axis.

18.8 Replot horizontal distance on the x-axis and vertical distance on the y-axis using the comet function. If the plot draws too quickly or too slowly on your computer, adjust the number of time values used in your calculations.

18.9 Calculate three new vectors for each of the vertical (v_1, v_2, v_3) and horizontal (h_1, h_2, h_3) distances traveled, assuming launch angles of $\pi/2$, $\pi/4$, and $\pi/6$.

- In a new figure window, graph horizontal distance on the x-axis and vertical distance on the y-axis, for all three cases. (You'll have three lines.)
- Make one line solid, one dashed, and one dotted. Add a legend to identify which line is which.

18.10 Re-create the plot from Problem 18.9. This time, create a matrix **theta** of the three angles, $\pi/2$, $\pi/4$, and $\pi/6$. Use the **meshgrid** function to create a mesh of **theta** and the time vector (**t**). Then use the two new meshed variables you create to recalculate vertical distance (**v**) and horizontal distance (**h**) traveled. Each of your results should be a 2001 × 3 matrix. Use the **plot** command to plot **h** on the x-axis and **v** on the y-axis.

18.11 A tensile testing machine such as the one shown in Figures P18.11a and P18.11b is used to determine the behavior of materials as they are deformed. In the typical test, a specimen is stretched at a steady rate. The force (load) required to deform the material is measured, as is the resulting deformation. An example set of data measured in one such test is shown in Table P18.11. These data can be used to calculate the applied stress and the resulting strain with the following equations.

$$\sigma = \frac{F}{A} \quad \text{and} \quad \varepsilon = \frac{l - l_0}{l_0}$$

where

σ is the stress in lb$_f$/in.^{2} (psi)

F is the applied force in lb$_f$

A is the sample cross sectional area in in.^{2}

ε is the strain in in./in.

l is the sample length

l_0 is the original sample length

(a) Use the provided data to calculate the stress and the corresponding strain for each data pair. The tested sample was a rod of diameter 0.505 in., so you'll need to find the cross sectional area to use in your calculations.

(b) Create an x–y plot with strain on the x-axis and stress on the y-axis. Connect the data points with a solid black line, and use circles to mark each data point.

(c) Add a title and appropriate axis labels.

(d) The point where the graph changes from a straight line with a steep slope to a flattened curve is called the yield stress or yield point. This corresponds to a significant change in the material behavior. Before the yield point the material is elastic, returning to its original shape if the load is removed—

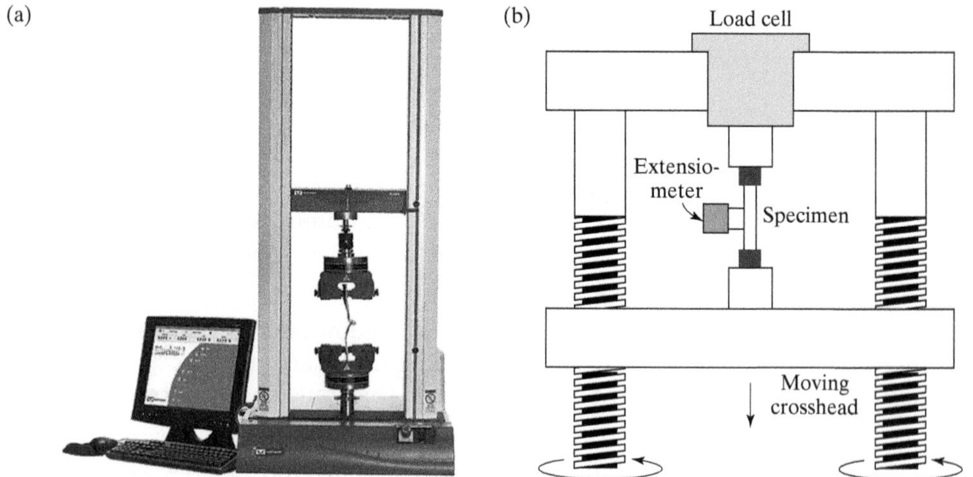

Figure P18.11a A tensile testing machine is used to measure stress and strain and to characterize the behavior of materials as they are deformed. (Photo courtesy of Instron®.)

Table P18.11 Tensile Testing Data

(From William Callister, *Materials Science and Engineering, An Introduction,* 5th ed., p. 149.)

load, lbf	length, inches
0	2
1650	2.002
3400	2.004
5200	2.006
6850	2.008
7750	2.010
8650	2.020
9300	2.040
10100	2.080
10400	2.120

much like a rubber band. Once the material has been deformed past the yield point, the change in shape becomes permanent and is called plastic deformation. Use a text box to mark the yield point on your graph.

Using Subplots

18.12 In Problem 18.1, you created four plots. Combine these into one figure with four subwindows, using the **subplot** function of MATLAB.

18.13 In Problems 18.6, 18.7 and 18.9, you created a total of four plots. Combine these into one figure with four subwindows, using the **subplot** function of MATLAB.

Polar Plots

18.14 Create a vector of angles from 0 to 2π. Use the **polar** plotting function to create graphs of the functions that follow. Remember, polar plots expect the angle and the radius as the two inputs to the **polar** function. Use the **subplot** function to put all four of your graphs in the same figure.

(a) $r = \sin^2(\theta) + \cos^2(\theta)$
(b) $r = \sin(\theta)$
(c) $r = e^{\theta/5}$
(d) $r = \sinh(\theta)$

Logarithmic Plots

18.15 When interest is compounded continuously, the following equation represents the growth of your savings:

$$P = P_0 e^{rt}$$

In this equation,

P = current balance,
P_0 = initial balance,
r = growth constant, expressed as a decimal fraction, and
t = time invested.

Determine the amount in your account at the end of each year if you invest \$1000 at 8% (0.08) for 30 years. (Make a table.)
Create a figure with four subplots. Plot time on the x-axis and current balance P on the y-axis.

(a) In the first quadrant, plot t versus P in a rectangular coordinate system.
(b) In the second quadrant, plot t versus P, scaling the x-axis logarithmically.
(c) In the third quadrant, plot t versus P, scaling the y-axis logarithmically.
(d) In the fourth quadrant, plot t versus P, scaling both axes logarithmically.

Which of the four plotting techniques do you think displays the data best?

Figure P18.17 Gordon Moore, a pioneer of the semiconductor industry. (Copyright © 2005 Intel Corporation.)

18.16 According to Moore's law (an observation made in 1965 by Gordon Moore, a cofounder of Intel Corporation; see Figure P18.17), the number of transistors that would fit per square inch on a semiconductor integrated circuit doubles approximately every two years. Although Moore's law is often reported as predicting doubling every 18 months, this is incorrect. A colleague of Moore's took into account the fact that transistor performance is also improving, and when combined with the increased number of transistors results in doubling of *performance* every 18 months. The year 2005 was the fortieth anniversary of the law. Over the last 40 years, Moore's projection has been consistently met. In 1965, the then state-of-the-art technology allowed for 30 transistors per square inch. Moore's law says that transistor density can be predicted by $d(t) = 30\,(2^{t/2})$, where t is measured in years.

(a) Letting $t = 0$ represent the year 1965 and $t = 45$ represent 2010, use this model to calculate the predicted number of transistors per square inch for the 45 years from 1965 to 2010. Let t increase in increments of two years. Display the results in a table with two columns—one for the year and one for the number of transistors.

(b) Using the **subplot** feature, plot the data in a linear x–y plot, a semilog x plot, a semilog y plot and a log–log plot. Be sure to title the plots and label the axes.

18.17 The total number of transistor count on integrated circuits produced over the last 35 years is shown in Table P18.18. Create a semilog plot (with the y-axis scaled logarithmically) of the actual data, using circles only to indicate the data points (no lines). Include a second line representing the predicted values using Moore's law, based on the 1971 count as the starting point. Add a legend to your plot.

Table P18.18 Exponential Increase in Transistor Count on Integrated Circuits*

Processor	Transistor Count	Date of Introduction	Manufacturer
Intel 4004	2300	1971	Intel
Intel 8008	2500	1972	Intel
Intel 8080	4500	1974	Intel
Intel 8088	29000	1979	Intel
Intel 80286	134000	1982	Intel
Intel 80386	275000	1985	Intel
Intel 80486	1200000	1989	Intel
Pentium	3100000	1993	Intel
AMD K5	4300000	1996	AMD
Pentium II	7500000	1997	Intel
AMD K6	8800000	1997	AMD
Pentium III	9500000	1999	Intel
AMD K6-III	21300000	1999	AMD
AMD K7	22000000	1999	AMD
Pentium 4	42000000	2000	Intel
Barton	54300000	2003	AMD
AMD K8	105900000	2003	AMD
Itanium 2	220000000	2003	Intel
Itanium 2 with 9MB cache	592000000	2004	Intel
Cell	241000000	2006	Sony/IBM/Toshiba
Core 2 Duo	291000000	2006	Intel
Core 2 Quad	582000000	2006	Intel
G80	681000000	2006	NVIDIA
POWER6	789000000	2007	IBM
Dual-Core Itanium 2	1700000000	2006	Intel
Quad-Core Itanium Tukwila (processor)[1]	2000000000	2008	Intel

*Data from *Wikipedia*, http://en.wikipedia.org/wiki/Transistor_count.

18.18 Many physical phenomena can be described by the Arrhenius equation. For example, reaction-rate constants for chemical reactions are modeled as

$$k = k_0 e^{(-Q/RT)}$$

where

k_0 = constant with units that depend upon the reaction,
Q = activation energy, kJ/kmol,
R = ideal gas constant, kJ/kmol K, and
T = temperature in K.

For a certain chemical reaction, the values of the constants are

$$Q = 1000 \text{ J/mol},$$
$$k_0 = 10 \text{ sec}^{-1}, \text{ and}$$
$$R = 8.314 \text{ J/mol K},$$

for T from 300 K to 1000 K. Find the values of k. Create the following two graphs of your data in a single figure window:

(a) Plot T on the x-axis and k on the y-axis.
(b) Plot your results as the $\log_{10}$ of k on the y-axis and $1/T$ on the x-axis.

Bar Graphs, Pie Charts, and Histograms

18.19 Let the vector

$$G = [68, 83, 61, 70, 75, 82, 57, 5, 76, 85, 62, 71, 96, 78, 76, 68, 72, 75, 83, 93]$$

represent the distribution of final grades in an engineering course.

(a) Use MATLAB to sort the data and create a bar graph of the scores.
(b) Create a histogram of the scores.

18.20 In the engineering class mentioned in Problem 18.20, there are

2 A's
4 B's
8 C's
4 D's
2 E's

(a) Create a vector of the grade distribution

$$\text{grades} = [2, 4, 8, 4, 2]$$

Create a pie chart of the grades vector. Add a legend listing the grade names (A, B, C, etc.)

(b) Use the **menu** text option instead of a legend to add a text box to each slice of pie, and save your modified graph as a **.fig** file.
(c) Create a three-dimensional pie chart of the same data. MATLAB has trouble with legends for many three-dimensional figures, so don't be surprised if your legend doesn't match the pie chart.

18.21 The inventory of a certain type of screw in a warehouse at the end of each month is listed in the following table:

	2004	2005
January	2345	2343
February	4363	5766
March	3212	4534
April	4565	4719
May	8776	3422
June	7679	2200
July	6532	3454
August	2376	7865
September	2238	6543
October	4509	4508
November	5643	2312
December	1137	4566

Plot the data in a bar graph.

18.22 Use the **randn** function to create 1000 values in a normal (Gaussian) distribution of numbers with a mean of 70 and a standard deviation of 3.5. Create a histogram of the data set you calculated.

Graphs with Two *y*-Axes

18.23 In the introduction to Problems 18.6 through 18.9, we learned that the equations for the distance traveled by a projectile as a function of time are

$$\text{Horizontal}(t) = tV_0\cos(\theta)$$

$$\text{Vertical}(t) = tV_0\sin(\theta) - \tfrac{1}{2}gt^2$$

For time from 0 to 20 s, plot both the horizontal distance versus time and the vertical distance versus time on the same graph, using separate *y*-axes for each line. Assume a launch angle of 45 degrees ($\pi/4$ radians) and an initial velocity of 100 m/s. Assume also that the acceleration due to gravity, g, is 9.8 m/s.

18.24 If the equation modeling the vertical distance traveled by a projectile as a function of time is

$$\text{Vertical}(t) = tV_0\sin(\theta) - 1/2\,gt^2$$

then, from calculus, the velocity in the vertical direction is

$$\text{Velocity}(t) = V_0\sin(\theta) - gt$$

Create a vector t from 0 to 20 s, and calculate both the vertical position and the velocity in the vertical direction, assuming a launch angle θ of $\pi/4$ radians and an initial velocity of 100 m/s. Plot both quantities on the same graph with separate *y*-axes.

The velocity should be zero at the point where the projectile is the highest in the vertical direction. Does your graph support this prediction?

18.25 For many metals, deformation changes their physical properties. In a process called *cold work*, metal is intentionally deformed to make it stronger. The following data tabulate both the strength and ductility of a metal that has been cold worked to different degrees:

Percent Cold Work	Yield Strength, MPa	Ductility, %
10	275	43
15	310	30
20	340	23
25	360	17
30	375	12
40	390	7
50	400	4
60	407	3
68	410	2

Plot these data on a single x–y plot with two y-axes.

Three-Dimensional Line Plots

18.26 Create a vector **x** of values from 0 to 20 π, with a spacing of $\pi/100$. Define vectors **y** and **z** as

$$y = x\sin(x)$$

and

$$z = x\cos(x)$$

(a) Create an x–y plot of **x** and **y**.
(b) Create a polar plot of **x** and **y**.
(c) Create a three-dimensional line plot of **x**, **y**, and **z**. Don't forget a title and labels.

18.27 Figure out how to adjust your input to **plot3** in Problem 18.27 so as to create a graph that looks like a tornado. (See Figure P18.28.) Use **comet3** instead of **plot3** to create the graph.

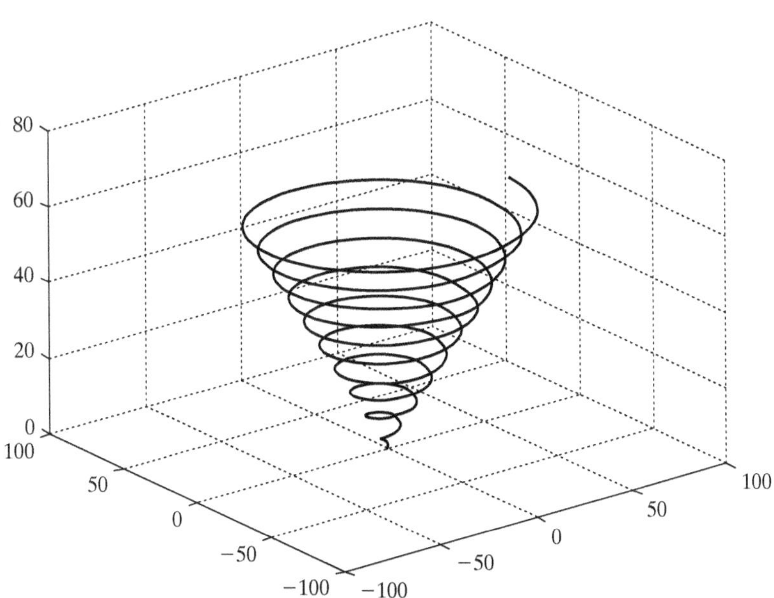

Figure P18.28 Tornado plot.

Three-Dimensional Surface and Contour Plots

18.28 Create **x** and **y** vectors from −5 to +5 with a spacing of 0.5. Use the **meshgrid** function to map **x** and **y** onto two new two-dimensional matrices called **X** and **Y**. Use your new matrices to calculate vector **Z**, with magnitude

$$Z = \sin\left(\sqrt{X^2 + Y^2}\right)$$

(a) Use the **mesh** plotting function to create a three-dimensional plot of **Z**.
(b) Use the **surf** plotting function to create a three-dimensional plot of **Z**. Compare the results you obtain with a single input (**Z**) with those obtained with inputs for all three dimensions (**X**, **Y**, **Z**).
(c) Modify your surface plot with interpolated shading. Try using different **colormaps**.
(d) Generate a contour plot of **Z**.
(e) Generate a combination surface and contour plot of **Z**.

CHAPTER 19
USER-DEFINED FUNCTIONS

Objectives

By learning the material in this chapter, you should be able to

- create and use your own MATLAB functions with both single and multiple inputs and outputs
- store and access your own functions in toolboxes
- create and use anonymous functions
- create and use function handles
- create and use subfunctions and nested subfunctions

Introduction

The MATLAB programming language is built around functions. A *function* is a piece of computer code that accepts an input argument from the user and provides output to the program. Functions allow us to program efficiently, enabling us to avoid rewriting the computer code for calculations that are performed frequently. For example, most computer programs contain a function that calculates the sine of a number. In MATLAB, **sin** is the function name used to call up a series of commands that perform the necessary calculations. The user needs to provide an angle, and MATLAB returns a result. It isn't necessary for the programmer to know how MATLAB calculates the value of **sin(x)**.

19.1 CREATING FUNCTION M-FILES

We have already explored many of MATLAB's built-in functions, but you may wish to define your own functions—those which are used commonly in your programming. User-defined functions are stored as M-files and can be accessed by MATLAB if they are in the current directory.

19.1.1 Syntax

Both built-in MATLAB functions and user-defined MATLAB functions have the same structure. Each consists of a name, user-provided input, and calculated output. For example, the function

```
cos(x)
```

- is named **cos**,
- takes user input inside the parentheses (in this case, **x**), and
- calculates a result.

Taken from *MATLAB® for Engineers,* Second Edition, by Holly Moore.

The user does not see the calculations performed, but just accepts the answer. User-defined functions work the same way. Imagine that you have created a function called **my_function**. Using

```
my_function(x)
```

in a program or from the command window will return a result, as long as **x** is defined and the logic in the function definition works.

Key Idea: Functions allow us to program more efficiently

User-defined functions are created in M-files. Each must start with a function-definition line that contains

- the word **function**,
- a variable that defines the function output,
- a function name, and
- a variable used for the input argument.

For example,

```
function   output = my_function(x)
```

is the first line of the user-defined function called **my_function**. It requires one input argument, which the program will call **x**, and will calculate one output argument, which the program will call **output**. The function name and the names of the input and output variables are arbitrary and are selected by the programmer. Here's an example of an appropriate first line for a function called **calculation**:

```
function    result = calculation(a)
```

In this case, the function name is **calculation**, the input argument will be called **a** in any calculations performed in the function program, and the output will be called **result**. Although any valid MATLAB names can be used, it is good programming practice to use meaningful names for all variables and for function names.

Function: a piece of computer code that accepts an input, performs a calculation, and provides an output

HINT

Students are often confused about the use of the word *input* as it refers to a function. We use it here to describe the input argument—the value that goes inside the parentheses when we call a function. In MATLAB, input arguments are different from the **input** command.

Here's an example of a very simple MATLAB function that calculates the value of a particular polynomial:

```
function output = poly(x)
%This function calculates the value of a third-order
%polynomial
output = 3*x.^3 + 5*x.^2 – 2*x +1;
```

The function name is **poly**, the input argument is **x**, and the output variable is named **output**.

Before this function can be used, it must be saved into the current directory. The file name *must be the same* as the function name in order for MATLAB to find it. All of the MATLAB naming conventions we learned for naming variables apply to naming user-defined functions. In particular,

- The function name must start with a letter.
- It can consist of letters, numbers, and the underscore.
- Reserved names cannot be used.
- Any length is allowed, although long names are not good programming practice.

Once the M-file has been saved, the function is available for use from the command window, from a script M-file, or from another function. You can not execute a function M-file directly from the M-file itself. This makes sense, since the input parameters have not been defined until you call the function from the command window or a script M-file. Consider the **poly** function just created. If, in the command window, we type

> ***Key Idea:*** name functions using standard MATLAB naming conventions for variables

```
poly(4)
```

then MATLAB responds with

```
ans =
        265
```

If we set **a** equal to 4 and use **a** as the input argument, we get the same result:

```
a = 4;
poly(a)
ans =
        265
```

If we define a vector, we get a vector of answers. Thus,

```
y = 1:5;
poly(y)
```

gives

```
ans =
        7   41   121   265   491
```

If, however, you try to execute the function by selecting the save-and-run icon from the function menu bar, the following error message is displayed:

```
???Input argument "x" is undefined.
Error in ==> poly at 3
output = 3*x.^3 + 5*x.^2 – 2*x +1;
```

The value of **x** must be passed to the function when it is used—either in the command window or from within a script M-file program.

HINT

While you are creating a function, it may be useful to allow intermediate calculations to print to the command window. However, once you complete your "debugging," make sure that all your output is suppressed. If you don't, you'll see extraneous information in the command window.

In-Class Activity

ICA 19-1

Create MATLAB functions to evaluate the following mathematical functions (make sure you select meaningful function names) and test them. To test your functions you'll need to call them from the command window, or use them in a script M-file program. Remember, each function requires its own M-file.

1. $y(x) = x^2$
2. $y(x) = e^{1/x}$
3. $y(x) = \sin(x^2)$

Create MATLAB functions for the following unit conversions (you may need to consult a textbook or the Internet for the appropriate conversion factors). Be sure to test your functions, either from the command window, or by using them in a script M-file program.

4. inches to feet
5. calories to joules
6. watts to BTU/hr
7. meters to miles
8. miles per hour (mph) to ft/s

EXAMPLE 19.1

Converting between Degrees and Radians

Figure 19.1 Trigonometric functions require angles to be expressed in radians. Trigonometry is regularly used in engineering drawings.

Engineers usually measure angles in degrees, yet most computer programs and many calculators require that the input to trigonometric functions be in radians. Write and test a function DR that changes degrees to radians and another function RD that changes radians to degrees. Your functions should be able to accept both scalar and matrix input.

1. State the Problem
   Create and test two functions, DR and RD, to change degrees to radians and radians to degrees (see Figure 19.1).
2. Describe the Input and Output

   Input A vector of degree values
   A vector of radian values

   Output A table converting degrees to radians
   A table converting radians to degrees
3. Develop a Hand Example

$$\text{degrees} = \text{radians} \times 180/\pi$$

$$\text{radians} = \text{degrees} \times \pi/180$$

Degrees to Radians	
Degrees	Radians
0	0
30	$30(\pi/180) = \pi/6 = 0.524$
60	$60(\pi/180) = \pi/3 = 1.047$
90	$90(\pi/180) = \pi/2 = 1.571$

4. Develop a MATLAB Solution

```
%Example 18.1
%
clear, clc
%Define a vector of degree values
degrees 5 0:15:180;
% Call the DR function, and use it to find radians
radians 5 DR(degrees);
%Create a table to use in the output
degrees_radians 5[degrees;radians]'
%Define a vector of radian values
```

```
radians 5 0:pi/12:pi;
%Call the RD function, and use it to find degrees
degrees 5 RD(radians);
radians_degrees 5 [radians;degrees]'
```

The functions called by the program are

```
function output 5 DR(x)
%This function changes degrees to radians
output 5 x*pi/180;
```

and

```
function output 5 RD(x)
%This function changes radians to degrees
output 5 x*180/pi;
```

Remember that in order for the script M-file to find the functions, they must be in the current directory and must be named **DR.m** and **RD.m**. The program generates the following results in the command window:

```
degrees_radians 5
  0        0.000
  15       0.262
  30       0.524
  45       0.785
  60       1.047
  75       1.309
  90       1.571
  105      1.833
  120      2.094
  135      2.356
  150      2.618
  165      2.880
  180      3.142

radians_degrees 5
  0.000      0.000
  0.262     15.000
  0.524     30.000
  0.785     45.000
  1.047     60.000
  1.309     75.000
  1.571     90.000
  1.833    105.000
  2.094    120.000
  2.356    135.000
  2.618    150.000
  2.880    165.000
  3.142    180.000
```

5. Test the Solution
   Compare the MATLAB solution with the hand solution. Since the output is a table, it is easy to see that the conversions generated by MATLAB correspond to those calculated by hand.

EXAMPLE 19.2

Figure 19.2 Typical microstructures of iron (400×). (From *Metals Handbook,* 9th ed., Vol. 1, American Society of Metals, Metals Park, Ohio, 1978.)

ASTM Grain Size

You may not be used to thinking of metals as crystals, but they are. If you look at a polished piece of metal under a microscope, the structure becomes clear, as seen in Figure 19.2. As you can see, every crystal (called a grain in metallurgy) is a different size and shape. The size of the grains affects the metal's strength; the finer the grains, the stronger the metal.

Because it is difficult to determine an "average" grain size, a standard technique has been developed by ASTM (formerly known as the American Society for Testing and Materials, but now known just by its initials). A sample of metal is examined under a microscope at a magnification of 100, and the number of grains in 1 square inch is counted. The parameters are related by

$$N = 2^{n-1}$$

where n is the ASTM grain size and N is the number of grains per square inch at 100×. The equation can be solved for n to give

$$n = \frac{(\log(N) + \log(2))}{\log(2)}$$

This equation is not hard to use, but it's awkward. Instead, let's create a MATLAB function called **grain_size.**

1. State the Problem
   Create and test a function called **grain_size** to determine the ASTM grain size of a piece of metal.
2. Describe the Input and Output
   To test the function, we'll need to choose an arbitrary number of grains. For example:

   Input 16 grains per square inch at 100×

   Output ASTM grain size
3. Develop a Hand Example

$$n = \frac{(\log(N) + \log(2))}{\log(2)}$$

$$n = \frac{(\log(16) + \log(2))}{\log(2)} = 5$$

4. Develop a MATLAB Solution
   The function, created in a separate M-file, is

```
function output 5 grain_size(N)
%Calculates the ASTM grain size n
output 5 (log10(N) + log10(2))./log10(2);
```

which was saved as **grain_size.m** in the current directory. To use this function, we can call it from the command window:

```
grain_size(16)
ans =
     5
```

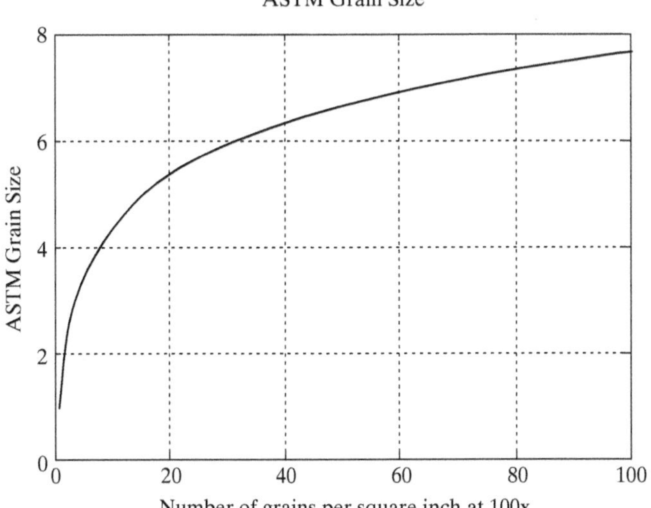

Figure 19.3 A plot of a function's behavior is a good way to help determine whether you've programmed it correctly.

5. Test the Solution
   The MATLAB solution is the same as the hand solution. It might be interesting to see how the ASTM grain size varies with the number of grains per square inch. We could use the function with an array of values and plot the results in Figure 19.3.

```
%Example 18.2
%ASTM Grain Size

N 5 1:100;
n 5 grain_size(N);
plot(N,n)
title('ASTM Grain Size')
xlabel('Number of grains per square inch at 100x')
ylabel('ASTM Grain Size')
grid
```

   As expected, the grain size increases as the number of grains per square inch increases.

Key Idea: Function comments are displayed when you use the help feature

19.1.2 Comments

As with any computer program, you should comment your code liberally so that it is easy to follow. However, in a MATLAB function, the comments on the line immediately following the very first line serve a special role. These lines are returned when the **help** function is queried from the command window. Consider, for example, the following function:

```
function results 5 f(x)
%This function converts seconds to minutes
results 5 x./60;
```

Querying the **help** function from the command window

```
help f
```

returns

```
This function converts seconds to minutes
```

19.1.3 Functions with Multiple Inputs and Outputs

Just as the predefined MATLAB functions may require multiple inputs and may return multiple outputs, more complicated user-defined functions can be written. Recall, for example, the remainder function. This predefined function calculates the remainder in a division problem and requires the user to input the dividend and the divisor. For the problem $\frac{5}{3}$, the correct syntax is

```
rem(5,3)
```

which gives

```
ans =
      2
```

Similarly, a user-defined function could be written to multiply two vectors together:

```
function output = g(x,y)
% This function multiplies x and y together
% x and y must be the same size matrices
a = x .*y;
output = a;
```

When **x** and **y** are defined in the command window and the function **g** is called, a vector of output values is returned:

```
x = 1:5;
y = 5:9;
g(x,y)
ans =
 5  12  21  32  45
```

You can use the comment lines to let users know what kind of input is required and to describe the function. In this example, an intermediate calculation (**a**) was performed, but the only output from this function is the variable we've named **output**. This output can be a matrix containing a variety of numbers, but it's still only one variable.

You can also create functions that return more than one output variable. Many of the predefined MATLAB functions return more than one result. For example, **max** returns both the maximum value in a matrix and the element number at which the maximum occurs. To achieve the same result in a user-defined function, make the output a matrix of answers instead of a single variable, as in

```
function    [dist, vel, accel] = motion(t)
% This function calculates the distance, velocity, and
% acceleration of a car for a given value of t
accel = 0.5 .*t;
vel = accel .* t;
dist = vel.*t;
```

Once saved as **motion** in the current directory, you can use the function to find values of **distance**, **velocity**, and **acceleration** at specified times:

```
[distance, velocity, acceleration] = motion(10)
distance =
      500
velocity =
      50
acceleration =
      5
```

If you call the **motion** function without specifying all three outputs, only the first output will be returned:

```
motion(10)
ans =
        500
```

Remember, all variables in MATLAB are matrices, so it's important in the preceding example to use the **.*** operator, which specifies element-by-element multiplication. For example, using a vector of time values from 0 to 30 in the motion function

```
time = 0:10:30;
[distance, velocity, acceleration] = motion(time)
```

returns three vectors of answers:

```
distance =
        0  500  4000  13500
velocity =
        0  50    200    450
acceleration =
        0  5     10     15
```

It's easier to see the results if you group the vectors together, as in

```
results =[time',distance',velocity',acceleration']
```

which returns

```
results =
            0      0          0       0
           10      500        50      5
           20      4000       200     10
           30      13500      450     15
```

Because **time, distance, velocity**, and **acceleration** were row vectors, the transpose operator was used to convert them into columns.

In-Class Activity

ICA 19-2

Assuming that the matrix dimensions agree, create and test MATLAB functions to evaluate the following simple mathematical functions with multiple input vectors and a single output vector:

1. $z(x, y) = x + y$
2. $z(a, b, c) = ab^c$
3. $z(w, x, y) = we^{(x/y)}$
4. $z(p, t) = p/\sin(t)$

Assuming that the matrix dimensions agree, create and test MATLAB functions to evaluate the following simple mathematical functions with a single input vector and multiple output vectors:

5. $f(x) = \cos(x)$
   $f(x) = \sin(x)$
6. $f(x) = 5x^2 + 2$
   $f(x) = \sqrt{5x^2 + 2}$

7. $f(x) = \exp(x)$
   $f(x) = \ln(x)$

Assuming that the matrix dimensions agree, create and test MATLAB functions to evaluate the following simple mathematical functions with multiple input vectors and multiple output vectors:

8. $f(x, y) = x + y$
   $f(x, y) = x - y$
9. $f(x, y) = ye^x$
   $f(x, y) = xe^y$

EXAMPLE 19.3

How Grain Size Affects Metal Strength: A Function with Three Inputs

Metals composed of small crystals are stronger than metals composed of fewer large crystals. The metal yield strength (the amount of stress at which the metal starts to permanently deform) is related to the average grain diameter by the *Hall–Petch equation:*

$$\sigma = \sigma_0 + Kd^{-1/2}$$

where the symbols σ_0 and K represent constants that are different for every metal.

Create a function called **HallPetch** that requires three inputs—σ_0, *K*, and *d*—and calculates the value of yield strength. Call this function from a MATLAB program that supplies values of σ_0 and *K*, then plots the value of yield strength for values of *d* from 0.1 to 10 mm.

1. State the Problem
   Create a function called **HallPetch** that determines the yield strength of a piece of metal, using the Hall–Petch equation. Use the function to create a plot of yield strength versus grain diameter.
2. Describe the Input and Output

   Input $K = 9600 \text{ psi}/\sqrt{\text{mm}}$
   $\sigma_0 = 12{,}000$ psi
   $d = 0.1$ to 10 mm

   Output Plot of yield strength versus diameter
3. Develop a Hand Example
   The Hall–Petch equation is

$$\sigma = \sigma_0 + Kd^{-1/2}$$

   Substituting values of 12,000 psi and 9600 psi/$\sqrt{\text{mm}}$ for σ_0 and *K*, respectively, then

$$\sigma = 12{,}000 + 9600d^{-1/2}$$

   For $d = 1$ mm,

$$\sigma = 12{,}000 + 9600 = 21{,}600$$

4. Develop a MATLAB Solution
   The desired function, created in a separate M-file, is

```
function output 5 HallPetch(sigma0,K,d)
%Hall–Petch equation to determine the yield
%strength of metals
output 5 sigma0 + K*d.^(–0.5);
```

and was saved as HallPetch.m in the current directory:

```
%Example 18.3
clear,clc
format compact
s0 5 12000
K 5 9600
%Define the values of grain diameter
diameter 5 0.1:0.1:10;
yield 5 HallPetch(s0,K,d);
%Plot the results
figure(1)
plot(diameter,yield)
title('Yield strengths found with the Hall–Petch equation')
xlabel('diameter, mm')
ylabel('yield strength, psi')
```

The graph shown in Figure 19.4 was generated by the program.

5. Test the Solution
   We can use the graph to compare the results to the hand solution.

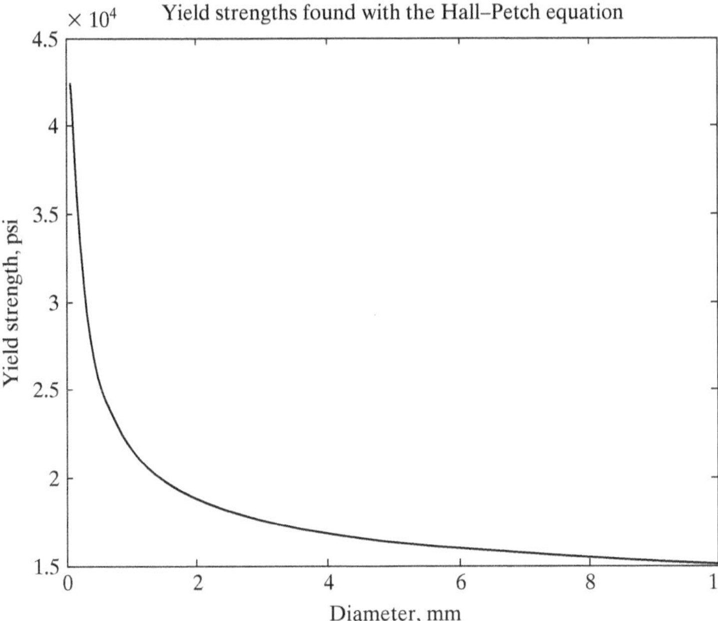

Figure 19.4 Yield strengths predicted with the Hall–Petch equation.

EXAMPLE 19.4

Kinetic Energy: A Function with Two Inputs

The kinetic energy of a moving object (Figure 19.5) is

$$KE = 1/2mv^2.$$

Create and test a function called KE to find the kinetic energy of a moving car if you know the mass *m* and the velocity *v* of the vehicle.

1. State the Problem
   Create a function called KE to find the kinetic energy of a car.
2. Describe the Input and Output

   Input Mass of the car, in kilograms
   Velocity of the car, in m/s

   Output Kinetic energy, in joules
3. Develop a Hand Example
   If the mass is 1000 kg, and the velocity is 25 m/s, then

$$\text{Ke} = 1/2 \times 1000 \text{ kg} \times (25 \text{ m/s})^2 = 312{,}500 \text{ J} = 312.5 \text{ kJ}$$

4. Develop a MATLAB Solution

```
function   output = ke(mass,velocity)
output = 1/2*mass*velocity.^2;
```

5. Test the Solution

```
v = 25;
m = 1000;
ke(m,v)
ans =
        312500
```

This result matches the hand example, confirming that the function works correctly and can now be used in a larger MATLAB program.

Figure 19.5 Race cars store a significant amount of kinetic energy. (Rick Graves/Getty Images.)

19.1.4 Functions with No Input or No Output

Although most functions need at least one input and return at least one output value, in some situations no inputs or outputs are required. For example, consider this function, which draws a star in polar coordinates:

```
function [ ] = star( )
theta = pi/2:0.8*pi:4.8*pi;
r=ones(1,6);
polar(theta,r)
```

The square brackets on the first line indicate that the output of the function is an empty matrix (i.e., no value is returned). The empty parentheses tell us that no input is expected. If, from the command window, you type

```
star
```

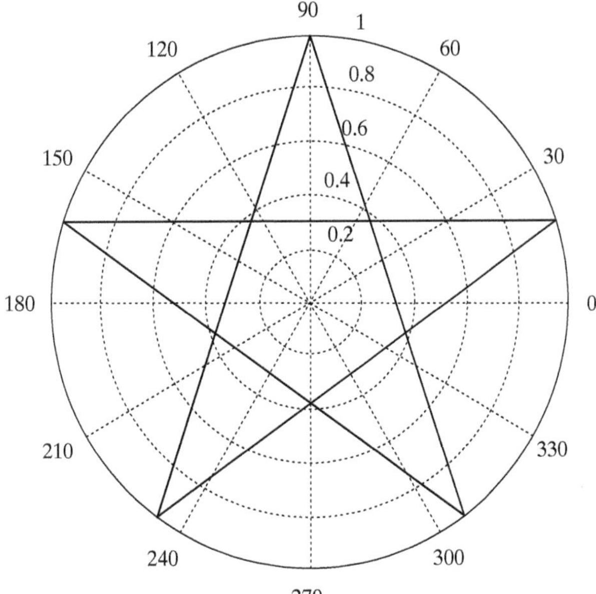

Figure 19.6 The user-defined function **star** requires no input and produces no output values, but it does draw a star in polar coordinates.

then no values are returned, but a figure window opens showing a star drawn in polar coordinates. (See Figure 19.6.)

HINT

You may ask yourself if the **star** function is really an example of a function that does not return an output; after all, it does draw a star. But the output of a function is defined as a *value* that is returned when you call the function. If we ask MATLAB to perform the calculation

```
A = Star
```

an error statement is generated, because the **star** function does not return anything! Thus, there is nothing to set **A** equal to.

> ***Key Idea:*** Not all functions require an input

There are numerous built-in MATLAB functions that do not require any input. For example,

```
A = clock
```

returns the current time:

```
A =
 1.0e+003 *
 Columns 1 through 4
  2.0050   0.0030   0.0200   0.0150
 Columns 5 through 6
  0.0250   0.0277
```

Also,

```
A = pi
```

returns the value of the mathematical constant π:

```
A =
  3.1416
```

However, if we try to set the MATLAB function **tic** equal to a variable name, an error statement is generated, because **tic** does not return an output value:

```
A = tic
???Error using ==> tic
Too many output arguments.
```

(The **tic** function starts a timer going for later use in the **toc** function.)

19.1.5 Determining the Number of Input and Output Arguments

There may be times when you want to know the number of input arguments or output values associated with a function. MATLAB provides two built-in functions for this purpose.

> ***Key Idea:*** Using the **nargin** or **nargout** functions is useful in programming functions with variable inputs and outputs

The **nargin** function determines the number of input arguments in either a user-defined function or a built-in function. The name of the function must be specified as a string, as, for example, in

```
nargin('sin')
ans =
  1
```

The remainder function, **rem**, requires two inputs; thus,

```
nargin('rem')
ans =
  2
```

When **nargin** is used inside a user-defined function, it determines how many input arguments were actually entered. This allows a function to have a variable number of inputs. Recall graphing functions such as **surf**. When **surf** has a single matrix input, a graph is created, using the matrix index numbers as the x- and y-coordinates. When there are three inputs, x, y, and z, the graph is based on the specified x- and y-values. The **nargin** function allows the programmer to determine how to create the plot, based on the number of inputs.

The **surf** function is an example of a function with a variable number of inputs. If we use **nargin** from the command window to determine the number of declared inputs, there isn't one correct answer. The **nargin** function returns a negative number to let us know that a variable number of inputs is possible:

```
nargin('surf')
ans =
  -1
```

The **nargout** function is similar to **nargin**, but it determines the number of outputs from a function:

```
nargout('sin')
ans =
  1
```

The number of outputs is determined by how many matrices are returned, not how many values are in the matrix. We know that **size** returns the number of rows and columns in a matrix, so we might expect **nargout** to return 2 when applied to size. However,

```
nargout('size')
ans =
   1
```

returns only one matrix, which has just two elements, as for example, in

```
x = 1:10;
size(x)
ans =
   1  10
```

An example of a function with multiple outputs is **max**:

```
nargout('max')
ans =
    3
```

When used inside a user-defined function, **nargout** determines how many outputs have been requested by the user. Consider this example, in which we have rewritten the function from Section 19.1.4 to create a star:

```
function A = star1( )
theta = pi/2:0.8*pi:4.8*pi;
r = ones(1,6);
polar(theta,r)
if nargout==1
   A = 'Twinkle twinkle little star';
end
```

If we use **nargout** from the command window, as in

```
nargout('star1')
ans =
   1
```

MATLAB tells us that one output is specified. If we call the function simply as

```
star1
```

nothing is returned to the command window, although the plot is drawn. If we call the function by setting it equal to a variable, as in

```
x = star1
x =
Twinkle twinkle little star
```

a value for **x** is returned, based on the **if** statement embedded in the function, which used **nargout** to determine the number of output values.

19.1.6 Local Variables

The variables used in function M-files are known as *local variables*. The only way a function can communicate with the workspace is through input arguments and the output it returns. Any variables defined within the function exist only for the function to use. For example, consider the **g** function previously described:

```
function output = g(x,y)
% This function multiplies x and y together
% x and y must be the same size matrices
a = x .*y;
output = a;
```

Local Variable: a variable that only has meaning inside a program or function

The variables **a**, **x**, **y**, and **output** are local variables. They can be used for additional calculations inside the **g** function, but they are not stored in the workspace. To confirm this, clear the workspace and the command window and then call the **g** function:

```
clear, clc
g(10,20)
```

The function returns

```
g(10,20)
ans =
    200
```

Notice that the only variable stored in the workspace window is **ans**, which is characterized as follows:

Name	Value	Size	Bytes	Class
ans	200	1 × 1	8	double array

Just as calculations performed in the command window or from a script M-file cannot access variables defined in functions, functions cannot access the variables defined in the workspace. This means that functions must be completely self-contained: The only way they can get information from your program is through the input arguments, and the only way they can deliver information is through the function output.

Consider a function written to find the distance an object falls due to gravity:

```
function  result = distance(t)
%This function calculates the distance a falling object
%travels due to gravity
g = 9.8      %meters per second squared
result = 1/2*g*t.^2;
```

The value of **g** must be included *inside* the function. It doesn't matter whether **g** has or has not been used in the main program. How **g** is defined is hidden to the distance function unless **g** is specified inside the function.

Of course, you could also pass the value of **g** to the function as an input argument:

```
function  result = distance(g,t)
%This function calculates the distance a falling object
%travels due to gravity
result = 1/2*g*t.^2;
```

HINT

The same matrix names can be used in both a function and the program that references it. However, they do not *have* to be the same. Since variable names are local to either the function or the program that calls the function, the variables are completely separate. As a beginning programmer, you would be wise to use different variable names in your functions and your programs—just so you don't confuse *yourself.*

19.1.7 Accessing M-File Code

The functions provided with MATLAB are of two types. One type is built in, and the code is not accessible for us to review. The other type consists of M-files, stored in toolboxes provided with the program. We can see these M-files (or the M-files we've written) with the **type** command. For example, the **sphere** function creates a three-dimensional representation of a sphere; thus,

```
type sphere
```

or

```
type('sphere')
```

returns the contents of the **sphere.m** file:

```
function [xx,yy,zz] = sphere(varargin)
%SPHERE Generate sphere.
%  [X,Y,Z] = SPHERE(N) generates three (N+1)-by-(N+1)
%  matrices so that SURF(X,Y,Z) produces a unit sphere.
%
%  [X,Y,Z] = SPHERE uses N = 20.
%
%  SPHERE(N) and just SPHERE graph the sphere as a SURFACE
%  and do not return anything.
%
%  SPHERE(AX,...) plots into AX instead of GCA.
%
%  See also ELLIPSOID, CYLINDER.

%  Clay M. Thompson 4-24-91, CBM 8-21-92.
%  Copyright 1984-2002 The MathWorks, Inc.
%  $Revision: 5.8.4.1 $  $Date: 2002/09/26 01:55:25 $

% Parse possible Axes input
error(nargchk(0,2,nargin));
[cax,args,nargs] = axescheck(varargin{:});

n = 20;
if nargs > 0, n = args{1}; end
% -pi <= theta <= pi is a row vector.
% -pi/2 <= phi <= pi/2 is a column vector.
theta = (-n:2:n)/n*pi;
phi = (-n:2:n)'/n*pi/2;
cosphi = cos(phi); cosphi(1) = 0; cosphi(n+1) = 0;
sintheta = sin(theta); sintheta(1) = 0; sintheta(n+1) = 0;

x = cosphi*cos(theta);
y = cosphi*sintheta;
z = sin(phi)*ones(1,n+1);

if nargout == 0
   cax = newplot(cax);
   surf(x,y,z,'parent',cax)
else
   xx = x; yy = y; zz = z;
end
```

HINT

Notice that the **sphere** function uses **varargin** to indicate that it will accept a variable number of input arguments. The function also makes use of the **nargin** and **nargout** functions. Studying this function may give you ideas on how to program your own function M-files. The **sphere** function also uses an if/else structure, which is introduced in a subsequent chapter of this text.

19.2 FUNCTION FUNCTIONS

Key Idea: Function functions require functions or function handles as input

One example of a MATLAB built-in function function is the function plot, **fplot**. This function requires two inputs: a function or a function handle, and a range over which to plot. We can demonstrate the use of **fplot** with the function handle **ln**, defined as

```
ln = @(x) log(x)
```

The function handle can now be used as input to the **fplot** function:

```
fplot(ln,[0.1, 10])
```

The result is shown in Figure 19.7. We could also use the **fplot** function without the function handle. We just need to insert the function syntax directly, as a string:

```
fplot('log(x)',[0.1, 10])
```

The advantage to using function handles isn't obvious from this example, but consider instead this anonymous function describing a particular fifth-order polynomial:

```
poly5 = @(x) -5*x.^5 + 400*x.^4 + 3*x.^3 + 20*x.^2 - x + 5;
```

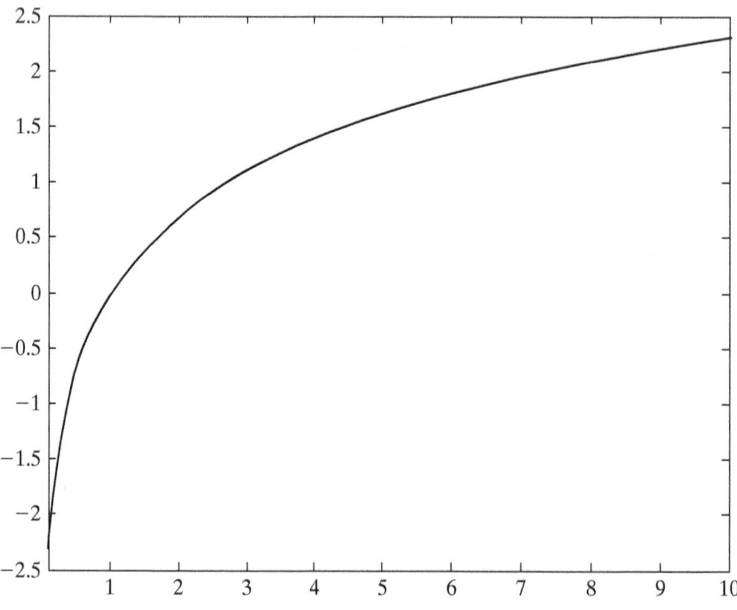

Figure 19.7 Function handles can be used as input to a function function, such as **fplot**.

Entering the equation directly into the **fplot** function would be awkward. Using the function handle is considerably simpler.

```
fplot(poly5,[-30,90])
```

The results are shown in Figure 19.8.

A wide variety of MATLAB functions accept function handles as input. For example, the **fzero** function finds the value of x when $f(x)$ is equal to 0. It accepts a function handle and a rough guess for x. From Figure 19.8 we see that our fifth-order polynomial probably has a zero between 75 and 85 so a rough guess for the zero point might be $x = 75$.

```
fzero(poly5,75)
ans =
   80.0081
```

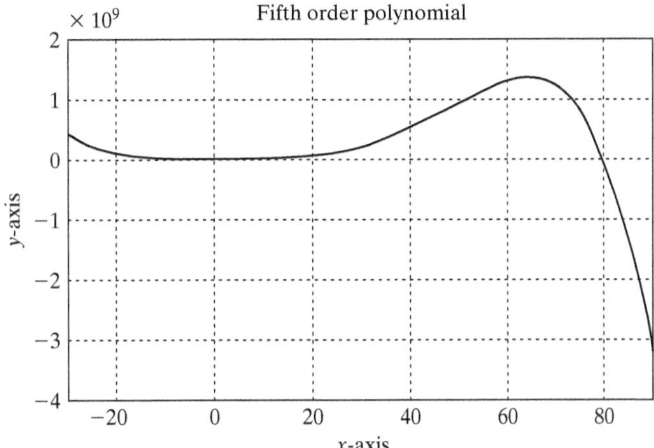

Figure 19.8 This fifth-order polynomial was plotted using the **fplot** function function, with a function handle as input.

SUMMARY

MATLAB contains a wide variety of built-in functions. However, you will often find it useful to create your own MATLAB functions. The most common type of user-defined MATLAB function is the function M-file, which must start with a function-definition line that contains

- the word **function**,
- a variable that defines the function output,
- a function name, and
- a variable used for the input argument.

For example,

```
function output = my_function(x)
```

The function name must also be the name of the M-file in which the function is stored. Function names follow the standard MATLAB naming rules.

Like the built-in functions, user-defined functions can accept multiple inputs and can return multiple results.

Comments immediately following the function-definition line can be accessed from the command window with the **help** command.

Variables defined within a function are local to that function. They are not stored in the workspace and cannot be accessed from the command window. Global variables can be defined with the **global** command used in both the command window (or script M-file) and a MATLAB function. Good programming style suggests that you define global variables with capital letters. In general, however, it is not wise to use global variables.

Groups of user-defined functions, called "toolboxes," may be stored in a common directory and accessed by modifying the MATLAB search path. This is accomplished interactively with the path tool, either from the menu bar, as in

File→Set Path

or from the command line, with

pathtool

MATLAB provides access to numerous toolboxes developed at The MathWorks or by the user community.

Another type of function is the anonymous function, which is defined in a MATLAB session or in a script M-file and exists only during that session. Anonymous functions are especially useful for very simple mathematical expressions or as input to the more complicated function functions.

MATLAB SUMMARY

The following MATLAB summary lists and briefly describes all of the special characters, commands, and functions that were defined in this chapter:

Special Characters	
@	identifies a function handle, such as that used with anonymous functions
%	Comment

Commands and Functions	
addpath	adds a directory to the MATLAB search path
fminbnd	a function function that accepts a function handle or function definition as input and finds the function minimum between two bounds
fplot	a function function that accepts a function handle or function definition as input and creates the corresponding plot between two bounds
fzero	a function function that accepts a function handle or function definition as input and finds the function zero point nearest a specified value
function	identifies an M-file as a function
global	defines a variable that can be used in multiple sections of code
meshgrid	maps two input vectors onto two two-dimensional matrices
nargin	determines the number of input arguments in a function
nargout	determines the number of output arguments from a function
pathtool	opens the interactive path tool
varargin	indicates that a variable number of arguments may be input to a function

KEY TERMS

anonymous	function	in-line
argument	function function	input argument
comments	function handle	local variable
directory	function name	M-file
file name	global variable	toolbox
folder		

EXERCISES AND ACTIVITIES

Function M-Files

As you create functions in this section, be sure to comment them appropriately. Remember that, although many of these problems could be solved without a function, the objective of this chapter is to learn to write and use functions. Each of these functions (except for the anonymous functions) must be created in its own M-file and then called from the command window or a script M-file program.

19.1 As described in Example 19.2, metals are actually crystalline materials. Metal crystals are called grains. When the average grain size is small, the metal is strong; when it is large, the metal is weaker. Since every crystal in a particular sample of metal is a different size, it isn't obvious how we should describe the average crystal size. The American Society for Testing and Materials (ASTM) has developed the following correlation for standardizing grain-size measurements:

$$N = 2^{n-1}$$

The ASTM grain size (n) is determined by looking at a sample of a metal under a microscope at a magnification of 100× (100 power). The number of grains in a 1-square-inch area (actual dimensions of 0.01 inch × 0.01 inch) is estimated (N) and used in the preceding equation to find the ASTM grain size.

(a) Write a MATLAB function called **num_grains** to find the number of grains in a 1-square-inch area (N) at 100× magnification when the ASTM grain size is known.

(b) Use your function to find the number of grains for ASTM grain sizes $n = 10$ to 100.

(c) Create a plot of your results.

19.2 Perhaps the most famous equation in physics is

$$E = mc^2$$

which relates energy E to mass m. The speed of light in a vacuum, c, is the property that links the two together. The speed of light in a vacuum is 2.9979×10^8 m/s.

(a) Create a function called **energy** to find the energy corresponding to a given mass in kg. Your result will be in joules, since 1 kg $m^2/s^2 = 1$ joule.

(b) Use your function to find the energy corresponding to masses from 1 kg to 10^6 kg. Use the **logspace** function (consult **help/logspace**) to create an appropriate mass vector.

(c) Create a plot of your results. Try using different logarithmic plotting approaches (e.g., **semilogy**, **semilogx**, and **loglog**) to determine the best way to graph your results.

19.3 The future-value-of-money formula relates how much a current investment will be worth in the future, assuming a constant interest rate.

$$FV = PV*(1 + i)^n$$

where

FV is the future value

PV is the present value or investment

I is the interest rate expressed as a fractional amount per compounding period—i.e., 5% is expressed as .05.

n is the number of compounding periods

(a) Create a MATLAB function called **future_value** with three inputs; the investment (present value), the interest rate expressed as a fraction, and the number of compounding periods.

(b) Use your function to determine the value of a $1000 investment in 10 years, assuming the interest rate is 0.5% per month, and the interest is compounded monthly.

19.4 In first-year chemistry, the relationship between moles and mass is introduced:

$$n = \frac{m}{\text{MW}}$$

where

n = number of moles of a substance,

m = mass of the substance, and

MW = molecular weight (molar mass) of the substance.

(a) Create a function M-file called **nmoles** that requires two vector inputs—the mass and molecular weight—and returns the corresponding number of moles. Because you are providing vector input, it will be necessary to use the **meshgrid** function in your calculations.

(b) Test your function for the compounds shown in the following table, for masses from 1 to 10 g:

Compound	Molecular Weight (Molar Mass)
Benzene	78.115 g/mol
Ethyl alcohol	46.07 g/mol
Refrigerant R134a (tetrafluoroethane)	102.3 g/mol

Your result should be a 10 × 3 matrix.

19.5 By rearranging the preceding relationship between moles and mass, you can find the mass if you know the number of moles of a compound:

$$m = n \times \text{MW}$$

(a) Create a function M-file called **mass** that requires two vector inputs—the number of moles and the molecular weight—and returns the corresponding mass. Because you are providing vector input, it will be necessary to use the **meshgrid** function in your calculations.

(b) Test your function with the compounds listed in the previous problem, for values of n from 1 to 10.

19.6 The distance to the horizon increases as you climb a mountain (or a hill). The expression

$$d = \sqrt{2rh + h^2}$$

where

d = distance to the horizon,

r = radius of the earth, and

h = height of the hill

can be used to calculate that distance. The distance depends on how high the hill is and on the radius of the earth (or another planetary body).

(a) Create a function M-file called **distance** to find the distance to the horizon. Your function should accept two vector inputs—radius and height—and should return the distance to the horizon. Don't forget that you'll need to use **meshgrid** because your inputs are vectors.

(b) Create a MATLAB program that uses your distance function to find the distance in miles to the horizon, both on the earth and on Mars, for hills from 0 to 10,000 feet. Remember to use consistent units in your calculations. Note that

- Earth's diameter = 7926 miles
- Mars' diameter = 4217 miles

Report your results in a table. Each column should represent a different planet, and each row a different hill height.

19.7 A rocket is launched vertically. At time $t = 0$, the rocket's engine shuts down. At that time, the rocket has reached an altitude of 500 meters and is rising at a velocity of 125 meters per second. Gravity then takes over. The height of the rocket as a function of time is

$$h(t) = -\frac{9.8}{2}t^2 + 125t + 500 \quad \text{for } t > 0$$

(a) Create a function called **height** that accepts time as an input and returns the height of the rocket. Use your function in your solutions to parts b and c.

(b) Plot **height** vs. time for times from 0 to 30 seconds. Use an increment of 0.5 second in your time vector.

(c) Find the time when the rocket starts to fall back to the ground. (The **max** function will be helpful in this exercise.)

19.8 The distance a freely falling object travels is

$$x = \frac{1}{2}gt^2$$

where

g = acceleration due to gravity, 9.8 m/s^2

t = time in seconds

x = distance traveled in meters.

If you have taken calculus, you know that we can find the velocity of the object by taking the derivative of the preceding equation. That is,

$$\frac{dx}{dt} = v = gt$$

We can find the acceleration by taking the derivative again:

$$\frac{dv}{dt} = a = g$$

(a) Create a function called **free_fall** with a single input vector **t** that returns values for distance **x**, velocity **v**, and acceleration **g**.

(b) Test your function with a time vector that ranges from 0 to 20 seconds.

19.9 Create a function called **polygon** that draws a polygon with any number of sides. Your function should require a single input: the number of sides desired. It should not return any value to the command window but should draw the requested polygon in polar coordinates.

Creating Your Own Toolbox

19.10 This problem requires you to generate temperature-conversion tables. Use the following equations, which describe the relationships between temperatures in degrees Fahrenheit (T_F), degrees Celsius (T_C), kelvins (T_K),and degrees Rankine (T_R), respectively:

$$T_F = T_R - 459.67°\text{R}$$

$$T_F = \frac{9}{5}T_C + 32°\text{F}$$

$$T_R = \frac{9}{5}T_K$$

You will need to rearrange these expressions to solve some of the problems.

(a) Create a function called **F_to_K** that converts temperatures in Fahrenheit to Kelvin. Use your function to generate a conversion table for values from 0°F to 200°F.

(b) Create a function called **C_to_R** that converts temperatures in Celsius to Rankine. Use your function to generate a conversion table from 0°C to 100°C. Print 25 lines in the table. (Use the **linspace** function to create your input vector.)

(c) Create a function called **C_to_F** that converts temperatures in Celsius to Fahrenheit. Use your function to generate a conversion table from 0°C to 100°C. Choose an appropriate spacing.

(d) Group your functions into a folder (directory) called **my_temp_conversions**. Adjust the MATLAB search path so that it finds your folder. (Don't save any changes on a public computer!)

Anonymous Functions and Function Handles

19.11 Barometers have been used for almost 400 years to measure pressure changes in the atmosphere. The first known barometer was invented by Evangelista Torricelli (1608–1647), a student of Galileo during his final years in Florence, Italy. The height of a liquid in a barometer is directly proportional to the atmospheric pressure, or

$$P = \rho g h$$

where P is the pressure, ρ is the density of the barometer fluid, and h is the height of the liquid column. For mercury barometers, the density of the fluid is 13,560 kg/m^3. On the surface of the earth, the acceleration due to gravity, g, is approximately 9.8 m/s^2. Thus, the only variable in the equation is the height of the fluid column, h, which should have the unit of meters.

(a) Create an anonymous function **P** that finds the pressure if the value of h is provided. The units of your answer will be

$$\frac{\text{kg}}{\text{m}^3}\frac{\text{m}}{\text{s}^2}\text{m} = \frac{\text{kg}}{\text{m}}\frac{1}{\text{s}^2} = \text{Pa}$$

(b) Create another anonymous function to convert pressure in Pa (Pascals) to pressure in atmospheres (atm). Call the function **Pa_to_atm**. Note that

$$1 \text{ atm} = 101{,}325 \text{ Pa}$$

(c) Use your anonymous functions to find the pressure for fluid heights from 0.5 m to 1.0 m of mercury.

(d) Save your anonymous functions as **.mat** files

19.12 The energy required to heat water at constant pressure is approximately equal to

$$E = mC_p\,\Delta T$$

where

m = mass of the water, in grams,

C_p = heat capacity of water, 1 cal/g K, and

ΔT = change in temperature, K.

(a) Create an anonymous function called **heat** to find the energy required to heat 1 gram of water if the change in temperature is provided as the input.

(b) Your result will be in calories:

$$\text{g}\frac{\text{cal}}{\text{g}}\frac{1}{\text{K}}\text{K} = \text{cal}$$

Joules are the unit of energy used most often in engineering. Create another anonymous function **cal_to_J** to convert your answer from part a into joules. (There are 4.2 joules/cal.)

(c) Save your anonymous functions as **.mat** files.

19.13 **(a)** Create an anonymous function called **my_function**, equal to

$$-x^2 - 5x - 3 + e^x$$

(b) Use the **fplot** function to create a plot from $x = -5$ to $x = +5$. Recall that the **fplot** function can accept a function handle as input.

(c) Use the **fminbnd** function to find the minimum function value in this range. The **fminbnd** function is an example of a function function, since it requires a function or function handle as input. The syntax is

```
fminbnd(function_handle, xmin, xmax)
```

Three inputs are required; the function handle, the minimum value of x and the maximum value of x. The function searches between the minimum value of x and the maximum value of x for the point where the function value is a minimum.

19.14 In Problem 19.7 you created an M-file function called **height** to evaluate the height of a rocket as a function of time. The relationship between time, t, and height, $h(t)$, is:

$$h(t) = -\frac{9.8}{2}t^2 + 125t + 500 \quad \text{for } t > 0$$

(a) Create a function handle to the **height** function called **height_handle**.

(b) Use **height_handle** as input to the **fplot** function, and create a graph from 0 to 60 seconds.

(c) Use the **fzero** function to find the time when the rocket hits the ground (i.e., when the function value is zero). The **fzero** function is an example of a function function, since it requires a function or function handle as input. The syntax is

```
fzero(function_handle, x_guess)
```

The **fzero** function requires two inputs—a function handle and your guess as to the time value where the function is close to zero. You can select a reasonable **x_guess** value by inspecting the graph created in part b.

Subfunctions

19.15 In Problem 19.10 you were asked to create and use three different temperature-conversion functions, based on the following conversion equations:

$$T_F = T_R - 459.67°\text{R}$$

$$T_F = \frac{9}{5}T_C + 32°\text{F}$$

$$T_R = \frac{9}{5}T_K$$

Recreate Problem 19.10 using nested subfunctions. The primary function should be called **temperature_conversions** and should include the subfunctions

```
F_to_K
C_to_R
C_to_F
```

Within the primary function use the subfunctions to:

(a) Generate a conversion table for values from 0°F to 200°F. Include a column for temperature in Fahrenheit and Kelvin.

(b) Generate a conversion table from 0°C to 100°C. Print 25 lines in the table. (Use the **linspace** function to create your input vector.) Your table should include a column for temperature in Celsius and Rankine.

(c) Generate a conversion table from 0°C to 100°C. Choose an appropriate spacing. Include a column for temperature in Celsius and Fahrenheit.

Recall that you will need to call your primary function from the command window or from a script M-file.

CHAPTER 20
USER-CONTROLLED INPUT AND OUTPUT

Objectives

By learning the material in this chapter, you should be able to

- prompt the user for input to an M-file program
- create output with the **disp** function
- create formatted output by using **fprintf**
- create formatted output for use in other functions with the **sprintf** function
- use graphical techniques to provide program input
- use the cell mode to modify and run M-file programs

Introduction

So far, we have explored the use of MATLAB in two modes: in the command window as a scratch pad and in the editing window to write simple programs (script M-files). The programmer has been the user. Now we move on to more complicated programs, written in the editing window, where the programmer and the user may be different people. That will make it necessary to use input and output commands to communicate with the user, instead of rewriting the actual code to solve similar problems. MATLAB offers built-in functions to allow a user to communicate with a program as it executes. The **input** command pauses the program and prompts the user for input; the **disp** and **fprintf** commands provide output to the command window.

20.1 USER-DEFINED INPUT

Although we have written programs in script M-files, we have assumed that the programmer (you) and the user are the same person. To run the program with different input values, we actually changed some of the code. We can create more general programs by allowing the user to input values of a matrix from the keyboard while the program is running. The **input** function allows us to do this. It displays a text string in the command window and then waits for the user to provide the requested input. For example,

```
z = input('Enter a value')
```

Taken from *MATLAB® for Engineers,* Second Edition, by Holly Moore.

displays

```
Enter a value
```

in the command window. If the user enters a value such as

```
5
```

the program assigns the value 5 to the variable **z**. If the **input** command does not end with a semicolon, the value entered is displayed on the screen:

```
z =
        5
```

The same approach can be used to enter a one- or two-dimensional matrix. The user must provide the appropriate brackets and delimiters (commas and semicolons). For example,

```
z = input('Enter values for z in brackets')
```

> ***Key Idea:*** The **input** function can be used to communicate with the program user

requests the user to input a matrix such as

```
[ 1, 2, 3; 4, 5, 6]
```

and responds with

```
z =
        1 2 3
        4 5 6
```

This input value of **z** can then be used in subsequent calculations by the script M-file.

Data entered with **input** does not need to be numeric information. Suppose we prompt the user with the command

```
x = input('Enter your name in single quotes')
```

and enter

```
'Holly'
```

when prompted. Because we haven't used a semicolon at the end of the **input** command, MATLAB will respond

```
x =
 Holly
```

Notice in the workspace window that **x** is listed as a 1×5 character array:

Name	Value	Size	Bytes	Class
abc x	'Holly'	1×5	6	char

If you are entering a string (in MATLAB, strings are character arrays), you must enclose the characters in single quotes. However, an alternative form of the input command alerts the function to expect character input without the single quotes by specifying string input in the second field:

```
x = input('Enter your name', 's')
```

Now you need only enter the characters, such as

```
Ralph
```

and the program responds with

```
x =
  Ralph
```

In-Class Activity

ICA 20-1

1. Create an M-file to calculate the area A of a triangle:

$$A = \frac{1}{2}\text{ base height}$$

Prompt the user to enter the values for the base and for the height.

2. Create an M-file to find the volume V of a right circular cylinder:

$$V = \pi r^2 h$$

Prompt the user to enter the values of r and h.

3. Create a vector from 0 to n, allowing the user to enter the value of n.
4. Create a vector that starts at a, ends at b, and has a spacing of c. Allow the user to input all of these parameters.

EXAMPLE 20.1

Freely Falling Objects

Consider the behavior of a freely falling object under the influence of gravity. (See Figure 20.1.)

The position of the object is described by

$$d = \frac{1}{2}gt^2$$

where d = distance the object travels,
g = acceleration due to gravity, and
t = elapsed time

Figure 20.1 The Leaning Tower of Pisa. (Courtesy of Tim Galligan.)

We shall allow the user to specify the value of g—the acceleration due to gravity—and a vector of time values.

1. State the Problem
   Find the distance traveled by a freely falling object and plot the results.
2. Describe the Input and Output
   Input Value of g, the acceleration due to gravity, provided by the user
   Time, provided by the user
   Output Distances
   Plot of distance versus time
3. Develop a Hand Example

$$d = \frac{1}{2}gt^2, \text{ so, on the moon at 100 seconds,}$$

$$d = \frac{1}{2} \times 1.6 \text{ m/s}^2 \times 100^2 \text{ s}^2$$

$$d = 8000 \text{ m}$$

4. Develop a MATLAB Solution

```
%Example 19.1
%Free fall
clear, clc
%Request input from the user
g = input('What is the value of acceleration due to
  gravity?')
start = input('What starting time would you like? ')
finish = input('What ending time would you like? ')
incr = input('What time increments would you like
  calculated? ')
time = start:incr:finish;
%Calculate the distance
distance = 1/2*g*time.^2;
%Plot the results
loglog(time,distance)
title('Distance Traveled in Free Fall')
xlabel('time, s'),ylabel('distance, m')
%Find the maximum distance traveled
final_distance = max(distance)
```

The interaction in the command window is:

```
What is the value of acceleration due to gravity? 1.6
g =
  1.6000
What starting time would you like? 0
start =
  0
What ending time would you like? 100
finish =
  100
What time increments would you like calculated? 10
incr =
  10
final_distance =
  8000
```

The results are plotted in Figure 20.2.

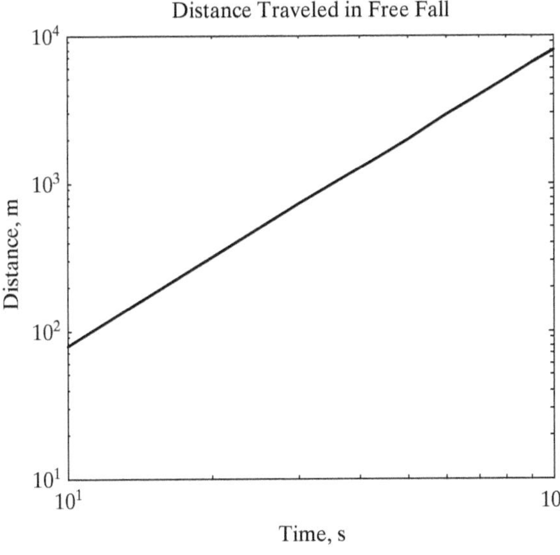

Figure 20.2 Distance traveled when the acceleration is 1.6 m/s^2. Notice that the figure is a loglog plot.

5. Test the Solution
   Compare the MATLAB solution with the hand solution. Since the user can control the input, we entered the data used in the hand solution. MATLAB tells us that the final distance traveled is 8000 m, which, since we entered 100 seconds as the final time, corresponds to the distance traveled after 100 seconds.

20.2 OUTPUT OPTIONS

There are several ways to display the contents of a matrix. The simplest is to enter the name of the matrix, without a semicolon. The name will be repeated, and the values of the matrix will be displayed, starting on the next line. For example, first define a matrix **x**:

```
x = 1:5;
```

Because there is a semicolon at the end of the assignment statement, the values in **x** are not repeated in the command window. However, if you want to display **x** later in your program, simply type in the variable name

```
x
```

which returns

```
x =
     1     2     3     4     5
```

> ***Key Idea:*** The **disp** function can display either character arrays or numeric arrays

MATLAB offers two other approaches to displaying results: the **disp** function and the **fprintf** function.

20.2.1 Display Function

The display (**disp**) function can be used to display the contents of a matrix without printing the matrix name. It accepts a single array as input. Thus,

```
disp(x)
```

returns

```
1    2    3    4    5
```

The display command can also be used to display a string (text enclosed in single quotation marks). For example,

```
disp('The values in the x matrix are:');
```

returns

```
The values in the x matrix are:
```

When you enter a string as input into the **disp** function, you are really entering an array of character information. Try entering the following on the command line:

```
'The values in the x matrix are:'
```

MATLAB responds

```
ans =
'The values in the x matrix are:'
```

Character Array: stores character information

The workspace window lists **ans** as a 1 × 32 character array.

Name	Size	Bytes	Class
abc ans	1×32	90	char array

Character arrays store character information in arrays similar to numerical arrays. Characters can be letters, numbers, punctuation, and even some nondisplayed characters. Each character, including spaces, is an element in the character array.

When we execute the two display functions

```
disp('The values in the x matrix are:');
disp(x)
```

Key Idea: Characters can be letters, numbers or symbols

MATLAB responds

```
The values in the x matrix are:
1 2 3 4 5
```

Notice that the two **disp** functions are displayed on separate lines. You can get around this feature by creating a combined matrix of your two outputs, using the **num2str** (number to string) function. The process is called concatenation and creates a single character array. Thus,

```
disp(['The values in the x array are: ' num2str(x)])
```

returns

```
The values in the x array are: 1 2 3 4 5
```

The **num2str** function changes an array of numbers into an array of characters. In the preceding example, we used **num2str** to transform the **x** matrix to a character array, which was then combined with the first string (by means of square brackets, [ ]) to make a bigger character array. You can see the resulting matrix by typing

```
A = ['The values in the x array are: ' num2str(x)]
```

which returns

```
A =
    The values in the x array are: 1 2 3 4 5
```

Checking in the workspace window, we see that **A** is a 1 × 45 matrix. The workspace window also tells us that the matrix contains character data instead of numeric information. This is evidenced both by the icon in front of **A** and in the class column.

Name	Size	Bytes	Class
abc A	1×45	90	char array

HINT

If you want to include an apostrophe in a string, you need to enter the apostrophe twice. If you don't do this, MATLAB will interpret the apostrophe as terminating the string. An example of the use of two apostrophes is

```
disp('The moon''s gravity is 1/6th that of the earth')
```

You can use a combination of the **input** and **disp** functions to mimic a conversation. Try creating and running the following M-file:

```
disp('Hi There');
disp('I''m your MATLAB program');
name = input('Who are you?','s');
disp(['Hi ',name]);
answer = input('Don't you just love computers?', 's');
disp([answer,'?']);
disp('Computers are very useful');
disp('You''ll use them a lot in college!!');
disp('Good luck with your studies')
pause(2);
disp('Bye bye')
```

This interaction made use of the **pause** function. If you execute **pause** without any input, the program waits until the user hits the Enter key. If a value is used as input to the **pause** function, the program waits for the specified number of seconds, and then continues.

20.2.2 Formatted Output—The fprintf Function

The **fprintf** function (formatted print function) gives you even more control over the output than you have with the **disp** function. In addition to displaying both text and matrix values, you can specify the format to be used in displaying the values, and you can specify when to skip to a new line. If you are a C programmer, you will be familiar with the syntax of this function. With few exceptions, the MATLAB **fprintf** function uses the same formatting specifications as the C **fprintf** function. This is hardly surprising, since MATLAB was written in C. (It was originally written in Fortran and then later rewritten in C.)

The general form of the **fprintf** command contains two arguments, one a string and the other a list of matrices:

```
fprintf(format-string, var,...)
```

Consider the following example:

```
cows = 5;
fprintf('There are %f cows in the pasture ', cows)
```

The string, which is the first argument inside the **fprintf** function, contains a placeholder (%) where the value of the variable (in this case, **cows**) will be inserted. The placeholder also contains formatting information. In this example, the **%f** tells MATLAB to display the value of **cows** in a default fixed-point format. The default format displays six places after the decimal point:

```
There are 5.000000 cows in the pasture
```

Besides defaulting to a fixed-point format, MATLAB allows you to specify an exponential format, **%e**, or lets you allow MATLAB to choose whichever is shorter, fixed point or exponential (**%g**). It also lets you display character information (**%c**) or a string of characters (**%s**). The decimal format (**%d**) is especially useful if the number you wish to display is an integer.

```
fprintf('There are %d cows in the pasture ', cows)
There are 5 cows in the pasture
```

Table 20.1 illustrates the various formats supported by **fprintf**, and the related **sprintf** functions.

> ***Key Idea:*** The **fprintf** function allows you to control how numbers are displayed

MATLAB does not automatically start a new line after an **fprintf** function is executed. If you tried out the preceding **fprintf** command example, you probably noticed that the command prompt is on the same line as the output:

```
There are 5.000000 cows in the pasture >>
```

If we execute another command, the results will appear on the same line instead of moving down. Thus, if we issue the new commands

```
cows = 6;
fprintf('There are %f cows in the pasture', cows);
```

from an M-file, MATLAB continues the command window display on the same line:

```
There are 5.000000 cows in the pasture There are 6.000000 cows in the pasture
```

> ***Key Idea:*** The **fprintf** function allows you to display both character and numeric information with a single command

To cause MATLAB to start a new line, you'll need to use **\n**, called a linefeed, at the end of the string. For example, the code

```
cows = 5;
fprintf('There are %f cows in the pasture \n', cows)
cows = 6;
fprintf('There are %f cows in the pasture \n', cows)
```

Table 20.1 Type Field Format

Type Field	Result
%f	fixed-point notation
%e	exponential notation
%d	decimal notation—does not include trailing zeros if the value displayed is an integer. If the number includes a fractional component, it is displayed using exponential notation.
%g	whichever is shorter, **%f** or **%e**
%c	character information (displays one character at a time)
%s	string of characters (displays the entire string)

Additional type fields are described in the help feature.

returns the following output:

```
There are 5.000000 cows in the pasture
There are 6.000000 cows in the pasture
```

HINT

The backslash (\) and forward slash (/) are different characters. It's a common mistake to confuse them—and then the linefeed command doesn't work! Instead, the output to the command window will be

```
There are 5.000000 cows in the pasture /n
```

Other special format commands are listed in Table 20.2. The tab (**\t**) is especially useful for creating tables in which everything lines up neatly.

You can further control how the variables are displayed by using the optional **width field** and **precision field** with the format command. The **width field** controls the minimum number of characters to be printed. It must be a positive decimal integer. The **precision field** is preceded by a period (**.**) and specifies the number of decimal places after the decimal point for exponential and fixed-point types. For example, **%8.2f** specifies that the minimum total width available to display your result is eight digits, two of which are after the decimal point. Thus, the code

```
voltage = 3.5;
fprintf('The voltage is %8.2f millivolts \n',voltage);
```

returns

```
The voltage is     3.50 millivolts
```

Notice the empty space before the number 3.50. This occurs because we reserved six spaces (eight total, two after the decimal) for the portion of the number to the left of the decimal point.

Often when you use the **fprintf** function, your variable will be a matrix—for example,

```
x = 1:5;
```

MATLAB will repeat the string in the **fprintf** command until it uses all the values in the matrix. Thus,

```
fprintf('%8.2f \n',x);
```

Table 20.2 Special Format Commands

Format Command	Resulting Action
/n	linefeed
/r	carriage return (similar to linefeed)
/t	tab
/b	backspace

returns

```
1.00
2.00
3.00
4.00
5.00
```

If the variable is a two-dimensional matrix, MATLAB uses the values one ***column*** at a time, going down the first column, then the second, and so on. Here's a more complicated example:

```
feet = 1:3;
inches = feet.*12;
```

Combine these two matrices:

```
table = [feet;inches]
```

MATLAB then returns

```
table =
          1  2  3
         12 24 36
```

Now we can use the **fprintf** function to create a table that is easier to interpret. For instance,

```
fprintf('%4.0f %7.2f \n',table)
```

sends the following output to the command window:

```
1 12.00
2 24.00
3 36.00
```

Why don't the two outputs look the same? The **fprintf** statement we created uses two values at a time. It goes through the **table** array one ***column*** at a time to find the numbers it needs. Thus, the first two numbers used in the **fprintf** output are from the first column of the **table** array.

The **fprintf** function can accept a variable number of matrices after the string. It uses all of the values in each of these matrices, in order, before moving on to the next matrix. As an example, suppose we wanted to use the feet and inches matrices without combining them into the table matrix. Then we could type

```
fprintf('%4.0f %7.2f \n', feet, inches)
 1  2.00
 3  12.00
24  36.00
```

The function works through the values of **feet** first and then uses the values in **inches**. It is unlikely that this is what you really want the function to do (in this example it wasn't), so the output values are almost always grouped into a single matrix to use in **fprintf**.

The **fprintf** command gives you considerably more control over the form of your output than MATLAB's simple format commands. It does, however, require some care and forethought to use.

In addition to creating formatted output for display in the command window, the **fprintf** function can be used to send formatted output to a file. First you'll need to create and open an output file and assign it a file identifier (nickname). You do this with the **fopen** function

```
file_id = fopen('my_output_file.txt', 'wt');
```

The first field is the name of the file, and the second field makes it possible for us to write data to the file (hence the string 'wt'). Once the file has been identified and opened for writing, we use the **fprintf** function, adding the file identifier as the first field in the function input.

```
fprintf(file_id, 'Some example output is %4.2f \n', pi*1000)
```

This form of the function sends the result of the formatted string

```
Some example output is 3141.59
```

to **my_output_file.txt**. To the command window the function sends a count of the number of bytes transferred to the file.

```
ans =
      32
```

HINT

A common mistake new programmers make when using **fprintf** is to forget to include the field type identifier, such as **f,** in the placeholder sequence. The **fprintf** function won't work, but no error message is returned either.

HINT

If you want to include a percentage sign in an **fprintf** statement, you need to enter the % twice. If you don't, MATLAB will interpret the % as a placeholder for data. For example,

```
fprintf('The interest rate is %5.2f %% \n', 5)
```

results in

```
The interest rate is 5.00 %
```

EXAMPLE 20.2

Free Fall: Formatted Output

Let's redo Example 20.1, but this time let's create a table of results instead of a plot, and let's use the **disp** and **fprintf** commands to control the appearance of the output.

1. State the Problem
   Find the distance traveled by a freely falling object.
2. Describe the Input and Output
   Input Value of *g*, the acceleration due to gravity, provided by the user
   Time *t*, provided by the user
   Output Distances calculated for each planet and the moon

3. Develop a Hand Example

$$d = \frac{1}{2}gt^2, \text{ so, on the moon at 100 seconds,}$$

$$d = \frac{1}{2} \times 1.6\ \text{m/s}^2 \times 100^2\ \text{s}^2$$

$$d = 8000\ \text{m}$$

4. Develop a MATLAB Solution

```
%Example 19.2
%Free Fall
clear, clc
%Request input from the user
g = input('What is the value of acceleration due to
        gravity? ')
start = input('What starting time would you like? ')
finish = input('What ending time would you like? ')
incr = input('What time increments would you like
        calculated? ')
time = start:incr:finish;
%Calculate the distance
distance = 1/2*g*time.^2;
%Create a matrix of the output data
table = [time;distance];
%Send the output to the command window
fprintf('For an acceleration due to gravity of %5.1f
        seconds \n the following data were calculated \n', g)
disp('Distance Traveled in Free Fall')
disp('time, s distance, m')
fprintf('%8.0f %10.2f\n',table)
```

This M-file produces the following interaction in the command window:

```
What is the value of acceleration due to gravity? 1.6
g =
  1.6000
What starting time would you like? 0
start =
 0
What ending time would you like? 100
finish =
 100
What time increments would you like calculated? 10
incr =
 10
For an acceleration due to gravity of 1.6 seconds
 the following data were calculated
Distance Traveled in Free Fall
time, s   distance, m
     0        0.00
    10       80.00
    20      320.00
    30      720.00
    40     1280.00
    50     2000.00
    60     2880.00
```

```
 70   3920.00
 80   5120.00
 90   6480.00
100   8000.00
```

5. Test the Solution
   Compare the MATLAB solution with the hand solution. Since the output is a table, it is easy to see that the distance traveled at 100 seconds is 8000 m. Try using other data as input, and using other data as input, and compare your results with the graph produced in Example 20.1.

In-Class Activity

ICA 20-2

In an M-file,

1. Use the **disp** command to create a title for a table that converts inches to feet.
2. Use the **disp** command to create column headings for your table.
3. Create an **inches** vector from 0 to 120 with an increment of 10.
   Calculate the corresponding values of **feet.**
   Group the **inch** vector and the **feet** vector together into a **table** matrix.
   Use the **fprintf** command to send your table to the command window.

20.3 READING AND WRITING DATA FROM FILES

> ***Key Idea:*** MATLAB can import data from files using a variety of formats

Data are stored in many different formats, depending on the devices and programs that created the data and on the application. For example, sound might be stored in a .wav file, and an image might be stored in a .jpg file. Many applications store data in Excel spreadsheets (.xls files). The most generic of these files is the ASCII file, usually stored as a .dat or a .txt file. You may want to import these data into MATLAB to analyze in a MATLAB program, or you might want to save your data in one of these formats to make the file easier to export to another application.

20.3.1 Importing Data

Import Wizard

If you select a data file from the current directory and double-click on the file name, the Import Wizard launches. The Import Wizard determines what kind of data is in the file and suggests ways to represent the data in MATLAB. Table 20.3 is a list of some of the data types MATLAB recognizes. Not every possible data format is supported by MATLAB. You can find a complete list by typing

```
doc fileformats
```

in the command window.

Table 20.3 Data File Types Supported by MATLAB

File Type	Extension	Remark
Text	.mat .dat .txt .csv	MATLAB workspace ASCII data ASCII data Comma-separated values ASCII data
Other common scientific data formats	.cdf .fits .hdf	common data format flexible image transport system data hierarchical data format
Spreadsheet data	.xls .wk1	Excel spreadsheet Lotus 123
Image data	.tiff .bmp .jpeg or jpg .gif	tagged image file format bit map joint photographics expert group graphics interchange format
Audio data	.au .wav	audio Microsoft wave file
Movie	.avi	audio/video interleaved file

The Import Wizard can be used for simple ASCII files and for Excel spreadsheet files. You can also launch the Import Wizard from the command line, using the **uiimport** function:

```
uiimport(' filename.extension ')
```

For example, to import the sound file **decision.wav**, type

```
uiimport(' decision.wav ')
```

The Import Wizard then opens, as shown in Figure 20.3

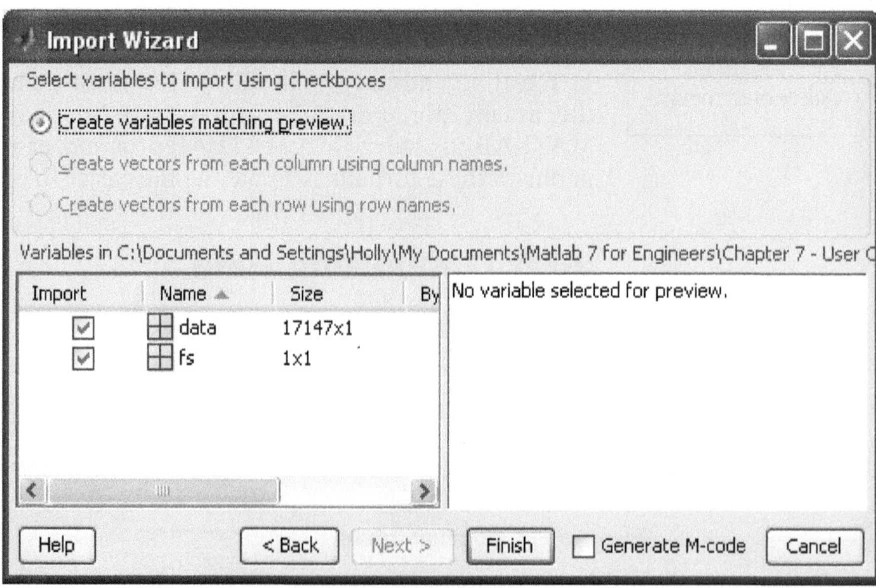

Figure 20.3 The Import Wizard launches when the **uiimport** command is executed.

Either technique for launching the Import Wizard requires an interaction with the user (through the Wizard). If you want to load a data file from a MATLAB program, you'll need a different approach.

Import Commands

You can bypass the Wizard interactions by using one of the functions that are especially designed to read each of the supported file formats. For example, to read in a .wav file, use the **wavread** function:

```
[data,fs] = wavread('decision.wav')
```

Clearly, you need to understand what kind of data to expect, so that you can name the created variables appropriately. Recall that you can find a list of import functions by typing

```
doc fileformats
```

EXAMPLE 20.3

2001: A Space Odyssey: Sound Files

One of the most memorable characters in the movie *2001: A Space Odyssey* is the computer Hal. Sound bites from Hal's dialogue in the movie have been popular for years with computer programmers and with engineers who use computers. You can find .wav files of some of Hal's dialogue at http://www.palantir.net/2001/ and at other popular-culture websites. Insert Hal's comments into a MATLAB program. (You'll need the **sound** function—consult the **help** tutorial for details on its use.)

1. State the Problem
   Load sound files into a MATLAB program, and play them at appropriate times.
2. Describe the Input and Output
   Input Sound files downloaded from the Internet. For this example, we'll assume that you've downloaded the following three files:
   dave.wav
   error.wav
   sure.wav
   Output Play the sound files inside a MATLAB program.
3. Develop a Hand Example
   Although working a hand example is not appropriate for this problem, you can listen to the sound files from the Internet before inserting them into the program.
4. Develop a MATLAB Solution
   Download the sound files and save them into the current directory before you run the following program:

```
%% Example 19.3
% Sound Files
%% First Clip
[dave,fs_dave] = wavread('dave.wav');
disp('Hit Enter once the sound clip is finished playing')
sound(dave,fs_dave)
pause
%% Second Clip
[error,fs_error] = wavread('error.wav');
disp('Hit Enter once the sound clip is finished playing')
sound(error,fs_error)
```

```
pause
%% Third Clip
[sure,fs_sure] = wavread('sure.wav');
disp('Hit Enter once the sound clip is finished playing')
sound(sure,fs_sure)
pause
disp('That was the last clip')
```

5. Test the Solution
   Many audio files are available to download from the Internet. Some are as simple as these, but others are complete pieces of music. Browse the Internet and insert a "sound byte" into another MATLAB program, perhaps as an error message for your users. Some of our favorites are from *Star Trek* (try http://services.tos.net/sounds/sound.html#tos) and *The Simpsons.*

20.3.2 Exporting Data

The easiest way to find the appropriate function for writing a file is to use the **help** tutorial to find the correct function to read it and then to follow the links to the **write** function. For example, to read an Excel spreadsheet file (.xls), we'd use **xlsread**:

```
xlsread('filename.xls')
```

At the end of the tutorial page, we are referred to the correct function for writing an Excel file, namely,

```
xlswrite('filename.xls', M)
```

where **M** is the array you want to store in the Excel spreadsheet.

SUMMARY

MATLAB provides functions that allow the user to interact with an M-file program and allow the programmer to control the output to the command window.

The **input** function pauses the program and sends a prompt determined by the programmer to the command window. Once the user has entered a value or values and hits the return key, program execution continues.

The display (**disp**) function allows the programmer to display the contents of a string or a matrix in the command window. Although the **disp** function is adequate for many display tasks, the **fprintf** function gives the programmer considerably more control over the way results are displayed. The programmer can combine text and calculated results on the same line and specify the number format used. The **sprintf** function behaves exactly the same way as the **fprintf** function. However, the result of **sprintf** is assigned a variable name and can be used with other functions that require strings as input. For example, the functions used to annotate graphs such as **title**, **text**, and **xlabel** all accept strings as input and therefore will accept the result of the **sprintf** function as input.

For applications in which graphical input is required, the **ginput** command allows the user to provide input to a program by selecting points from a graphics window.

The cell mode allows the programmer to group M-file code into sections and to run each section individually. The **publish to HTML** tool creates a report containing both the M-file code and results as well as any figures generated when the program executes. The Increment and Decrement icons on the cell toolbar allow the user to automatically change the value of a parameter each time the code is executed, making it easy to test the result of changing a variable.

MATLAB includes functions that allow the user to import and export data in a number of popular file formats. A complete list of these formats is available in the **help** tutorial on the File Formats page (doc fileformats). The **fprintf** function can also be used to export formatted output to a text file.

MATLAB SUMMARY

The following MATLAB summary lists all the special characters, commands, and functions that were defined in this chapter:

Special Characters	
'	begins and ends a string
%	placeholder used in the **fprintf** command
%f	fixed-point, or decimal, notation
%e	exponential notation
%g	either fixed-point or exponential notation
%s	string notation
%%	cell divider
\n	linefeed
\r	carriage return (similar to linefeed)
\t	tab
\b	backspace

Commands and Functions	
disp	displays a string or a matrix in the command window
fprintf	creates formatted output which can be sent to the command window or to a file
ginput	allows the user to pick values from a graph
input	allows the user to enter values
num2str	changes a number to a string
pause	pauses the program
sound	plays MATLAB data through the speakers
sprintf	similar to **fprintf** creates formatted output which is assigned to a variable name and stored as a character array
uiimport	launches the Import Wizard
wavread	reads wave files
xlsimport	imports Excel data files
xlswrite	exports data as an Excel file

KEY TERMS

cell
cell mode
character array
formatted output
precision field
string
width field

EXERCISES AND ACTIVITIES

Input Function

20.1 Create an M-file that prompts the user to enter a value of x and then calculates the value of $\sin(x)$.

20.2 Create an M-file that prompts the user to enter a matrix and then use the **max** function to determine the largest value entered. Use the following matrix to test your program:

$$[1, 5, 3, 8, 9, 22]$$

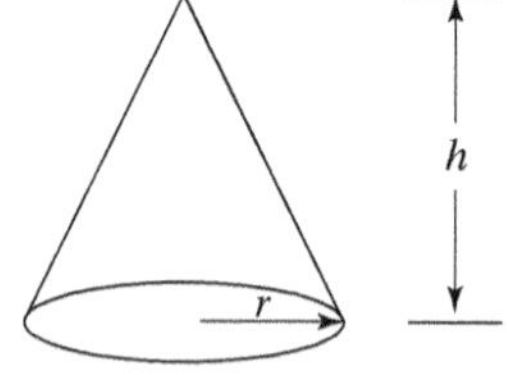

Figure P20.3 Volume of a cone.

20.3 The volume of a cone is

$$V = \frac{1}{3} \times \text{area\_of\_the\_base} \times \text{height}$$

Prompt the user to enter the area of the base and the height of the cone (Figure P20.3). Calculate the volume of the cone.

Disp Function

20.4 One of the first computer programs many students write is called "Hello, World." The only thing the program does is print this message to the computer screen. Write a "Hello, World" program in an M-file, using the **disp** function.

20.5 Use two separate **input** statements to prompt a user to enter his or her first and last names. Use the **disp** function to display those names on one line. (You'll need to combine the names and some spaces into an array.)

20.6 Prompt the user to enter his or her age. Then use the **disp** function to report the age back to the command window. If, for example, the user enters 5 when prompted for her age, your display should read

```
Your age is 5
```

This output requires combining both character data (a string) and numeric data in the **disp** function—which can be accomplished by using the **num2str** function.

20.7 Prompt the user to enter an array of numbers. Use the **length** function to determine how many values were entered, and use the **disp** function to report your results to the command window.

fprintf

20.8 Repeat Problem 20.7, and use **fprintf** to report your results.

20.9 Use **fprintf** to create the multiplication tables from 1 to 13 for the number 6. Your table should look like this.

1 times 6 is 6

2 times 6 is 12

3 times 6 is 18

⋮

20.10 Before calculators were readily available (about 1974), students used tables to determine the values of mathematical functions like sine, cosine, and log. Create such a table for sine, using the following steps:

- Create a vector of angle values from 0 to 2π in increments of $\pi/10$.
- Calculate the sine of each of the angles, and group your results into a table that includes the angle and the sine.
- Use **disp** to create a title for the table and a second **disp** command to create column headings.
- Use the **fprintf** function to display the numbers. Display only two values past the decimal point.

20.11 Very small dimensions—those on the atomic scale—are often measured in angstroms. An angstrom is represented by the symbol Å and corresponds to a length of 10^{-10} meter. Create an inches-to-angstroms conversion table as follows for values of inches from 1 to 10:

- Use **disp** to create a title and column headings.
- Use **fprintf** to display the numerical information.
- Because the length represented in angstroms is so big, represent your result in scientific notation, showing two values after the decimal point. This corresponds to three significant figures (one before and two after the decimal point).

20.12 Use your favorite Internet search engine and World Wide Web browser to identify recent currency conversions for British pounds sterling, Japanese yen, and the European euro to U.S. dollars. Use the conversion tables to create the following tables (use the **disp** and **fprintf** commands in your solution, which should include a title, column labels, and formatted output):

(a) Generate a table of conversions from yen to dollars. Start the yen column at 5 and increment by 5 yen. Print 25 lines in the table.

(b) Generate a table of conversions from the euros to dollars. Start the euro column at 1 euro and increment by 2 euros. Print 30 lines in the table.

(c) Generate a table with four columns. The first should contain dollars, the second the equivalent number of euros, the third the equivalent number of pounds, and the fourth the equivalent number of yen. Let the dollar column vary from 1 to 10.

Problems Combining the input, disp, and fprintf Commands

20.13 This problem requires you to generate temperature conversion tables. Use the following equations, which describe the relationships between temperatures in degrees Fahrenheit (T_F), degrees Celsius (T_C), kelvins (T_K), and degrees Rankine (T_R), respectively:

$$T_F = T_R - 459.67°R$$

$$T_F = \frac{9}{5}T_C + 32°F$$

$$T_R = \frac{9}{5}T_K$$

You will need to rearrange these expressions to solve some of the problems.

(a) Generate a table of conversions from Fahrenheit to Kelvin for values from 0°F to 200°F. Allow the user to enter the increments in degrees F between lines. Use **disp** and **fprintf** to create a table with a title, column headings, and appropriate spacing.

(b) Generate a table of conversions from Celsius to Rankine. Allow the user to enter the starting temperature and the increment between lines. Print 25 lines in the table. Use **disp** and **fprintf** to create a table with a title, column headings, and appropriate spacing.

(c) Generate a table of conversions from Celsius to Fahrenheit. Allow the user to enter the starting temperature, the increment between lines, and the number of lines for the table. Use **disp** and **fprintf** to create a table with a title, column headings, and appropriate spacing.

20.14 Engineers use both English and SI (Système International d'Unités) units on a regular basis. Some fields use primarily one or the other, but many combine the two systems. For example, the rate of energy input to a steam power plant from burning fossil fuels is usually measured in Btu/hour. However, the electricity produced by the same plant is usually measured in joules/sec (watts). Automobile engines, by contrast, are often rated in horsepower or in ft lb_f/s. Here are some conversion factors relating these different power measurements:

$$1 \text{ kW} = 3412.14 \text{ Btu/h} = 737.56 \text{ ft lb}_f\text{/s}$$

$$1 \text{ hp} = 550 \text{ ft lb}_f\text{/s} = 2544.5 \text{ Btu/h}$$

(a) Generate a table of conversions from kW to hp. The table should start at 0 kW and end at 15 kW. Use the **input** function to let the user define the increment between table entries. Use **disp** and **fprintf** to create a table with a title, column headings, and appropriate spacing.

(b) Generate a table of conversions from ft lb_f/s to Btu/h. The table should start at 0 ft lb_f/s but let the user define the increment between table entries and the final table value. Use **disp** and **fprintf** to create a table with a title, column headings, and appropriate spacing.

(c) Generate a table that includes conversions from kW to Btu/h, hp, and ft lb_f/s. Let the user define the initial value of kW, the final value of kW, and the number of entries in the table. Use **disp** and **fprintf** to create a table with a title, column headings, and appropriate spacing.

ginput

20.15 At time $t = 0$, when a rocket's engine shuts down, the rocket has reached an altitude of 500 meters and is rising at a velocity of 125 meters per second. At this point, gravity takes over. The height of the rocket as a function of time is

$$h(t) = -\frac{9.8}{2}t^2 + 125t + 500 \text{ for } t > 0$$

Plot the height of the rocket from 0 to 30 seconds, and

- Use the **ginput** function to estimate the maximum height the rocket reaches and the time when the rocket hits the ground.
- Use the **disp** command to report your results to the command window.

20.16 The **ginput** function is useful for picking distances off a graph. Demonstrate this feature by doing the following:

- Create a graph of a circle by defining an array of angles from 0 to 2π, with a spacing of $\pi/100$.
- Use the **ginput** function to pick two points on the circumference of the circle.
- Use **hold on** to keep the figure from refreshing, and plot a line between the two points you picked.
- Use the data from the points to calculate the length of the line between them. (*Hint*: Use the Pythagorean theorem in your calculation.)

20.17 In recent years the price of gasoline has increased dramatically. Automobile companies have responded with more fuel-efficient cars, in particular hybrid models. But will you save money by purchasing to purchase a hybrid such as the Toyota Camry rather a Camry with a standard engine? The hybrid vehicles are considerably more expensive, but get better gas mileage. Consider the vehicle prices and gas efficiencies

CHAPTER 21

NUMERICAL TECHNIQUES

Objectives

By learning the material in this chapter, you should be able to

- prompt the user for input to an M-file program
- create output with the **disp** function
- create formatted output by using **fprintf**
- create formatted output for use in other functions with the **sprintf** function
- use graphical techniques to provide program input
- use the cell mode to modify and run M-file programs

21.1 CURVE FITTING

Although we could use interpolation techniques to find values of y between measured x-values, it would be more convenient if we could model experimental data as $y = f(x)$. Then we could just calculate any value of y we wanted. If we know something about the underlying relationship between x and y, we may be able to determine an equation on the basis of those principles. For example, the ideal/gas law is based on two underlying assumptions:

Key Idea: Curve fitting is a technique for modeling data with an equation

- All the molecules in a gas collide elastically.
- The molecules don't take up any room in their container.

Neither assumption is entirely accurate, so the ideal gas law works only when they are a good approximation of reality, but that is true for many situations, and the ideal gas law is extremely valuable. However, when real gases deviate from this simple relationship, we have two choices for how to model their behavior. Either we can try to understand the physics of the situation and adjust the equation accordingly, or we can just take the data and model them empirically. Empirical equations are not related to any theory of why a behavior occurs; they just do a good job of predicting how a parameter changes in relationship to another parameter.

MATLAB has built-in curve-fitting functions that allow us to model data empirically. It's important to remind ourselves that these models are good only in the region where we've collected data. If we don't understand why a parameter such as y changes as it does with x, we can't predict whether our data-fitting equation will still work outside the range where we've collected data.

Section 21.1 was taken from *MATLAB® for Engineers,* Second Edition, by Holly Moore.

Sections 21.2 and 21.3 were taken from *MATLAB®: An Introduction with Applications,* Third Edition, by Amos Gilat.

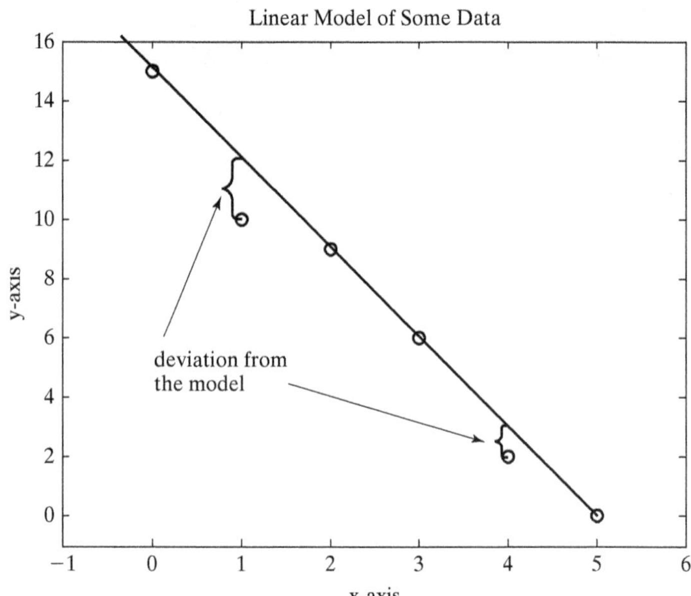

Figure 21.1 A linear model: the line was "eyeballed."

21.1.1 Linear Regression

The simplest way to model a set of data is as a straight line.

```
x = 0:5;
y = [15, 10, 9, 6, 2, 0];
```

If we plot the data in Figure 21.1, we can try to draw a straight line through the data points to get a rough model of the data's behavior. This process is sometimes called "eyeballing it"—meaning that no calculations were done, but it looks like a good fit.

Looking at the plot, we can see that several of the points appear to fall exactly on the line, but others are off by varying amounts. In order to compare the quality of the fit of this line to other possible estimates, we find the difference between the actual y-value and the value calculated from the estimate.

We can find the equation of the line in Figure 21.1 by noticing that at $x = 0$, $y = 15$, and at $x = 5$, $y = 0$. Thus, the slope of the line is

$$\frac{\text{rise}}{\text{run}} = \frac{\Delta y}{\Delta x} = \frac{y_2 - y_1}{x_2 - x_1} = \frac{0 - 15}{5 - 0} = -3$$

The line crosses the y-axis at 15, so the equation of the line is

$$y = -3x + 15$$

The differences between the actual values and the calculated values are listed in Table 21.1.

Linear Regression: a technique for modeling data as a straight line

The *linear regression* technique uses an approach called least squares to compare how well different equations model the behavior of the data. In this technique, the differences between the actual and calculated values are squared and added together. This has the advantage that positive and negative deviations don't cancel each other out. We could use MATLAB to calculate this parameter for our data. We have

```
sum_of_the_squares = sum((y-y_calc).^2)
```

Table 21.1 Difference between Actual and Calculated Values

x	y (actual)	y_calc (calculated)	difference = y − y_calc
0	15	15	0
1	10	12	−2
2	9	9	0
3	6	6	0
4	2	3	−1
5	0	0	0

which gives us

```
sum_of_the_squares =
 5
```

It's beyond the scope of this text to explain how the linear regression technique works, except to say that it compares different models and chooses the model in which the sum of the squares is the smallest. Linear regression is accomplished in MATLAB with the **polyfit** function. Three fields are required by **polyfit**: a vector of x-values, a vector of y-values, and an integer indicating what order of polynomial should be used to fit the data. Since a straight line is a first-order polynomial, we'll enter the number 1 into the **polyfit** function:

```
polyfit(x,y,1)
ans =
 -2.9143 14.2857
```

The results are the coefficients corresponding to the best-fit first-order polynomial equation:

$$y = -2.9143x + 14.2857$$

Is this really a better fit than our "eyeballed" model? We can calculate the sum of the squares to find out:

```
best_y = -2.9143*x+14.2857;
new_sum = sum((y-best_y).^2)
new_sum =
  3.3714
```

Since the result of the sum-of-the-squares calculation is indeed less than the value found for the "eyeballed" line, we can conclude that MATLAB found a better fit to the data. We can plot the data and the best-fit line determined by linear regression (see Figure 21.2) to try to get a visual sense of whether the line fits the data well:

```
plot(x,y,'o',x,best_y)
```

21.1.2 Polynomial Regression

Of course, straight lines are not the only equations that could be analyzed with the regression technique. For example, a common approach is to fit the data with a higher-order polynomial of the form

$$y = a_0x^n + a_1x^{n-1} + a_2x^{n-2} + \cdots + a_{n-1}x + a_n$$

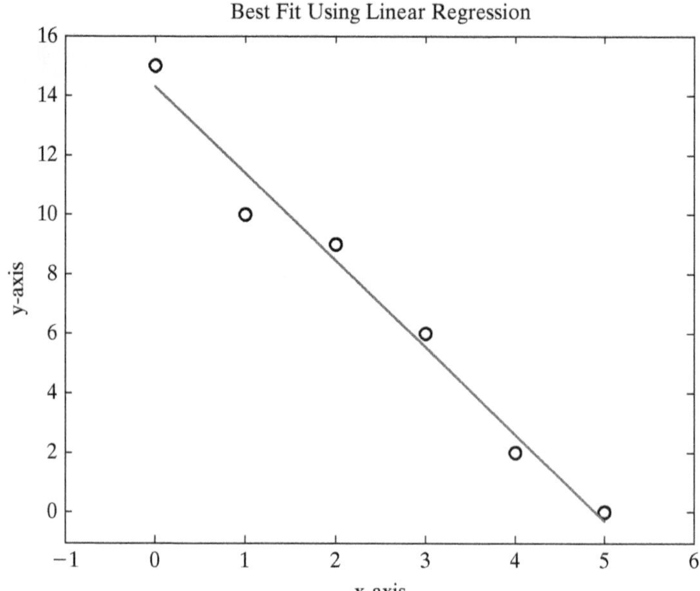

Figure 21.2 Data and best-fit line using linear regression.

Polynomial regression is used to get the best fit by minimizing the sum of the squares of the deviations of the calculated values from the data. The **polyfit** function allows us to do this easily in MATLAB. We can fit our sample data to second- and third-order equations with the commands

```
polyfit(x,y,2)
ans =
  0.0536 -3.1821 14.4643
```

and

```
polyfit(x,y,3)
ans =
 -0.0648 0.5397 -4.0701 14.6587
```

which correspond to the following equations

$$y_2 = 0.0536x^2 - 3.1821x + 14.4643$$
$$y_3 = -0.0648x^3 + 0.5397x^2 - 4.0701x + 14.6587$$

We can find the sum of the squares to determine whether these models fit the data better:

```
y2 = 0.0536*x.^2-3.182*x + 14.4643;
sum((y2-y).^2)
ans =
  3.2643
y3 = -0.0648*x.^3+0.5398*x.^2-4.0701*x + 14.6587
sum((y3-y).^2)
ans =
  2.9921
```

As we might expect, the more terms we add to our equation, the "better" is the fit, at least in the sense that the distance between the measured and predicted data points decreases.

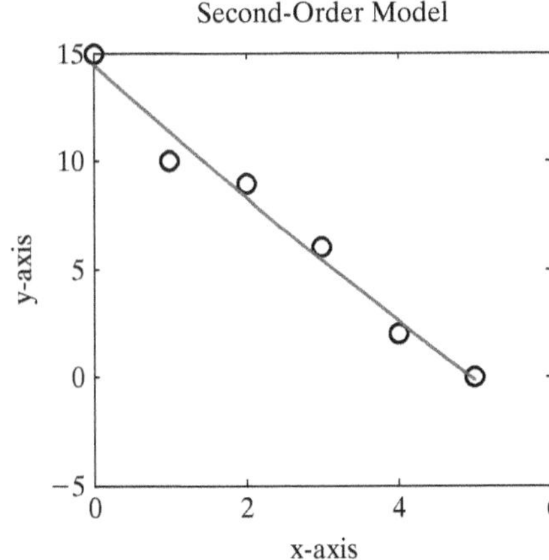

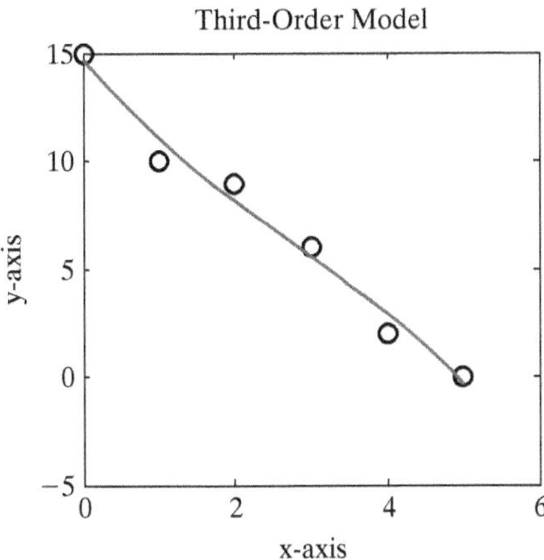

Figure 21.3 Second- and third-order polynomial fits.

In order to plot the curves defined by these new equations, we'll need more than the six data points used in the linear model. Remember that MATLAB creates plots by connecting calculated points with straight lines, so if we want a smooth curve, we'll need more points. We can get more points and plot the curves with the following code:

```
smooth_x = 0:0.2:5;
smooth_y2 = 0.0536*smooth_x.^2-3.182*smooth_x + 14.4643;
subplot(1,2,1)
plot(x,y,'o',smooth_x,smooth_y2)
smooth_y3 = -0.0648*smooth_x.^3+0.5398*smooth_x.^2-4.0701* smooth_x +
14.6587;
subplot(1,2,2)
plot(x,y,'o',smooth_x,smooth_y3)
```

> ***Key Idea:*** Modeling of data should be based not only on the data collected but also on a physical understanding of the process

The results are shown in Figure 21.3. Notice the slight curvature in each model. Although mathematically these models fit the data better, they may not be as good a representation of reality as the straight line. As an engineer or scientist, you'll need to evaluate any modeling you do. You'll need to consider what you know about the physics of the process you're modeling and how accurate and reproducible your measurements are.

21.1.3 The polyval Function

The **polyfit** function returns the coefficients of a polynomial that best fits the data, at least on the basis of a regression criterion. In the previous section, we entered those coefficients into a MATLAB expression for the corresponding polynomial and used it to calculate new values of y. The **polyval** function can perform the same job without our having to reenter the coefficients.

The **polyval** function requires two inputs. The first is a coefficient array, such as that created by **polyfit**. The second is an array of x-values for which we would like to calculate new y-values. For example, we might have

```
coef = polyfit(x,y,1)
y_first_order_fit = polyval(coef,x)
```

These two lines of code could be shortened to one line by nesting functions:

```
y_first_order_fit = polyval(polyfit(x,y,1),x)
```

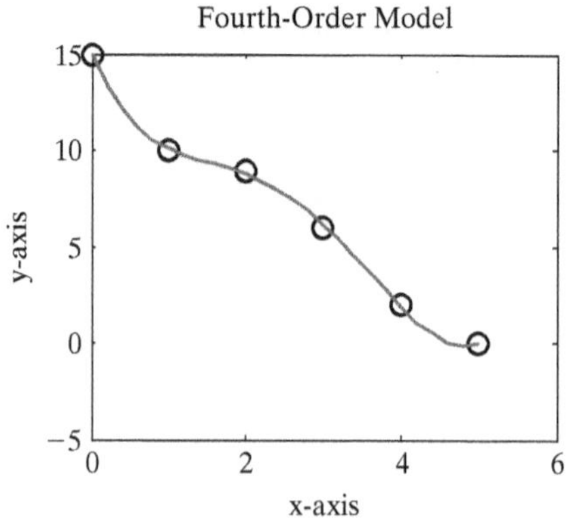

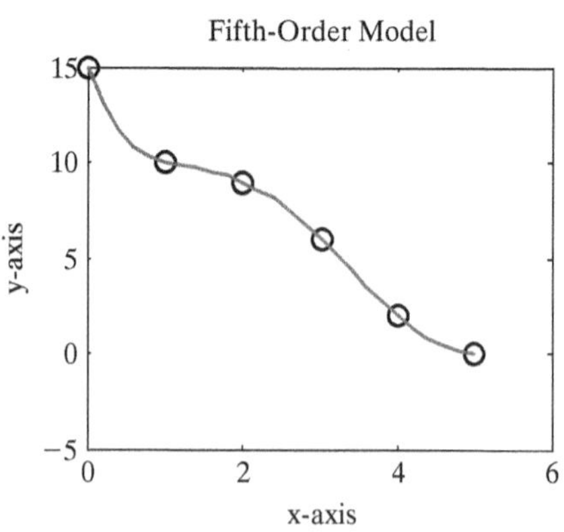

Figure 21.4 Fourth- and fifth-order model of six data points.

We can use our new understanding of the **polyfit** and **polyval** functions to write a program to calculate and plot the fourth- and fifth-order fits for the data:

```
y4 = polyval(polyfit(x,y,4),smooth_x);
y5 = polyval(polyfit(x,y,5),smooth_x);

subplot(1,2,1)
plot(x,y,'o',smooth_x,y4)
axis([0,6,-5,15])
subplot(1,2,2)
plot(x,y,'o',smooth_x,y5)
axis([0,6,-5,15])
```

Figure 21.4 gives the results of our plot

As expected, the higher-order fits match the data better and better. The fifth-order model matches exactly, because there were only six data points.

HINT

You could create all four of the graphs shown in Figures 21.3 and Figure 21.4 by using a **for** loop, which makes use of subplots and the **sprintf** function.

```
x = 0:5;
y = [15, 10, 9, 6, 2, 0];
smooth_x = 0:0.2:5;
for k = 1:4
  subplot(2,2,k)
  plot(x,y,'o',smooth_x,polyval(polyfit(x,y,k+1),smooth_x))
  axis([0,6,-5,15])
  a = sprintf('Polynomial plot of order %1.0f \n',k+1);
  title(a)
end
```

In-Class Activity

ICA 21-1

Create x and y vectors to represent the following data:

z = 15		z = 30	
x	y	x	y
10	23	10	33
20	45	20	55
30	60	30	70
40	82	40	92
50	111	50	121
60	140	60	150
70	167	70	177
80	198	80	198
90	200	90	210
100	220	100	230

1. Use the **polyfit** function to fit the data for $z = 15$ to a first-order polynomial.
2. Create a vector of new x values from 10 to 100 in intervals of 2. Use your new vector in the **polyval** function together with the coefficient values found in Exercise 1 to create a new y vector.
3. Plot the original data as circles without a connecting line and the calculated data as a solid line on the same graph. How well do you think your model fits the data?
4. Repeat Exercises 1 through 3 for the x and y data corresponding to $z = 30$.

EXAMPLE 21.1

Water in a Culvert

Determining how much water will flow through a culvert is not as easy as it might first seem. The channel could have a nonuniform shape (see Figure 21.5), obstructions might influence the flow, friction is important, and so on. A numerical approach allows us to fold all those concerns into a model of how the water actually behaves.

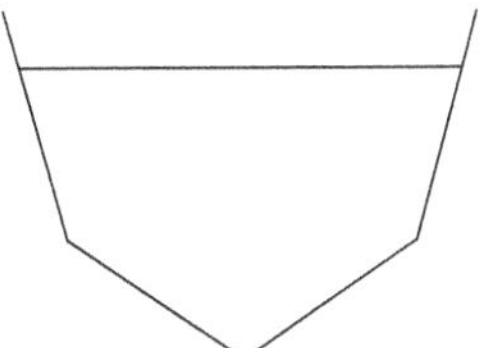

Figure 21.5 Culverts do not necessarily have a uniform cross section.

Consider the following data collected from an actual culvert.

Height, ft	Flow, ft^3/s
0	0
1.7	2.6
1.95	3.6
2.60	4.03
2.92	6.45
4.04	11.22
5.24	30.61

Compute a best-fit linear, quadratic, and cubic equation for the data, and plot them on the same graph. Which model best represents the data? (Linear is first order, quadratic is second order, and cubic is third order.)

1. State the Problem
   Perform a polynomial regression on the data, plot the results, and determine which order best represents the data.
2. Describe the Input and Output
   Input Height and flow data
   Output Plot of the results
3. Develop a Hand Example
   Draw an approximation of the curve by hand. Be sure to start at zero, since, if the height of water in the culvert is zero, no water should be flowing (see Figure 21.6).
4. Develop a MATLAB Solution
   Create the MATLAB solution in an M-file, then run it in the command environment:

```
%20.1 Example - Water in a Culvert
height = [1.7, 1.95, 2.6, 2.92, 4.04, 5.24];
flow = [2.6, 3.6, 4.03, 6.45, 11.22, 30.61];
new_height = 0:0.5:6;
```

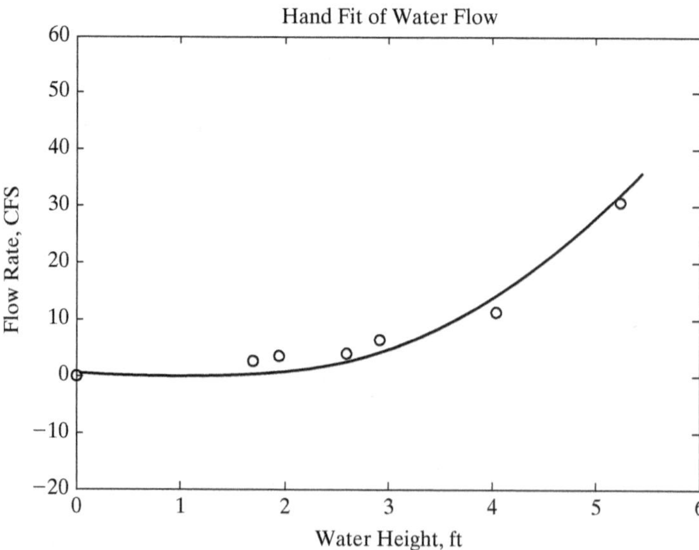

Figure 21.6 Hand fit of water flow.

```
newf1 = polyval(polyfit(height,flow,1),new_height);
newf2 = polyval(polyfit(height,flow,2),new_height);
newf3 = polyval(polyfit(height,flow,3),new_height);
plot(height,flow,'o',new_height,newf1,new_height,newf2,
new_height,newf3)
title('Fit of Water Flow')
xlabel('Water Height, ft')
ylabel('Flow Rate, CFS')
legend('Data','Linear Fit','Quadratic Fit', 'Cubic Fit')
```

The MATLAB code generates the plot shown in Figure 21.7.

5. Test the Solution

The question of which line best represents the data is difficult to answer. The higher-order polynomial approximation will follow the data points better, but it doesn't necessarily represent reality better.

The linear fit predicts that the water flow rate will be approximately −5 CFS at a height of zero, which doesn't match reality. The quadratic fit goes back up after a minimum at a height of approximately 1.5 meters—again a result inconsistent with reality. The cubic (third-order) fit follows the points the best and is probably the best polynomial fit. We should also compare the MATLAB solution with the hand solution. The third-order (cubic) polynomial fit approximately matches the hand solution.

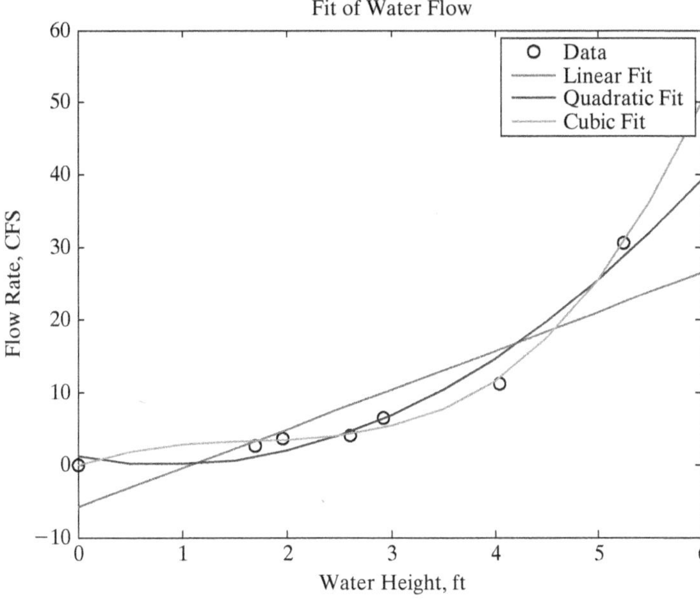

Figure 21.7 Different curve-fitting approaches.

EXAMPLE 21.2

Heat Capacity of a Gas

The amount of energy necessary to warm a gas 1 degree (called the *heat capacity* of the gas) depends not only on the gas, but on its temperature as well. This relationship is commonly modeled with polynomials. For example, consider the data for carbon dioxide in Table 21.2.

Table 21.2 Heat Capacity of Carbon Dioxide

Temperature, T, in K	Heat capacity, C_p, in kJ/(kg K)
250	0.791
300	0.846
350	0.895
400	0.939
450	0.978
500	1.014
550	1.046
600	1.075
650	1.102
700	1.126
750	1.148
800	1.169
900	1.204
1000	1.234
1500	1.328

Source: Tables of Thermal Properties of Gases, NBS circular 564, 1955.

Use MATLAB to model these data as a polynomial. Then compare the results with those obtained from the model published in B. G. Kyle, *Chemical and Process Thermodynamics* (Upper Saddle River, NJ: Prentice Hall PTR, 1999), namely,

$$C_p = 1.698 \times 10^{-10}T^3 - 7.957 \times 10^{-7}T^2 + 1.359 \times 10^{-3}T + 5.059 \times 10^{-1}$$

1. State the Problem
   Create an empirical mathematical model that describes heat capacity as a function of temperature. Compare the results with those obtained from published models.
2. Describe the Input and Output
   Input Use the table of temperature and heat-capacity data provided.
   Output Find the coefficients of a polynomial that describes the data.
   Plot the results.
3. Develop a Hand Example
   By plotting the data (Figure 21.8) we can see that a straight-line fit (first-order polynomial) is not a good approximation of the data. We'll need to evaluate several different models—for example, from first to fourth order.
4. Develop a MATLAB Solution

```
%Example 20.2 Heat Capacity of a Gas

%Define the measured data
T=[250:50:800,900,1000,1500];
Cp=[0.791, 0.846, 0.895, 0.939, 0.978, 1.014, 1.046, ... 1.075, 1.102, 1.126, 1.148,
1.169, 1.204, 1.234, 1.328];
```

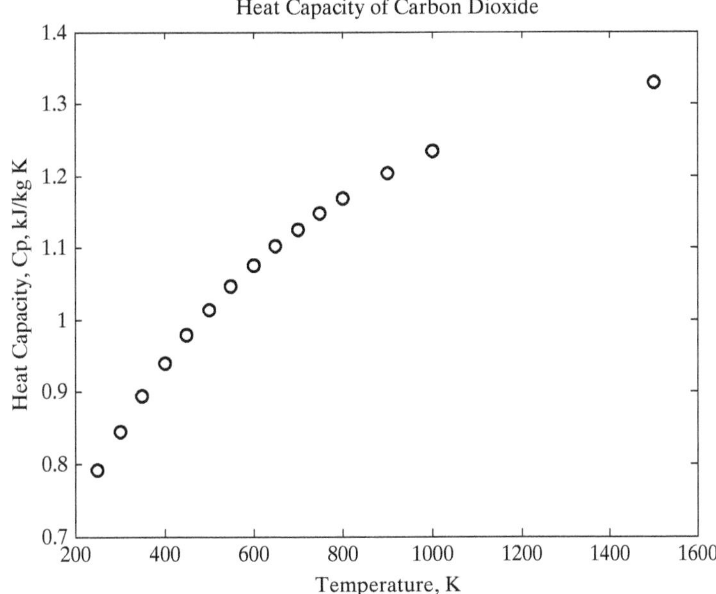

Figure 21.8 Heat capacity of carbon dioxide as a function of temperature.

```
%Define a finer array of temperatures
new_T = 250:10:1500;

%Calculate new heat capacity values, using four different polynomial models
Cp1 = polyval(polyfit(T,Cp,1),new_T);
Cp2 = polyval(polyfit(T,Cp,2),new_T);
Cp3 = polyval(polyfit(T,Cp,3),new_T);
Cp4 = polyval(polyfit(T,Cp,4),new_T);

%Plot the results
subplot(2,2,1)
plot(T,Cp,'o',new_T,Cp1)
axis([0,1700,0.6,1.6])
subplot(2,2,2)
plot(T,Cp,'o',new_T,Cp2)
axis([0,1700,0.6,1.6])
subplot(2,2,3)
plot(T,Cp,'o',new_T,Cp3)
axis([0,1700,0.6,1.6])
subplot(2,2,4)
plot(T,Cp,'o',new_T,Cp4)
axis([0,1700,0.6,1.6])
```

By looking at the graphs shown in Figure 21.9, we can see that a second- or third-order model adequately describes the behavior in this temperature region. If we decide to use a third-order polynomial model, we can find the coefficients with **polyfit**:

```
polyfit(T,Cp,3)
ans =
2.7372e-010 -1.0631e-006 1.5521e-003 4.6837e-001
```

The results correspond to the equation

$$C_p = 2.7372 \times 10^{-10}T^3 - 1.0631 \times 10^{-6}T^2 + 1.5521 \times 10^{-3}T + 4.6837 \times 10^{-1}$$

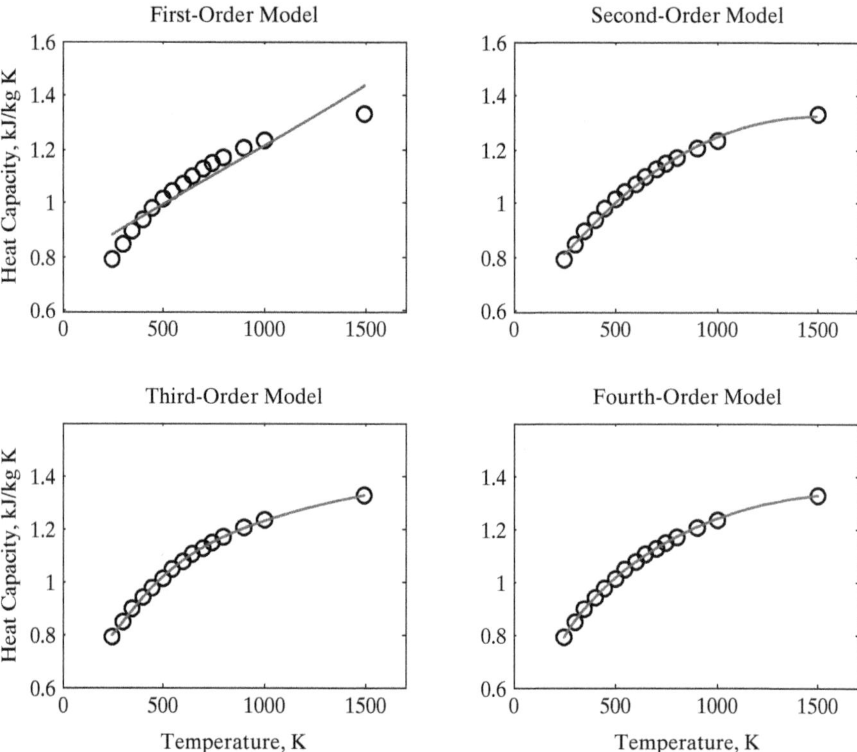

Figure 21.9 A comparison of different polynomials used to model the heat-capacity data of carbon dioxide.

5. Test the Solution

   Comparing our result with that reported in the literature, we see that they are close, but not exact:

   $$C_p = 2.737 \times 10^{-10}T^3 - 10.63 \times 10^{-7}T^2 + 1.552 \times 10^{-3}T + 4.683 \times 10^{-1}$$

   (our fit)

   $$C_p = 1.698 \times 10^{-10}T^3 - 7.957 \times 10^{-7}T^2 + 1.359 \times 10^{-3}T + 5.059 \times 10^{-1}$$

   (literature)

   This is not too surprising, since we modeled a limited number of data points. The models reported in the literature use more data and are therefore probably more accurate.

21.2 SOLVING AN EQUATION WITH ONE VARIABLE

An equation with one variable can be written in the form $f(x) = 0$. The solution is the value of x where the function crosses the x axis (the value of the function is zero), which means that the function changes sign at x. An exact solution is a value of x for which the value of the function is exactly zero. If such a value does not exist or is difficult to determine, a numerical solution can be determined by finding an x that is very close to the point where the function changes its sign (crosses the x-axis). This is done by the iterative process where in each iteration the computer determines a value of x that is closer to the solution. The iterations stop when the difference in x between two iterations is smaller than some measure. In general, a function can have none, one, several, or infinite number of solutions.

In MATLAB a zero of a function can be determined with the command (built-in function) **fzero** that has the form:

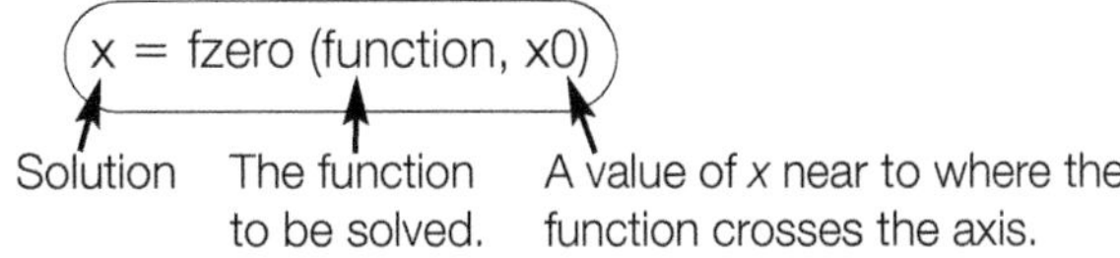
x = fzero (function, x0)
Solution
The function to be solved.
A value of x near to where the function crosses the axis.

The built-in function **fzero** is a MATLAB function function, which means that it accepts another function (the function to be solved) as an input argument.

Additional Details on the Arguments of fzero:

- x is the solution, which is a scalar.
- function is the function to be solved. It can be entered in several different ways:
  1. The simplest way is to enter the mathematical expression as a string.
  2. The function is first created as a user-defined function in a function file and then the function handle is entered.
  3. The function is first created as an anonymous function and then the name of the anonymous function (which is the name of the handle) is entered.

  (As explained, it is also possible to pass a user-defined function and an inline function into a function function by using its name. However, function handles are more efficient and easier to use, and should be the preferred method.)
- The function has to be written in a standard form. For example, if the function to be solved is $xe^{-x} = 0.2$, it has to be written as $f(x) = xe^{-x} - 0.2 = 0$. If this function is entered into the fzero command as a string, it is typed as: 'x*exp (−x) −0.2'.
- When a function is entered as an expression (string), it cannot include predefined variables. For example, if the function to be entered is $f(x) = xe^{-x} - 0.2$, it is not possible to define b = 0.2 and then enter 'x*exp (−x) −b'.
- x0 can be a scalar or a two-element vector. If it is entered as a scalar, it has to be a value of x near the point where the function crosses the x axis. If x0 is entered as a vector, the two elements have to be points on opposite sides of the solution such that $f(x0(1))$ has a different sign than $f(x0(2))$. When a function has more than one solution, each solution can be determined separately by using the fzero function and entering values for x0 that are near each of the solutions.
- A good way to find approximately where a function has a solution is to make a plot of the function. In many applications in science and engineering the domain of the solution can be estimated. Often when a function has more than one solution only one of the solutions will have a physical meaning.

In-Class Activity

ICA 21-2

Solving a Nonlinear Equation

Determine the solution of the equation $xe^{-x} = 0.2$.

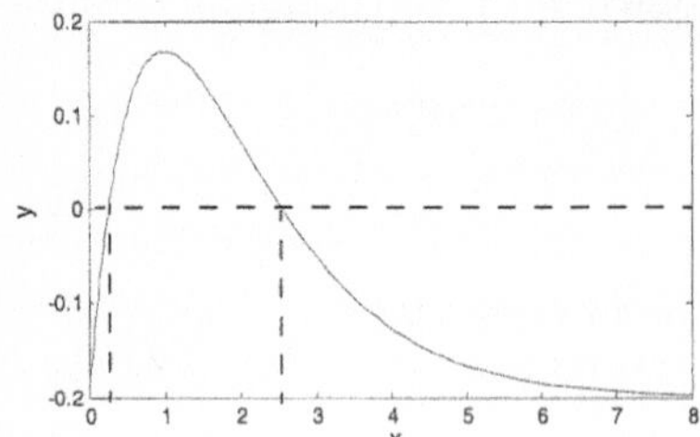

Solution

The equation is first written in a form of a function: $f(x) = xe^{-x} - 0.2$. A plot of the function, shown on the left, shows that the function has one solution between 0 and 1 and another solution between 2 and 3. The plot is obtained by typing

```
>> fplot ('x*exp (–x) –0.2', [0 8])
```

in the Command Window. The solutions of the function are found by using the fzero command twice. First, the equation is entered as a string expression, and a value of x0 between 0 and 1, (x0 = 0.7) is used. Second, the equation to be solved is written as an anonymous function, which is then used in fzero with x0 between 2 and 3, (x0 = 2.8). This is shown below:

```
>> x1=fzero ('x*exp (–x) –0.2', 0.7)     The function is entered as a string expression.
x1 =
  0.2592                                  The first solution is 0.2592.
>> F=@ (x) x*exp (–x) –0.2
F =                                       Creating an anonymous function.
  @ (x) x*exp (–x) –0.2
>> fzero (F, 2.8)                         Using the name of the anonymous function in fzero.
ans =
  2.5426                                  The second solution is 2.5426.
```

Additional Comments:

- The fzero command finds zeros of a function only where the function crosses the x-axis. The command does not find a zero at points where the function touches but does not cross the x-axis.
- If a solution cannot be determined, NaN is assigned to x.
- The fzero command has additional options (see the Help Window). Two of the more important options are:
  [x fval]=fzero (function, x0) assigns the value of the function at x to the variable fval.
  x=fzero (function, x0, optimset ('display', 'iter')) displays the output of each iteration during the process of finding the solution.
- When the function can be written in the form of a polynomial, the solution, or the roots, can be found with the roots command.
- The fzero command can also be used to find the value of x where the function has a specific value. This is done by translating the function up or down. For example, in the function of In Class Activity 21.2 the first value of x where the function is equal to 0.1 can be determined by solving the equation $xe^{-x} - 0.3 = 0$. This is shown below:

```
>> x=fzero ('x*exp (–x) –0.3', 0.5)
x =
  0.4894
```

21.3 FINDING A MINIMUM OR A MAXIMUM OF A FUNCTION

In many applications there is a need to determine the local minimum or the maximum of a function of the form $y = f(x)$. In calculus the value of x that corresponds to a local minimum or the maximum is determined by finding the zero of the derivative of the function. The value of y is determined by substituting the x into the function. In MATLAB the value of x where a one-variable function $f(x)$ within the interval $x_1 \le x \le x_2$ has a minimum can be determined with the **fminbnd** command, which has the form:

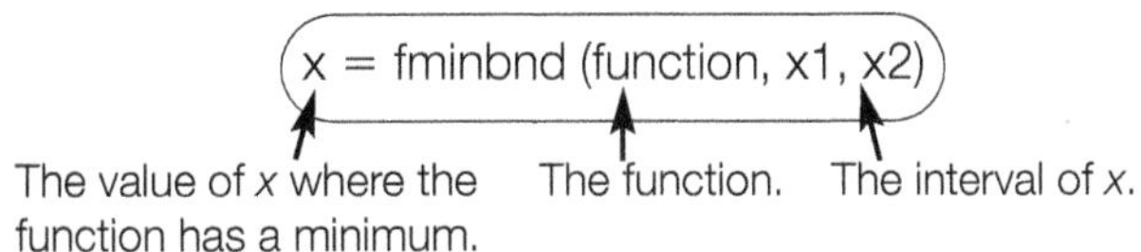
x = fminbnd (function, x1, x2)
The value of x where the function has a minimum.
The function.
The interval of x.

- The function can be entered as a string expression, or as a function handle, in the same way as with the fzero command. See Section 21.2 for details.
- The value of the function at the minimum can be added to the output by using the option:

  [x fval]=fminbnd (function, x1, x2)

  where the value of the function at x is assigned to the variable fval.
- Within a given interval, the minimum of a function can either be at one of the end points of the interval, or at a point within the interval where the slope of the function is zero (local minimum). When the fminbnd command is executed, MATLAB looks for a local minimum. If a local minimum is found, its value is compared to the value of the function at the end points of the interval. MATLAB returns the point with the actual minimum value of the interval.

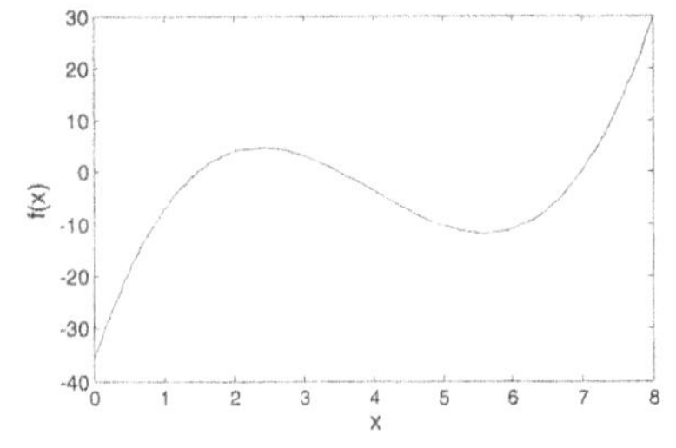

For example, consider the function $f(x) = x^3 - 12x^2 + 40.25x - 36.5$ which is plotted in the interval $0 \le x \le 8$ in the figure on the left. It can be observed that there is a local minimum between 5 and 6, and that the absolute minimum is at $x = 0$. Using the fminbnd command with the interval $3 \le x \le 8$ to find the location of the local minimum and the value of the function at this point gives:

```
>> [x fval]=fminbnd ('x^3-12*x^2+40.25*x-36.5', 3, 8)
x =
  5.6073
fval =
 -11.8043
```

The local minimum is at $x = 5.6073$. The value of the function at this point is -11.8043.

Notice that the fminbnd command gives the local minimum. If the interval is changed to $0 \le x \le 8$, the fminbnd gives:

```
>> [x fval]=fminbnd ('x^3-12*x^2+40.25*x-36.5', 0, 8)
x =
  0
fval =
 -36.5000
```

The minimum is at $x = 0$. The value of the function at this point is -36.5.

For this interval the fminbnd command gives the absolute minimum which is at the end point $x = 0$.

- The fminbnd command can also be used to find the maximum of a function. This is done by multiplying the function by -1 and finding the minimum. For example, the maximum of the function $f(x) = xe^{-x} - 0.2$, (from In-Class Activity 21.2) in the interval $0 \leq x \leq 8$ can be determined by finding the minimum of the function $f(x) = -xe^{-x} + 0.2$ as shown below:

```
>> [x fval]=fminbnd ('-x*exp (-x) + 0.2', 0, 8)
x =
  1.0000
fval =
  -0.1679
```

The maximum is at $x = 1.0$. The value of the function at this point is 0.1679.

CHAPTER 22
LOGICAL FUNCTIONS AND CONTROL STRUCTURES

Objectives

By learning the material in this chapter, you should be able to

- understand how MATLAB interprets relational and logical operators
- be able to use the **find** function
- understand the appropriate uses of the **if/else** family of commands
- understand the **switch/case** structure
- be able to write and use **for** loops and **while** loops

Introduction

One way to think of a computer program (not just MATLAB) is to consider how the statements that compose it are organized. Usually, sections of computer code can be categorized as ***sequences***, ***selection structures***, and ***repetition structures***. (See Figure 22.1.) So far, we have written code that contains sequences but none of the other structures:

- A sequence is a list of commands that are executed one after another.
- A selection structure allows the programmer to execute one command (or set of commands) if some criterion is true and a second command (or set of commands) if the criterion is false. A selection statement provides the means of choosing between these paths, based on a ***logical condition***. The conditions that are evaluated often contain both ***relational*** and ***logical*** operators or functions.
- A repetition structure, or loop, causes a group of statements to be executed multiple times. The number of times a loop is executed depends on either a counter or the evaluation of a logical condition.

22.1 RELATIONAL AND LOGICAL OPERATORS

The selection and repetition structures used in MATLAB depend on relational and logical operators. MATLAB has six relational operators for comparing two matrices of equal size, as shown in Table 22.1.

Comparisons are either true or false, and most computer programs (including MATLAB) use the number 1 for true and 0 for false. (MATLAB actually takes any number that is not 0 to be true.) If we define two scalars

```
x = 5;
y = 1;
```

Taken from *MATLAB® for Engineers,* Second Edition, by Holly Moore.

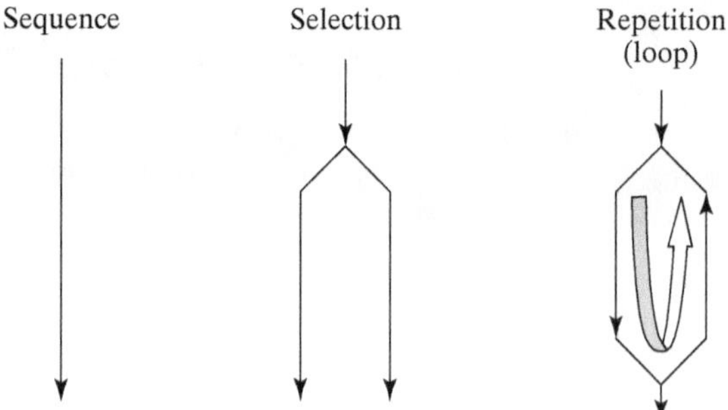

Figure 22.1 Programming structures used in MATLAB.

Table 22.1 Relational Operators

Relational Operator	Interpretation
<	less than
<=	less than or equal to
>	greater than
>=	greater than or equal to
==	equal to
~=	not equal to

Key Idea: Relational operators compare values

and use a relational operator such as <, the result of the comparison

```
x<y
```

is either true or false. In this case, **x** is not less than **y**, so MATLAB responds

```
ans =
     0
```

indicating that the comparison is false. MATLAB uses this answer in selection statements and in repetition structures to make decisions.

Of course, variables in MATLAB usually represent entire matrices. If we redefine **x** and **y**, we can see how MATLAB handles comparisons between matrices. For example,

```
x = 1:5;
y = x –4;
x<y
```

returns

```
ans =
     0  0  0  0  0
```

MATLAB compares corresponding elements and creates an answer matrix of zeros and ones. In the preceding example, **x** was greater than **y** for every comparison of elements, so every comparison was false and the answer was a string of zeros. If, instead, we have

```
x = [ 1, 2, 3, 4, 5];
y = [–2, 0, 2, 4, 6];
x<y
```

Table 22.2 Logical Operators

Logical Operator	Interpretation
&	and
~	not
|	or
xor	exclusive or

then

```
ans =
   0  0  0  0  1
```

The results tell us that the comparison was false for the first four elements, but true for the last. For a comparison to be true for an entire matrix, it must be true for *every* element in the matrix. In other words, all of the results must be ones.

MATLAB also allows us to combine comparisons with the logical operators `and`, `not`, and `or`. (See Table 22.2)

Key Idea: Logical operators are used to combine comparison statements

The code

```
x = [ 1, 2, 3, 4, 5];
y = [-2, 0, 2, 4, 6];
z = [ 8, 8, 8, 8, 8];
z>x & z>y
```

returns

```
ans =
      1  1  1  1  1
```

because **z** is greater than both **x** and **y** for every element. The statement

```
x>y | x>z
```

is read as "**x** is greater than **y** or **x** is greater than **z**" and returns

```
ans =
      1  1  1  0  0
```

This means that the condition is true for the first three elements and false for the last two.

These relational and logical operators are used in both selection structures and loops to determine what commands should be executed.

22.2 FLOWCHARTS AND PSEUDOCODE

With the addition of selection structures and repetition structures to your group of programming tools, it becomes even more important to plan your program before you start coding. Two common approaches are to use flowcharts and to use pseudocode. Flowcharts are a graphical approach to creating your coding plan, and pseudocode is a verbal description of your plan. You may want to use either or both for your programming projects.

For simple programs, pseudocode may be the best (or at least the simplest) planning approach:

Key Idea: Flowcharts and pseudocode are used to plan programming tasks

- Outline a set of statements describing the steps you will take to solve a problem.
- Convert these steps into comments in an M-file.
- Insert the appropriate MATLAB code into the file between the comment lines.

Here's a really simple example: Suppose you've been asked to create a program to convert mph to ft/s. The output should be a table, complete with a title and column headings. Here's an outline of the steps you might follow:

- Define a vector of mph values.
- Convert mph to ft/s.
- Combine the mph and ft/s vectors into a matrix.
- Create a table title.
- Create column headings.
- Display the table.

Once you've identified the steps, put them into a MATLAB M-file as comments:

```
%Define a vector of mph values
%Convert mph to ft/s
%Create a table title
%Combine the mph and ft/s vectors into a matrix
%Create a column headings
%Display the table
```

Now you can insert the appropriate MATLAB code into the M-file.

```
%Define a vector of mph values
  mph = 0:10:100;
%Convert mph to ft/s
  fps = mph*5280/3600;
%Combine the mph and ft/s vectors into a matrix
  table = [mph;fps]
%Create a table title
  disp('Velocity Conversion Table')
%Create column headings
  disp('     mph      f/s')
%Display the table
  fprintf('%8.0f    %8.2f \n',table)
```

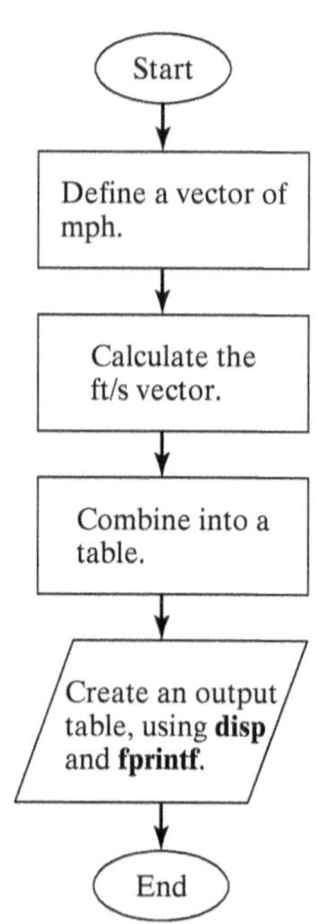

Figure 22.2 Flowcharts make it easy to visualize the structure of a program.

If you put some time into your planning, you probably won't need to change the pseudocode much, once you start programming.

Flowcharts alone or flowcharts combined with pseudocode are especially appropriate for more complicated programming tasks. You can create a "big picture" of your program graphically and then convert your project to pseudocode suitable to enter into the program as comments. Before you can start flowcharting, you'll need to be introduced to some standard flowcharting symbols. (See Table 22.3)

Figure 22.2 is an example of a flowchart for the mph-to-ft/s problem. For a problem this simple, you would probably never actually create a flowchart. However, as

Table 22.3 Flowcharting for Designing Computer Programs

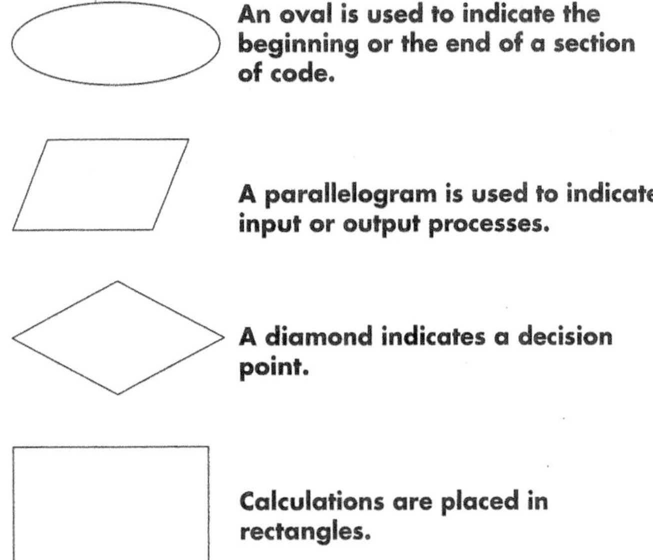

problems become more complicated, flowcharts become an invaluable tool, allowing you to organize you thoughts.

An oval is used to indicate the beginning or the end of a section of code.
A parallelogram is used to indicate input or output processes.
A diamond indicates a decision point.
Calculations are placed in rectangles.

> ***Key Idea:*** A flowchart is a pictorial representation of a computer program

Once you've created a flowchart, you should transfer the ideas into comment lines in an M-file and then add the appropriate code between the comments.

Remember, both flowcharts and pseudocode are tools intended to help you create better computer programs. They can also be used effectively to illustrate the structure of a program to nonprogrammers, since they emphasize the logical progression of ideas over programming details.

22.3 SELECTION STRUCTURES

Most of the time, the **find** command can and should be used instead of an **if** statement. In some situations, however, the **if** statement is required. This section describes the syntax used in **if** statements.

22.3.1 The Simple If

A simple **if** statement has the following form:

```
if comparison
  statements
end
```

If the comparison (a logical expression) is true, the statements between the **if** statement and the **end** statement are executed. If the comparison is false, the program jumps immediately to the statement following **end**. It is good programming practice to indent the statements within an **if** structure for readability. However, recall that MATLAB ignores white space. Your programs will run regardless of whether you do or do not indent any of your lines of code.

Here's a really simple example of an **if** statement:

```
if G<50
  disp('G is a small value equal to:')
  disp(G);
end
```

Key Idea: **if** statements usually work best with scalars

This statement (from **if** to **end**) is easy to interpret if **G** is a scalar. If **G** is less than 50, then the statements between the **if** and the **end** lines are executed. For example, if **G** has a value of 25, then

```
G is a small value equal to:
  25
```

is displayed on the screen. However, if **G** is not a scalar, then the **if** statement considers the comparison true **only if it is true for every element**! Thus, if **G** is defined from 0 to 80,

```
G = 0:10:80;
```

the comparison is false, and the statements inside the **if** statement are not executed! In general, **if** statements work best when dealing with scalars.

22.3.2 The If/Else Structure

The simple **if** allows us to execute a series of statements if a condition is true and to skip those steps if the condition is false. The **else** clause allows us to execute one set of statements if the comparison is true and a different set if the comparison is false. Suppose you would like to take the logarithm of a variable x. You know from basic algebra classes that the input to the **log** function must be greater than 0. Here's a set of **if/else** statements that calculates the logarithm if the input is positive and sends an error message if the input to the function is 0 or negative:

```
if x >0
  y = log(x)
else
  disp('The input to the log function must be positive')
end
```

When **x** is a scalar, this is easy to interpret. However, when **x** is a matrix, the comparison is true only if it is true for every element in the matrix. So, if

```
x = 0:0.5:2;
```

then the elements in the matrix are not all greater than 0. Therefore, MATLAB skips to the **else** portion of the statement and displays the error message. The **if/else** statement is probably best confined to use with scalars, although you may find it to be of limited use with vectors.

HINT

MATLAB includes a function called **beep** that causes the computer to "beep" at the user. You can use this function to alert the user to an error. For example, in the **if/else** clause, you could add a beep to the portion of the code that includes an error statement:

```
x = input('Enter a value of x greater than 0: ');
if x >0
  y = log(x)
else
  beep
  disp('The input to the log function must be positive')
end
```

22.3.3 The Elseif Structure

When we nest several levels of **if/else** statements, it may be difficult to determine which logical expressions must be true (or false) in order to execute each set of statements. The **elseif** function allows you to check multiple criteria while keeping the code easy to read. Consider the following lines of code that evaluate whether to issue a driver's license, based on the applicant's age:

```
if age<16
  disp('Sorry – You'll have to wait')
elseif age<18
  disp('You may have a youth license')
elseif age<70
  disp('You may have a standard license')
else
  disp('Drivers over 70 require a special license')
end
```

In this example, MATLAB first checks to see if **age < 16.** If the comparison is true, the program executes the next line or set of lines, displays the message **Sorry–You'll have to wait**, and then exits the **if** structure. If the comparison is false, MATLAB moves on to the next **elseif** comparison, checking to see if **age < 18** this time. The program continues through the **if** structure until it finally finds a true comparison or until it encounters the **else**. Notice that the **else** line does not include a comparison, since it executes if the **elseif** immediately before it is false.

The flowchart for this sequence of commands (Figure 22.3) uses the diamond shape to indicate a selection structure.

This structure is easy to interpret if **age** is a scalar. If it is a matrix, the comparison must be true for every element in the matrix. Consider this age matrix

```
age = [15,17,25,55,75]
```

The first comparison, **if age<16**, is false, because it is not true for every element in the array. The second comparison, **elseif age<18**, is also false. The third comparison, **elseif age<70**, is false as well, since not all of the ages are below 70. The result is **Drivers over 70 require a special license**—a result that won't please the other drivers.

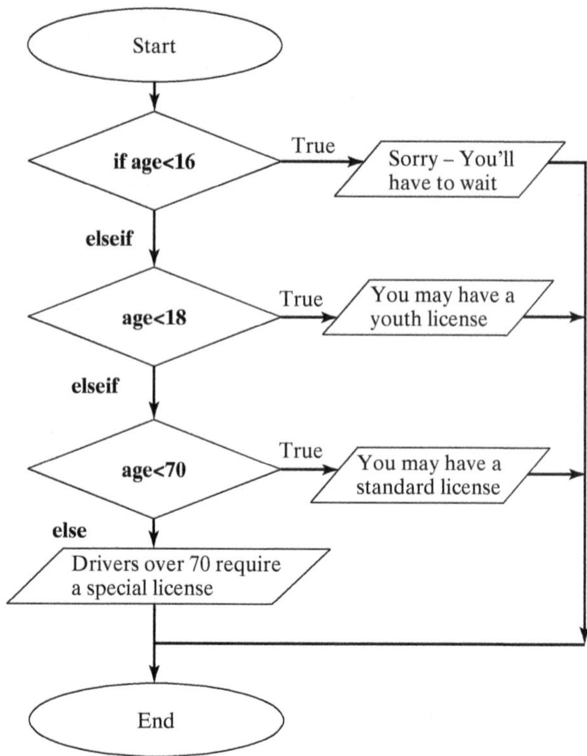

Figure 22.3 Flowchart using multiple if statements.

HINT

One common mistake new programmers make when using if statements is to overspecify the criteria. In the preceding example, it is enough to state that **age** < **18** in the second if clause, because age cannot be less than 16 and still reach this statement. You don't need to specify **age** < 18 and **age** > = 16. If you overspecify the criteria, you risk defining a calculational path for which there is no correct answer. For example, in the code

```
if age<16
  disp('Sorry – You''ll have to wait')
elseif age<18 & age>16
  disp('You may have a youth license')
elseif age<70 & age>18
  disp('You may have a standard license')
elseif age>70
  disp('Drivers over 70 require a special license')
end
```

there is no correct choice for age = 16, 18, or 70.

In general, **elseif** structures work well for scalars, but **find** is probably a better choice for matrices. Here's an example that uses **find** with an array of ages and generates a table of results in each category:

```
age = [15,17,25,55,75];
set1 = find(age<16);
set2 = find(age>=16 & age<18);
set3 = find(age>=18 & age<70);
set4 = find(age>=70);
```

```
fprintf('Sorry – You'll have to wait - you're only %3.0f
  \n',age(set1))
fprintf('You may have a youth license because you're %3.0f
  \n',age(set2))
fprintf('You may have a standard license because you're
  %3.0f \n',age(set3))
fprintf('Drivers over 70 require a special license. You're
  %3.0f \n',age(set4))
```

These commands return

```
Sorry – You'll have to wait - you're only 15
You may have a youth license because you're 17
You may have a standard license because you're 25
You may have a standard license because you're 55
Drivers over 70 require a special license. You're 75
```

Since every **find** in this sequence is evaluated, it is necessary to specify the range completely (for example, **age>=16 & age<18**).

EXAMPLE 22.1

Assigning Grades

The if family of statements is used most effectively when the input is a scalar. Create a function to determine test grades based on the score and assuming a single input into the function. The grades should be based on the following criteria:

Grade	Score
A	90 to 100
B	80 to 90
C	70 to 80
D	60 to 70
E	< 60

1. State the Problem
   Determine the grade earned on a test.
2. Describe the Input and Output

   Input Single score, not an array

   Output Letter grade
3. Develop a Hand Example
   85 should be a B
   But should 90 be an A or a B? We need to create more exact criteria.

Grade	Score
A	≥ 90 to 100
B	≥ 80 to < 90
C	≥ 70 to < 80
D	≥ 60 to < 70
E	< 60

4. Develop a MATLAB Solution
   Outline the function, using the flowchart shown in Figure 22.4.

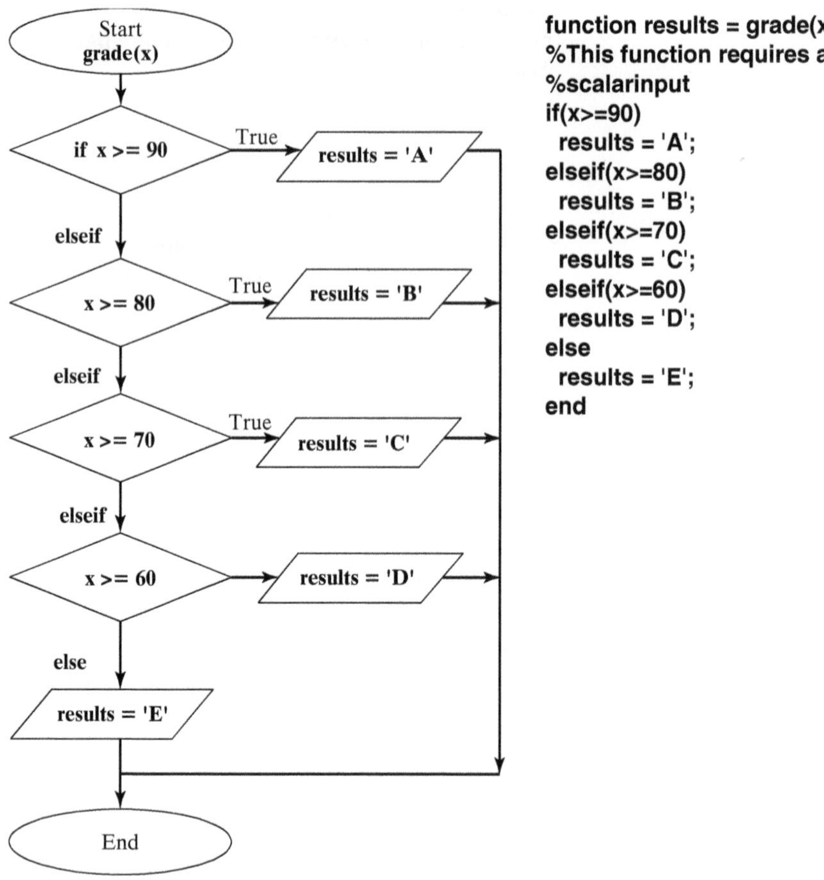


```
function results = grade(x)
%This function requires a
%scalarinput
if(x>=90)
  results = 'A';
elseif(x>=80)
  results = 'B';
elseif(x>=70)
  results = 'C';
elseif(x>=60)
  results = 'D';
else
  results = 'E';
end
```

Figure 22.4 Flowchart for a grading scheme.

5. Test the Solution
   Now test the function in the command window:

```
grade(25)
ans =
E
grade(80)
ans =
B
grade(–52)
ans =
E
grade(108)
ans =
A
```

Notice that although the function seems to work properly, it returns grades for values over 100 and values less than 0. If you'd like, you can now go back and add the logic to exclude those values:

```
function results = grade(x)
%This function requires a scalar input
```

```
    if(x>=0 & x<=100)
    if(x>=90)
      results = 'A';
    elseif(x>=80)
      results = 'B';
    elseif(x>=70)
      results = 'C';
    elseif(x>=60)
      results = 'D';
    else
      results = 'E';
    end
    else
      results = 'Illegal Input';
end
```

We can test the function again in the command window:

```
grade(–10)
ans =
Illegal Input
grade(108)
ans =
Illegal Input
```

This function will work great for scalars, but if you send a vector to the function, you may get some unexpected results, such as

```
score = [95,42,83,77];
grade(score)
ans =
E
```

In-Class Activity

ICA 22-1

The **if** family of functions is particularly useful in functions. Write and test a function for each of these problems, assuming that the input to the function is a scalar:

1. Suppose the legal drinking age is 21 in your state. Write and test a function to determine whether a person is old enough to drink.
2. Many rides at amusement parks require riders to be a certain minimum height. Assume that the minimum height is 48″ for a certain ride. Write and test a function to determine whether the rider is tall enough.
3. When a part is manufactured, the dimensions are usually specified with a tolerance. Assume that a certain part needs to be 5.4 cm long, plus or minus 0.1 cm (5.4 ± 0.1 cm). Write a function to determine whether a part is within these specifications.
4. Unfortunately, the United States currently uses both metric and English units. Suppose the part in Exercise 3 was inspected by measuring the length in inches instead of cm. Write and test a function that determines whether the part is within specifications and that accepts input into the function in inches.
5. Many solid-fuel rocket motors consist of three stages. Once the first stage burns out, it separates from the missile and the second stage lights. Then the second stage burns out

and separates, and the third stage lights. Finally, once the third stage burns out, it also separates from the missile. Assume that the following data approximately represent the times during which each stage burns:

Stage 1	0–100 seconds
Stage 2	100–170 seconds
Stage 3	170–260 seconds

Write and test a function to determine whether the missile is in Stage 1 flight, Stage 2 flight, Stage 3 flight, or free flight (unpowered).

22.4 REPETITION STRUCTURES: LOOPS

Loops are used when you need to repeat a set of instructions multiple times. MATLAB supports two different types of loops: the **for** loop and the **while** loop. **For** loops are the easiest choice when you know how many times you need to repeat the loop. **While** loops are the easiest choice when you need to keep repeating the instructions until a criterion is met. If you have previous programming experience, you may be tempted to use loops extensively. However, usually you can compose MATLAB programs that avoid loops, either by using the **find** command or by vectorizing the code. (In vectorization, we operate on entire vectors at a time instead of one element at a time.) It's a good idea to avoid loops whenever possible, because the resulting programs run faster and often require fewer programming steps.

22.4.1 For Loops

The structure of the **for** loop is simple. The first line identifies the loop and defines an index, which is a number that changes on each pass through the loop. After the identification line comes the group of commands we want to execute. Finally, the end of the loop is identified by the command **end**. In sum, we have

```
for index = [matrix]
    commands to be executed
end
```

The loop is executed once for each element of the index matrix identified in the first line. Here's a really simple example:

```
for k = [1,3,7]
  k
end
```

This code returns

```
k =
   1
k =
   3
k =
   7
```

The index in this case is **k**. Programmers often use **k** as an index variable as a matter of style. The index matrix can also be defined with the colon operator or, indeed, in a number of other ways as well. Here's an example of code that finds the value of 5 raised to powers between 1 and 3:

Key Idea: Loops allow you to repeat sequences of commands until some criterion is met

```
for k = 1:3
  a = 5^k
end
```

On the first line, the index, **k**, is defined as the matrix [1, 2, 3]. The first time through the loop, **k** is assigned a value of 1, and 5^1 is calculated. Then the loop repeats, but now **k** is equal to 2 and 5^2 is calculated. The last time through the loop, **k** is equal to 3 and 5^3 is calculated. Because the statements in the loop are repeated three times, the value of **a** is displayed three times in the command window:

```
a =
   5
a =
   25
a =
   125
```

Although we defined **k** as a matrix in the first line of the **for** loop, because **k** is an index number when it is used in the loop, it can equal only one value at a time. After we finish executing the loop, if we call for **k**, it has only one value: the value of the index the final time through the loop. For the preceding example,

```
k
```

returns

```
k =
   3
```

Notice that **k** is listed as a 1×1 matrix in the workspace window.

A common way to use a **for** loop is in defining a new matrix. Consider, for example, the code

```
for k = 1:5
  a(k) = k^2
end
```

This loop defines a new matrix, **a**, one element at a time. Since the program repeats its set of instructions five times, a new element is added to the **a** matrix each time through the loop, with the following output in the command window:

```
a =
   1
a =
   1  4
a =
   1  4  9
a =
   1  4  9  16
a =
   1  4  9  16  25
```

HINT

Most computer programs do not have MATLAB's ability to handle matrices so easily; therefore, they rely on loops similar to the one just presented to define arrays. It would be easier to create the vector **a** in MATLAB with the code

```
k = 1:5
a = k.^2
```

which returns

```
k =
   1 2 3 4 5
a =
   1 4 9 16 25
```

This is an example of *vectorizing* the code.

Another common use for a **for** loop is to combine it with an **if** statement and determine how many times something is true. For example, in the list of test scores shown in the first line, how many are above 90?

```
scores = [76,45,98,97];
count = 0;
for k=1:length(scores)
  if scores(k)>90
     count = count + 1;
  end
end
disp(count)
```

Each time through the loop, if the score is greater than 90, the count is incremented by 1.

Most of the time, **for** loops are created which use an index matrix that is a single row. However, if a two-dimensional matrix is defined in the index specification, MATLAB uses an entire column as the index each time through the loop. For example, suppose we define the index matrix as

$$k = \begin{bmatrix} 1 & 2 & 3 \\ 1 & 4 & 9 \\ 1 & 8 & 27 \end{bmatrix}$$

Then

```
for k = [1,2,3; 1,4,9; 1,8,27]
  a = k'
end
```

returns

```
a =
   1 1 1
a =
   2 4 8
a =
   3 9 27
```

Notice that **k** was transposed when it was set equal to **a**, so our results are rows instead of columns.

We can summarize the use of for loops with the following rules:

> ***Key Idea:*** Use for loops when you know how many times you need to repeat a sequence of commands

- The loop starts with a **for** statement and ends with the word **end.**
- The first line in the loop defines the number of times the loop will repeat, using an index matrix.
- The index of a **for** loop must be a variable. (The index is the number that changes each time through the loop.) Although **k** is often used as the symbol for the index, any variable name may be employed. The use of **k** is a matter of style.
- Any of the techniques learned to define a matrix can be used to define the index matrix. One common approach is to use the colon operator, as in

```
for index = start:inc:final
```

- If the expression is a row vector, the elements are used one at a time—once for each time through the loop.
- If the expression is a two-dimensional matrix (this alternative is not common), each time through the loop the index will contain the next *column* in the matrix. This means that the index will be a column vector!
- Once you've completed a **for** loop, the index is the last value used.
- **For** loops can often be avoided by vectorizing the code.

The basic flowchart for a **for** loop includes a diamond, which reflects the fact that a **for** loop starts each pass with a check to see if there is a new value in the index matrix (Figure 22.5). If there isn't, the loop is terminated and the program continues with the statements after the loop.

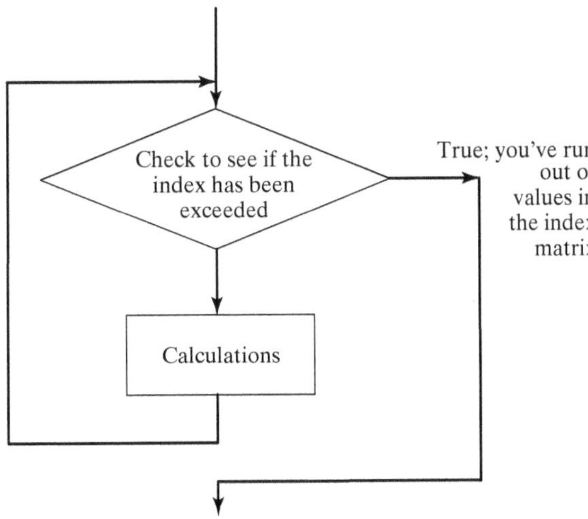

Figure 22.5 Flowchart for a for loop.

EXAMPLE 22.2

Creating a Degrees-to-Radians Table

Although it would be much easier to use MATLAB's vector capability to create a degrees-to-radians table, we can demonstrate the use of **for** loops with this example.

1. State the Problem
   Create a table that converts angle values from degrees to radians, from 0 to 360 degrees, in increments of 10 degrees.
2. Describe the Input and Output

   Input An array of angle values in degrees

   Output A table of angle values in both degrees and radians
3. Develop a Hand Example
   For 10 degrees,

$$\text{radians} = (10)\frac{\pi}{180} = 0.1745$$

4. Develop a MATLAB Solution
   First develop a flowchart (Figure 22.6) to help you plan your code.
   The command window displays the following results:

```
Degrees to Radians
Degrees    Radians
  10       0.17
  20       0.35
  30       0.52   etc.
```

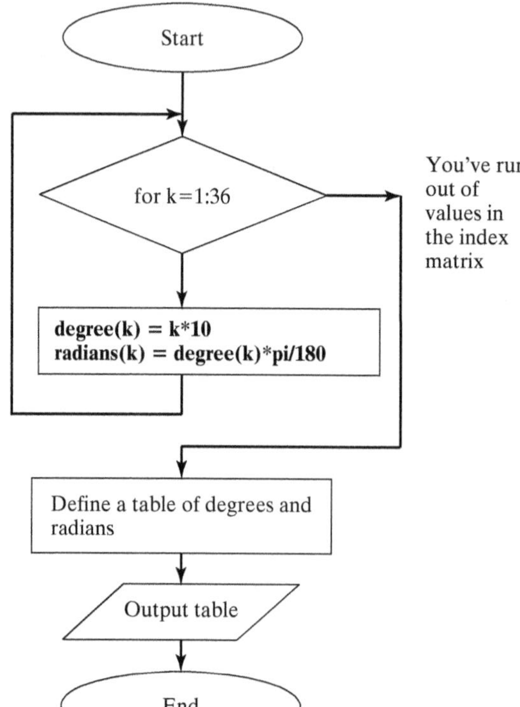


```
%Example 22.2
%Create a table of degrees to
%radians
clear, clc
%Use a for loop for
the%calculations

for k=1:36
  degree(k) = k*10;
  radians(k)=degree(k)*pi/180;
end

%Create a table

table = [degree;radians]

%Send the table to the
%command window

disp('Degrees to Radians')
disp('Degrees Radians')
fprintf('%8.0f %8.2f
\n',table)
```

Figure 22.6 Flowchart for changing degrees to radians.

5. Test the Solution
   The value for 10 degrees calculated by MATLAB is the same as the hand calculation.
   Clearly, it is much easier to use MATLAB's vector capabilities for this calculation. You get exactly the same answer, and it takes significantly less computing time. This approach is called vectorization of your code and is one of the strengths of MATLAB. The vectorized code is

```
degrees = 0:10:360;
radians = degrees * pi/180;
table = [degree;radians]
disp('Degrees to Radians')
disp('Degrees    Radians')
fprintf('%8.0f %8.2f \n',table)
```

EXAMPLE 22.3

Calculating Factorials with a For Loop

A factorial is the product of all the integers from 1 to *N*. For example, 5 factorial is

$$1 \cdot 2 \cdot 3 \cdot 4 \cdot 5$$

In mathematics texts, factorial is usually indicated with an exclamation point:

5! is five factorial.

MATLAB contains a built-in function for calculating factorials, called **factorial**. However, suppose you would like to program your own factorial function called **fact**.

1. State the Problem
   Create a function called **fact** to calculate the factorial of any number. Assume scalar input.
2. Describe the Input and Output

   Input A scalar value *N*

   Output The value of *N*!
3. Develop a Hand Example

$$5! = 1 \cdot 2 \cdot 3 \cdot 4 \cdot 5 = 120$$

4. Develop a MATLAB Solution
   First develop a flowchart (Figure 22.7) to help you plan your code.
5. Test the Solution
   Test the function in the command window:

```
fact(5)
ans =
  120
```

   This function works only if the input is a scalar. If an array is entered, the **for** loop does not execute, and the function returns a value of 1:

```
x=1:10;
  fact(x)
ans =
   1
```

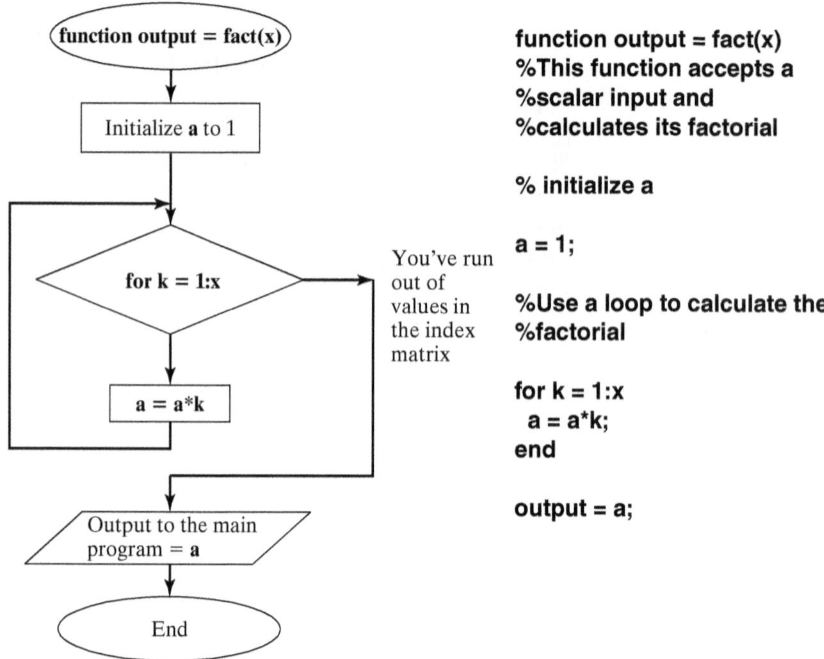
function output = fact(x)
Initialize a to 1
for k = 1:x
a = a*k
You've run out of values in the index matrix
Output to the main program = a
End
function output = fact(x)
%This function accepts a
%scalar input and
%calculates its factorial
% initialize a
a = 1;
%Use a loop to calculate the
%factorial
for k = 1:x
a = a*k;
end
output = a;

Figure 22.7 Flowchart for finding a factorial, using a **for** loop.

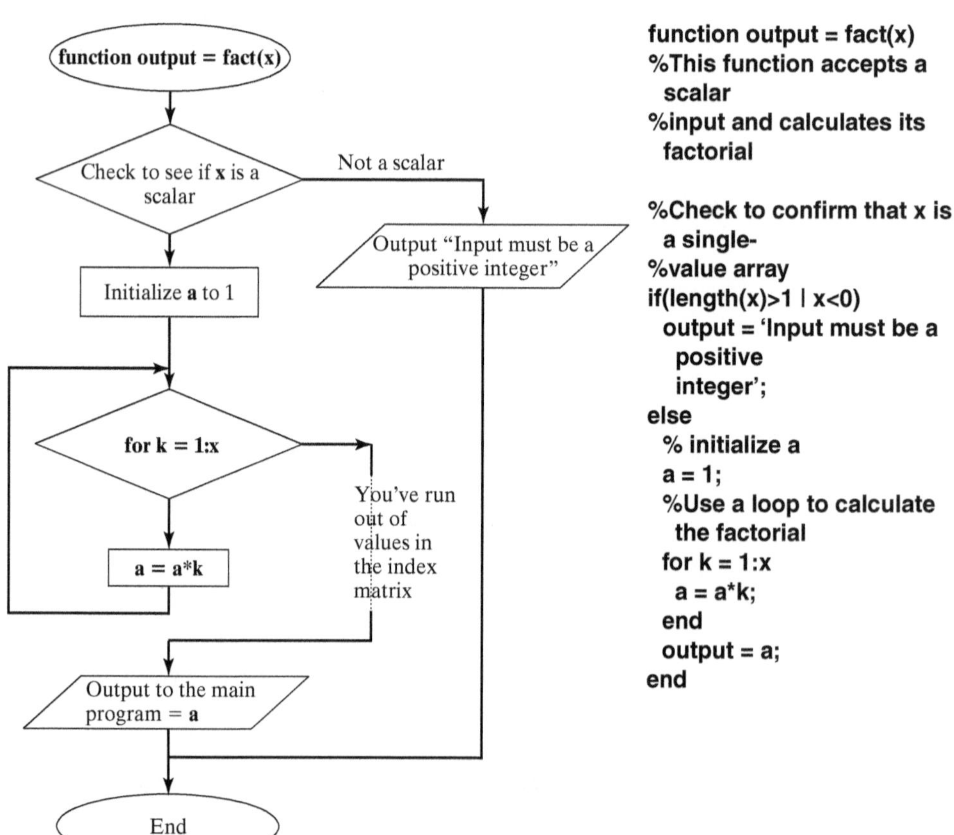
function output = fact(x)
Check to see if x is a scalar
Not a scalar
Output "Input must be a positive integer"
Initialize a to 1
for k = 1:x
a = a*k
You've run out of values in the index matrix
Output to the main program = a
End
function output = fact(x)
%This function accepts a scalar
%input and calculates its factorial
%Check to confirm that x is a single-
%value array
if(length(x)>1 | x<0)
output = 'Input must be a positive integer';
else
% initialize a
a = 1;
%Use a loop to calculate the factorial
for k = 1:x
a = a*k;
end
output = a;
end

Figure 22.8 Flowchart for finding a factorial, including error checking.

You can add an **if** statement to confirm that the input is a positive integer and not an array, as shown in the flowchart in Figure 22.8 and the accompanying code.
Check the new function in the command window:

```
fact(-4)
ans =
Input must be a positive integer

fact(x)
ans =
Input must be a positive integer
```

In-Class Activity

ICA 22-2

Use a **for** loop to solve the following problems:

1. Create a table that converts inches to feet.
2. Consider the following matrix of values:

$$x = [45, 23, 17, 34, 85, 33]$$

   How many values are greater than 30? (Use a counter.)
3. Repeat Exercise 2, this time using the **find** command.
4. Use a **for** loop to sum the elements of the matrix in Problem 2. Check your results with the **sum** function. (Use the **help** feature if you don't know or remember how to use **sum**.)
5. Use a **for** loop to create a vector containing the first 10 elements in the harmonic series, i.e.,

   1/1 1/2 1/3 1/4 1/5 . . . . 1/10

6. Use a **for** loop to create a vector containing the first 10 elements in the alternating harmonic series, i.e.,

   1/1 −1/2 1/3 −1/4 1/5 . . . . −1/10

22.4.2 While Loops

> ***Key Idea:*** Use while loops when you don't know how many times a sequence of commands will need to be repeated

While loops are similar to **for** loops. The big difference is the way MATLAB decides how many times to repeat the loop. **While** loops continue until some criterion is met. The format for a **while** loop is

```
while criterion
    commands to be executed
end
```

Here's an example:

```
k = 0;
while k<3
  k = k+1
end
```

In this case, we initialized a counter, **k**, before the loop. Then the loop repeated as long as **k** was less than 3. We incremented **k** by 1 every time through the loop, so the loop repeated three times, giving

```
k =
   1
k =
   2
k =
   3
```

We could use **k** as an index number to define a matrix or just as a counter. Most **for** loops can also be coded as **while** loops. Recall the **for** loop in Section 22.4.1 used to calculate the first three powers of 5. The following **while** loop accomplishes the same task:

```
k = 0;
while k<3
  k = k+1;
  a(k) = 5^k
end
```

The code returns

```
a =
   5
a =
   5  25
a =
   5  25  125
```

> ***Key Idea:*** Any problem that can be solved using a while loop could also be solved using a **for** loop

Each time through the loop, another element is added to the matrix **a**.

As another example, first initialize **a**:

```
a = 0;
```

Then find the first multiple of 3 that is greater than 10:

```
while(a<10)
        a = a + 3
end;
```

The first time through the loop, **a** is equal to 0, so the comparison is true. The next statement (**a = a + 3**) is executed, and the loop is repeated. This time **a** is equal to 3 and the condition is still true, so execution continues. In succession, we have

```
a =
   3
a =
   6
a =
   9
a =
   12
```

The last time through the loop, **a** starts out as 9 and then becomes 12 when 3 is added to 9. The comparison is made one final time, but since **a** is now equal to 12—which is greater than 10—the program skips to the end of the **while** loop and no longer repeats.

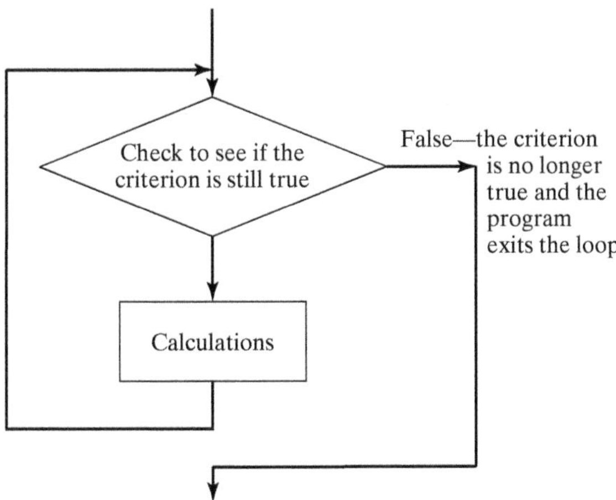

Figure 22.9 Flowchart for a while loop.

While loops can also be used to count how many times a condition is true by incorporating an **if** statement. Recall the test scores we counted in a **for** loop earlier. We can also count them with a **while** loop:

```
scores = [76,45,98,97];
count = 0;
k = 0;
while k<length(scores)
 k = k+1;
  if scores(k)>90
    count = count + 1;
 end
end
disp(count)
```

The variable **count** is used to count how many values are greater than 90. The variable **k** is used to count how many times the loop is executed.

The basic flow chart for a **while** loop is the same as that for a **for** loop (Figure 22.9).

One common use for a **while** loop is error checking of user input. Consider a program where we prompt the user to input a positive number, and then we calculate the log base 10 of that value. We can use a **while** loop to confirm that the number is positive, and if it is not, to prompt the user to enter an allowed value. The program keeps on prompting for a positive value until the user finally enters a valid number.

HINT

The variable used to control the **while** loop must be updated every time through the loop. If not, you'll generate an endless loop. When a calculation is taking a long time to complete, you can confirm that the computer is really working on it by checking the lower left-hand corner for the "busy" indicator. If you want to exit the calculation manually, type **Ctrl c**. Make sure that the command window is the active window when you execute this command.

```
x = input('Enter a positive value of x')
while (x<=0)
  disp('log(x) is not defined for negative numbers')
  x = input('Enter a positive value of x')
end
  y = log10(x);
fprintf('The log base 10 of %4.2f is %5.2f \n',x,y)
```

If, when the code is executed, a positive value of **x** is entered, the **while** loop does not execute (since **x** is not less than 0). If, instead, a zero or negative value is entered, the **while** loop is executed, an error message is sent to the command window, and the user is prompted to re-enter the value of **x**. The **while** loop continues to execute until a positive value of **x** is finally entered.

HINT

Many computer texts and manuals indicate the control key with the ^ symbol. This is confusing at best. The command ^c usually means to strike the Ctrl key and the c key at the same time.

EXAMPLE 22.4

Creating a Table for Converting Degrees to Radians with a While Loop

Just as we used a **for** loop to create a table for converting degrees to radians in Example 22.2, we can use a **while** loop for the same purpose.

1. State the Problem
   Create a table that converts degrees to radians, from 0 to 360 degrees, in increments of 10 degrees.
2. Describe the Input and Output
   Input An array of angle values in degrees
   Output A table of angle values in both degrees and radians
3. Develop a Hand Example
   For 10 degrees,
   $$\text{radians} = (10)\frac{\pi}{180} = 0.1745$$
4. Develop a MATLAB Solution
   First develop a flowchart (Figure 22.10) to help you plan your code.
   The command window displays the following results:

```
Degrees to Radians
Degrees   Radians
  10        0.17
  20        0.35
  30        0.52   etc.
```

5. Test the Solution
   The value for 10 degrees calculated by MATLAB is the same as the hand calculation.

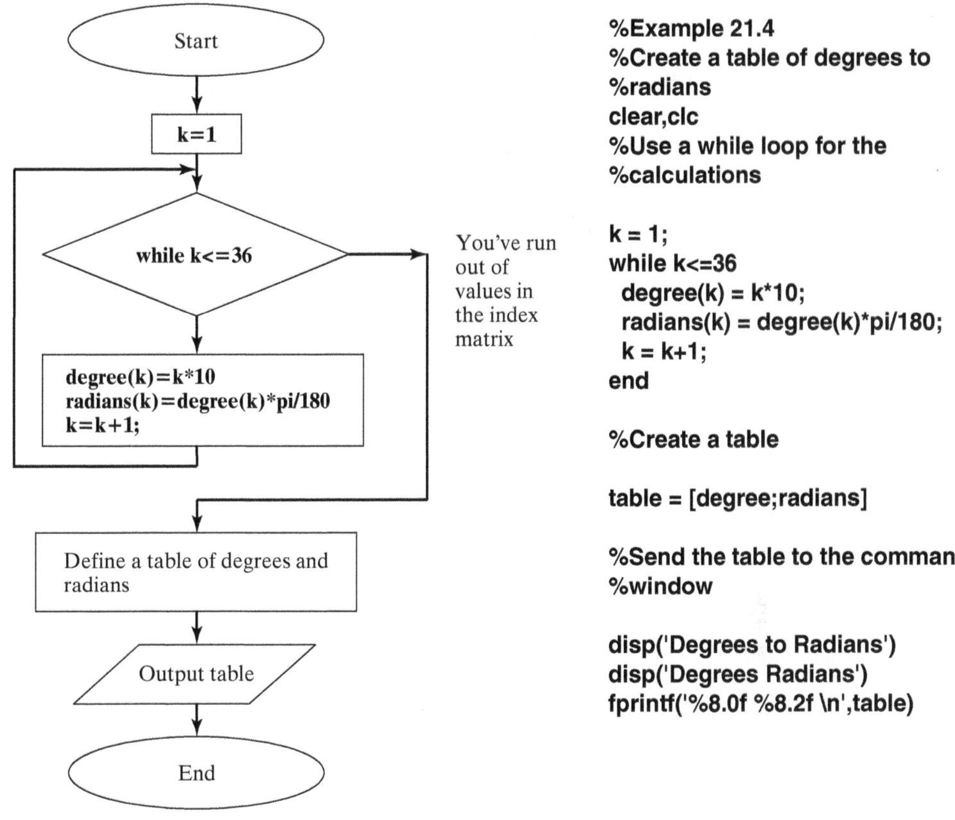

Figure 22.10 Flowchart for converting degrees to radians with a **while** loop.

EXAMPLE 22.5

Calculating Factorials with a While Loop

Create a new function called **fact2** that uses a **while** loop to find *N*!. Include an **if** statement to check for negative numbers and to confirm that the input is a scalar.

1. State the Problem
   Create a function called **fact2** to calculate the factorial of any number.
2. Describe the Input and Output
   Input A scalar value N
   Output The value of N!
3. Develop a Hand Example

$$5! = 1 \cdot 2 \cdot 3 \cdot 4 \cdot 5 = 120$$

4. Develop a MATLAB Solution
   First develop a flowchart (Figure 22.11) to help you plan your code.
5. Test the Solution
   Test the function in the command window:

```
fact2(5)
ans =
120
fact2(–10)
ans =
The input must be a positive integer
fact2([1:10])
ans =
The input must be a positive integer
```

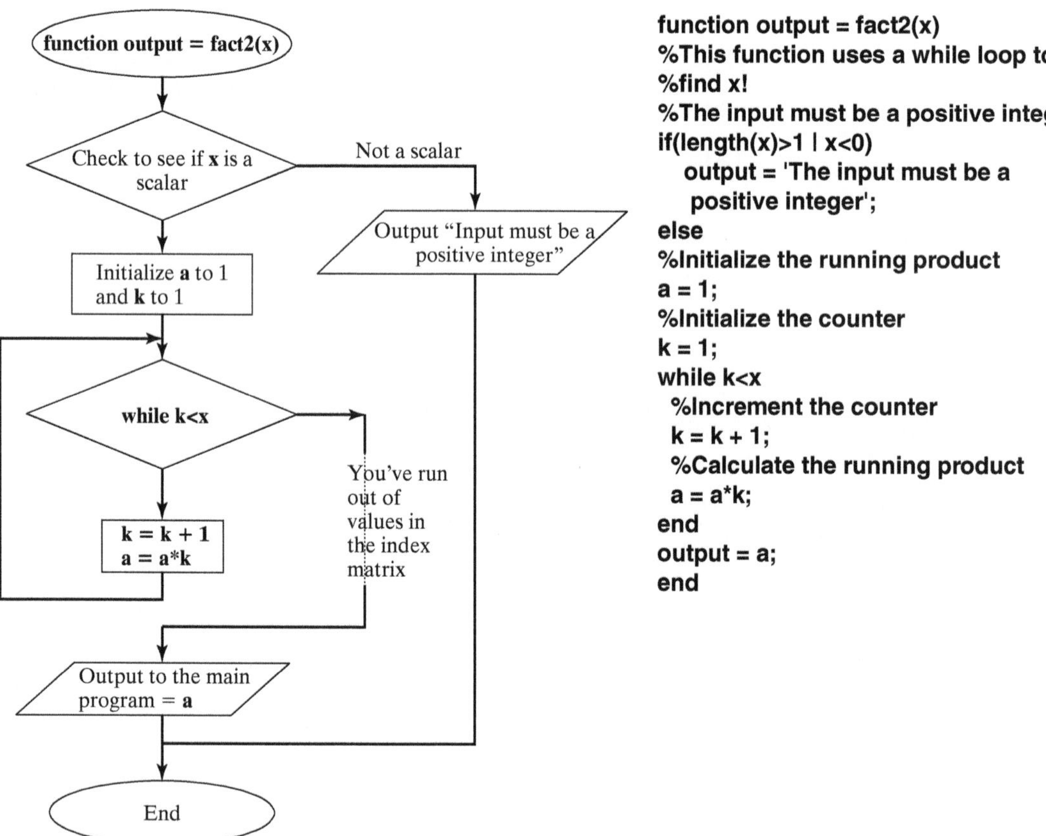


```
function output = fact2(x)
%This function uses a while loop to
%find x!
%The input must be a positive integer
if(length(x)>1 | x<0)
   output = 'The input must be a
    positive integer';
else
%Initialize the running product
a = 1;
%Initialize the counter
k = 1;
while k<x
  %Increment the counter
  k = k + 1;
  %Calculate the running product
  a = a*k;
end
output = a;
end
```

Figure 22.11 Flowchart for finding a factorial with a **while** loop.

EXAMPLE 22.6

The Alternating Harmonic Series

The *alternating harmonic series* converges to the natural log of 2:

$$\sum_{k=1}^{\infty} \frac{(-1)^{k+1}}{k} = 1 - \frac{1}{2} + \frac{1}{3} - \frac{1}{4} + \frac{1}{5} - \cdots = \ln(2) = 0.6931471806$$

Because of this, we can use the alternating harmonic series to approximate the ln(2). But how far out do you have to take the series to get a good approximation of the final answer? We can use a **while** loop to solve this problem.

1. State the Problem
   Use a **while** loop to calculate the members of the alternating harmonic sequence and the value of the series until it converges to values that vary by less than .001. Compare the result to the natural log of 2.

2. Describe the Input and Output
   Input The description of the alternating harmonic series

$$\sum_{k=1}^{\infty} \frac{(-1)^{k+1}}{k} = 1 - \frac{1}{2} + \frac{1}{3} - \frac{1}{4} + \frac{1}{5} - \cdots \frac{1}{\infty}$$

   Output The value of the truncated series, once the convergence criterion is met. Plot the cumulative sum of the series elements, up to the point where the convergence criterion is met.

3. Develop a Hand Example
   Let's calculate the value of the alternating harmonic series for 1 to 5 terms. First find the value for each of the first five terms in the sequence

   1.0000 −0.5000 0.3333 −0.2500 0.2000

   Now calculate the sum of the series assuming 1 to 5 terms

   1.0000 0.5000 0.8333 0.5833 0.7833

   The calculated sums are getting closer together, as we can see if we find the difference between adjacent pairs

   −0.5000 0.3333 −0.2500 0.2000

4. Develop a MATLAB Solution
   First develop a flowchart (Figure 22.12) to help you plan your code, then convert it to a MATLAB program. When we run the program, the following results are displayed in the command window.

```
The sequence converges when the final element is equal
 to  0.001
At which point the value of the series is 0.6936
This compares to the value of the ln(2), 0.6931
The sequence took 1002 terms to converge
```

   The series is pretty close to the ln(2), but perhaps we could get closer with more terms. If we change the convergence criterion to 0.0001 and run the program, we get the following results.

```
The sequence converges when the final element is equal
 to  -0.000
At which point the value of the series is 0.6931
This compares to the value of the ln(2), 0.6931
The sequence took 10001 terms to converge
```

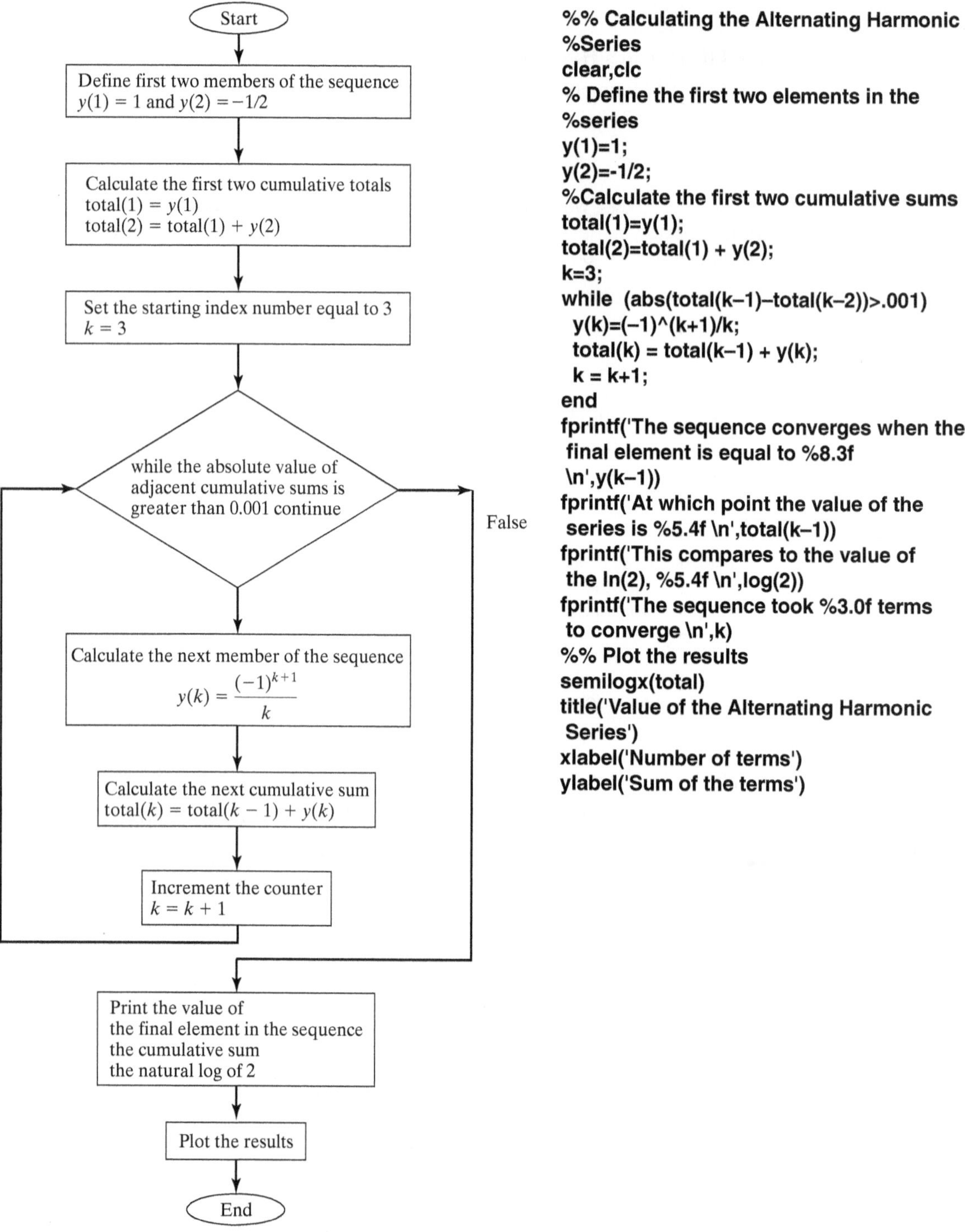


```
%% Calculating the Alternating Harmonic
%Series
clear,clc
% Define the first two elements in the
%series
y(1)=1;
y(2)=-1/2;
%Calculate the first two cumulative sums
total(1)=y(1);
total(2)=total(1) + y(2);
k=3;
while (abs(total(k-1)-total(k-2))>.001)
  y(k)=(-1)^(k+1)/k;
  total(k) = total(k-1) + y(k);
  k = k+1;
end
fprintf('The sequence converges when the
 final element is equal to %8.3f
 \n',y(k-1))
fprintf('At which point the value of the
 series is %5.4f \n',total(k-1))
fprintf('This compares to the value of
 the ln(2), %5.4f \n',log(2))
fprintf('The sequence took %3.0f terms
 to converge \n',k)
%% Plot the results
semilogx(total)
title('Value of the Alternating Harmonic
 Series')
xlabel('Number of terms')
ylabel('Sum of the terms')
```

Figure 22.12 Flowchart to evaluate the alternating harmonic series until it converges.

5. Test the Solution
   Compare the result of the hand solution to the MATLAB solution, by examining the graph (Figure 22.13). The first five values for the series match those displayed in the graph. We can also see that the series seems to be converging to approximately 0.69, which is approximately the natural log of 2.

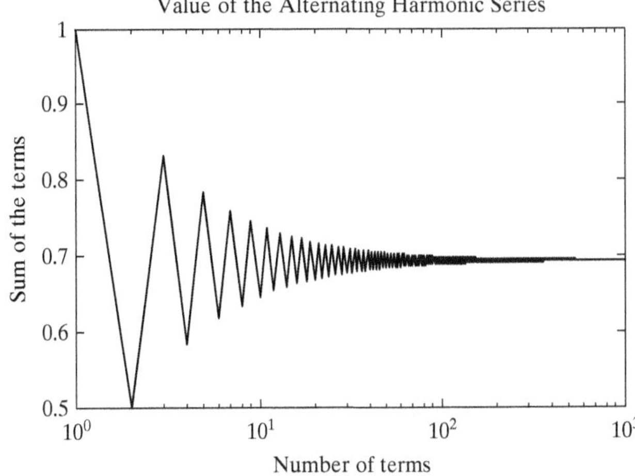

Figure 22.13 The alternating harmonic series converges to the ln(2)

In-Class Activity

ICA 22-3

Use a **while** loop to solve the following problems:

1. Create a table that converts inches to feet.
2. Consider the following matrix of values:

$$x = [45, 23, 17, 34, 85, 33]$$

   How many values are greater than 30? (Use a counter.)
3. Repeat Exercise 2, this time using the **find** command.
4. Use a **while** loop to sum the elements of the matrix in Exercise 1. Check your results with the **sum** function. (Use the **help** feature if you don't know or remember how to use **sum**.)
5. Use a **while** loop to create a vector containing the first 10 elements in the harmonic series, i.e.,

   1/1 1/2 1/3 1/4 1/5 .. .. 1/10

6. Use a **while** loop to create a vector containing the first 10 elements in the alternating harmonic series—i.e.,

   1/1 −1/2 1/3 −1/4 1/5 .. .. −1/10

SUMMARY

Sections of computer code can be categorized as sequences, selection structures, and repetition structures. Sequences are lists of instructions that are executed in order. Selection structures allow the programmer to define criteria (conditional statements) that the program uses to choose execution paths. Repetition structures define loops in which a sequence of instructions is repeated until some criterion is met (also defined by conditional statements).

MATLAB uses the standard mathematical relational operators, such as greater than (>) and less than (<). The not-equal-to (~=) operator's form is not usually seen in mathematics texts. MATLAB also includes logical operators such as *and* (&) and *or* (|). These operators are used in conditional statements, allowing MATLAB to make decisions regarding which portions of the code to execute.

The **find** command is unique to MATLAB and should be the primary conditional function used in your programming. This command allows the user to specify a condition by using both logical and relational operators. The command is then used to identify elements of a matrix that meet the condition.

Although the **if**, **else**, and **elseif** commands can be used for both scalars and matrix variables, they are useful primarily for scalars. These commands allow the programmer to identify alternative computing paths on the basis of the results of conditional statements.

For loops are used mainly when the programmer knows how many times a sequence of commands should be executed. **While** loops are used when the commands should be executed until a condition is met. Most problems can be structured so that either **for** or **while** loops are appropriate.

The **break** and **continue** statements are used to exit a loop prematurely. They are usually used in conjunction with **if** statements. The **break** command causes a jump out of a loop and execution of the remainder of the program. The **continue** command skips execution of the current pass through a loop, but allows the loop to continue until the completion criterion is met.

Vectorization of MATLAB code allows it to execute much more efficiently and therefore more quickly. Loops in particular should be avoided in MATLAB. When loops are unavoidable, they can be improved by defining "dummy" variables with placeholder values, such as ones or zeros. These placeholders can then be replaced in the loop. Doing this will result in significant improvements in execution time, a fact that can be confirmed with timing experiments.

The **clock** and **etime** functions are used to poll the computer clock and then determine the time required to execute pieces of code. The time calculated is the "elapsed" time. During this time, the computer not only has been running MATLAB code, but also has been executing background jobs and housekeeping functions. The **tic** and **toc** functions perform a similar task. Either **tic/toc** or **clock/etime** functions can be used to compare execution time for different code options.

MATLAB SUMMARY

The following MATLAB summary lists and briefly describes all of the special characters, commands, and functions that were defined in this chapter:

Special Characters	
<	less than
<=	less than or equal to
>	greater than
>=	greater than or equal to
==	equal to
~=	not equal to
&	and
|	or
~	not

Commands and Functions	
all	checks to see if a criterion is met by all the elements in an array
any	checks to see if a criterion is met by any of the elements in an array
break	causes the execution of a loop to be terminated
case	sorts responses
clock	determines the current time on the CPU clock
continue	terminates the current pass through a loop, but proceeds to the next pass
else	defines the path if the result of an if statement is false
elseif	defines the path if the result of an if statement is false, and specifies a new logical test
end	identifies the end of a control structure
etime	finds elapsed time
find	determines which elements in a matrix meet the input criterion
for	generates a loop structure
	(Continued)

Commands and Functions (*Continued*)	
if	checks a condition, resulting in either true or false
menu	creates a menu to use as an input vehicle
ones	creates a matrix of ones
otherwise	part of the case selection structure
switch	part of the case selection structure
tic	starts a timing sequence
toc	stops a timing sequence
while	generates a loop structure

KEY TERMS

control structure
index
local variable
logical condition
logical operator
loop
relational operator
repetition
selection
sequence
subscript

EXERCISES AND ACTIVITIES

Logical Operators: Find

22.1 A sensor that monitors the temperature of a backyard hot tub records the data shown in Table 22.4.

(a) The temperature should never exceed 105°F. Use the **find** function to find the index numbers of the temperatures that exceed the maximum allowable temperature.
(b) Use the **length** function with the results from part (a) to determine how many times the maximum allowable temperature was exceeded.
(c) Determine at what times the temperature exceeded the maximum allowable temperature, using the index numbers found in part (a).
(d) The temperature should never be lower than 102°F. Use the **find** function together with the **length** function to determine how many times the temperature was less than the minimum allowable temperature.
(e) Determine at what times the temperature was less than the minimum allowable temperature.
(f) Determine at what times the temperature was within the allowable limits (i.e., between 102°F and 105°F, inclusive).
(g) Use the **max** function to determine the maximum temperature reached and the time at which it occurred.

22.2 The height of a rocket (in meters) can be represented by the following equation:

$$\text{height} = 2.13t^2 - 0.0013t^4 + 0.000034t^{4.751}$$

Table 22.4 Hot-Tub Temperature Data

Time of Day	Temperature, °F	Time of Day	Temperature, °F
0:00 A.M.	100	1:00 P.M.	103
1:00 A.M.	101	2:00 P.M.	101
2:00 A.M.	102	3:00 P.M.	100
3:00 A.M.	103	4:00 P.M.	99
4:00 A.M.	103	5:00 P.M.	100
5:00 A.M.	104	6:00 P.M.	102
6:00 A.M.	104	7:00 P.M.	104
7:00 A.M.	105	8:00 P.M.	106
8:00 A.M.	106	9:00 P.M.	107
9:00 A.M.	106	10:00 P.M.	105
10:00 A.M.	106	11:00 P.M.	104
11:00 A.M.	105	12:00 A.M.	104
12:00 P.M.	104		

Create a vector of time (t) values from 0 to 100 at 2-second intervals.

(a) Use the **find** function to determine when the rocket hits the ground to within 2 seconds. (*Hint:* The value of **height** will be positive for all values until the rocket hits the ground.)

(b) Use the **max** function to determine the maximum height of the rocket and the corresponding time.

(c) Create a plot with t on the horizontal axis and height on the vertical axis for times until the rocket hits the ground. Be sure to add a title and axis labels.*

Figure P22.3 Solid-fuel rocket booster to a Titan missile. (Courtesy of NASA.)

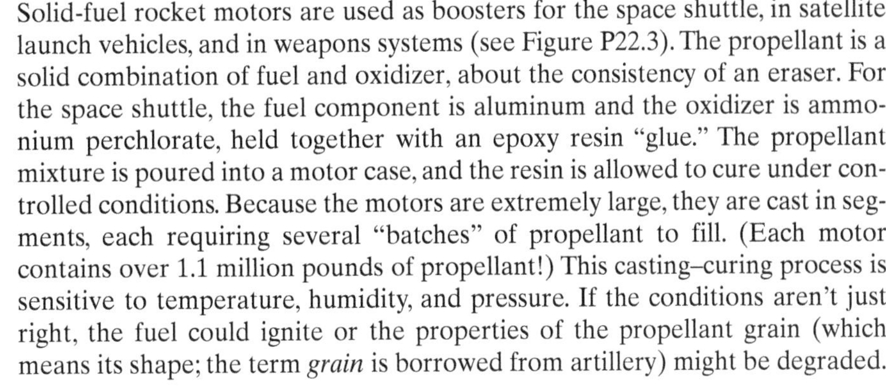

22.3 Solid-fuel rocket motors are used as boosters for the space shuttle, in satellite launch vehicles, and in weapons systems (see Figure P22.3). The propellant is a solid combination of fuel and oxidizer, about the consistency of an eraser. For the space shuttle, the fuel component is aluminum and the oxidizer is ammonium perchlorate, held together with an epoxy resin "glue." The propellant mixture is poured into a motor case, and the resin is allowed to cure under controlled conditions. Because the motors are extremely large, they are cast in segments, each requiring several "batches" of propellant to fill. (Each motor contains over 1.1 million pounds of propellant!) This casting–curing process is sensitive to temperature, humidity, and pressure. If the conditions aren't just right, the fuel could ignite or the properties of the propellant grain (which means its shape; the term *grain* is borrowed from artillery) might be degraded.

*From Etter, Kancicky, and Moore, *Introduction to Matlab 7* (Upper Saddle River, NJ: Pearson/Prentice Hall, 2005).

Table 22.5 Casting–Curing Data

Batch Number	Temperature, °F	Humidity, %	Pressure, torr
1	116	45	110
2	114	42	115
3	118	41	120
4	124	38	95
5	126	61	118

Solid-fuel rocket motors are extremely expensive as well as dangerous and clearly must work right every time, or the results will be disastrous. Failures can cause loss of human life and irreplaceable scientific data and equipment. Highly public failures can destroy a company. Actual processes are tightly monitored and controlled. However, for our purposes, consider these general criteria:

The temperature should remain between 115°F and 125°F.
The humidity should remain between 40% and 60%.
The pressure should remain between 100 and 200 torr.

Imagine that the data in Table 22.5 were collected during a casting–curing process.

(a) Use the **find** command to determine which batches did and did not meet the criterion for temperature.
(b) Use the **find** command to determine which batches did and did not meet the criterion for humidity.
(c) Use the **find** command to determine which batches did and did not meet the criterion for pressure.
(d) Use the **find** command to determine which batches failed for any reason and which passed.
(e) Use your results from the previous questions, along with the **length** command, to determine what percentage of motors passed or failed on the basis of each criterion and to determine the total passing rate.

22.4 Two gymnasts are competing with each other. Their scores are shown in Table 22.6.

(a) Write a program that uses **find** to determine how many events each gymnast won.
(b) Use the **mean** function to determine each gymnast's average score.

Table 22.6 Gymnastics Scores

Event	Gymnast 1	Gymnast 2
Pommel horse	9.821	9.700
Vault	9.923	9.925
Floor	9.624	9.83
Rings	9.432	9.987
High bar	9.534	9.354
Parallel bars	9.203	9.879

22.5 Create a function called **f** that satisfies the following criteria:

$$\text{For values of } x > 2, f(x) = x^2$$
$$\text{For values of } x \leq 2, f(x) = 2x$$

Plot your results for values of x from –3 to 5. Choose your spacing to create a smooth curve. You should notice a break in the curve at $x = 2$.

22.6 Create a function called g that satisfies the following criteria:

$$\text{For } x < -\pi, \quad g(x) = -1$$
$$\text{For } x \geq -\pi \text{ and } x \leq \pi, \quad g(x) = \cos(x)$$
$$\text{For } x > \pi, \quad g(x) = -1$$

Plot your results for values of x from -2π to $+2\pi$. Choose your spacing to create a smooth curve.

22.7 A file named **temp.dat** contains information collected from a set of thermocouples. The data in the file are shown in Table 22.7. The first column consists of time measurements (one for each hour of the day), and the remaining

Table 22.7 Temperature Data

Hour	Temp1	Temp2	Temp3
1	68.70	58.11	87.81
2	65.00	58.52	85.69
3	70.38	52.62	71.78
4	70.86	58.83	77.34
5	66.56	60.59	68.12
6	73.57	61.57	57.98
7	73.57	67.22	89.86
8	69.89	58.25	74.81
9	70.98	63.12	83.27
10	70.52	64.00	82.34
11	69.44	64.70	80.21
12	72.18	55.04	69.96
13	68.24	61.06	70.53
14	76.55	61.19	76.26
15	69.59	54.96	68.14
16	70.34	56.29	69.44
17	73.20	65.41	94.72
18	70.18	59.34	80.56
19	69.71	61.95	67.83
20	67.50	60.44	79.59
21	70.88	56.82	68.72
22	65.99	57.20	66.51
23	72.14	62.22	77.39
24	74.87	55.25	89.53

Figure P22.8 Glen Canyon Dam at Lake Powell. (Courtesy of Getty Images, Inc.)

columns correspond to temperature measurements at different points in a process.

(a) Write a program that prints the index numbers (rows and columns) of temperature data values greater than 85.0. (*Hint*: You'll need to use the **find** command.)

(b) Find the index numbers (rows and columns) of temperature data values less than 65.0.

(c) Find the maximum temperature in the file and the corresponding hour value and thermocouple number.

22.8 The Colorado River Drainage Basin covers parts of seven western states. A series of dams has been constructed on the Colorado River and its tributaries to store runoff water and to generate low-cost hydroelectric power. (See Figure P22.8.) The ability to regulate the flow of water has made the growth of agriculture and population in these arid desert states possible. Even during periods of extended drought, a steady, reliable source of water and electricity has been available to the basin states. Lake Powell is one of these reservoirs. The file **lake_powell.dat** contains data on the water level in the reservoir for the eight years from 2000 to 2007. These data are shown in Table 22.8. Use the data in the file to answer the following questions:

(a) Determine the average elevation of the water level for each year and for the eight-year period over which the data were collected.

(b) Determine how many months each year exceed the overall average for the eight-year period.

(c) Create a report that lists the month and the year for each of the months that exceed the overall average.

(d) Determine the average elevation of the water for each month for the eight-year period.

If Structures

22.9 Create a program that prompts the user to enter a scalar value of temperature. If the temperature is greater than 98.6°F, send a message to the command window telling the user that he or she has a fever.

22.10 Create a program that first prompts the user to enter a value for **x** and then prompts the user to enter a value for **y**. If the value of **x** is greater than the

Table 22.8 Water-Level Data for Lake Powell, Measured in Feet above Sea Level

	2000	2001	2002	2003	2004	2005	2006	2007
January	3680.12	3668.05	3654.25	3617.61	3594.38	3563.41	3596.26	3601.41
February	3678.48	3665.02	3651.01	3613	3589.11	3560.35	3591.94	3598.63
March	3677.23	3663.35	3648.63	3608.95	3584.49	3557.42	3589.22	3597.85
April	3676.44	3662.56	3646.79	3605.92	3583.02	3557.52	3589.94	3599.75
May	3676.76	3665.27	3644.88	3606.11	3584.7	3571.60	3598.27	3604.68
June	3682.19	3672.19	3642.98	3615.39	3587.01	3598.06	3609.36	3610.94
July	3682.86	3671.37	3637.53	3613.64	3583.07	3607.73	3608.79	3609.47
August	3681.12	3667.81	3630.83	3607.32	3575.85	3604.96	3604.93	3605.56
September	3678.7	3665.45	3627.1	3604.11	3571.07	3602.20	3602.08	3602.27
October	3676.96	3663.47	3625.59	3602.92	3570.7	3602.31	3606.12	3601.27
November	3674.93	3661.25	3623.98	3601.24	3569.69	3602.65	3607.46	3599.71
December	3671.59	3658.07	3621.65	3598.82	3565.73	3600.14	3604.96	3596.79

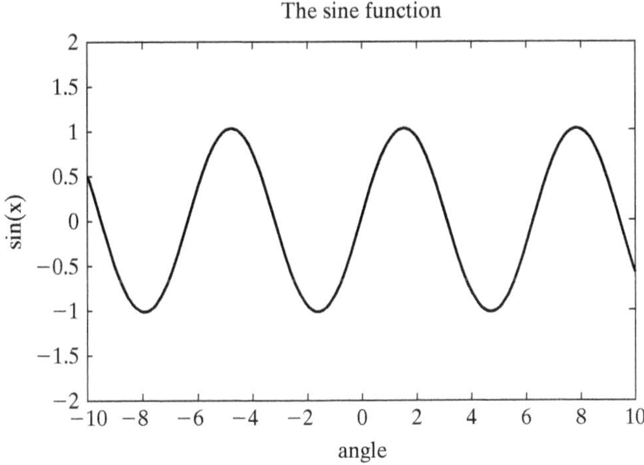

Figure P22.11 The sine function varies between −1 and +1. Thus, the inverse sine (**asin**) is not defined for values greater than 1 and values less than −1.

value of **y**, send a message to the command window telling the user that **x > y**. If **x** is less than or equal to **y**, send a message to the command window telling the user that **y > = x**.

22.11 The inverse sine (**asin**) and inverse cosine (**acos**) functions are valid only for inputs between –1 and +1 because both the sine and the cosine have values only between –1 and +1 (Figure P22.11). MATLAB interprets the result of **asin** or **acos** for a value outside the range as a complex number. For example, we might have

```
acos(-2)
ans =
 3.1416 - 1.3170i
```

which is a questionable mathematical result. Create a function called **my_asin** that accepts a single value of **x** and checks to see if it is between –1 and +1 (**−1 < = x < = 1**). If **x** is outside the range, send an error message to the screen. If it is inside the allowable range, return the value of **asin**.

22.12 Create a program that prompts the user to enter a scalar value for the outside air temperature. If the temperature is equal to or above 80°F, send a message to the command window telling the user to wear shorts. If the temperature is between 60°F and 80°F send a message to the command window telling the user that it is a beautiful day. If the temperature is equal to or below 60°F, send a message to the command window telling the user to wear a jacket or coat.

22.13 Suppose the following matrix represents the number of saws ordered from your company each month over the last year.

```
saws = [1,4,5,3,7,5,3,10,12,8, 7, 4]
```

All the numbers should be zero or positive.

(a) Use an **if** statement to check whether any of the values in the matrix are invalid. (Evaluate the whole matrix at once in a single **if** statement.) Send the message "All valid" or else "Invalid number found" to the screen, depending on the results of your analysis.

(b) Change the **saws** matrix to include at least one negative number, and check your program to make sure that it works for both cases.

22.14 Most large companies encourage employees to save by matching their contributions to a 401(k) plan. The government limits how much you can save in these plans, because they shelter income from taxes until the money is withdrawn during your retirement. The amount you can save is tied to your income, as is the amount your employer can contribute. The government will allow you to save additional amounts without the tax benefit. These plans change from year to year, so this example is just a made-up "what if."

Suppose the Quality Widget Company has the savings plan described in Table 22.9. Create a function that finds the total yearly contribution to your savings plan, based on your salary and the percentage you contribute. Remember, the total contribution consists of the employee contribution and the company contribution.

Table 22.9 Quality Widget Company Savings Plan

Income	Maximum You Can Save Tax Free	Maximum the Company Will Match
Up to \$30,000	10%	10%
Between \$30,000 and \$60,000	10%	10% of the first \$30,000 and 5% of the amount above \$30,000
Between \$60,000 and \$100,000	10% of the first \$60,000 and 8% of the amount above \$60,000	10% of the first \$30,000 and 5% of the amount between \$30,000 and \$60,000; nothing for the remainder above \$60,000
Above \$100,000	10% of the first \$60,000 and 8% of the amount between \$60,000 and \$100,000; nothing on the amount above \$100,000	Nothing—highly compensated employees are exempt from this plan and participate in stock options instead

Switch/Case

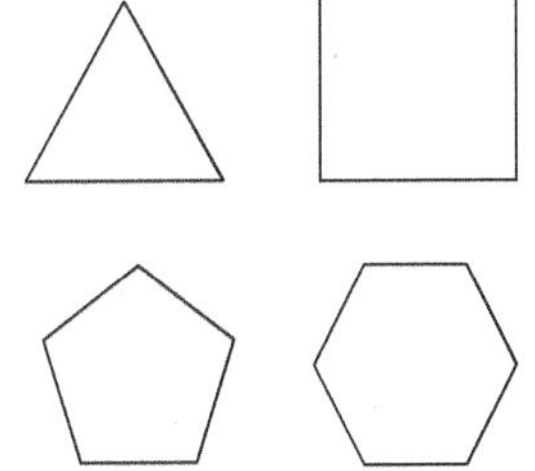

Figure P22.15 Regular polygons.

22.15 In order to have a closed geometric figure composed of straight lines (Figure P22.15), the angles in the figure must add to

$$(n - 2)(180 \text{ degrees})$$

where n is the number of sides.

(a) Prove this statement to yourself by creating a vector called n from 3 to 6 and calculating the angle sum from the formula. Compare what you know about geometry with your answer.

(b) Write a program that prompts the user to enter one of the following:

triangle
square
pentagon
hexagon

Use the input to define the value of n via a **switch/case** structure; then use n to calculate the sum of the interior angles in the figure.

(c) Reformulate your program from part (b) so that it uses a menu.

22.16 At the University of Utah, each engineering major requires a different number of credits for graduation. For example, in 2005 the requirements for some of the departments were as follows:

Civil Engineering	130
Chemical Engineering	130
Computer Engineering	122
Electrical Engineering	126.5
Mechanical Engineering	129

Prompt the user to select an engineering program from a menu. Use a **switch/case** structure to send the minimum number of credits required for graduation back to the command window.

22.17 The easiest way to draw a star in MATLAB is to use polar coordinates. You simply need to identify points on the circumference of a circle and draw lines between those points. For example, to draw a five-pointed star, start at the top of the circle ($\theta = \pi/2, r = 1$) and work counterclockwise (Figure P22.17).

Prompt the user to specify either a five-pointed or a six-pointed star, using a menu. Then create the star in a MATLAB figure window. Note that a six-pointed star is made of three triangles and requires a strategy different from that used to create a five-pointed star.

Repetition Structures: Loops

22.18 Use a **for** loop to sum the elements in the following vector:

$$x = [1, 23, 43, 72, 87, 56, 98, 33]$$

Check your answer with the **sum** function.

22.19 Repeat the previous problem, this time using a **while** loop.

22.20 Use a **for** loop to create a vector of the squares of the numbers 1 through 5.

22.21 Use a while loop to create a vector of the squares of the numbers 1 through 5.

22.22 Use the **primes** function to create a list of all the primes below 100. Now use a **for** loop to multiply adjacent values together. For example, the first 4 prime numbers are

$$2 \quad 3 \quad 5 \quad 7$$

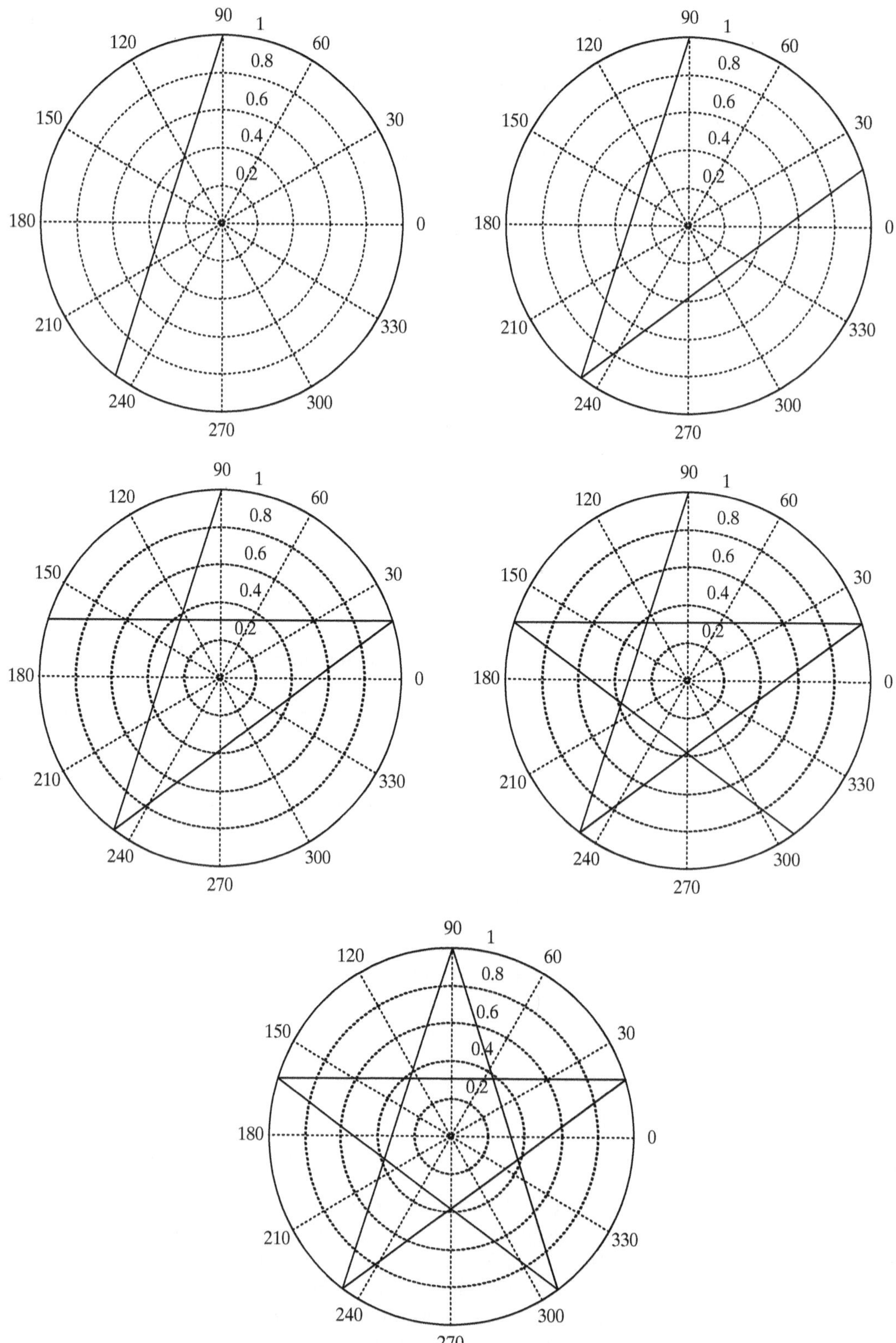

Figure P22.17 Steps required to draw a five-pointed star in polar coordinates.

Your calculation would be

2*3 3*5 5*7

which gives

6 15 35

Figure P22.23 Chambered nautilus. (Colin Keates © Dorling Kindersley, Courtesy of the Natural History Museum, London.)

22.23 A Fibonacci sequence is composed of elements created by adding the two previous elements. The simplest Fibonacci sequence starts with 1, 1 and proceeds as follows:

$$1, 1, 2, 3, 5, 8, 13, \ldots$$

However, a Fibonacci sequence can be created with any two starting numbers. Fibonacci sequences appear regularly in nature. For example, the shell of the chambered nautilus (Figure P22.23) grows in accordance with a Fibonacci sequence.

Prompt the user to enter the first two numbers in a Fibonacci sequence and the total number of elements requested for the sequence. Find the sequence and store it in an array by using a **for** loop. Now plot your results on a **polar** graph. Use the element number for the angle and the value of the element in the sequence for the radius.

22.24 Repeat the preceding problem, this time using a **while** loop.

22.25 One interesting property of a Fibonacci sequence is that the ratio of the values of adjacent members of the sequence approaches a number called "the golden ratio" or (phi). Create a program that accepts the first two numbers of a Fibonacci sequence as user input and then calculates additional values in the sequence until the ratio of adjacent values converges to within 0.001. You can do this in a **while** loop by comparing the ratio of element **k** to element **k – 1** and the ratio of element **k – 1** to element **k – 2**. If you call your sequence **x**, then the code for the **while** statement is

```
while abs(x(k)/x(k-1) – x(k-1)/x(k-2))>0.001
```

22.26 Recall from trigonometry that the tangent of both $\pi/2$ and $-\pi/2$ is infinity. This may be seen from the fact that

$$\tan(\theta) = \sin(\theta)/\cos(\theta)$$

and since

$$\sin(\pi/2) = 1$$

and

$$\cos(\pi/2) = 0$$

it follows that

$$\tan(\pi/2) = \text{infinity}$$

Because MATLAB uses a floating-point approximation of π, it calculates the tangent of $\pi/2$ as a very large number, but not infinity.

Prompt the user to enter an angle θ between $\pi/2$ and $-\pi/2$ inclusive. If it is between $\pi/2$ and $\pi/2$ but not equal to either of those values, calculate $\tan(\theta)$ and display the result in the command window. If it is equal to $\pi/2$ or $-\pi/2$ set the result equal to **Inf** and display the result in the command window. If it is outside the specified range, send the user an error message in the command window and prompt the user to enter another value. Continue prompting the user for a new value of theta until he or she enters a valid number.

22.27 Imagine that you are a proud new parent. You decide to start a college savings plan now for your child, hoping to have enough in 18 years to pay the sharply rising cost of an education. Suppose that your folks give you $1000 to get started and that each month you can contribute $100. Suppose also that the interest rate is 6% per year compounded monthly, which is equivalent to 0.5% each month.

Because of interest payments and your contribution, each month your balance will increase in accordance with the formula

New Balance = Old Balance + interest + you contribution

Use a **for** loop to find the amount in the savings account each month for the next 18 years. (Create a vector of values.) Plot the amount in the account as a function of time. (Plot time on the horizontal axis and dollars on the vertical axis.)

22.28 Imagine that you have a crystal ball and can predict the percentage increases in tuition for the next 22 years. The following vector **increase** shows your predictions, in percent, for each year:

```
increase = [10, 8, 10, 16, 15, 4, 6, 7, 8, 10, 8, 12, 14,
 15, 8, 7, 6, 5, 7, 8, 9, 8]
```

Use a **for** loop to determine the cost of a four-year education, assuming that the current cost for one year at a state school is $5000.

22.29 Use an **if** statement to compare your results from the previous two problems. Are you saving enough? Send an appropriate message to the command window.

22.30 **Faster Loops**. Whenever possible, it is better to avoid using **for** loops, because they are slow to execute.

(a) Generate a 100,000-item vector of random digits called **x**; square each element in this vector and name the result **y**; use the commands **tic** and **toc** to time the operation.

(b) Next, perform the same operation element by element in a **for** loop. Before you start, clear the values in your variables with

```
clear x y
```

Use **tic** and **toc** to time the operation.

Depending on how fast your computer runs, you may need to stop the calculations by issuing the **Ctrl c** command in the command window.

(c) Now convince yourself that suppressing the printing of intermediate answers will speed execution of the code by allowing these same operations to run and print the answers as they are calculated. You will almost undoubtedly need to cancel the execution of this loop because of the large amount of time it will take. Recall that Ctrl c terminates the program.

(d) If you are going to be using a constant value several times in a **for** loop, calculate it once and store it, rather than calculating it each time through the loop. Demonstrate the increase in speed of this process by adding **(sin(0.3) + cos(pi/3))*5!** to every value in the long vector in a **for** loop. (Recall that ! means factorial, which can be calculated with the MATLAB function **factorial**.)

(e) As discussed in this chapter, if MATLAB must increase the size of a vector every time through a loop, the process will take more time than if the vector were already the appropriate size. Demonstrate this fact by repeating part (b) of this problem. Create the following vector of **y**-values, in which every element is equal to zero before you enter the **for** loop:

```
y = zeros(1,100000);
```

You will be replacing the zeros one at a time as you repeat the calculations in the loop.

Challenge Problems

22.31 **(a)** Create a function called **polygon** that draws a polygon in a polar plot. Your function should have a single input parameter—the number of sides.

(b) Use a **for** loop to create a figure with four subplots, showing a triangle in the first subplot, a square in the second subplot, a pentagon in the third subplot and a hexagon in the fourth subplot. You should use the function you created in part (a) to draw each polygon. Use the index parameter from the **for** loop to specify the subplot in which each polygon is drawn, and in an expression to determine the number of sides used as input to the **polygon** function.

22.32 Most major airports have separate lots for long-term and short-term parking. The cost to park depends on the lot you select, and how long you stay. Consider this rate structure from the Salt Lake International Airport during the summer of 2008.

- Long-Term (Economy) Parking
  - The first hour is $1.00, and each additional hour or fraction thereof is $1.00
  - Daily maximum $6.00
  - Weekly maximum $42.00
- Short-Term Parking
  - The first 30 minutes are free and each additional 20 minutes or fraction thereof is $1.00
  - Daily maximum $25.00

Write a program that asks the user the following:

- Which lot are you using?
- How many weeks, hours, days and minutes did you park?

Your program should then calculate the parking bill.

CHAPTER 23
GRAPHICAL USER INTERFACES

Objectives

By learning the material in this chapter, you should be able to

- construct a GUI layout
- explain the purpose of the following GUI-related MATLAB functions and variables
  - Functions: get, set, guidata
  - Variable: handles
- write code to enable each component of the GUI layout to function appropriately

A graphical user interface (GUI) is a pictorial interface to a program. A good GUI can make programs easier to use by providing them with a consistent appearance, and with intuitive controls such as pushbuttons, edit boxes, list boxes, sliders, and menus. The GUI should behave in an understandable and predictable manner, so that a user knows what to expect when he or she performs an action. For example, when a mouse click occurs on a pushbutton, the GUI should initiate the action described on the label of the button.

This chapter contains an introduction to the basic elements of the MATLAB GUIs. It does not contain a complete description of components or GUI features, but it does provide us with the basics required to create functional GUIs for your programs.

23.1 HOW A GRAPHICAL USER INTERFACE WORKS

A graphical user interface provides the user with a familiar environment in which to work. It contains pushbuttons, toggle buttons, lists, menus, text boxes, and so forth, all of which are already familiar to the user, so that he or she can concentrate on the purpose of the application instead of the mechanics involved in doing things. However, GUIs are harder for the programmer, because a GUI-based program must be prepared for mouse clicks (or possibly keyboard input) for any GUI element at any time. Such inputs are known as **events,** and a program that responds to events is said to be *event driven.*

The three principal elements required to create a MATLAB Graphical User Interface are:

1. **Components.** Each item on a MATLAB GUI (e.g., pushbuttons, labels, edit boxes) is a graphical component. The types of components include graphical **controls** (pushbuttons, toggle buttons, edit boxes, lists, sliders, etc.) static elements (text boxes), **menus, toolbars,** and **axes.** Graphical controls and text boxes are

---

Taken from *MATLAB® Programming for Engineers,* Third Edition, by Stephen J. Chapman.

created by the function **uicontrol**, and menus are created by the functions **uimenu** and **uicontextmenu.** Toolbars are created by the function **uitoolbar**. Axes, which are used to display graphical data, are created by the function **axes**.

2. **Containers.** The components of a GUI must be arranged within a **container**, which is a window on the computer screen. The most common container is a **figure.** A figure is a window on the computer screen that has a title bar along the top, and that can optionally have menus attached. In the past, figures have been created automatically whenever we plotted data. However, empty figures can be created with the function **figure**, and they can be used to hold any combination of components and other containers.

   The other types of containers are **panels** (created by the function **uipanel**) and **button groups** (created by the function **uibutton-group**). Panels can contain components or other containers, but they do not have a title bar and cannot have menus attached. Button groups are special panels that can manage groups of radio buttons or toggle buttons to ensure that no more than one button in the group is on at any time.
3. **Callbacks.** Finally, there must be some way to perform an action if a user clicks a mouse on a button or types information on a keyboard. A mouse click or a key press is an **event,** and the MATLAB program must respond to each event if the program is to perform its function. For example, if a user clicks on a button, then that event must cause the MATLAB code that implements the function of the button to be executed. The code executed in response to an event is known as a **callback.** There must be a callback to implement the function of each graphical component on the GUI.

The basic GUI elements are summarized in Table 23.1, and some sample elements are shown in Figure 23.1 on page 642. We will study examples of these elements and then build working GUIs from them.

Table 23.1 Some Basic GUI Components

Component	Created By	Description
		Containers
Figure	**figure**	Creates a figure, which is a container that can hold components and other containers. Figures are separate windows that have title bars, and can have menus.
Panel	**uipanel**	Creates a panel, which is a container that can hold components and other containers. Unlike figures, panels do not have title bars or menus. Panels can be placed inside figures or other panels.
Button Group	**uibuttongroup**	Creates a button group, which is a special kind of panel. Button groups automatically manage groups of radio buttons or toggle buttons to ensure that only one item of the group is on at any given time.
		Graphical Controls
Pushbutton	**uicontrol**	A graphical component that implements a pushbutton. It triggers a callback when clicked with a mouse.
		(Continued)

Table 23.1 Some Basic GUI Components (*continued*)

Component	Created By	Description
Toggle Button	**uicontrol**	A graphical component that implements a toggle button. A toggle button is either "on" or "off," and it changes state each time that it is clicked. Each mouse button click also triggers a callback.
Radio Button	**uicontrol**	A radio button is a type of toggle button that appears as a small circle with a dot in the middle when it is "on." Groups of radio buttons are used to implement mutually exclusive choices. Each mouse click on a radio button triggers a callback.
Check Box	**uicontrol**	A checkbox is a type of toggle button that appears as a small square with a check mark in it when it is "on." Each mouse click on a check box triggers a callback.
Edit Box	**uicontrol**	An edit box displays a text string and allows the user to modify the information displayed. A callback is triggered when the user presses the **Enter** key, or when the user clicks in a different object with the mouse.
List Box	**uicontrol**	A list box is a graphical control that displays a series of text strings. A user may select one of the text strings by single- or double-clicking on them. A callback is triggered when the user selects a string.
Popup Menus	**uicontrol**	A popup menu is a graphical control that displays a series of text strings in response to a mouse click. When the popup menu is not clicked on, only the currently selected string is visible.
Slider	**uicontrol**	A slider is a graphical control to adjust a value in a smooth, continuous fashion by dragging the control with a mouse. Each slider change triggers a callback.
		Static Elements
Frame	**uicontrol**	Creates a frame, which is a rectangular box within a figure. Frames are used to group sets of controls together. Frames never trigger callbacks. (This is a deprecated component, which should not be used in new GUIs.)
Text Field	**uicontrol**	Creates a label, which is a text string located at a point on the figure. Text fields never trigger callbacks.
		Menus, Toolbars, Axes
Menu Items	**uimenu**	Creates a menu item. Menu items trigger a callback when a mouse button is released over them.
Context Menus	**uicontextmenu**	Creates a context menu, which is a menu that appears over a graphical object when a user right-clicks the mouse on that object.
Toolbar	**uitoolbar**	Creates a toolbar, which is a bar across the top of the figure containing quick-access buttons.
Toolbar Pushbutton	**uipushtool**	Creates a pushbutton to go in a toolbar.
Toolbar Toggle	**uitoggletool**	Creates a toggle button to go in a toolbar.
Button Axes	**axes**	Creates a new set of axes to display data on. Axes never trigger callbacks.

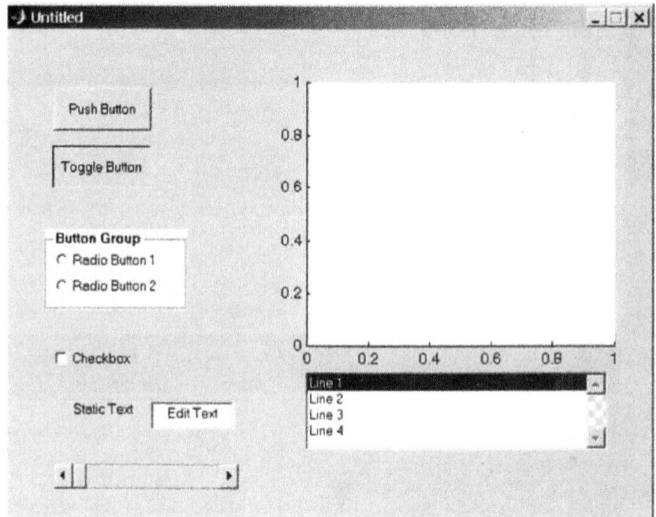

Figure 23.1 A Figure Window showing examples of MATLAB GUI elements. From top to bottom and left to right, the elements are: (1) a pushbutton; (2) a toggle button in the 'on' state; (3) two radio buttons within a button group; (4) a check box; (5) a label and an edit box; (6) a slider; (7) a set of axes; and (8) a list box.

23.2 CREATING AND DISPLAYING A GRAPHICAL USER INTERFACE

MATLAB graphical user interfaces are created using a tool called **guide**, the GUI Development Environment. This tool allows a programmer to lay out the GUI, selecting and aligning the GUI components to be placed in it. Once the components are in place, the programmer can edit their properties: name, color, size, font, text to display, and so forth. When **guide** saves the GUI, it creates a working program, including skeleton functions that the programmer can modify to implement the behavior of the GUI.

When **guide** is executed, it creates the Layout Editor, shown in Figure 23.2. The large gray area with grid lines is the *layout area*, where a programmer can lay out the GUI. The Layout Editor window has a palette of GUI components along the left-hand side of the layout area. A user can create any number of GUI components by first clicking on the desired component and then dragging its outline in the layout area. The top of the window has a toolbar with a series of useful tools that allow the user to distribute and align GUI components, modify the properties of GUI components, and add menus to GUIs, among other things.

The basic steps required to create a MATLAB GUI are:

1. Decide what elements are required for the GUI and what the function of each element will be. Make a rough layout of the components by hand on a piece of paper.
2. Use the MATLAB tool called **guide** (GUI Development Environment) to lay out the components on a figure. The size of the figure as well as the alignment and spacing of components on the figure can be adjusted using the tools built into **guide**.
3. Use a MATLAB tool called the Property Inspector (built into **guide**) to give each component a name (a "tag") and to set the characteristics of each component, such as its color or the text it displays.

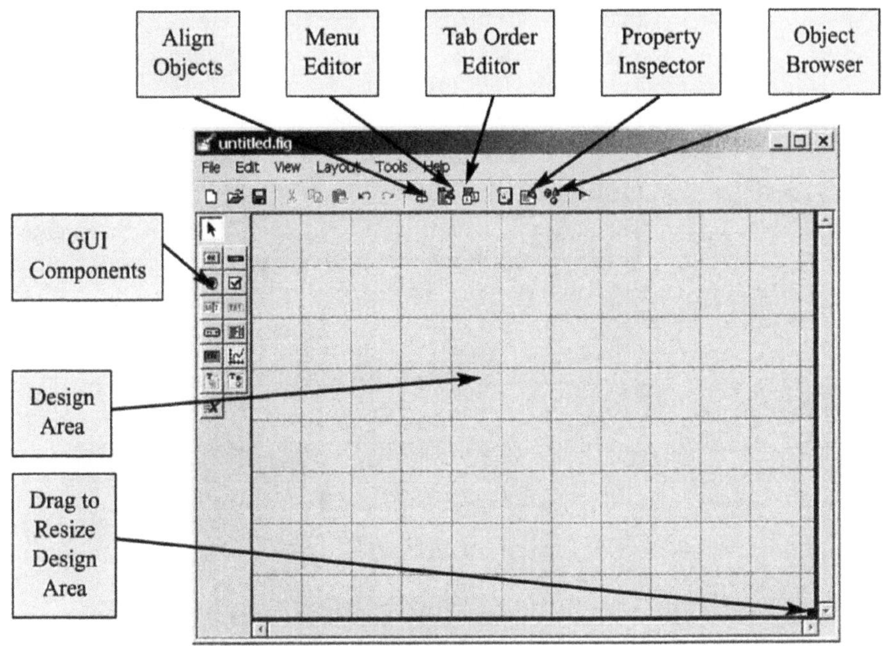

Figure 23.2 The **guide** tool window.

4. Save the figure to a file. When the figure is saved, two files will be created on disk with the same name but different extents. The **fig** file contains the GUI layout and the components of the GUI; the M-file contains the code to load the figure along with skeleton callback functions for each GUI element.
5. Write code to implement the behavior associated with each callback function.

As an example of this stepwise procedure, let's consider a simple GUI that contains a single pushbutton and a single text string. Each time that the pushbutton is clicked, the text string will be updated to show the total number of clicks since the GUI started.

Step 1: The design of this GUI is very simple. It contains a single pushbutton and a single text field. The callback from the pushbutton will cause the number displayed in the text field to increase by one each time that the button is pressed. A rough sketch of the GUI is shown in Figure 23.3.

Step 2: To lay out the components on the GUI, run the MATLAB function **guide**. When **guide** is executed, it creates the window shown in Figure 23.2.

First, we must set the size of the layout area, which will become the size of the final GUI. We do this by dragging the small square on the lower right-hand corner of the layout area until it has the desired size and shape. Then, click on the "pushbutton" button in the list of GUI components and create the shape of the pushbutton in the layout area. Finally, click on the "text" button in the list of GUI components and create the shape of the text field in the layout area. The resulting figure after these steps is shown in Figure 23.4. We could now adjust the alignment of these two elements using the Alignment Tool, if desired.

Step 3: To set the properties of the pushbutton, click on the button in the layout area and then select "Property Inspector" ( ) from the toolbar. Alternatively, right-click on the button and select "Property Inspector" from the popup menu. The Property Inspector window shown in Figure 23.5 will appear. Note that this window lists every property available for the pushbutton and allows us to set each value using a

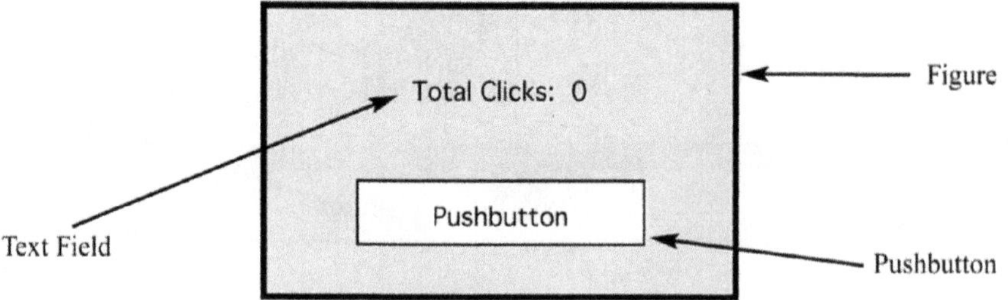

Figure 23.3 Rough layout for a GUI containing a single pushbutton and a single label field.

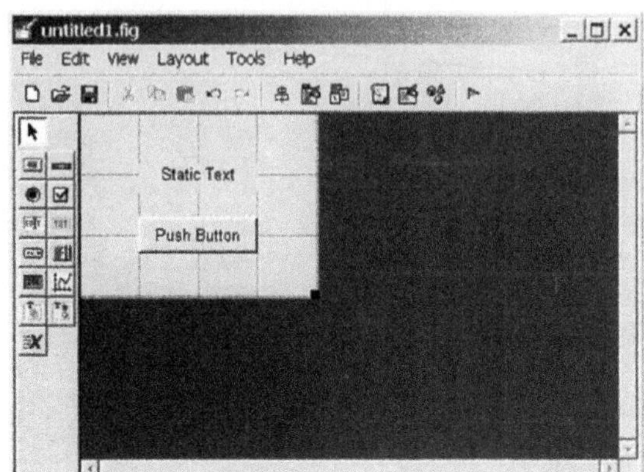

Figure 23.4 The completed GUI layout within the **guide** window.

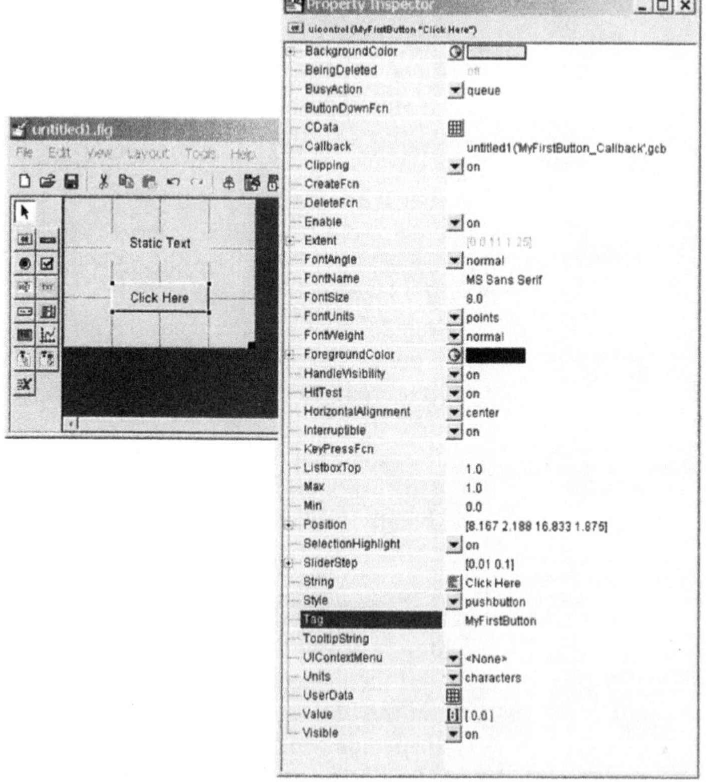

Figure 23.5 The Property Inspector showing the properties of the pushbutton. Note that the String is set to '**Click Here**', and the Tag is set to '**MyFirstButton**'.

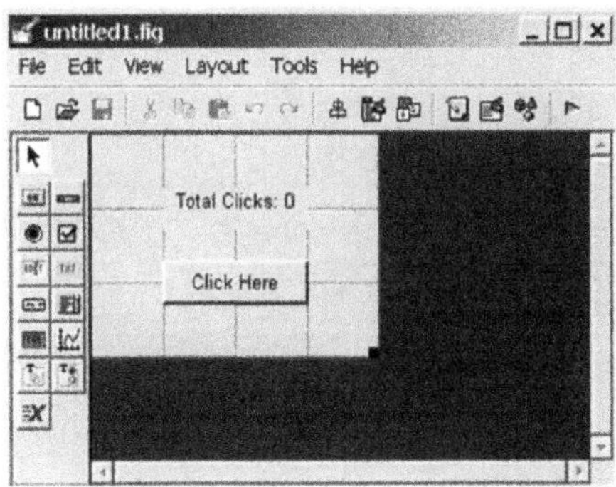

Figure 23.6 The design area after the properties of the pushbutton and the text field have been modified.

GUI interface. The Property Inspector performs the same function as the **get** and **set** functions, but in a much more convenient form.

For the pushbutton, we may set many properties such as color, size, font, and text alignment. However, we *must* set two properties: the **String** property, which contains the text to be displayed, and the **Tag** property, which is the name of the pushbutton. In this case, the **String** property will be set to **'Click Here'**, and the **Tag** property will be set to **MyFirstButton.**

For the text field, we *must* set two properties: the **String** property, which contains the text to be displayed, and the **Tag** property, which is the name of the text field. This name will be needed by the callback function to locate and update the text field. In this case, the **String** property will be set to **'Total Clicks: 0'**, and the Tag property defaulted to **'MyFirstText'**. The layout area after these steps is shown in Figure 23.6.

It is possible to set the properties of the figure itself by clicking on a clear spot in the Layout Editor, and using the Property Inspector to examine and set the figure's properties. Although not required, it is a good idea to set the figure's Name property. The string in the Name property will be displayed in the title bar of the resulting GUI when it is executed. In this program, we will set the **Name** to **'MyFirstGUI'.**

Step 4: We will now save the layout area under the name **MyFirstGUI**. Select the "File/Save As" menu item, type the name **MyFirstGUI** as the file name, and click "Save". This action will automatically create two files—**MyFirstGUI.fig** and **MyFirstGUI.m**. The figure file contains the actual GUI that we have created. The M-file contains code that loads the figure file and creates the GUI, plus a skeleton callback function for each active GUI component.

At this point, we have a complete GUI, but one that does not yet do the job it was designed to do. You can start this GUI by typing **MyFirstGUI** in the Command Window, as shown in Figure 23.7. If the button is clicked on this GUI, nothing happens.

A portion of the M-file automatically created by **guide** is shown in Figure 23.8. This file contains the main function **MyFirstGUI**, plus sub-functions to specify the behavior of the active GUI components. The file contains a *dummy callback function for every active GUI component* that you defined. In this case, the only active GUI component was the pushbutton, so there is a callback function called **MyFirstButton_Callback,** which is executed when the user clicks on the button.

If function **MyFirstGUI** is called *without* arguments, then the function displays the GUI contained in file **MyFirstGUI.fig.** If function **MyFirstGUI** is called *with* arguments, then the function assumes that the first argument is the name of a subfunction, and it calls that subfunction using **feval,** passing the other arguments on to that subfunction.

Each callback function handles events from a single GUI component. If a mouse click (or keyboard input for edit fields) occurs on the GUI component, then the

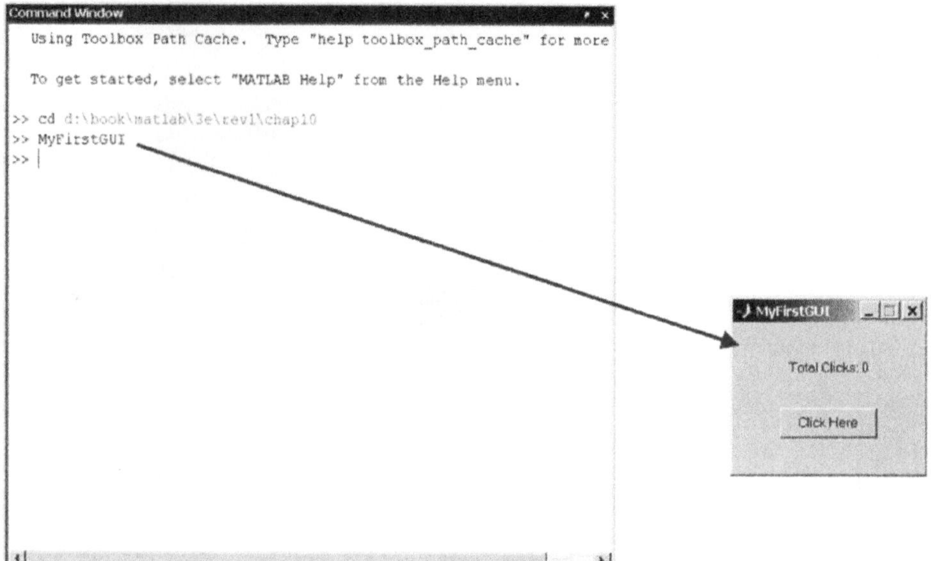

Figure 23.7 Typing **MyFirstGUI** in the Command Window starts the GUI.

component's callback function will be automatically called by MATLAB. The name of the callback function will be the value in the Tag property of the GUI component plus the characters "**_Callback.**" Thus, the callback function for **MyFirstButton** will be named **MyFirstButton_Callback.**

M-files created by **guide** contain callbacks for each active GUI component, but these callbacks don't do anything yet.

Step 5: Now, we need to write the callback subfunction code for the pushbutton. This function will include a **persistent** variable that can be used to count the number of clicks that have occurred. When a click occurs on the pushbutton, MATLAB will call the function **MyFirstGUI** with **MyFirstButton_Callback** as the first argument. Then function **MyFirstGUI** will call subfunction **MyFirstButton_Callback,** as shown in Figure 23.9. This function should increase the count of clicks by one, create a new text string containing the count, and store the new string in the **String** property of the text field **MyFirstText.** A function to perform this step is shown below:

```
Function MyFirstButton_Callback(hObject, eventdata, handles)
% hObject        handle to MyFirstButton (see GCBO)
% eventdata      reserved – to be defined in a future version of MATLAB
% handles        structure with handles and user data (see GUIDATA)

%Declare and initialize variable to store the count
persistent count
if isempty(count)
        count = 0;
end

%Update count
count = count + 1;

% Create new string
str = sprintf('Total Clicks : %d',count);

% Update the text field
set (handles.MyFirstText,'String',str);
```

```
function varargout = MyFirstGUI(varargin)
% MYFIRSTGUI M-file for MyFirstGUI.fig
%      MYFIRSTGUI, by itself, creates a new MYFIRSTGUI or raises the existing
%      singleton*.
%
%      H = MYFIRSTGUI returns the handle to a new MYFIRSTGUI or the handle to
%      the existing singleton*.
%
%      MYFIRSTGUI('CALLBACK',hObject,eventData,handles,...) calls the local
%      function named CALLBACK in MYFIRSTGUI.M with the given input arguments.
%
%      MYFIRSTGUI('Property','Value',...) creates a new MYFIRSTGUI or raises the
%      existing singleton*.  Starting from the left, property value pairs are
%      applied to the GUI before MyFirstGUI_OpeningFunction gets called.  An
%      unrecognized property name or invalid value makes property application
%      stop.  All inputs are passed to MyFirstGUI_OpeningFcn via varargin.
%
%      *See GUI Options on GUIDE's Tools menu.  Choose "GUI allows only one
%      instance to run (singleton)".
%
% See also: GUIDE, GUIDATA, GUIHANDLES

% Edit the above text to modify the response to help MyFirstGUI

% Last Modified by GUIDE v2.5 21-Feb-2004 16:17:45

% Begin initialization code - DO NOT EDIT
gui_Singleton = 1;
gui_State = struct('gui_Name',       mfilename, ...
                   'gui_Singleton',  gui_Singleton, ...
                   'gui_OpeningFcn', @MyFirstGUI_OpeningFcn, ...
                   'gui_OutputFcn',  @MyFirstGUI_OutputFcn, ...
                   'gui_LayoutFcn',  [] , ...
                   'gui_Callback',   []);
if nargin & isstr(varargin{1})
    gui_State.gui_Callback = str2func(varargin{1});
end

if nargout
    [varargout{1:nargout}] = gui_mainfcn(gui_State, varargin{:});
else
    gui_mainfcn(gui_State, varargin{:});
end
% End initialization code - DO NOT EDIT


% --- Executes just before MyFirstGUI is made visible.
function MyFirstGUI_OpeningFcn(hObject, eventdata, handles, varargin)
% This function has no output args, see OutputFcn.
% hObject    handle to figure
% eventdata  reserved - to be defined in a future version of MATLAB
% handles    structure with handles and user data (see GUIDATA)
% varargin   command line arguments to MyFirstGUI (see VARARGIN)

% Choose default command line output for MyFirstGUI
handles.output = hObject;

% Update handles structure
guidata(hObject, handles);
```

Main Function

Figure Opening Function

Figure 23.8 The M-file for **MyFirstGUI**, automatically created by **guide**.

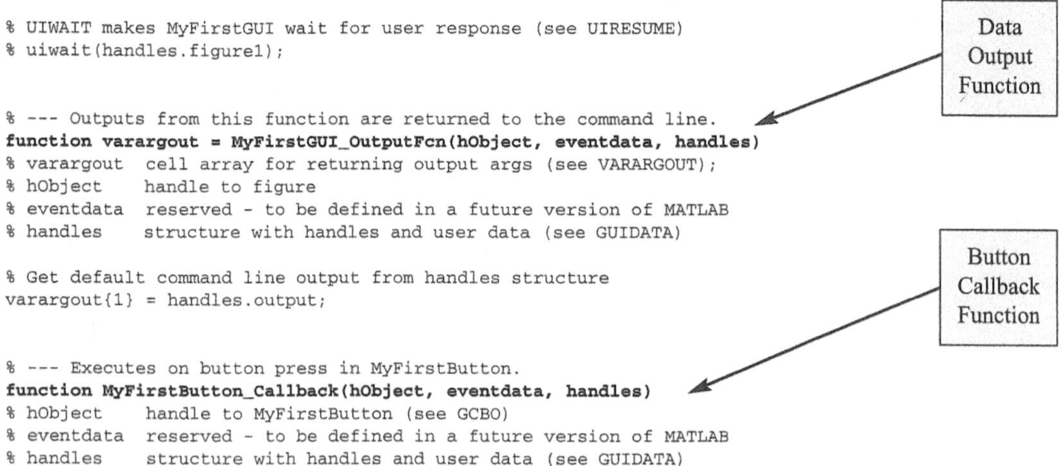

```
% UIWAIT makes MyFirstGUI wait for user response (see UIRESUME)
% uiwait(handles.figure1);


% --- Outputs from this function are returned to the command line.
function varargout = MyFirstGUI_OutputFcn(hObject, eventdata, handles)
% varargout  cell array for returning output args (see VARARGOUT);
% hObject    handle to figure
% eventdata  reserved - to be defined in a future version of MATLAB
% handles    structure with handles and user data (see GUIDATA)

% Get default command line output from handles structure
varargout{1} = handles.output;


% --- Executes on button press in MyFirstButton.
function MyFirstButton_Callback(hObject, eventdata, handles)
% hObject    handle to MyFirstButton (see GCBO)
% eventdata  reserved - to be defined in a future version of MATLAB
% handles    structure with handles and user data (see GUIDATA)
```


Figure 23.8 *(continued)*

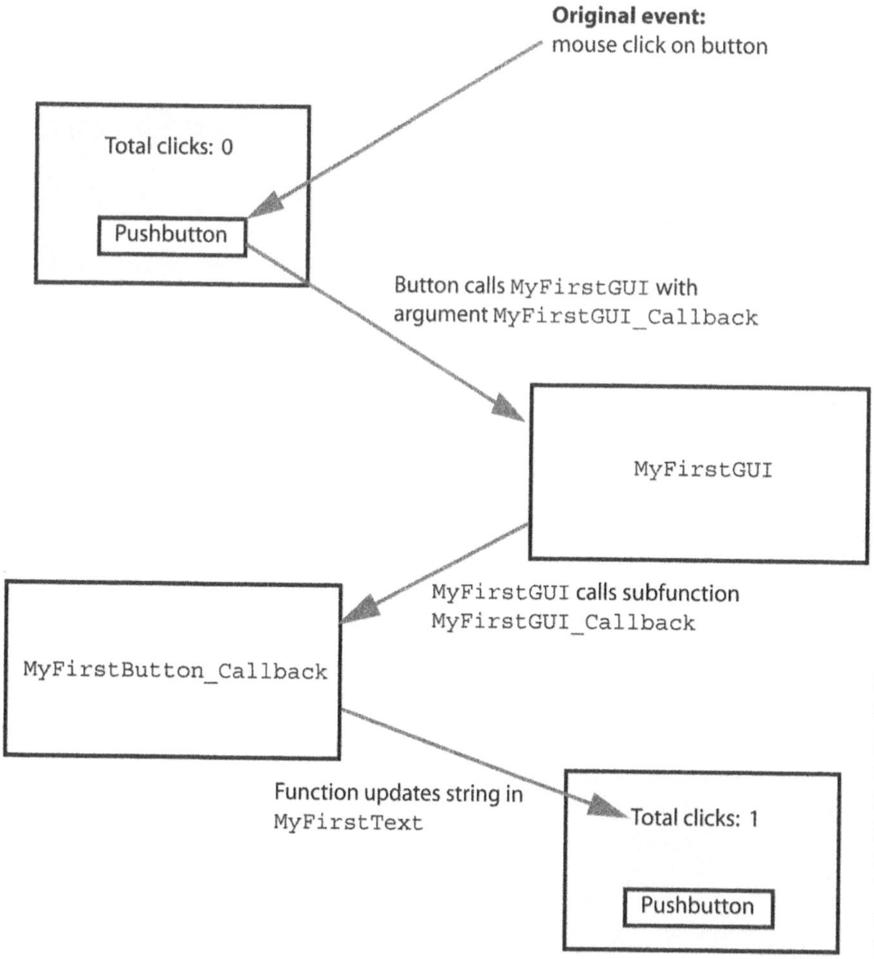

Figure 23.9 Event handling in program **MyFirstGUI**. When a user clicks on the button with the mouse, the function **MyFirstGUI** is called automatically with the argument **MyFirstButton_Callback**. Function **MyFirstGUI** in turn calls subfunction **MyFirstButton_Callback**. This function increments **count**, and then saves the new count in the text field on the GUI.

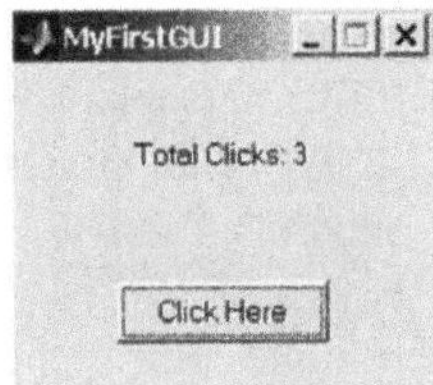

Figure 23.10 The resulting program after three button pushes.

Note that this function declares a persistent variable **count** and initializes it to zero. Each time the function is called, it increments **count** by 1 and creates a new string containing the count. Then, it updates the string displayed in the text field **MyFirstText.**

The resulting program is executed by typing **MyFirstGUI** in the Command Window. When the user clicks on the button, MATLAB automatically calls function **MyFirstGUI** with **MyFirstButton_Callback** as the first argument, and function **MyFirstGUI** calls subfunction **MyFirstButton_Callback.** This function increments variable **count** by one and updates the value displayed in the text field. The resulting GUI after three button pushes is shown in Figure 23.10.

Good Programming Practice

Use **guide** to lay out a new GUI, and use the Property Inspector to set the initial properties of each component, such as the text displayed on the component, the color of the component, and the name of the callback function, if required.

Good Programming Practice

After creating a GUI with **guide,** manually edit the resulting M-file to add comments describing its purpose and components, and to implement the behavior of callbacks.

23.2.1 A Look Under the Hood

Figure 23.8 shows the M-file that was automatically generated by **guide** for **MyFirstGUI.** We will now examine this M-file more closely to understand how it works.

First, let's look at the main **function** declaration itself. Note that this function uses **varargin** to represent its input arguments and **varargout** to represent its output results. Function **varargin** can represent an arbitrary number of input arguments, and function **varargout** can represent a varying number of output arguments. Therefore, *a user can call function* **MyFirstGUI** *with any number of arguments.*

The main function begins with a series of comments that serve as the help message displayed when the user types "**help MyFirstGUI.**" You should edit these comments to reflect the actual function of your program.

Next, the main function creates a structure called **gui_State.** The code to create this structure is shown below:

```
gui_Singleton = 1;
gui_State = struct('gui_Name',          mfilename, ...
                   'gui_Singleton',     gui_Singleton, ...
                   'gui_OpeningFcn',    @MyFirstGUI_OpeningFcn, ...
                   'gui_OutputFcn',     @MyFirstGUI_OutputFcn, ...
                   'gui_LayoutFcn',     [] , ...
                   'gui_Callback',      []);
if nargin & isstr(varargin{1})
   gui_State.gui_Callback = str2func(varargin{1});
End
```

The structure contains some control information, plus function handles for some of the subfunctions in the file. Other MATLAB GUI functions use these function handles to call the subfunctions from outside of the M-file. Note that the first argument is converted into a callback function handle, if it exists.

The value **gui_Singleton** specifies whether there can be one or more simultaneous copies of the GUI. If **gui_Singleton** is 1, then there can be only one copy of the GUI. If **gui_Singleton** is 0, then there can be many simultaneous copies of the GUI.

The main function calls the MATLAB function **gui_mainfcn**, and passes the **gui_State** structure and all of the input arguments to it. Function **gui_mainfcn** is standard MATLAB function. It actually does the work of creating the GUI, or of calling the appropriate subfunction in response to a callback.

23.2.2 Calling the M-File Without Arguments

If the user calls **MyFirstGUI** *without* arguments, function **gui_mainfcn** loads the GUI from the figure file **MyFirstGUI.fig** using the **openfig** function. The form of this function is

```
fig = openfig(mfilename,reuse);
```

where **mfilename** is the name of the figure file to load. The second argument in the function specifies whether there can be only one copy of the figure running at a given time, or multiple copies can be run. If **gui_State.gui_Singleton** is 1, then the second argument is set to **'reuse'**, and only one copy of the figure can be run. If **openfig** is called with the **'reuse'** option and the specified figure already exists, the preexisting figure will be brought to the top of the screen and reused. In contrast, if **gui_State.gui_Singleton** is 0, then the argument is set to **'new'** and a new copy of the figure will be created each time that **MyFirstGUI** is called without arguments. By default, a GUI created by **guide** has the **gui_State.gui_Singleton** set to 1, so only one copy of the figure can exist at any time. If you wish to have multiple copies of the GUI, turn off the "GUI allows only one instance to run" flag in the GUI Options selection on **guide's** Tools menu.

After the figure is loaded, the **gui_mainfcn** function executes the statement

```
set(fig, 'Color', get(0, 'defaultUicontrolBackgroundColor'));
```

This function sets the background color of the figure to match the default background color used by the computer that MATLAB is executing on. It makes the color of the GUI match the color of native windows on the computer. Therefore, a GUI can be written on a Windows-based PC and used on a Unix-based computer, and vice versa. It will look natural in either environment.

Then, function **gui_mainfcn** creates a structure containing the handles of all the objects in the current figure and stores that structure as application data in the figure.

```
guidata(gui_hFigure, guihandles(gui_hFigure));
```

Function **guihandles** creates a structure containing handles to all of the objects within the specified figure. The element names in the structure correspond to the Tag properties of each GUI component, and the values are the handles of each component. For example, the handle structure returned in **MyFirstGUI.m** is

```
>> handles = guihandles(fig)
handles =
              figure1: 99.0005
          MyFirstText: 3.0021
        MyFirstButton: 100.0007
```

There are three GUI components in this figure—the figure itself, plus a text field and a pushbutton. Function **guidata** saves the handles structure as application data in the figure, using the **setappdata** function.

Finally, just before making the figure visible, function **gui_mainfcn** calls the function specified in **gui_OpeningFcn**. This function provides a way for the programmer to customize the GUI before showing it to the user. For example, a programmer could load initial data values here, change background colors, and so forth.

23.2.3 Calling the M-File with Arguments

When the user clicks on an active GUI element, MATLAB calls **MyFirstGUI** with the name of the GUI element's callback function in the first argument. If **MyFirstGUI** is called *with* arguments, the value returned by **nargin** will be greater than zero. In this case, function **MyFirstGUI** converts the callback function name into a function handle using the following code.

```
If nargin & isstr(varargin{1})
  gui_State.gui_Callback = str2func(varargin{1});
end
```

When function **gui_mainfcn** is called this time, it calls the callback function using this function handle. The callback executes and responds to the mouse click or keyboard input, as appropriate.

Figure 23.11 summarizes the operation of **MyFirstGUI** on first and subsequent calls.

23.2.4 The Structure of a Callback Subfunction

Every callback subfunction has the standard form

```
function ComponentTag_Callback(hObject, eventdata, handles)
```

where **ComponentTag** is the name of the component generating the callback (the string in its Tag **property**). The arguments of this subfunction are:

- **hObject**—The handle of the parent figure
- **eventdata**—A currently unused (in MATLAB 7) array.
- **Handles**—The handles structure contains the handles of all GUI components on the figure.

Note that each callback function has full access to the **handles** structure; therefore, each callback function can modify any GUI component in the figure. We took advantage of this structure in the callback function for the pushbutton in **MyFirstGUI**, where the callback function for the pushbutton modified the text displayed in the text field.

```
% Update the text field
set (handles.MyFirstText, 'String',str);
```

23.2.5 Adding Application Data to a Figure

It is possible to store any application-specific information needed by a GUI program in the **handles** structure instead of using global or persistent memory for that data. The resulting GUI design is more robust, since other MATLAB programs cannot accidentally modify the global GUI data and since multiple copies of the same GUI cannot interfere with each other.

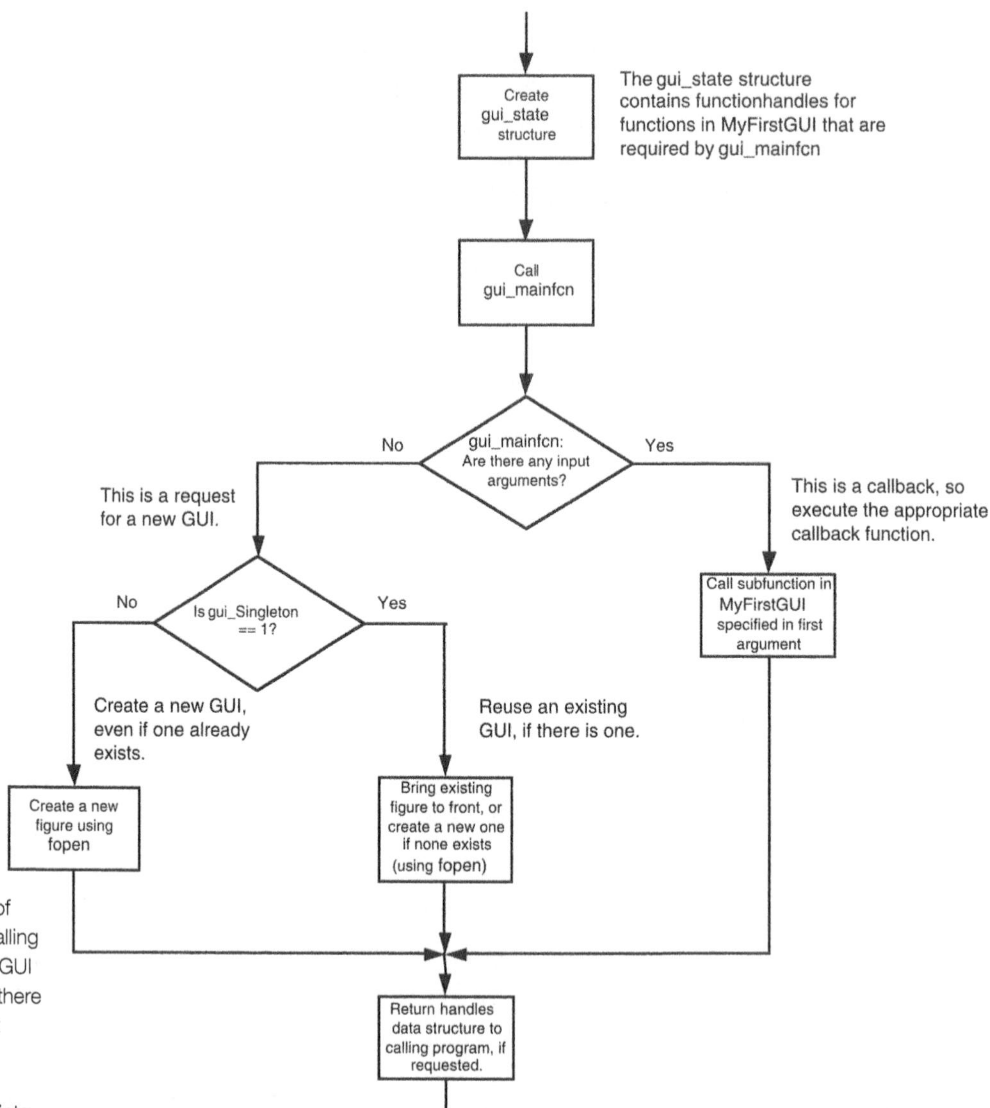

Figure 23.11 The operation of **MyFirstGUI**. If there are no calling arguments, it either creates a GUI or displays an existing GUI. If there are calling arguments, the first argument is assumed to be a callback function name, and **MyFirstGUI** calls the appropriate callback function.

To add local data to the **handles** structure, we must manually modify the M-file after it is created by **guide**. A programmer first adds the required local data to the handles structure, and then calls **guidata** to update the handles structure stored in the figure. For example, to add the number of mouse clicks **count** to the **handles** structure, we would modify the **MyFirstButton_Callback** function as follows:

```
function MyFirstButton_Callback(hObject, eventdata, handles)
% hObject      handle to MyFirstButton (see GCBO)
% eventdata    reserved – to be defined in a future version of MATLAB
% handles      structure with handles and user data (see GUIDATA)

% Create the count field if it does not exist
if ~isfield(handles, 'count')
        handles.count = 0;
end
```

```
% Update count
handles.count = handles.count + 1;

%Save the updated handles structure
quidata(hObject, handles);

%Create new string
str = sprintf('Total Clicks: %d',handles.count);

% Update the text field
set (handles.MyFirstText, 'String',str);
```

Good Programming Practice

Store GUI application data in the **handles** structure, so that it will automatically be available to any callback function.

Good Programming Practice

If you modify any of the GUI application data in the **handles** structure, be sure to save the structure with a call to **guidata** before exiting the function where the modifications occurred.

23.3 OBJECT PROPERTIES

Every GUI object includes an extensive list of properties that can be used to customize the object. These properties are slightly different for each type of object (figures, axes, **uicontrols**, etc.). All of the properties for all types of objects are documented on the on-line Help Browser, but a few of the more important properties for **figure** and **uicontrol** objects are summarized in Tables 23.2 and 23.3.

Object properties can be modified using either the Property Inspector or the **get** and **set** functions. Although the Property Inspector is a convenient way to adjust properties during GUI design, we must use **get** and **set** to adjust them dynamically from within a program, such as in a callback function.

Table 23.2 Important **figure** Properties

Property	Description
Color	Specifies the color of the figure. The value is either a predefined color such as **'r'** , **'g'**, or **'b'**, or else a 3-element vector specifying the red, green, and blue components of the color on a 0–1 scale. For example, the color magenta would be specified by [**1 0 1**].
CurrentCharacter	Contains the character corresponding to the last key pressed in this figure.
CurrentPoint	Location of the last button click in this figure, measured from the lower left-hand corner of the figure in units specified in the **Units** property.
Dockable	Specifies whether or not the figure can be docked to the desktop. Possible values are **'on'** or **'off'**.
MenuBar	Specifies whether or not the default set of menus appears on the figure. Possible values are **'figure'** to display the default menus or **'none'** to delete them.

Table 23.2 *(continued)*

Property	Description
Name	A string containing the name that appears in the title bar of a figure.
NumberTitle	Specifies whether or not the figure number appears in the title bar. Possible values are **'on'** or **'off'**.
Position	Specifies the position of a figure on the screen, in the units specified by the **'units'** property. This value accepts a 4-element vector in which the first two elements are the *x* and *y* positions of the lower left-hand corner of the figure and the next two elements are the width and height of the figure.
SelectionType	Specifies the type of selection for the last mouse click on this figure. A single click returns type **'normal'**, while a double click returns type **'open'**. There are additional options; see the MATLAB on-line documentation.
Tag	The "name" of the figure, which can be used to locate it.
Units	The units used to describe the position of the figure. Possible choices are **'inches'**, **'centimeters'**, **'normalized'**, **'points'**, **'pixels'**, or **'characters'**. The default units are **'pixels'**.
Visible	Specifies whether or not this figure is visible. Possible values are **'on'** or **'off'**.
WindowStyle	Specifies whether this figure is normal or modal. Possible values are **'normal'** or **'modal'**.

Table 23.3 Important **uicontrol** Properties

Property	Description
BackgroundColor	Specifies the background color of the object. The value is either a predefined color such as **'r'**, **'g'**, or **'b'**, or else a 3-element vector specifying the red, green, and blue components of the color on a 0–1 scale. For example, the color magenta would be specified by [**1 0 1**].
Callback	Specifies the name and parameters of the function to be called when the object is activated by a keyboard or text input.
Enable	Specifies whether or not this object is selectable. If it is not enabled, it will not respond to mouse or keyboard input. Possible values are **'on'** or **'off'**.
FontAngle	A string containing the font angle for text displayed on the object. Possible values are **'normal'**, **'italic'**, and **'oblique'**.
FontName	A string containing the font name for text displayed on the object.
FontSize	A number specifying the font size for text displayed on the object.
FontUnits	The units in which the font size is defined. Possible choices are **'inches'**, **'centimeters'**, **'normalized'**, **'points'**, and **'pixels'**. The default font units are **'points'**.

Table 23.3 *(continued)*

Property	Description
FontWeight	A string containing the font weight for text displayed on the object. Possible values are **'light'**, **'normal'**, **'demi'**, and **'bold'**. The default font weight is **'normal'**.
ForegroundColor	Specifies the foreground color of the object.
HorizontalAlignment	Specifies the horizontal alignment of a text string within the object. Possible values are **'left'**, **'center'**, and **'right'**.
Max	The maximum size of the **value** property for this object.
Min	The minimum size of the **value** property for this object.
Parent	The handle of the figure containing this object.
Position	Specifies the position of the object on the screen, in the units specified by the **'units'** property. This value accepts a 4-element vector in which the first two elements are the *x* and *y* positions of the lower left-hand corner of the object *relative the figure containing it*, and the next two elements are the width and height of the object.
Tag	The "name" of the object, which can be used to locate it.
TooltipString	Specifies the help text to be displayed when a user places the mouse pointer over an object.
Units	The units used to describe the position of the figure. Possible choices are **'inches'**, **'centimeters'**, **'normalized'**, **'points'**, **'pixels'**, or **'characters'**. The default units are **'pixels'**.
Value	The current value of the **uicontrol**. For toggle buttons, check boxes, and radio buttons, the value is **max** when the button is on and **min** when the button is off. Other controls have different meanings for this term.
Visible	Specifies whether or not this object is visible. Possible values are **'on'** or **'off'**.

23.4 GRAPHICAL USER INTERFACE COMPONENTS

This section summarizes the basic characteristics of common graphical user interface components. It describes how to create and use each component, as well as the types of events each component can generate. The components discussed in this section are:

- Static Text Fields
- Edit Boxes
- Pushbuttons
- Toggle Buttons
- Checkboxes
- Radio Buttons
- Popup Menus
- List Boxes
- Sliders

23.4.1 Static Text Fields

A **static text field** is a graphical object that displays one or more text strings, which are specified in the text field's **String** property. The **String** property accepts a string or a cell array of strings. If the input value is a string, it will be displayed on a single line. If the input value is a cell array of strings, the first element will be displayed on the first line of the text box, the second element will be displayed on the second line of the text box, and so forth. You can specify how the text is aligned in the display area by setting the horizontal alignment property. By default, text fields are horizontally centered. A text field is created by a **uicontrol** whose style property is **'text'**. A text field may be added to a GUI by using the text tool ( ) in the Layout Editor.

Text fields do not create callbacks, but the value displayed in the text field can be updated from another component's callback function by changing the text field's **String** property, as shown in program **MyFirstGUI** in Section 23.2.

23.4.2 Edit Boxes

An **edit box** is a graphical object that allows a user to enter one or more text strings. It is created by a **uicontrol** whose style property is **'edit'**. If the **min** property and **max** property are both set to 1, then *the edit box will accept a single line of text*, and it will generate a callback when the user presses the Enter key or the ESC key after typing the text.

Figure 23.12 shows a simple GUI containing an edit box named **'EditBox'** and a text field named **'TextBox'**. When a user presses Enter or ESC after typing a string into the edit box, the program automatically calls the function **EditBox_Callback**. This function locates the edit box using the **handles** structure, and recovers the string typed by the user. Then, it locates the text field and displays the string in the text field. Figure 23.13

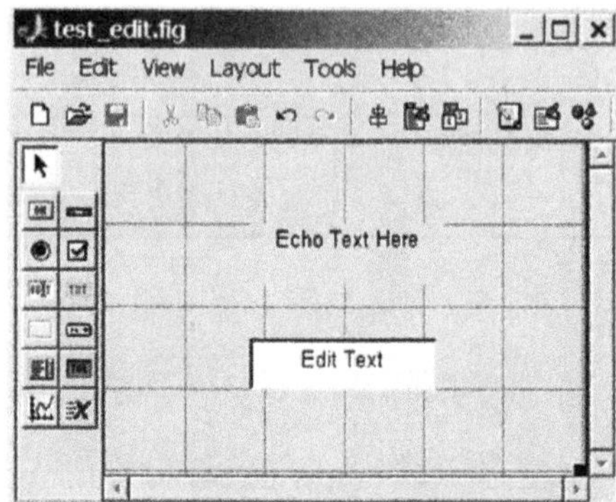


```
function EditBox_Callback(hObject, eventdata, handles)

% Find the value typed into the edit box
str = get (handles.EditBox,'String');

% Place the value into the text field
set (handles.TextBox,'String',str);
```

Figure 23.12 Layout of a simple GUI with a single-line edit box and a text field and the callback function for this GUI.

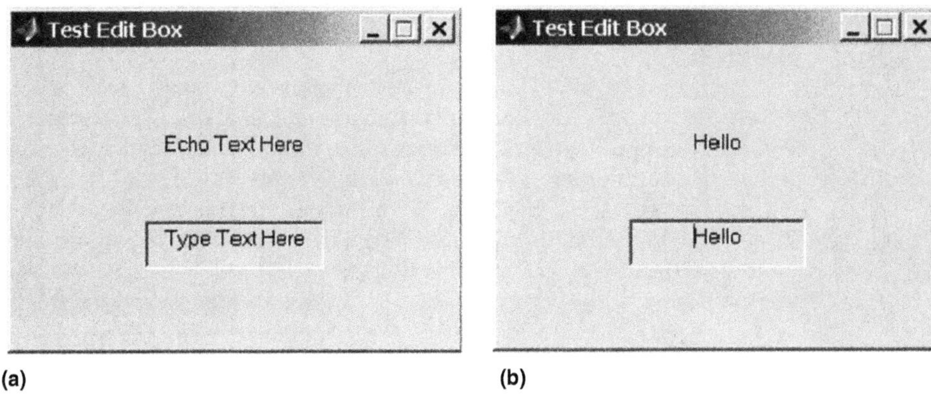

Figure 23.13 **(a)** The GUI produced by program **test_edit**. **(b)** The GUI after a user types '**Hello**' into the edit box and presses Enter.

shows this GUI just after it has started, and after the user has typed the word "Hello" in the edit box.

If the **max** property is set to a number greater than the **min** property, *the edit box will accept as many lines of text as the user wishes to enter.* The textbox will include a vertical scrollbar to allow the user to move up and down through the data. Either the scrollbar or the up and down arrows can be used to move between the input lines. If the user presses the Enter key in a multi-line edit box, the current line is finished and the cursor moves down to the next line for additional input. If the user presses the ESC key or clicks a point on the figure background with the mouse, a callback will be generated and the data typed into the edit box will be available as a cell array of strings in the **uicontrol's String** property.

Figure 23.14 shows a simple GUI containing a multi-line edit box named **'EditBox2'** and a text field named **'TextBox2'**. When a user presses ESC after typing a set of lines into the edit box, the program automatically calls the function **EditBox2_Callback.** This function locates the edit box using the **handles** structure and recovers the strings typed by the user. Then, it locates the text field and displays the strings in the text field. Figure 23.15 shows this GUI just after it has started, and after the user has typed four lines in the edit box.

23.4.3 Pushbuttons

A **pushbutton** is a component that a user can click on to trigger a specific action. The pushbutton generates a callback when the user clicks on it with the mouse. A pushbutton is created by creating a **uicontrol** whose style property is **'pushbutton'**. It can be added to a GUI by using the pushbutton tool ( ) in the Layout Editor.

Function **MyFirstGUI** in Figure 23.10 illustrates the use of pushbuttons.

23.4.4 Toggle Buttons

A toggle button is a type of button that has two states: on (depressed) and off (not depressed). A toggle button switches between these two states whenever the mouse clicks on it, and it generates a callback each time. The **'Value'** property of the toggle button is set to **max** (usually 1) when the button is on, and **min** (usually 0) when the button is off.

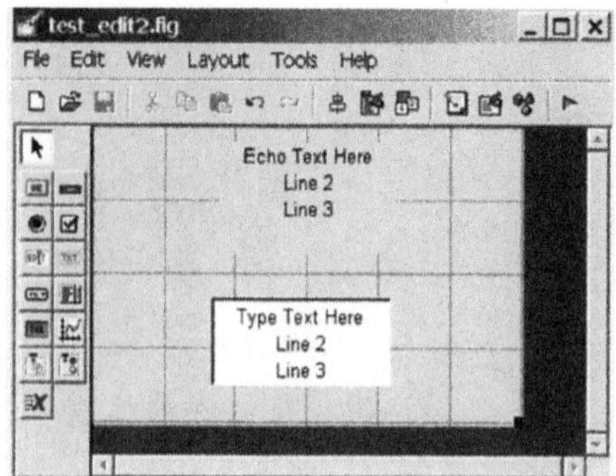


```
function EditBox2_Callback(hObject, eventdata, handles)

% Find the value typed into the edit box
str = get (handles.EditBox,'String');

% Place the value into the text field
set (handles.TextBox2,'String',str);
```

Figure 23.14 Layout of a simple GUI with a multi-line edit box and a text field and the callback function for this GUI.

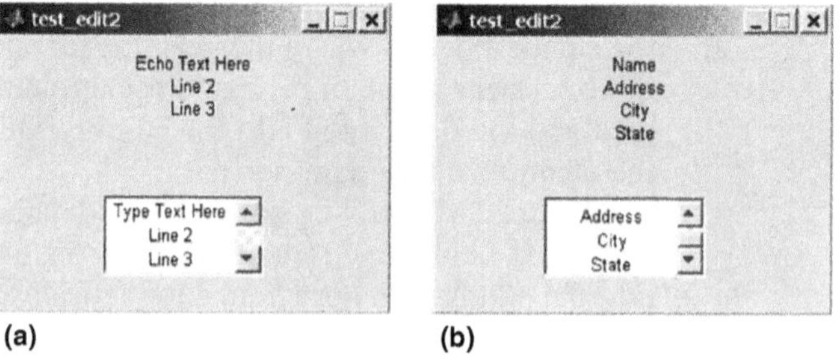

Figure 23.15 **(a)** The GUI produced by program **test_edit2**. **(b)** The GUI after a user types four lines into the edit box and presses ESC.

A toggle button is created by a **uicontrol** whose style property is '**togglebutton**'. It can be added to a GUI by using the toggle button tool () in the Layout Editor.

Figure 23.16 shows a simple GUI containing a toggle button named '**ToggleButton**' and a text field named '**TextBox**'. When a user clicks on the toggle button, it automatically calls the function **ToggleButton_Callback**. This function locates the toggle button using the **handles** structure and recovers its state from the '**Value**' property. Then, it locates the text field and displays the state in the text field. Figure 23.17 shows this GUI just after it has started, and after the user has clicked on the toggle button for the first time.

23.4.5 Checkboxes and Radio Buttons

Checkboxes and radio buttons are essentially identical to toggle buttons except that they have different shapes. Like toggle buttons, they have two states: on and off. They switch between these two states whenever the mouse clicks on them, generating a callback each time. The 'Value' property of the checkbox or radio button is set to max

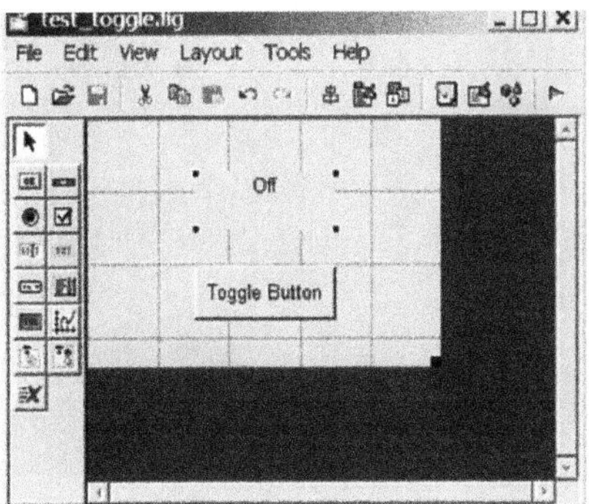


```
% Find the state of the toggle button
state = get(handles.ToggleButton,'Value');

% Place the value into the text field
if state == 0
   set (handles.TextBox,'String','Off');
else
   set (handles.TextBox,'String','On');
end
```

Figure 23.16 Layout of a simple GUI with a toggle button and a text field and the callback function for this GUI.

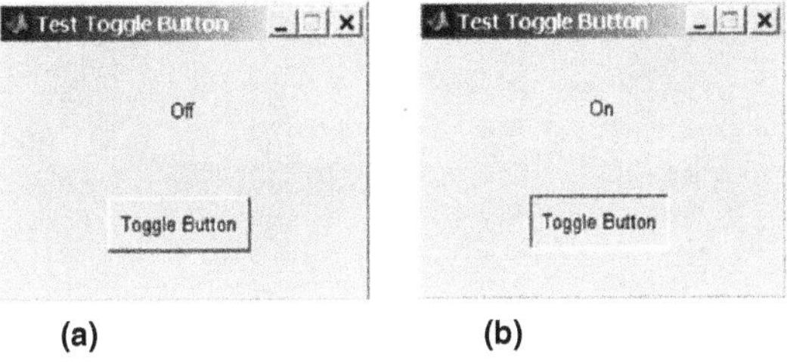

Figure 23.17 **(a)** The GUI produced by program **test_togglebutton** when the toggle button is off. **(b)** The GUI when the toggle button is on.

(usually 1) when they are on, and min (usually 0) when they are off. Both checkboxes and radio buttons are illustrated in Figure 23.1.

A checkbox is created by a **uicontrol** whose style property is **'checkbox'**, and a radio button is created by a **uicontrol** whose style property is **'radiobutton'**. A checkbox may be added to a GUI by using the checkbox tool (☑) in the Layout Editor, and a radio button may be added to a GUI by using the radio button tool (◉) in the Layout Editor.

Checkboxes are traditionally used to display on/off options, and groups of radio buttons are traditionally used to select among mutually exclusive options.

Figure 23.18 shows a simple GUI containing a checkbox named **'CheckBox'** and a text field named **'TextBox'**. When a user clicks on the checkbox, it automatically calls the function **CheckButton_Callback**. This function locates the checkbox using the **handles** structure and recovers its state from the **'Value'** property. Then, it locates the text field

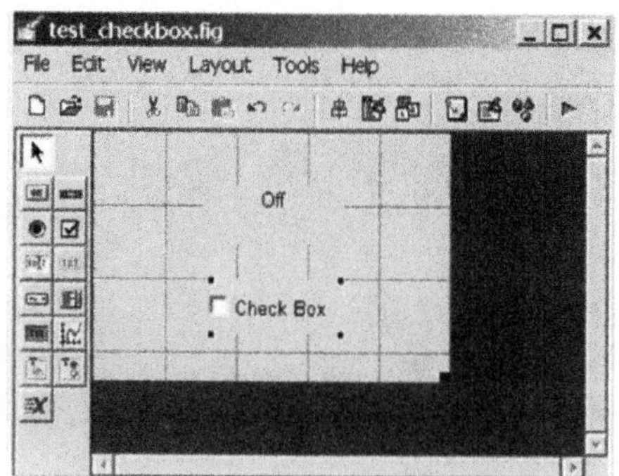


```
function CheckBox_Callback(hObject, eventdata, handles)

% Find the state of the checkbox
state = get(handles.CheckBox,'Value');

% Place the value into the text field
if state == 0
   set (handles.TextBox,'String','Off');
else
   set (handles.TextBox,'String','On');
end ;
```

Figure 23.18 Layout of a simple GUI with a CheckBox and a text field and the callback function for this GUI.

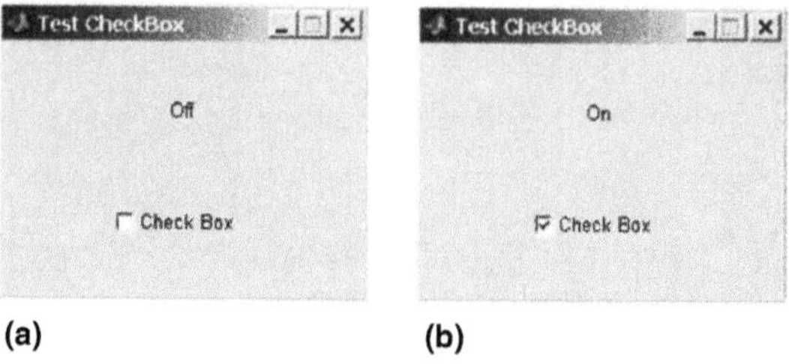

Figure 23.19 **(a)** The GUI produced by program **test_checkbox** when the toggle button is off. **(b)** The GUI when the toggle button is on.

and displays the state in the text field. Figure 23.19 shows this GUI just after it has started, and after the user has clicked on the toggle button for the first time.

Figure 23.20 shows an example of how to create a group of mutually exclusive options with radio buttons. The GUI in this figure creates three radio buttons, labeled "Option 1," "Option 2," and "Option 3," plus a text field to display the currently selected results.

The corresponding callback functions are shown in Figure 23.20. When the user clicks on a radio button, the corresponding callback function is executed. That function sets the text box to display the current option, turns on that radio button, and turns off all other radio buttons.

Figure 23.21 on page 662 shows this GUI after Option 2 has been selected.

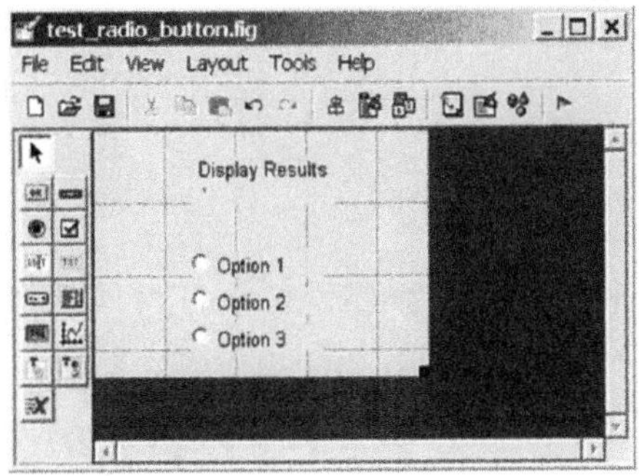


```
function Option1_Callback(hObject, eventdata, handles)

% Display the radio button clicked in the text field
set (handles.TextBox,'String','Option 1');

% Update all text fields
set (handles.Option1,'Value',1);
set (handles.Option2,'Value',0);
set (handles.Option3,'Value',0);

function Option2_Callback(hObject, eventdata, handles)

% Display the radio button clicked in the text field
set (handles.TextBox,'String','Option 2');

% Update all text fields
set (handles.Option1,'Value',0);
set (handles.Option2,'Value',1);
set (handles.Option3,'Value',0);

function Option3_Callback(hObject, eventdata, handles)

% Display the radio button clicked in the text field
set (handles.TextBox,'String','Option 3');

% Update all text fields
set (handles.Option1,'Value',0);
set (handles.Option2,'Value',0);
set (handles.Option3,'Value',1);
```

Figure 23.20 Layout of a simple GUI with three radio buttons and a text field and the callback functions for this GUI. When a user clicks on a radio button, it is set to 'on' and all other radio buttons are set to 'off'.

23.4.6 Popup Menus

Popup menus are graphical objects that allow a user to select one of a mutually exclusive list of options. The list of options that the user can select among is specified by a cell array of strings, and the '**Value**' property indicates which of the strings is currently selected. A popup menu may be added to a GUI by using the popup menu tool ( ) in the Layout Editor.

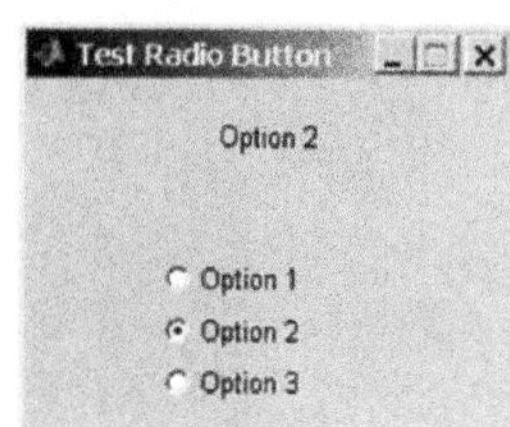

Figure 23.21 The GUI produced by program **test_radio_button** when Option 2 has been selected.

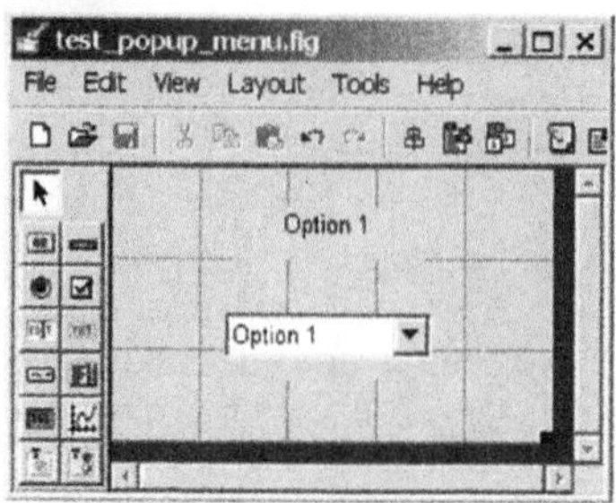


```
function Popup1_Callback(hObject, eventdata, handles)

% Find the value of the popup menu
value = get(handles.Popup1,'Value');

% Place the value into the text field
str = ['Option ' num2str(value)];
set (handles.Label1,'String',str);
```

Figure 23.22 Layout of a simple GUI with a popup menu and a text field to display the current selection and the callback functions for this GUI.

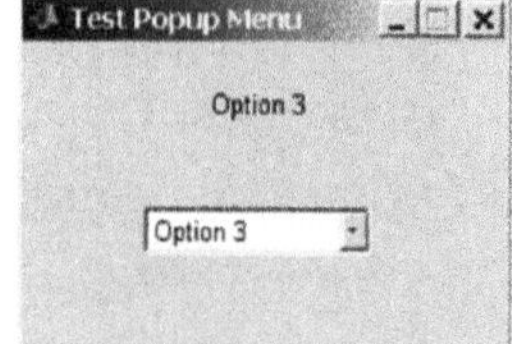

Figure 23.23 The GUI produced by program **test_popup_menu**.

Figure 23.22 show an example of a popup menu. This GUI in this figure creates a popup menu with five options, labeled "Option 1," "Option 2," and so forth.

The corresponding callback function is shown in Figure 23.22. The callback function recovers the selected option by checking the **'Value'** parameter of the popup menu and creates and displays a string containing that value in the text field. Figure 23.23 shows this GUI after Option 4 has been selected.

23.4.7 List Boxes

List boxes are graphical objects that display many lines of text and allow a user to select one or more of those lines. If there are more lines of text than can fit in the list box, a scroll bar will be created to allow the user to scroll up and down within the list box. The lines of text that the user can select among are specified by a cell array of strings, and the **'Value'** property indicates which of the strings are currently selected.

A list box is created by a uicontrol whose style property is **'list-box'**. A list box may be added to a GUI by using the listbox tool ( ) in the Layout Editor.

List boxes can be used to select a single item from a selection of possible choices. In normal GUI usage, a single mouse click on a list item selects that item but does not cause an action to occur. Instead, the action waits on some external trigger, such as a pushbutton. However, a double mouse click causes an action to happen immediately. Single-click and double-click events can be distinguished using the **SelectionType** property of the figure in which the clicks occurred. A single mouse click will place the string **'normal'** in the **SelectionType** property, and a double mouse click will place the string **'open'** in the **SelectionType** property.

It is also possible for a list box to allow multiple selections from the list. If the difference between the max and min properties of the list box is greater than one, multiple selection is allowed. Otherwise, only one item may be selected from the list.

Figure 23.24 shows an example of a single-selection list box. The GUI in this figure creates a list box with eight options, labeled "Option 1," "Option 2," and so forth. In addition, it creates a pushbutton to perform selection and a text field to display the selected choice. Both the list box and the pushbutton generate callbacks.

The corresponding callback functions are shown in Figure 23.24. If a selection is made in the list box, function **Listbox1_Callback** will be executed. This function will check the *figure producing the callback* (using function **gcbf**) to see whether the selecting action was a single-click or a double-click. If it was a single-click, the function does nothing. If it was a double-click, then the function gets the selected value from the listbox and writes an appropriate string into the text field.

If the pushbutton is selected, function **Button1_Callback** will be executed. This function gets the selected value from the listbox and writes an appropriate string into the text field.

23.4.8 Sliders

Sliders are graphical objects that allow a user to select values from a continuous range between a specified minimum value and a specified maximum value by moving a bar with a mouse. The **'Value'** property of the slider is set to a value between **min** and **max** depending on the position of the slider.

A slider is created by a **uicontrol** whose style property is **'slider'**. A slider may be added to a GUI by using the slider tool ( ) in the Layout Editor.

Figure 23.26 shows the layout for a simple GUI containing a slider and a text field. The **'Min'** property for this slider is set to zero, and the **'Max'** property is set to one. When a user drags the slider, it automatically calls the function **Slider1_Callback**. This function get the value of the slider from the **'Value'** property and displays the value in the text field. Figure 23.27 shows this GUI with the slider at some intermediate position in its range.

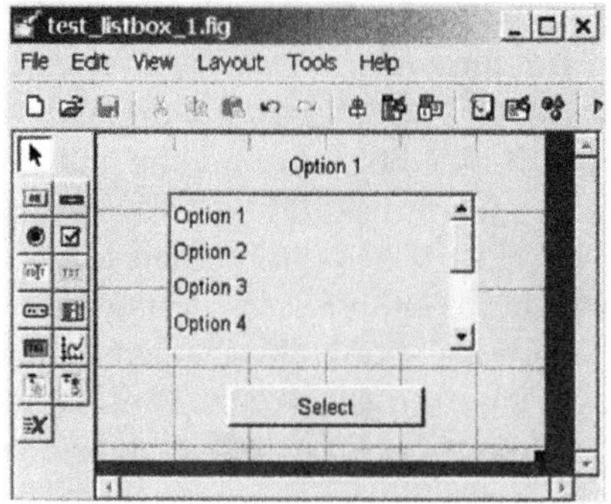


```
function Button1_Callback(hObject, eventdata, handles)

% Find the value of the popup menu
value = get(handles.Listbox1,'Value');

% Update text label
str = ['Option ' num2str(value)];
set (handles.Label1,'String',str);


function Listbox1_Callback(hObject, eventdata, handles)

% If this was a double click, update the label.
selectiontype = get(gcbf,'SelectionType');
if selectiontype(1) == 'o'

   % Find the value of the popup menu
   value = get(handles.Listbox1,'Value');

   % Update text label
   str = ['Option ' num2str(value)];
   set (handles.Label1,'String',str);
end
```

Figure 23.24 Layout of a simple GUI with a list box, a pushbutton, and a text field and the callback functions for this GUI.

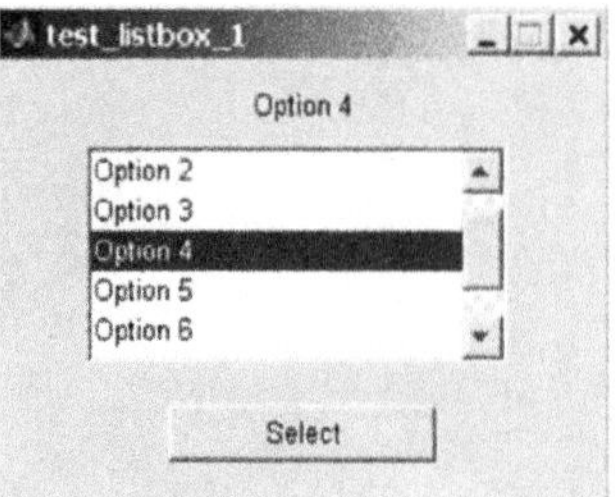

Figure 23.25 The GUI produced by program **test_listbox**.

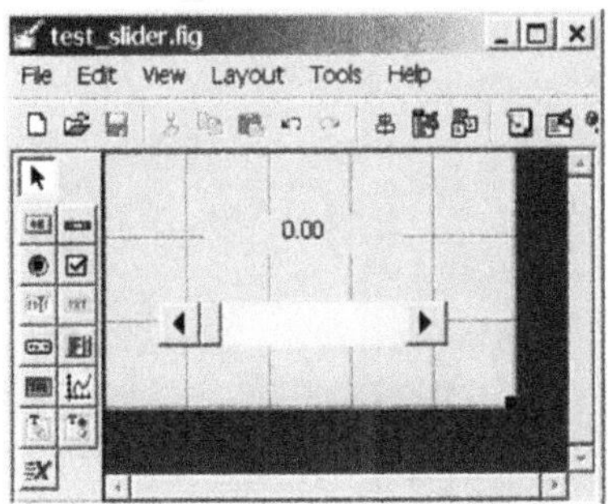


```
function Slider1_Callback(hObject, eventdata, handles)

% Find the value of the slider
value = get(handles.Slider1,'Value');

% Place the value in the text field
str = sprintf('%.2f',value);
set (handles.Label1,'String',str);
```

Figure 23.26 Layout of a simple GUI with a slider and a text field and the callback function for this GUI.

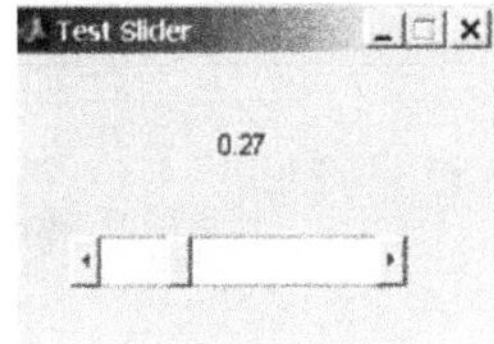

Figure 23.27 The GUI produced by program **test_slider**.

EXAMPLE 23.1

Temperature Conversion

Write a program that converts temperature from degrees Fahrenheit to degrees Celsius and vice versa over the range 0–100°C, using a GUI to accept data and display results. The program should include an edit box for the temperature in degrees Fahrenheit, an edit box for the temperature in degrees Celsius, and a slider to allow for the continuous adjustment of temperature. The user should be able to enter temperatures in either edit box or by moving the slider, and all GUI elements should adjust to the corresponding values.

Solution

To create this program, we will need a text field and an edit box for the temperature in degrees Fahrenheit, another text field and an edit box for the temperature in degrees Celsius, and a slider. We will also need a function to convert degrees Fahrenheit to degrees Celsius and a function to convert degrees Celsius to degrees Fahrenheit. Finally, we will need to write a callback function to support user inputs.

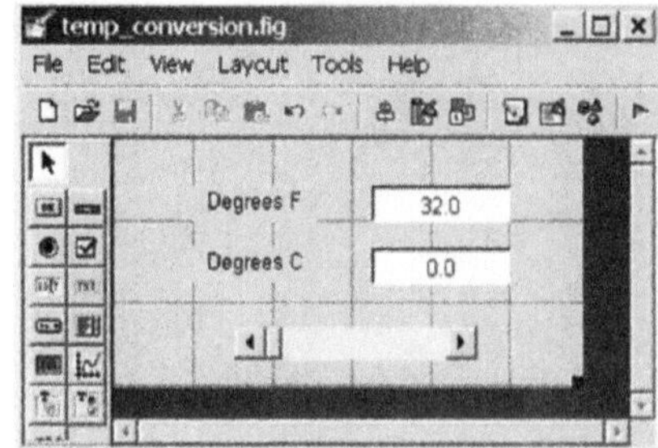

Figure 23.28 Layout of the temperature conversion GUI.

The range of values to convert will be 32–212°F or 0–100°C, so it will be convenient to set up the slider to cover the range 0–100, and to treat the value of the slider as a temperature in degrees C.

The first step in this process is to use **guide** to design the GUI. We can use **guide** to create the five required GUI elements and locate them in approximately the correct positions. Then, we can use the Property Inspector to perform the following steps:

1. Select appropriate names for each GUI element and store them in the appropriate **Tag** properties. The names will be **'Label1'**, **'Label2'**, **'Edit1'**, **'Edit2'**, and **'Slider1'**.
2. Store **'Degrees F'** and **'Degrees C'** in the **String** properties of the two labels.
3. Set the slider's minimum and maximum limits to 0 and 100, respectively.
4. Store initial values in the **String** property of the two edit fields and in the **Value** property of the slider. We will initialize the temperature to 32°F or 0°C, which corresponds to a slider value of 0.
5. Set the **Name** property of the figure containing the GUI to **'Temperature Conversion'**.

Once these changes have been made, the GUI should be saved to file **temp_conversion.fig**. This will produce both a figure file and a matching M-file. The M-file will contain stubs for the three callback functions needed by the edit fields and the slider. The resulting GUI is shown during the layout process in Figure 23.28.

The next step in the process is to create the functions to convert degrees Fahrenheit to degrees Celsius. Function **to_c** will convert temperature from degrees Fahrenheit to degrees Celsius. It must implement the equation

$$\text{deg } C = \frac{5}{9}(\text{deg } F - 32)$$

The code for this function is

```
function deg_c = to_c(deg_f)

% Convert degrees Fahrenheit to degrees C.
deg_c = (5/9) * (deg_f – 32);
end % function deg_c
```

Function **to_f** will convert temperature from degrees Celsius to degrees Fahrenheit. It must implement the equation

$$\text{deg } F = \frac{5}{9}(\text{deg } C + 32)$$

The code for this function is

```
function deg_f = to_f(deg_c)

% Convert degrees Celsius to degrees Fahrenheit.
deg_f = (9/5) * deg_c + 32;
end % function deg_f
```

Finally, we must write the callback functions to tie it all together. The functions must respond to either the edit box or to the slider and must update all three components. (Note that we will update even the edit box that the user types into, so that the data can be displayed with a consistent format at all times as well as to correct errors if the user types an out-of-range input value.)

There is an extra complication here, because the values entered into edit boxes are *strings* and we wish to treat them as *numbers*. If a user types the value 100 into an edit box, he or she has really created the string **'100'**, not the number 100. The callback function must convert the strings into numbers so that the conversion can be calculated. This conversion is done with the **str2num** function, which converts a string into a numerical value.

Also, the callback function will have to limit user entries to the valid temperature range, which is 0–100°C and 32–212°F.

The resulting callback functions are shown in Figure 23.29.

The program is now complete. Execute it and enter several different values using both the edit boxes and the sliders. Be sure to use some out-of-range values. Does it appear to be functioning properly?

```
function Edit1_Callback(hObject, eventdata, handles)

% Update all temperature values
deg_f = str2num( get(hObject,'String') );
deg_f = max( [ 32 deg_f] );
deg_f = min( [212 deg_f] );
deg_c = to_c(deg_f);

% Now update the fields
set (handles.Edit1,'String',sprintf('%.1f',deg_f));
set (handles.Edit2,'String',sprintf('%.1f',deg_c));
set (handles.Slider1,'Value',deg_c);


function Edit2_Callback(hObject, eventdata, handles)

% Update all temperature values
deg_c = str2num( get(hObject,'String') );
deg_c = max( [  0 deg_c] );
deg_c = min( [100 deg_c] );
deg_f = to_f(deg_c);

% Now update the fields
set (handles.Edit1,'String',sprintf('%.1f',deg_f));
set (handles.Edit2,'String',sprintf('%.1f',deg_c));
set (handles.Slider1,'Value',deg_c);


function Slider1_Callback(hObject, eventdata, handles)

% Update all temperature values
deg_c = get(hObject,'Value');
deg_f = to_f(deg_c);

% Now update the fields
set (handles.Edit1,'String',sprintf('%.1f',deg_f));
set (handles.Edit2,'String',sprintf('%.1f',deg_c));
set (handles.Slider1,'Value',deg_c);
```

Figure 23.29 Callback functions for the temperature conversion GUI.

23.5 ADDITIONAL CONTAINERS: PANELS AND BUTTON GROUPS

MATLAB GUIs include two other types of containers: **panels** (created by the function **uipanel**) and **button groups** (created by the function **uibutton-group**).

23.5.1 Panels

Panels are containers that can contain components or other containers, but they do *not* have a title bar and cannot have menus attached. A panel can contain GUI elements such as uicontrols, axes, other panels, or button groups. Any elements placed in a panel will be positioned relative to the panel. If the panel is moved on the GUI, then all of the elements within it are moved as well. Panels provide a great way to group related controls on a GUI.

A panel is created by a **uipanel** function. It can be added to a GUI by using the panel tool ( ) in the Layout Editor.

Each panel has a title, and is usually surrounded by an etched or beveled line marking the edges of the panel. The title of a panel can be located at the left, center, or right side of either the top or bottom of the panel. Samples of panels with several combinations of title positions and edge styles are shown in Figure 23.30.

Let's look at a simple example using panels. Suppose that we wanted to create a GUI to plot the function $y = ax^2 + bx + c$ between two specified values x_{min} and x_{max}. The GUI should allow the user to specify the values *a, b, c,* x_{min}, and x_{max}. In addition, it should allow the user to specify the style, color, and thickness of the line being plotted. These two sets of values (the ones specifying the line and the ones specifying what the line looks like) are logically distinct, so we can group them together in two panels on the GUI. One possible layout is shown in Figure 23.31.

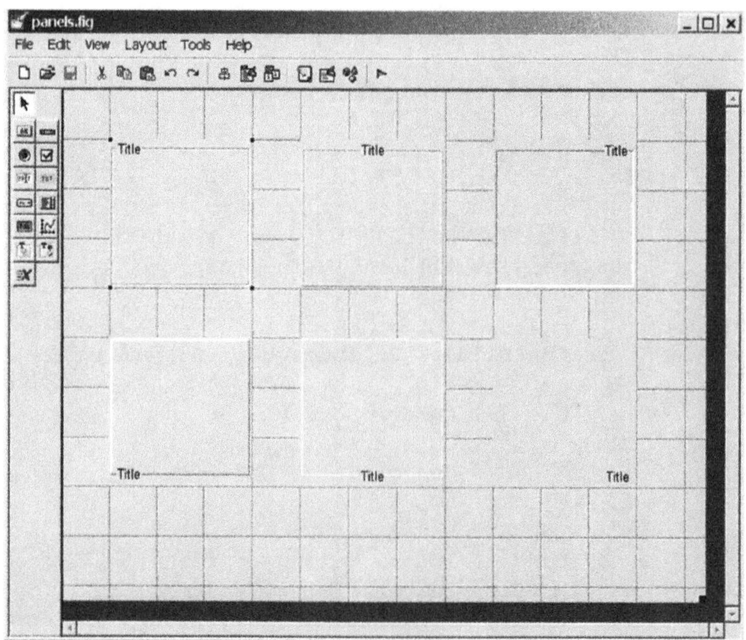

Figure 23.30 Examples of various panel styles.

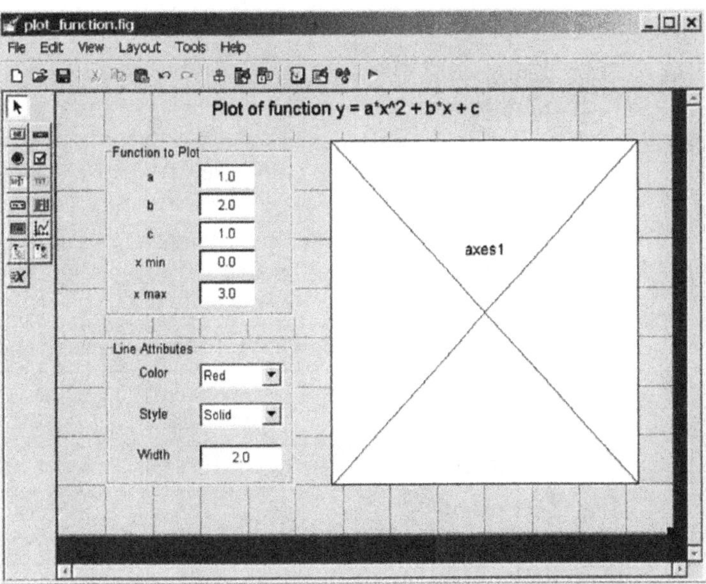

Figure 23.31 Layout of the Plot Function GUI, using panels to group related characteristics together.

Table 23.4 contains a list of some important uipanel properties. These properties can be modified by the Property Inspector during the design phase, or they can be modified during execution with get and set functions.

23.5.2 Button Groups

Button groups are a special type of panel that can manage groups of radio buttons or toggle buttons to ensure that *no more than one button in the group is on at any time.* A button group is just like any other panel, except that the button group ensures that at most one radio button or toggle button is on at any given time. If one of them is turned on, the button group turns off any buttons that were already on.

A button group is created by a **uibuttongroup** function. It can be added to a GUI by using the button group tool ( ) in the Layout Editor.

If a radio button or a toggle button is controlled by a Button Group, the user must attach the name of the function to execute when that button is selected in a special property called **SelectionChangeFcn**. This callback is executed by the GUI whenever a radio button or toggle button changes state. Do *not* place the function in the usual **Callback** property, because the Button Group overwrites the callback property for every radio button or toggle button that it controls.

Figure 23.32 shows a simple GUI containing a Button Group and three radio buttons, labeled **'Option 1'**, **'Option 2'**, and **'Option 3'**. When a user clicks on one radio button in the group, the button is turned on and all other buttons in the group are turned off.

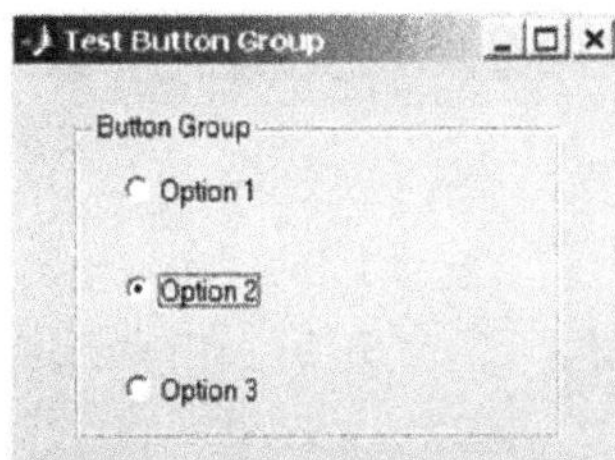

Figure 23.32 A button group controlling three radio buttons.

Table 23.4 Important uipanel and uibuttongroup Properties

Property	Description
BackgroundColor	Specifies the color of the **uipanel** background. The value is either a predefined color such as **'r'**, **'g'**, or **'b'**, or else a 3-element vector specifying the red, green, and blue components of the color on a 0–1 scale. For example, the color magenta would be specified by [**1 0 1**].
BorderType	Type of border around the **uipanel**. Options are **'none'**, **'etchedin'**, **'etchedout'**, **'beveledin'**, **'beveledout'**, or **'line'**. The default border type is **'etchedin'**.
BorderWidth	Width of border around the **uipanel**.
FontAngle	A string containing the font angle for the title text. Possible values are **'normal'**, **'italic'**, and **'oblique'**.
FontName	A string containing the font name for the title text.
FontSize	A number specifying the font size for the title text.
FontUnits	The units in which the font size is defined. Possible choices are **'inches'**, **'centimeters'**, **'normalized'**, **'points'**, and **'pixels'**. The default font units are **'points'**.
FontWeight	A string containing the font weight for the title text. Possible values are **'light'**, **'normal'**, **'demi'**, and **'bold'**. The default font weight is **'normal'**.
ForegroundColor	Specifies the color of the title font and the border.
HighlightColor	Specifies the 3D border highlight color.
Position	Specifies the position of a panel relative to its parent **figure**, **uipanel**, or **uibuttongroup**, in the units specified by the **'units'** property. This value accepts a 4-element vector in which the first two elements are the *x* and *y* positions of the lower left-hand corner of the panel, and the next two elements are the width and height of the panel.
ShadowColor	Specifies the color of the 3D border shadow.
Tag	The “name” of the **uipanel**, which can be used to access it.
Title	The title string.
TitlePosition	Location of the title string on the uipanel. Possible values are **'lefttop'**, **'centertop'**, **'righttop'**, **'leftbottom'**, **'centerbottom'**, and **'rightbottom'**. The default value is **'lefttop'**.
Units	The units used to describe the position of the **uipanel**. Possible choices are **'inches'**, **'centimeters'**, **'normalized'**, **'points'**, **'pixels'**, or **'characters'**. The default units are ‘normalized’.
Visible	Specifies whether or not this **uipanel** is visible. Possible values are **'on'** or **'off'**.

23.6 MENUS

Menus can also be added to MATLAB GUIs. A menu allows a user to select actions without additional components appearing on the GUI display. They are useful for selecting less commonly used options without cluttering up the GUI with a lot of extra buttons.

There are two types of menus in MATLAB: **standard menus**, which are pulled down from the menu bar at the top of a figure, and **context menus**, which pop up over the figure when a user right-clicks the mouse over a graphical object. We will learn how to create and use both types of menus in this section.

Standard menus are created with **uimenu** objects. Each item in a menu is a separate **uimenu** object, including items in submenus. These **uimenu** objects are similar to **uicontrol** objects, and they have many of the same properties such as **Parent, Callback, Enable,** and so forth. A list of the more important uimenu properties is given in Table 23.5.

Each menu item is attached to a parent object, which is a figure for the top-level menus, or another menu item for submenus. All of the **uimenus** connected to the same parent appear on the same menu, and the cascade of items forms a tree of submenus. Figure 23.33*a* shows a typical MATLAB menu in operation, and Figure 23.33*b* shows the relationship among the objects making up the menu.

MATLAB menus are created using the Menu Editor, which can be selected by clicking the ( ) icon on the toolbar in the guide Layout Editor. Figure 23.33*c* shows the Menu Editor with the menu items that generate this menu structure. The additional properties in Table 23.5 that are not shown in the Menu Editor can be set with the Property Editor (**propedit**).

Top-level context menus are created by **uicontextmenu** objects, and the lower level items within context menus are created by **uimenu** objects. Context menus are basically the same as standard menus, except that they can be associated with any GUI object (e.g., axes, lines, text, figures).

23.6.1 Suppressing the Default Menu

Every MATLAB figure comes with a default set of standard menus. If you wish to delete these menus from a figure and create your own menus, you must first turn the default menus off. The display of default menus is controlled by the figure's MenuBar property. The possible values of this property are **'figure'** and **'none'**. If the property is set to 'figure', the default menus are displayed. If the property is set to 'none', the default menus are suppressed. You can use the Property Inspector to set the MenuBar property for your GUIs when you create them.

23.6.2 Creating Your Own Menus

Creating your own standard menus for a GUI is basically a three-step process.

1. First, create a new menu structure with the Menu Editor. Use the Menu Editor to define the structure, giving each menu item a **Label** to display and a unique Tag value. You can also specify whether or not there is a separator bar between menu items, and whether or not each menu item has a check mark by it. A dummy callback function will be generated automatically for each menu item.
2. If necessary, edit the properties of each menu item using the Property Inspector. The Property Inspector can be started by clicking the "More Options" button on

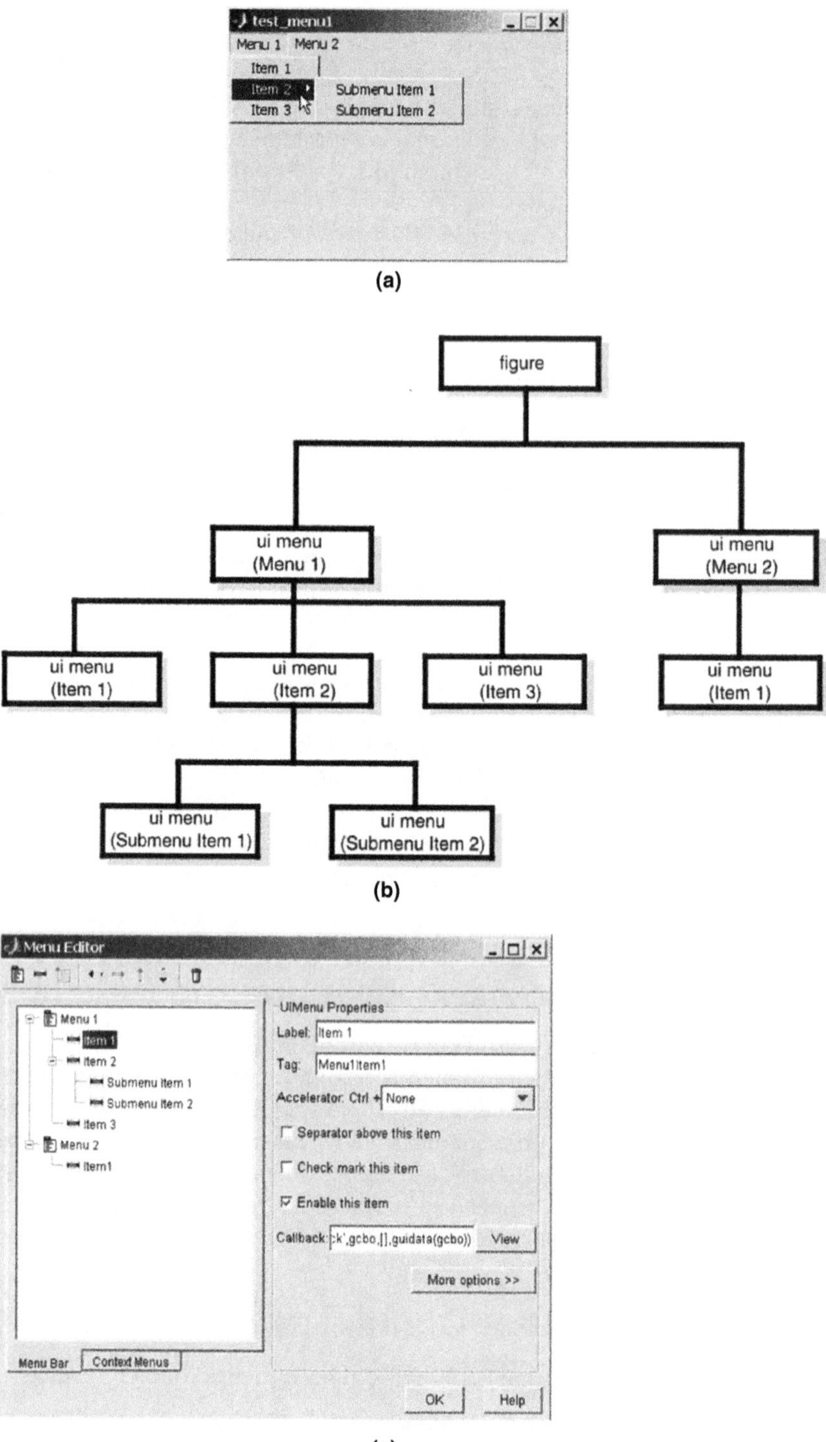

Figure 23.33 **(a)** A typical menu structure. **(b)** The relationships among the uimenu items creating the menu. **(c)** The Menu Editor structure that generated these menus.

Table 23.5 Important uimenu Properties

Property	Description
Accelerator	A single character specifying the keyboard equivalent for the menu item. The keyboard combination CTRL+key allows a user to activate the menu item from the keyboard.
Callback	Specifies the name and parameters of the function to be called when the menu item is activated. It the menu item has a submenu, the callback executes *before the submenu is displayed.* If the menu item does not have submenus, the callback executes when the mouse button is *released.*
Checked	When this property is **'on'**, a checkmark is placed to the left of the menu item. This property can be used to indicate the status of menu items that toggle between two states. Possible values are **'on'** or **'off'**.
Enable	Specifies whether or not this menu item is selectable. If it not enabled, the menu item will not respond to mouse clicks or accelerator keys. Possible values are **'on'** or **'off'**.
ForegroundColor	Set color of text in the menu item.
Label	Specifies the text to be displayed on the menu. The ampersand character (&) can be used to specify a keyboard mnemonic for this menu item; it will not appear on the label. For example, the string **'&File'** will create a menu item displaying the text **'File'** and responding to the F key.
Parent	The handle of the parent object for this menu item. The parent object could be a figure or another menu item.
Position	Specifies the position of a menu item on the menu bar or within a menu. Position 1 is the left-most menu position for a top-level menu, and the highest position within a submenu.
Separator	When this property is **'on'**, a separating line is drawn above this menu item. Possible values are **'on'** or **'off'**.
Tag	The "name" of the menu item, which can be used to access it.
Visible	Specifies whether or not this menu item is visible. Possible values are **'on'** or **'off'**.

the Menu Editor. Because the most important menu item properties (Label, Tag, Callback, Checked, and Separator) can be set on the Menu Editor, the Property Inspector is usually not needed. However, if you must set any of the other properties listed in Table 23.5, you will need to use the Property Inspector.

3. Third, implement a callback function to perform the actions required by your menu items. The prototype function is created automatically, but you must add the code to make each menu item behave properly.

Table 23.6 Important uicontextmenu Properties

Property	Description
Callback	Specifies the name and parameters of the function to be called when the context menu is activated. The callback executes before the context menu is displayed.
Parent	The handle of the parent object for this context menu.
Tag	The "name" of the context menu, which can be used to access it.
Visible	Specifies whether or not this context menu is visible. This property is set automatically, and should normally not be modified.

Programming Pitfalls

Only the **Label, Tag, Callback, Checked,** and **Separator** properties of a menu item can be set from the Menu Editor. If you need to set any of the other properties, you will have to use the Property Inspector on the figure and select the appropriate menu item to edit.

EXAMPLE 23.2

Creating a Histogram GUI

Write a program that opens a user-specified data file and calculates a histogram of the data in the file. The program should calculate the mean, median, and standard deviation of the data in the file. It should include a File menu, with Open and Exit menu items. It should also include a means to allow the user to change the number of bins in the histogram.

Select a color other than the default color for the figure and the text label backgrounds, use keyboard mnemonics for menu items, and add tool tips where appropriate.

Solution

This program should include a standard menu with Open and Exit menu items, a set of axes on which to plot the histogram, and a set of six text fields for the mean, median, and standard deviation of the data. Three of these text fields will hold labels, and three will hold the read-only mean, median, and standard deviation values. It must also include a label and an edit field to allow the user to selected the number of bins to display in the histogram.

We will select a light blue color [0.6 1.0 1.0] for the background of this GUI. To make the GUI have a light blue background, this color vector must be loaded into the **'Color'** property of the figure and into the **'BackgroundColor'** property of each text label with the Property Inspector during the GUI layout. Since MATLAB GUIs automatically reset their figure color to match the system default, we will also need to set this figure color in the **histGUI_OpeningFcn** callback, which is called just before the figure becomes visible.

The first step in creating this program is to use guide to lay out the required GUI (see Figure 23.34*a*). Then, use the Property Inspector to set the properties of the seven text fields and the edit field. The fields must be given unique tags so that we can locate them from the callback functions. Next, use the Menu Editor to create the File menu (see Figure 23.34*b*). Finally, the resulting GUI should be saved as **histGUI**, creating **histGUI.fig** and **histGUI.m**.

After **histGUI.m** has been saved, the function **histGUI_OpeningFcn** must be edited to initialize the background color of the figure and to save the initial number of histogram bins in the handles structure. The modified code for the opening function is:

```
% —- Executes just before histGUI is made visible.
function hisGUI_OpeningFcn(hObject, eventdata, handles, varargin)
% This function has no output args, see OutputFcn.
```

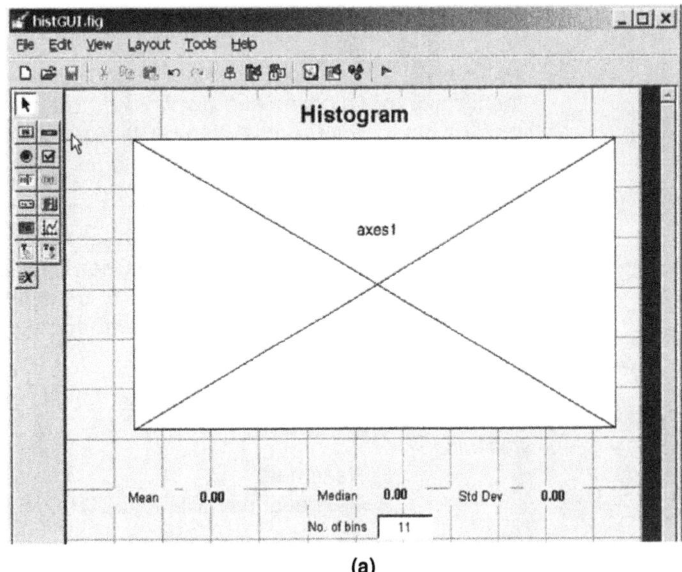

(a)

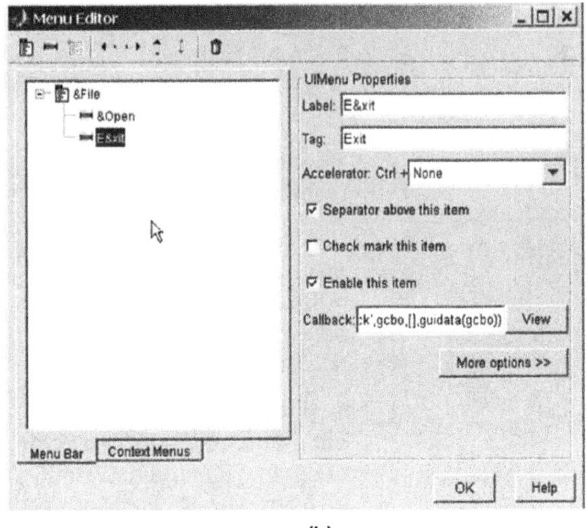

(b)

Figure 23.34 **(a)** The layout for **histGUI**. **(b)** The File menu in the Menu Editor.

```
% hObject      handle to figure
% eventdata    reserved – to be defined in a future version of MATLAB
% handles      structure with handles and user data (see GUIDATA)
% varargin     command line arguments to histGUI (see VARARGIN)

% Choose default command line output for histGUI
handles.output = hObject;

% Set the figure background color
set (hObject, 'Color', [0.6 1 1]);

% Set the initial number of bins
handles.nbins = 11;

% Update handles structure
guidata(hObject, handles);
```

Next, we must create callback functions for the File/Open menu item, the File/Exit menu item, and the "number of bins" edit box.

The File/Open callback must prompt the user for a file name and then read the data from the file. It must calculate and display the histogram and update the statistics text fields. Note that the data in the file must also be saved in the **handles** structure so that it will be available for recalculation if the user changes the number of bins in the historgram. The callback function to perform these steps is shown below:

```
function Open_Callback(hObject, eventdata, handles)
% hObject      handle to Open (see GCBO)
% eventdata    reserved – to be defined in a future verson of MATLAB
% handles      structure with handles and user data (see GUIDATA)

% Get file name
[filename,path] = uigetfile('*.dat','Load Data File');
if filename ~= 0

    % Read data
    x = textread([path filename],'%f');

    % Save in handles structure
    handles.x = x;
    guidata(gcbf, handles);

    % Create histogram
    hist(handles.x,handles.nbins);

    % Set axis labels
    xlabel('\bfValue');
    ylabel('\bfCount');

    % Calculate statistics
    ave = mean(x);
    med = median(x);
    sd = std(x);
    n = length(x);

    % Update fields
    set (handles.MeanData,'String',sprintf('%f7.2f',ave));
    set (handles.MedianData,'String',sprintf('%7.2f',med));
    set (handles.StdDevData,'String',sprintf('%7.2f',sd));
    set (handles.TitleString,'String',['Histogram (N = 'int2str(n)')']);
end
```

The File/Exit callback is trivial. All it has to do is close the figure.

```
function Exit>Callback(hObject, eventdata, handles)
% hObject      handle to Exit (see GCBO)
% eventdata    reserved – to be defined in a future version of MATLAB
% handles      structure with handles and user data (see GUIDATA)

close(gcbf);
```

The **NBins** callback must read a numeric input value, round it off to the nearest integer, display that integer in the Edit Box, and recalculate and display the histogram. Note that the number of bins must also be saved in the **handles** structure, so that it will be available for recalculation if the user loads a new data file. The callback function to perform these steps is shown below:

```
function NBins_Callback(hObject, eventdata, handles)
% hObject      handle to NBins (see GCBO)
% eventdata    reserved – to be defined in a future version of MATLAB
% handles      structure with handles and user data (see GUIDATA)
```

```
% Get number of bins, round to integer, and update field
nbins = str2num(get(hObject,'String'));
nbins = round(nbins);
if nbins < 1
    nbins = 1;
end
set (handles.NBins,'String',int2str(nbins));

% Save in handles structure
handles.nbins = nbins;
guidata(gcbf, handles);

% Re-display data, if available
if handles.bins > 0 & ~isempty(handles.x)

    %Create histogram
    hist(handles.x,handles.nbins);

end
```

The final program is shown in Figure 23.35. Experiment with it on your own computer to verify that it behaves properly.

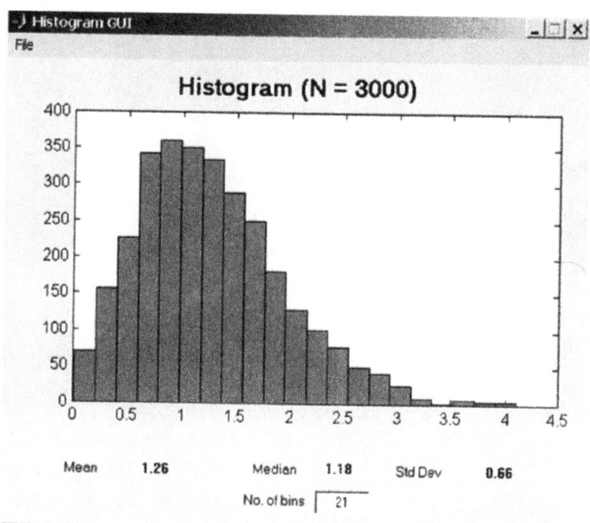

Figure 23.35 The GUI produced by program **histGUI**.

INDEX

Note: Boldface denotes commands/functions